Stanley Gi

Coll

Channel Islands
and Isle of Man
Stamps

2016 edition

STANLEY GIBBONS LTD

London and Ringwood

By Appointment to
Her Majesty The Queen
Philatelists
Stanley Gibbons Ltd
London

Published by Stanley Gibbons Ltd
Editorial, Publications Sales Offices
and Distribution Centre:
7 Parkside, Christchurch Road, Ringwood,
Hants BH24 3SH

30th COMBINED EDITION

© Stanley Gibbons Ltd 2016

British Library Cataloguing in
Publication Data.
A catalogue record for this book is available
from the British Library.

Errors and omissions excepted
the colour reproduction of stamps is only as
accurate as the printing process will allow.

ISBN-10: 0-85259-962-5
ISBN-13: 978-0-85259-962-4

Item No. R2855-16

Printed by
Latimer Trend

Contents

Introductory Notes

Scope. The listing of **stamps** for Guernsey and Jersey comprises German Occupation issues, the 1958–69 Regionals and the issues of the Independent Postal Administrations from their inception in 1969. Isle of Man sections cover the 1958–71 Regionals and the issues of the Independent Postal Administration from 1973 onwards.

Information is given on:

- Designers and printers
- The different printings for definitives and postage dues
- Distinctive papers
- Such varieties as imperforates and missing colours
- Phosphors
- Cylinder and plate numbers
- Sheet sizes and imprints
- Quantities sold (where known)
- Withdrawal and invalidation dates

The 'Notes' on page 1 may be found helpful in further explanation.

The checklist also covers:

- Miniature sheets
- First day covers
- Presentation packs and Yearbooks
- Gutter pairs
- Stamp booklets
- Stamp sachets (listed, but unpriced)
- Postal stationery commemorative cards and covers

Items outside the scope and therefore omitted are: cylinder and plate varieties; non-postage stamps, such as revenues and local Carriage labels; and other classes of postal stationery.

Layout. Stamps are set out chronologically by date of issue. In the catalogue lists the first numeral is the Stanley Gibbons catalogue number; the black (boldface) numeral alongside is the type number referring to the respective illustration. The denomination and colour of the stamp are then shown.

Before February 1971 British currency was:

£1=20s One Pound = twenty shillings and
1s=12d One shilling = twelve pence.

Upon decimalisation this became:

£1=100p One pound = one hundred (new) pence

The catalogue list then shows two price columns. The left-hand is for unused stamps and the right-hand for used.

Our method of indicating prices is:

Numerals for pence, e.g. 5 denotes 5p (5 pence). Numerals for pounds and pence, e.g. 4.25 denotes £4.25 (4 pounds and 25 pence). For £100 and above, prices are in whole pounds and so include the £ sign and omit the zeros for pence.

Size of illustrations. To comply with Post Office regulations illustrations of stamps and booklets are three-quarters linear size. Where illustrations are further reduced (miniature sheets and some booklet covers) actual sizes are given. Illustrations of watermarks are actual size.

Prices. Prices quoted in this catalogue are our selling prices at the time the book went to press. They are for stamps in fine condition; in issues where condition varies we may ask more for the superb and less for the sub-standard. With unused stamps prices are for unmounted mint (though where not available unmounted, mounted mint stamps are often supplied at a lower price). Used prices are normally for stamps fine postally used but may be for stamps cancelled-to-order where this practice exists. All prices are subject to change without prior notice and we give no guarantee to supply all stamps priced, since it is not possible to keep every catalogue item perpetually in stock. Commemoratives may, at times, only be available in complete sets.

The minimum price quoted is 10 pence. For individual stamps prices between 10 pence and 95 pence are provided as a guide for catalogue users. The lowest price charged for individual stamps or sets purchased from Stanley Gibbons Ltd is £1.

Perforations. The 'perforation' is the number of holes in a length of 2 cm, as measured by the Gibbons Instanta gauge. The stamp is viewed against a dark background with the transparent gauge put on top of it. Perforations are quoted to the nearest half. Stamps without perforation are termed 'imperforate'.

Se-tenant **combinations.** *Se-tenant* means 'joined together'. Some sets include stamps of different design arranged *se-tenant* as blocks or strips and, in mint condition, these are usually collected unsevered as issued. Where such combinations exist, the individual stamps are priced normally as mint and used singles. **The set prices refer to the unsevered combination plus singles of any other values in the set.**

First Day Covers. Prices for first day covers are for complete sets used on special covers, the stamps of which bear an official postmark for first day of issue. Where the stamps in a set were issued on different days, prices are for a cover from each day.

Catalogue numbers used. The checklist uses the same catalogue numbers as the Stanley Gibbons *Stamps of the World* catalogue, 2016 edition.

Latest stamps recorded in this edition appeared in November 2015.

Specialist Philatelic Society. Channel Islands Specialists Society. Membership Secretary: Moira Edwards, 86 Hall Lane, Sandon, Chelmsford, Essex CM2 7RQ.

Amendments to the 2016 edition

A number of additions, amendments and corrections have been made to this edition and we would particularly like to thank Ray Dixon for his assistance. Help and information have also been provided by David Aggersberg, Peter Barrett, John Embrey, David Gurney, Stuart Leigh, David Smythe and Frank Spencer.

Stanley Gibbons
Stamp Catalogues

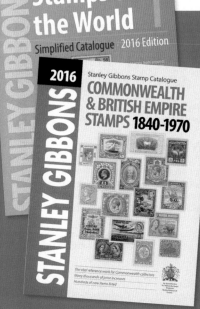

Stamps of the World 1
Simplified Catalogue 2016 Edition

2016 Stanley Gibbons Stamp Catalogue
COMMONWEALTH & BRITISH EMPIRE STAMPS 1840-1970

The vital reference work for Commonwealth collectors
Many thousands of price increases
Hundreds of new items listed

We have catalogues to suit every aspect of stamp collecting

Our catalogues cover stamps issued from across the globe - from the Penny Black to the latest issues. Whether you're a specialist in a certain reign or a thematic collector, we should have something to suit your needs. All catalogues include the famous SG numbering system, making it as easy as possible to find the stamp you're looking for.

Commonwealth & British Empire Stamps 1840–1970 (117th edition, 2015)

Commonwealth Country Catalogues

Australia & Dependencies (9th Edition, 2014)
Bangladesh, Pakistan & Sri Lanka (3rd edition, 2015)
Belize, Guyana, Trinidad & Tobago (2nd edition, 2013)
Brunei, Malaysia & Singapore (4th edition, 2013)
Canada (5th edition, 2014)
Central Africa (2nd edition, 2008)
Cyprus, Gibraltar & Malta (4th edition, 2014)
East Africa with Egypt & Sudan (3rd edition, 2014)
Eastern Pacific (3rd edition, 2015)
Falkland Islands (6th edition, 2013)
Hong Kong (5th edition, 2015)
India (including Convention & Feudatory States) (4th edition, 2013)
Indian Ocean (2nd edition, 2012)
Ireland (6th edition, 2015)
Leeward Islands (2nd edition, 2012)
New Zealand (5th edition, 2014)
Northern Caribbean, Bahamas & Bermuda (3rd edition, 2013)
St. Helena & Dependencies (5th edition, 2014)
Southern Africa (2nd edition, 2008)
Southern & Central Africa (2nd edition, 2014)
West Africa (2nd edition, 2012)
Western Pacific (3rd edition, 2014)
Windward Islands & Barbados (3rd edition, 2015)

Stamps of the World 2016

Volume 1 Abu Dhabi – Charkhari
Volume 2 Chile – Georgia
Volume 3 German Commands – Jasdan
Volume 4 Jersey – New Republic
Volume 5 New South Wales – Singapore
Volume 6 Sirmoor – Zululand

Great Britain Catalogues

Collect British Stamps (67th edition, 2016)
Collect Channel Islands & Isle of Man (30th edition, 2016)
Great Britain Concise Stamp Catalogue (30th edition, 2015)

Great Britain Specialised

Volume 1 *Queen Victoria* (16th edition, 2012)
Volume 2 *King Edward VII to King George VI* (14th edition, 2015)
Volume 3 *Queen Elizabeth II Pre-decimal issues* (12th edition, 2011)
Volume 4 *Queen Elizabeth II Decimal Definitive Issues – Part 1* (10th edition, 2008)
Queen Elizabeth II Decimal Definitive Issues – Part 2 (10th edition, 2010)

Foreign Countries

Austria & Hungary (8th edition, 2014)
Balkans (5th edition, 2009)
Belgium & Luxembourg (1st edition, 2015)
Central America (3rd edition, 2007)
Central Asia (4th edition, 2006)
China (11th edition, 2015)
Czech Republic, Slovakia & Poland (7th edition, 2012)
France, Andorra and Monaco (1st edition, May 2015)
Germany (11th edition, 2014)
Italy & Switzerland (8th edition, 2013)
Japan & Korea (5th edition, 2008)
Middle East (7th edition, 2009)
Portugal & Spain (6th edition, 2011)
Poland (1st edition, 2015)
Russia (7th edition, 2014)
Scandinavia (7th edition, 2013)
South America (4th edition, 2008)
South-East Asia (5th edition, 2012)
United States of America (8th edition, 2015)

Est 1856
STANLEY GIBBONS

Stanley Gibbons
7 Parkside, Christchurch Road, Ringwood, Hants, BH24 3SH
+44 (0)1425 472 363
www.stanleygibbons.com

International Philatelic Glossary

English	French	German	Spanish	Italian
Agate	Agate	Achat	Agata	Agata
Air stamp	Timbre de la poste aérienne	Flugpostmarke	Sello de correo aéreo	Francobollo per posta aerea
Apple Green	Vert-pomme	Apfelgrün	Verde manzana	Verde mela
Barred	Annulé par barres	Balkenentwertung	Anulado con barras	Sbarrato
Bisected	Timbre coupé	Halbiert	Partido en dos	Frazionato
Bistre	Bistre	Bister	Bistre	Bistro
Bistre-brown	Brun-bistre	Bisterbraun	Castaño bistre	Bruno-bistro
Black	Noir	Schwarz	Negro	Nero
Blackish Brown	Brun-noir	Schwärzlichbraun	Castaño negruzco	Bruno nerastro
Blackish Green	Vert foncé	Schwärzlichgrün	Verde negruzco	Verde nerastro
Blackish Olive	Olive foncé	Schwärzlicholiv	Oliva negruzco	Oliva nerastro
Block of four	Bloc de quatre	Viererblock	Bloque de cuatro	Bloco di quattro
Blue	Bleu	Blau	Azul	Azzurro
Blue-green	Vert-bleu	Blaugrün	Verde azul	Verde azzuro
Bluish Violet	Violet bleuâtre	Bläulichviolett	Violeta azulado	Violtto azzurrastro
Booklet	Carnet	Heft	Cuadernillo	Libretto
Bright Blue	Bleu vif	Lebhaftblau	Azul vivo	Azzurro vivo
Bright Green	Vert vif	Lebhaftgrün	Verde vivo	Verde vivo
Bright Purple	Mauve vif	Lebhaftpurpur	Púrpura vivo	Porpora vivo
Bronze Green	Vert-bronze	Bronzegrün	Verde bronce	Verde bronzo
Brown	Brun	Braun	Castaño	Bruno
Brown-lake	Carmin-brun	Braunlack	Laca castaño	Lacca bruno
Brown-purple	Pourpre-brun	Braunpurpur	Púrpura castaño	Porpora bruno
Brown-red	Rouge-brun	Braunrot	Rojo castaño	Rosso bruno
Buff	Chamois	Sämisch	Anteado	Camoscio
Cancellation	Oblitération	Entwertung	Cancelación	Annullamento
Cancelled	Annulé	Gestempelt	Cancelado	Annullato
Carmine	Carmin	Karmin	Carmín	Carminio
Carmine-red	Rouge-carmin	Karminrot	Rojo carmín	Rosso carminio
Centred	Centré	Zentriert	Centrado	Centrato
Cerise	Rouge-cerise	Kirschrot	Color de ceresa	Color Ciliegia
Chalk-surfaced paper	Papier couché	Kreidepapier	Papel estucado	Carta gessata
Chalky Blue	Bleu terne	Kreideblau	Azul turbio	Azzurro smorto
Charity stamp	Timbre de bienfaisance	Wohltätigkeitsmarke	Sello de beneficenza	Francobollo di beneficenza
Chestnut	Marron	Kastanienbraun	Castaño rojo	Marrone
Chocolate	Chocolat	Schokolade	Chocolate	Cioccolato
Cinnamon	Cannelle	Zimtbraun	Canela	Cannella
Claret	Grenat	Weinrot	Rojo vinoso	Vinaccia
Cobalt	Cobalt	Kobalt	Cobalto	Cobalto
Colour	Couleur	Farbe	Color	Colore
Comb-perforation	Dentelure en peigne	Kammzähnung, Reihenzähnung	Dentado de peine	Dentellatura e pettine
Commemorative stamp	Timbre commémoratif	Gedenkmarke	Sello conmemorativo	Francobollo commemorativo
Crimson	Cramoisi	Karmesin	Carmesí	Cremisi
Deep Blue	Blue foncé	Dunkelblau	Azul oscuro	Azzurro scuro
Deep bluish Green	Vert-bleu foncé	Dunkelbläulichgrün	Verde azulado oscuro	Verde azzurro scuro

English	French	German	Spanish	Italian
Design	Dessin	Markenbild	Diseño	Disegno
Die	Matrice	Urstempel. Type, Platte	Cuño	Conio, Matrice
Double	Double	Doppelt	Doble	Doppio
Drab	Olive terne	Trüboliv	Oliva turbio	Oliva smorto
Dull Green	Vert terne	Trübgrün	Verde turbio	Verde smorto
Dull purple	Mauve terne	Trübpurpur	Púrpura turbio	Porpora smorto
Embossing	Impression en relief	Prägedruck	Impresión en relieve	Impressione a relievo
Emerald	Vert-eméraude	Smaragdgrün	Esmeralda	Smeraldo
Engraved	Gravé	Graviert	Grabado	Inciso
Error	Erreur	Fehler, Fehldruck	Error	Errore
Essay	Essai	Probedruck	Ensayo	Saggio
Express letter stamp	Timbre pour lettres par exprès	Eilmarke	Sello de urgencia	Francobollo per espresso
Fiscal stamp	Timbre fiscal	Stempelmarke	Sello fiscal	Francobollo fiscale
Flesh	Chair	Fleischfarben	Carne	Carnicino
Forgery	Faux, Falsification	Fälschung	Falsificación	Falso, Falsificazione
Frame	Cadre	Rahmen	Marco	Cornice
Granite paper	Papier avec fragments de fils de soie	Faserpapier	Papel con filamentos	Carto con fili di seta
Green	Vert	Grün	Verde	Verde
Greenish Blue	Bleu verdâtre	Grünlichblau	Azul verdoso	Azzurro verdastro
Greenish Yellow	Jaune-vert	Grünlichgelb	Amarillo verdoso	Giallo verdastro
Grey	Gris	Grau	Gris	Grigio
Grey-blue	Bleu-gris	Graublau	Azul gris	Azzurro grigio
Grey-green	Vert gris	Graugrün	Verde gris	Verde grigio
Gum	Gomme	Gummi	Goma	Gomma
Gutter	Interpanneau	Zwischensteg	Espacio blanco entre dos grupos	Ponte
Imperforate	Non-dentelé	Geschnitten	Sin dentar	Non dentellato
Indigo	Indigo	Indigo	Azul indigo	Indaco
Inscription	Inscription	Inschrift	Inscripción	Dicitura
Inverted	Renversé	Kopfstehend	Invertido	Capovolto
Issue	Émission	Ausgabe	Emisión	Emissione
Laid	Vergé	Gestreift	Listado	Vergato
Lake	Lie de vin	Lackfarbe	Laca	Lacca
Lake-brown	Brun-carmin	Lackbraun	Castaño laca	Bruno lacca
Lavender	Bleu-lavande	Lavendel	Color de alhucema	Lavanda
Lemon	Jaune-citron	Zitrongelb	Limón	Limone
Light Blue	Bleu clair	Hellblau	Azul claro	Azzurro chiaro
Lilac	Lilas	Lila	Lila	Lilla
Line perforation	Dentelure en lignes	Linienzähnung	Dentado en linea	Dentellatura lineare
Lithography	Lithographie	Steindruck	Litografía	Litografia
Local	Timbre de poste locale	Lokalpostmarke	Emisión local	Emissione locale
Lozenge roulette	Percé en losanges	Rautenförmiger Durchstich	Picadura en rombos	Perforazione a losanghe
Magenta	Magenta	Magentarot	Magenta	Magenta
Margin	Marge	Rand	Borde	Margine
Maroon	Marron pourpré	Dunkelrotpurpur	Púrpura rojo oscuro	Marrone rossastro
Mauve	Mauve	Malvenfarbe	Malva	Malva
Multicoloured	Polychrome	Mehrfarbig	Multicolores	Policromo
Myrtle Green	Vert myrte	Myrtengrün	Verde mirto	Verde mirto
New Blue	Bleu ciel vif	Neublau	Azul nuevo	Azzurro nuovo
Newspaper stamp	Timbre pour journaux	Zeitungsmarke	Sello para periódicos	Francobollo per giornali

English	French	German	Spanish	Italian
Obliteration	Oblitération	Abstempelung	Matasello	Annullamento
Obsolete	Hors (de) cours	Ausser Kurs	Fuera de curso	Fuori corso
Ochre	Ocre	Ocker	Ocre	Ocra
Official stamp	Timbre de service	Dienstmarke	Sello de servicio	Francobollo di
Olive-brown	Brun-olive	Olivbraun	Castaño oliva	Bruno oliva
Olive-green	Vert-olive	Olivgrün	Verde oliva	Verde oliva
Olive-grey	Gris-olive	Olivgrau	Gris oliva	Grigio oliva
Olive-yellow	Jaune-olive	Olivgelb	Amarillo oliva	Giallo oliva
Orange	Orange	Orange	Naranja	Arancio
Orange-brown	Brun-orange	Orangebraun	Castaño naranja	Bruno arancio
Orange-red	Rouge-orange	Orangerot	Rojo naranja	Rosso arancio
Orange-yellow	Jaune-orange	Orangegelb	Amarillo naranja	Giallo arancio
Overprint	Surcharge	Aufdruck	Sobrecarga	Soprastampa
Pair	Paire	Paar	Pareja	Coppia
Pale	Pâle	Blass	Pálido	Pallido
Pane	Panneau	Gruppe	Grupo	Gruppo
Paper	Papier	Papier	Papel	Carta
Parcel post stamp	Timbre pour colis postaux	Paketmarke	Sello para paquete postal	Francobollo per pacchi postali
Pen-cancelled	Oblitéré à plume	Federzugentwertung	Cancelado a pluma	Annullato a penna
Percé en arc	Percé en arc	Bogenförmiger Durchstich	Picadura en forma de arco	Perforazione ad arco
Percé en scie	Percé en scie	Bogenförmiger Durchstich	Picado en sierra	Foratura a sega
Perforated	Dentelé	Gezähnt	Dentado	Dentellato
Perforation	Dentelure	Zähnung	Dentar	Dentellatura
Photogravure	Photogravure, Heliogravure	Rastertiefdruck	Fotograbado	Rotocalco
Pin perforation	Percé en points	In Punkten durchstochen	Horadado con alfileres	Perforato a punti
Plate	Planche	Platte	Plancha	Lastra, Tavola
Plum	Prune	Pflaumenfarbe	Color de ciruela	Prugna
Postage Due stamp	Timbre-taxe	Portomarke	Sello de tasa	Segnatasse
Postage stamp	Timbre-poste	Briefmarke, Freimarke, Postmarke	Sello de correos	Francobollo postale
Postal fiscal stamp	Timbre fiscal-postal	Stempelmarke als Postmarke verwendet	Sello fiscal-postal	Fiscale postale
Postmark	Oblitération postale	Poststempel	Matasello	Bollo
Printing	Impression, Tirage	Druck	Impresión	Stampa, Tiratura
Proof	Épreuve	Druckprobe	Prueba de impresión	Prova
Provisionals	Timbres provisoires	Provisorische Marken. Provisorien	Provisionales	Provvisori
Prussian Blue	Bleu de Prusse	Preussischblau	Azul de Prusia	Azzurro di Prussia
Purple	Pourpre	Purpur	Púrpura	Porpora
Purple-brown	Brun-pourpre	Purpurbraun	Castaño púrpura	Bruno porpora
Recess-printing	Impression en taille douce	Tiefdruck	Grabado	Incisione
Red	Rouge	Rot	Rojo	Rosso
Red-brown	Brun-rouge	Rotbraun	Castaño rojizo	Bruno rosso
Reddish Lilac	Lilas rougeâtre	Rötlichlila	Lila rojizo	Lilla rossastro
Reddish Purple	Poupre-rouge	Rötlichpurpur	Púrpura rojizo	Porpora rossastro
Reddish Violet	Violet rougeâtre	Rötlichviolett	Violeta rojizo	Violetto rossastro
Red-orange	Orange rougeâtre	Rotorange	Naranja rojizo	Arancio rosso
Registration stamp	Timbre pour lettre chargée (recommandée)	Einschreibemarke	Sello de certificado lettere	Francobollo per raccomandate
Reprint	Réimpression	Neudruck	Reimpresión	Ristampa
Reversed	Retourné	Umgekehrt	Invertido	Rovesciato

English	French	German	Spanish	Italian
Rose	Rose	Rosa	Rosa	Rosa
Rose-red	Rouge rosé	Rosarot	Rojo rosado	Rosso rosa
Rosine	Rose vif	Lebhaftrosa	Rosa vivo	Rosa vivo
Roulette	Percage	Durchstich	Picadura	Foratura
Rouletted	Percé	Durchstochen	Picado	Forato
Royal Blue	Bleu-roi	Königblau	Azul real	Azzurro reale
Sage green	Vert-sauge	Salbeigrün	Verde salvia	Verde salvia
Salmon	Saumon	Lachs	Salmón	Salmone
Scarlet	Écarlate	Scharlach	Escarlata	Scarlatto
Sepia	Sépia	Sepia	Sepia	Seppia
Serpentine roulette	Percé en serpentin	Schlangenliniger Durchstich	Picado a serpentina	Perforazione a serpentina
Shade	Nuance	Tönung	Tono	Gradazione de colore
Sheet	Feuille	Bogen	Hoja	Foglio
Slate	Ardoise	Schiefer	Pizarra	Ardesia
Slate-blue	Bleu-ardoise	Schieferblau	Azul pizarra	Azzurro ardesia
Slate-green	Vert-ardoise	Schiefergrün	Verde pizarra	Verde ardesia
Slate-lilac	Lilas-gris	Schierferlila	Lila pizarra	Lilla ardesia
Slate-purple	Mauve-gris	Schieferpurpur	Púrpura pizarra	Porpora ardesia
Slate-violet	Violet-gris	Schieferviolett	Violeta pizarra	Violetto ardesia
Special delivery stamp	Timbre pour exprès	Eilmarke	Sello de urgencia	Francobollo per espressi
Specimen	Spécimen	Muster	Muestra	Saggio
Steel Blue	Bleu acier	Stahlblau	Azul acero	Azzurro acciaio
Strip	Bande	Streifen	Tira	Striscia
Surcharge	Surcharge	Aufdruck	Sobrecarga	Soprastampa
Tête-bêche	Tête-bêche	Kehrdruck	Tête-bêche	Tête-bêche
Tinted paper	Papier teinté	Getöntes Papier	Papel coloreado	Carta tinta
Too-late stamp	Timbre pour lettres en retard	Verspätungsmarke	Sello para cartas retardadas	Francobollo per le lettere in ritardo
Turquoise-blue	Bleu-turquoise	Türkisblau	Azul turquesa	Azzurro turchese
Turquoise-green	Vert-turquoise	Türkisgrün	Verde turquesa	Verde turchese
Typography	Typographie	Buchdruck	Tipografia	Tipografia
Ultramarine	Outremer	Ultramarin	Ultramar	Oltremare
Unused	Neuf	Ungebraucht	Nuevo	Nuovo
Used	Oblitéré, Usé	Gebraucht	Usado	Usato
Venetian Red	Rouge-brun terne	Venezianischrot	Rojo veneciano	Rosso veneziano
Vermilion	Vermillon	Zinnober	Cinabrio	Vermiglione
Violet	Violet	Violett	Violeta	Violetto
Violet-blue	Bleu-violet	Violettblau	Azul violeta	Azzurro violetto
Watermark	Filigrane	Wasserzeichen	Filigrana	Filigrana
Watermark sideways	Filigrane couché	Wasserzeichen liegend	Filigrana acostado	Filigrana coricata
Wove paper	Papier ordinaire, Papier uni	Einfaches Papier	Papel avitelado	Carta unita
Yellow	Jaune	Gelb	Amarillo	Giallo
Yellow-brown	Brun-jaune	Gelbbraun	Castaño amarillo	Bruno giallo
Yellow-green	Vert-jaune	Gelbgrün	Verde amarillo	Verde giallo
Yellow-olive	Olive-jaunâtre	Gelboliv	Oliva amarillo	Oliva giallastro
Yellow-orange	Orange jaunâtre	Gelborange	Naranja amarillo	Arancio giallastro
Zig-zag roulette	Percé en zigzag	Sägezahnartiger Durchstich	Picado en zigzag	Perforazione a zigzag

Stanley Gibbons

399 Strand

Unsure how to progress your collection?

Visit 399 Strand to get advice from our experienced and knowledgeable staff. They will help you choose the stamps and philatelic accessories that will enhance and develop your collection. They will also offer guidance on techniques for the care and storage of your stamps and covers.

We have a superb range of stamps albums and philatelic accessories.

We strive to cater for every need a collector might have, and if we don't have the exact item you need, we will recommend an equivalent or an alternative.

Come in, browse our range and choose what's best for you.

Before you commit to a particular album, take the time to talk to our staff who will help you weigh up the pros and cons before you make your decision. We are always happy to demonstrate anything we sell from tweezers to Frank Godden luxury albums.

Everything for the philatelic collector.

Just down the road from the Savoy Hotel, two minutes from Charing Cross Tube station

For more information, please contact Stephen Bowyer on:
Tel. +44 (0)207 557 4436 or sbowyer@stanleygibbons.com
399 Strand opening hours   **Mon-Fri 9am-5.30pm   Sat 9:30am-5.30pm   Sun Closed**

Est 1856
STANLEY GIBBONS

Stanley Gibbons Limited
399 Strand, London, WC2R 0LX
+44 (0)20 7557 4444
www.stanleygibbons.com

Enhance your collection with Jersey stamps

Jersey Post is proud to have been issuing its own stamps since becoming an independent postal administration operator in 1969. The island of Jersey is rich in history and culture and over the years Jersey Post has produced stamps on a wide range of topics and a number of innovative world firsts.

A constant mix of heritage, technical innovation and creatively packaged special issues keeps Jersey Post at the forefront of the philatelic world and helps to make Jersey stamps such sought-after collections.

Flora & Fauna
Links with China - Garden Flowers

Fascinating themes
Hubble - 25 Years of
Space Exploration

The Royal Family
Queen Elizabeth II, the Longest Reigning British Monarch
Silk Miniature Sheet

Innovative techniques
2015 Definitives
The Crest of Jersey Hologram

Striking illustrations
The Great War 100 Years, Part Two: Change

Stunning photography
Jersey Seasons: Autumn

Myths and Folklore
Dragons

Nostalgia
Europa 2015 Traditional Toys - Hornby

Events and anniversaries
Victory & Liberation - Sir Winston Churchill

The Battle of Britain - Sir Winston Churchill

Contact us to find out more

Jersey Post's subscription customers benefit from free postage and packaging on all orders as well as the expertise of a friendly and knowledgeable customer services team.

www.jerseystamps.com

Email: stamps@jerseypost.com Tel: +44(0) 1534 516320
www.facebook.com/jerseystamps @JerseyStamps

Jersey Post

NOTES ON THE CATALOGUE LISTINGS

Printings

For definitives and postage due stamps released by the independent Postal Administrations we give the dates of the printings as announced, and relate them in the listings to the actual stamps involved. Users will therefore be able to see at a glance how many printings have been made of any particular item.

Cylinder and Plate Numbers

Following the listing of each issue we give the printers' cylinder or plate numbers known to us.

Sheet size

In describing the sheet arrangement we always give the number of stamps across the sheet first. For example, '50 (5×10)' indicates a sheet of fifty stamps in ten horizontal rows of five stamps each.

Paper

Only distinctive types are mentioned. Granite paper can be easily distinguished by the coloured lines in its texture. Chalky or chalk-surfaced applies to paper which shows a characteristic sheen when light is reflected off its surface. Under high magnification tiny bubbles or pock-marks may be seen in the paper coating.

Perforations

Perforations are normally given to the nearest half and the Instanta gauge is our standard. In this checklist we state if a perforation is by a line (L) or a comb (C) machine. A line machine only perforates one line at a time and consequently it requires two operations to do the horizontal and vertical perforations and where these intersect an irregular-shaped hole often results. A comb machine perforates three sides at a time and therefore produces a single hole at all corner intersections. The differences are easily seen in blocks of four.

The various perforations in this checklist are expressed as follows:

Perf 14:   Perforated alike on all sides.
Perf 14×15: Compound perforation. The first figure refers to top and bottom, the second to left and right sides.

Abbreviations

des = designer, designed
eng = engraver, engraved
litho = lithographed
mm = millimetres
MS = miniature sheet
No. = number
perf = perforated
photo = photogravure
recess = recess-printed
typo = typographed
wmk(d) = watermark(ed)

Channel Islands

C **1** Gathering Vraic   C **2** Islanders gathering Vraic

Broken Wheel (R.20/5)

Third Anniversary of Liberation

(Des J. R. R. Stobie (1d.), or from drawing by E. Blampied (2½d.). Photo Harrison and Sons)

1948 (10 May). Wmk Mult G VI R. P 15×14 (C).

C1	C **1**	1d. scarlet	25	55
C2	C **2**	2½d. ultramarine	25	60
		a. Broken wheel	75·00	
First Day Cover				35·00

These stamps were primarily intended for use in the Channel Islands although they were also available at eight head post offices in Great Britain.

Cylinder Nos.: 1d. 2; 2½d. 4.
Sheets: 120 (6×20).
Quantities sold: 1d. 5,934,000; 2½d. 5,398,000.

Guernsey

THE GERMAN OCCUPATION 1940–1945

The first German soldiers to arrive in Guernsey set foot on the island on 30 June 1940 and an official notice appeared in the local newspaper the following day announcing the occupation.

The first evidence of the occupation, philatelically, came towards the end of the year when supplies of Great Britain 1d. stamps then in use began to dry up. It was decided that the bisecting of 2d. stamps for use as 1d.'s be allowed and this commenced on 27 December. The decision to print 1d. stamps locally had been taken in October, but these were not ready and were eventually issued on 18 February 1941. In the meantime the two currently available 2d. stamps, the 1937 definitive and the 1940 Postal Centenary, were bisected and used, as were 2d. stamps of the reign of George V which were in collectors' hands. Other values are also known to have been bisected and used, and were allowed to pass through the post in most instances without a postage due charge being made.

The Swastika overprints, previously listed as Nos. SW1 and SW2 are now considered to be bogus.

As previously mentioned, the locally printed 1d. stamps were issued on 18 February 1941. The ½d. stamp was released on 7 April 1941 and the 2½d. on 12 April 1944. This last stamp was issued in an effort to economise on the use of paper as it was found that sealed letters were franked with two 1d. stamps and one ½d. or a larger number of ½d.'s, a gross waste in times of shortage. Many printings of these stamps were made, the most notable being on the French bank-note paper in 1942.

Shades of these issues abound, the more outstanding ones being the bluish green (4th) and olive-green (8th) printings of the ½d., and the pale vermilion (11th) printing of the 1d. During the occupation Guernsey stamps were only valid on mail within the Channel Islands. Letters sent overseas were despatched via the German Feldpost system. The stamps continued to be used after the liberation in 1945 until 13 April 1946.

Example of bisected 2d.
King George VI definitive (B55)

The Bisects

1940 (27 Dec).

(a) Stamps of King George V

Cat. No.		Price on Cover
BS1	1912–22 2d. orange	£400
BS2	1924–26 2d. orange	£400
BS3	1934–36 2d. orange	£450

(b) Stamps of King George VI

BS4	1937 1d. scarlet	£950
BS5	1938 2d. orange	50·00
BS6	1940 Stamp Centenary 1d. scarlet	£950
BS7	1940 Stamp Centenary 2d. orange	40·00
BS8	1940 Stamp Centenary 2½d. ultramarine	£2000
BS9	1940 Stamp Centenary 3d. violet	

Forged postmarks on fake bisects are known from Guernsey Head Post Office ('2 JA 41'), Market Place ('19 FE 41' or '7 AP 41'), St. Sampson ('27 DE 40') and The Vale ('18 FE 41').

The bisects are priced on philatelic cover. Those which were used commercially are worth more, particularly Nos. BS5 and BS7.

Invalidated: 22.2.41 (last postings were postmarked 24.2.41.)

1 Arms of Guernsey

1a Loops

Stamps issued during the German Occupation

(Des E. W. Vaudin. Typo Guernsey Press Co Ltd)

1941–44. Rouletted.

(a) White paper. No wmk

Cat. No.	Type No.		Unused	Used
1	1	½d. light green (7.4.41)	6·00	3·50
		a. Emerald-green (6.41)	6·00	2·00
		b. Bluish green (11.41)	35·00	13·00
		c. Bright green (2.42)	22·00	10·00
		d. Dull green (9.42)	4·00	2·00
		e. Olive-green (2.43)	45·00	25·00
		f. Pale yellowish green (7.43 and later) (*shades*)	4·00	3·00
		g. Imperf (pair)	£250	
		h. Imperf between (horizontal pair)	£800	
		i. Imperf between (vertical pair)	£900	
2		1d. scarlet (18.2.41)	3·25	2·00
		a. Pale vermilion (7.43) (etc)	5·00	2·00
		b. Carmine (1943)	3·50	2·00
		c. Imperf (pair)	£200	90·00
		d. Imperf between (horizontal pair)	£800	
		da. Imperf vert (centre stamp of horizontal strip of 3)		
		e. Imperf between (vertical pair)	£950	
		f. Ptd double (scarlet shade)	£150	
3		2½d. ultramarine (12.4.44)	18·00	15·00
		a. Pale ultramarine (7.44)	15·00	12·00
		b. Imperf (pair)	£600	
		c. Imperf between (horizontal pair)	£1250	
1	*First Day Cover*			10·00
2	*First Day Cover*			15·00
3	*First Day Cover*			20·00

*(b) Bluish French bank-note paper. Wmk **1a** (sideways)*

4	1	½d. bright green (11.3.42)	32·00	25·00
5		1d. scarlet (9.4.42)	18·00	25·00
4	*First Day Cover*			£325
5	*First Day Cover*			£125

The dates for the shades of Nos. 1/3 are the months in which they were printed as indicated on the printer's imprints (see below). Others are issue dates.

Printings and imprint: The various printings can be identified from the sheet imprints as follows:

½d.	1st Printing 240M/341
	2nd Printing 2×120M/6/41
	3rd Printing 3×120M/6/41
	4th Printing 4×120M/11/41
	5th Printing 5×120M/2/42
	6th Printing 6×240M/2/42
	7th Printing 7×120M/9/42
	8th Printing 8×120M/2/43
	9th Printing 9×120M/7/43
	10th Printing 10×120M/10/43
	11th Printing Guernsey Press Co., (stop and comma)
	12th Printing Guernsey Press Co. (stop only, margin at bottom 23 to 27 *mm*)
	13th Printing Guernsey Press Co. (stop only, margin at bottom 15 *mm*)
1d.	1st Printing 120M/41
	2nd Printing 2×120M/2/41
	3rd Printing 3×120M/6/41
	4th Printing 4×120M/6/41
	5th Printing 5×120M/9/41
	6th Printing 6×240M/11/41
	7th Printing 7×120M/2/42
	8th Printing 8×240M/4/42
	9th Printing 9×240M/9/42
	10th Printing 10×240M/1/43
	11th Printing 11×240M/7/43
	12th Printing Guernsey Press Co.
	13th Printing PRESS TYP.
	14th Printing 'PRESS' (inverted commas unlevel)
	15th Printing 'PRESS' (inverted commas level, margin at bottom 28 *mm*)
	16th Printing 'PRESS' (inverted commas level, margin at bottom 12 *mm*)
2½d.	1st Printing Guernsey Press Co.
	2nd Printing 'PRESS' (inverted commas unlevel)
	3rd Printing 'PRESS' (inverted commas level, margin at bottom 22 *mm*)

4th Printing 'PRESS' (inverted commas level, margin at bottom 15 mm)

The numbered imprints occur in the left-hand corner, bottom margin on the 1st printing of the 1d., and central, bottom margin on all other printings of all three values.

In the numbered imprints, for example, 2×120M/6/41, the '2' indicates the number of the printing; '120M' denotes the number of stamps printed in thousands, in this case 120,000; and '6/41' denotes the date of the printing, June 1941.

In the first ten printings of the ½d. and the first eleven printings of the 1d. the printing details are prefixed by the name of the printer, 'Guernsey Press Co.'

Sheets: 60 (6×10).

Quantities printed: ½d. 1,772,160; 1d. 2,478,000; 2½d. 416,640.

Withdrawn and invalidated: 13.4.46.

REGIONAL ISSUES

Although specifically issued for regional use, these issues were initially valid for use throughout Great Britain. However, they ceased to be valid for use in Guernsey and Jersey from 1 October 1969 when these islands each established their own independent postal administration and introduced their own stamps.

DATES OF ISSUE. Conflicting dates of issue have been announced for some of the regional issues, partly explained by the stamps being released on different dates by the Philatelic Bureau in Edinburgh or the Philatelic Counter in London and in the regions. We have adopted the practice of giving the earliest known dates, since once released the stamps could have been used anywhere in the U.K.

INVALIDATION. The regional issues of Guernsey were invalidated for use in Guernsey and Jersey on 1 November 1969. The stamps continued to be valid for use in the rest of the United Kingdom until 29 February 1972. Those still current remained on sale at philatelic sales counters until 30 September 1970.

1b Multiple Crowns　　　　　2　　　　　　　3

(Des E. A. Piprell. Portrait by Dorothy Wilding Ltd.
Photo Harrison and Sons)

1958–67. Wmk Type **1b**. P 15×14 (C).

6	**2**	2½d. rose-red (8.6.64)	40	50
7	**3**	3d. deep lilac (18.8.58)	30	40
		p. One centre phosphor band (24.5.67)	20	30
8		4d. ultramarine (7.2.66)	40	50
		p. Two phosphor bands (24.10.67)	15	25
6/8p	Set of 3		70	1·00
6	First Day Cover			30·00
7	First Day Cover			20·00
8	First Day Cover			8·00

Cylinder Nos.: 2½d. 1, 3; 3d. (ord) 4, 5; 3d. (phos) 5; 4d. (ord) 1; 4d. (phos) 1.

Sheets: 240 (12×20).

Quantities sold (ordinary only): 2½d. 3,485,760; 3d. 25,812,360; 4d. 4,415,040.

Withdrawn: 31.8.66 2½d.

Sold out: 6.3.68 3d. and 4d. (ordinary); 10.68 4d. (phosphor); 11.68 3d. (phosphor).

1968–69. No wmk. Chalk-surfaced paper. One centre phosphor band (Nos. 10/11) or two phosphor bands (others). P 15×14 (C).

9	**3**	4d. pale ultramarine (16.4.68)	10	20
		Ey. Phosphor omitted	45·00	
10		4d. olive-sepia (4.9.68)	10	15
		Ey. Phosphor omitted	45·00	
11		4d. bright vermilion (26.2.69)	20	25
12		5d. royal blue (4.9.68)	30	40
9/12	Set of 4		60	90
10, 12	First Day Cover			3·00

No. 9 was not issued in Guernsey until 22 April.

Cylinder Nos. 4d. (pale ultramarine) 1; 4d. (olive-sepia) 1; 4d. (bright vermilion) 1; 5d. 1.

Sold out: 3.69 4d. ultramarine.

Withdrawn: 30.9.69 (locally), 30.9.70 (British Philatelic Counters) 4d. olive-sepia, 4d. bright vermilion and 5d.

INDEPENDENT POSTAL ADMINISTRATION

Guernsey established their own independent postal administration on 1 October 1969 and introduced their own stamps.

NO WATERMARK. All the following issues are on unwatermarked paper.

4 Castle Cornet and Edward the Confessor

5 Map and William I

6 Martello Tower and Henry II

7 Arms of Sark and King John

8 Arms of Alderney and Edward III

9 Guernsey Lily and Henry V

10 Arms of Guernsey and Elizabeth I

11 Arms of Alderney and Charles II

12 Arms of Sark and George III

13 Arms of Guernsey and Queen Victoria

14 Guernsey Lily and Elizabeth I

15 Martello Tower and King John

16 View of Sark

17 View of Alderney

18 View of Guernsey

Two types of 1d. and 1s.6d.

I Latitude inscr '40° 30' N'

II Corrected to '49° 30' N'

(Des R. Granger Barrett. Photo Harrison (½d. to 2s.6d.), Delrieu (others))

1969 (1 Oct)–**70**. P 14 (½d. to 2s.6d.) or 12½ (others), all comb.

13	**4**	½d. deep magenta and black (a)	10	10
		a. Thin paper	60	60
14	**5**	1d. bright blue and black (I) (a)	10	10
		a. Thin paper (b)	50	50
14b		1d. bright blue and black (thin paper) (II) (eg)	30	30
		c. Booklet stamp with margins (thick paper) (C)	40	40
15	**6**	1½d. yellow-brown and black (a)	10	10
16	**7**	2d. gold, brt red, dp blue and blk (a)	10	10
		a. Thin paper (g)	40	40
17	**8**	3d. gold, pale greenish yellow, orange-red and black (a)	15	15
		a. Error. Wmk Block CA	£1400	
		ai. Wmk inverted	£1250	
		b. Thin paper (g)	50	50
18	**9**	4d. multicoloured (a)	20	25
		a. Booklet stamp with margins (C)	40	45
		ab. Yellow omitted	£775	
		ac. Emerald (stem) omitted	£775	
19	**10**	5d. gold, bright vermilion, bluish violet and black (a)	20	20
		a. Booklet stamp with margins (C)	50	50
		b. *gold* (inscription etc.) omitted (booklets)	£1400	
20	**11**	6d. gold, pale greenish yellow, light bronze-green and black (a)	20	40
		a. Thin paper (g)	45	45
21	**12**	9d. gold, brt red, crimson and blk (a)	30	40
		a. Thin paper (g)	3·00	1·70
22	**13**	1s. gold, brt verm, bistre and blk (a)	30	35
		a. Thin paper (g)	1·00	75
23	**5**	1s.6d. turquoise-grn and blk (I) (a)	25	30
		a. Thin paper (d)	1·70	3·25
23b		1s.6d. turquoise-green and black (thin paper) (II) (eg)	2·00	1·70
24	**14**	1s.9d. multicoloured (a)	1·00	1·00
		a. Emerald (stem) omitted	£875	
		b. Thin paper (g)	2·20	1·90
25	**15**	2s.6d. brt reddish violet and black (a)	4·00	4·50
		a. Thin paper (g)	5·50	4·50
26	**16**	5s. multicoloured (a)	2·50	2·75
27	**17**	10s. multicoloured (a)	16·00	18·00
		a. Perf 13½×13 (f)	35·00	36·00
28	**18**	£1 multicoloured (a)	2·20	2·20
		a. Perf 13½×13 (fh)	2·20	2·20
13/28a *Set of 16*			24·00	27·00
13/28 *First Day Cover*				29·00
13/28 *Presentation Packs* (incl. both 1d. *and* 1s.6d.) (3) (9.70)			40·00	
13/25 *Set of 13 Gutter Pairs*				

Thinner paper – see note after Jersey No. 29.

There was no postal need for the ½d. and 1½d. values as the ½d. coin had been withdrawn prior to their issue in anticipation of decimalisation. These values were only on sale at the Philatelic Bureau and at the Crown Agents as well as in the U.S.A.

Type **18** was re-issued as a booklet pane in 2001. See No. 927.

Printings: (a) 1.10.69; (b) 24.11.69; (c). 12.12.69; (d) 1.70; (e) 4.2.70; (f) 4.3.70; (g) 18.5.70; (h) 7.71.

Cylinder Nos.: ½d., 1½d., 2s.6d. 1A–1A, 1B–1B; 1d. (I) 1A–1A (a); 2A–2A, 2B–2B (b); 1d. (II) 2A–2A, 2B–2B (e); 3A–3A, 3B–3B (g) 2d.,3d/, 5d., 6d., 9d., 1s. 1A, 1B (each×4); 4d., 1s.9d. 1A, 1B (each×5); 1s.6d. (I) 1A–1A, 1B–1B (a); 1A–2A, 1B–2B (d); 1s6d. (II) 1B–1B, 1A–2A, 1B–2B (e); 2A–3A, 2B–2B (g) 2B–3B; 5s to £1 None. Sheets: 60 (2 panes (5×6) most sheets of the 5s., 10s. and £1 were divided into two panes before issue.

Imprint: Central, bottom margin (½d. to 2s.6d.).

Quantities sold ½d. 2,480,000; 1d. (Nos. 14/14b) 1,560,971; 1½d. 980,000; 2d. 574,610; 3d. 487,199; 4d. 2,782,490; 5d. 1,393,193; 6d. 456,275; 9d. 374,975; 1s 435,773; 1s.6d. (Nos. 23/23b) 627,003; 1s.9d. 255,111; 2s.6d. 225,732; 5s. 165,047; 10s. (No. 27) 114,000; 10s. (No. 27a) 55,200; £1 (No. 28) 120,000; £1 (No. 28a) 141,802.

Sold out: 8.71 10s. (No. 27a).

Withdrawn: 6.10.69, ½d., 1½d.; 4.2.70, 1d. (No. 14), 1s.6d. (No. 23); others 14.2.72 (except for No. 28a which remained on sale with Decimal definitives until 31.3.76).

Although officially withdrawn the ½d., 1d. (No. 14), 1½d. and 1s.6d. (No. 23) were subsequently included in *Presentation Packs*, whilst the ½d. and 1½d. remained on sale at the Philatelic Bureau until 14 February 1972.

Invalidated: 14.2.72. (except £1).

19 Isaac Brock as Colonel   **20** Sir Isaac Brock as major-General

21 Isaac Brock as Ensign   **22** Arms and Flags

Birth Bicentenary of Sir Isaac Brock

(Litho Format)

1969 (1 Dec). P 13½×14 (2s.6d.) or 14×13½ (others), all comb.

29	**19**	4d. multicoloured	20	20
30	**20**	5d. multicoloured	20	20
31	**21**	1s.9d. multicoloured	90	75
32	**22**	2s.6d. multicoloured	90	75
29/32 *Set of 4*			2·00	1·70
First Day Cover				3·25
Presentation Pack			3·75	
Set of 4 Gutter Pairs			£120	

Plate Nos. 4d., 2s.6d. 1A, 1B, 1C, 1D. (each×6); 5d. 1A, 1B, 1C, 1D. (each×7); 1s.9d. 1A, 1B, 1C, 1D. (each×5).

Sheets: 60 (2 panes 5×6) 2s.6d.; (2 panes 6×5) others.

Imprint: Right-hand corner, bottom margin.

Quantities sold: 4d. 940,956; 5d. 732,658; 1s.9d. 224,157; 2s.6d. 218,955.

Withdrawn: 30.11.70.

Invalidated: 14.2.72.

23 H.M.S. *L103* (landing craft) entering St. Peter's Harbour

24 H.M.S. *Bulldog* and H.M.S. *Beagle* (destroyers) entering St. Peter Port   **25** Brigadier Snow reading the Proclamation

25th Anniversary of Liberation

(Des and photo Courvoisier)

1970 (9 May). Granite paper. P 11½ (C).

33	**23**	4d. blue and pale blue	20	20
34	**24**	5d. brown-lake and pale grey	40	20
35	**25**	1s.6d. bistre-brown and buff	1·20	1·20
33/5 *Set of 3*			1·50	1·50
First Day Cover				2·40
Presentation Pack			4·00	

Cylinder Nos.: A1–1, B1–1 (all values).

Sheets: 25 (5×5).

Imprint: Left-hand corner, top margin (4d., 5d.); bottom corner, left-hand margin (1s.6d.).

Quantities sold: 4d. 968,873; 5d. 817,958; 1s.6d. 248,532.

Withdrawn: 8.5.71.

Invalidated: 14.2.72.

26 Guernsey 'Toms'   **27** Guernsey Cow

28 Guernsey Bull   **29** Freesias

Agriculture and Horticulture

(Des and Photo Courvoisier)

1970 (12 Aug). Granite paper. P 11½ (C).

36	**26**	4d. multicoloured	55	20
37	**27**	5d. multicoloured	70	20
38	**28**	9d. multicoloured	2·50	1·30
39	**29**	1s.6d. multicoloured	2·75	2·40
36/9 *Set of 4*			5·00	4·00
First Day Cover				5·00
Presentation Pack			18·00	

Cylinder Nos.: A1–1–1–1, B1–1–1–1, C1–1–1–1, D1–1–1–1 (all values).

Sheets: 25 (5×5).

Imprint: Central, bottom margin.

Quantities sold: 4d. 1,082.608; 5d. 1,000,000; 9d. 237,685; 1s.6d. 241,816.

Withdrawn: 11.8.71.

Invalidated: 14.2.72.

30 St. Anne's Church, Alderney   **31** St. Peter's Church, Guernsey

32 St. Peters Church, Sark   **33** St. Tugual Chapel, Herm

Christmas. Guernsey Churches (1st series)

(Des and photo Courvoisier)

1970 (11 Nov). Granite paper. P 11½ (C).

40	**30**	4d. multicoloured	20	10
41	**31**	5d. multicoloured	20	10
42	**32**	9d. multicoloured	1·20	1·00
43	**33**	1s.6d. multicoloured	1·50	1·20
40/3	*Set of 4*		2·50	2·00
First Day Cover				2·25
Presentation Pack			5·00	

See also Nos. 63/6.
Cylinder Nos.: A1–1–1–1 or B1–1–1–1 (all values).
Sheets: 50 (5×10) 4d., 5d.; (10×5) others.
Quantities sold: 4d. 815,737; 5d. 668.886; 9d. 236,833; 1s.6d. 223,907.
Withdrawn: 10.11.71.
Invalidated: 14.2.72.

34 Martello Tower and King John

Decimal Currency

(Photo Harrison (½p. to 10p.), Delrieu (others))

1971 (6 Jan)–**73**. Designs as Type **4** etc., but values inscribed in decimal currency as in Type **34**. Chalk-surfaced paper. P 14 (½p. to 10p.) or (13½×13) (others), all comb.

44	**4**	½p. deep magenta and black (b)	10	15
		a. Booklet stamp with margins.		
		Glazed, ordinary paper	15	20
		ab. Ditto. Chalk-surfaced paper (f)	15	20
45	**5**	1p. bright blue and black (ll) (b)	10	10
46	**6**	1½p. yellow-brown and black (b)	15	15
47	**9**	2p. multicoloured (b)	15	15
		a. Booklet stamp with margins.		
		Glazed, ordinary paper	20	20
		ab. Ditto. Chalk-surfaced paper (f)	20	20
		ac. Emerald (stem) omitted	£2750	
		b. Glazed, ordinary paper (b)	20	20
48	**10**	2½p. gold, bright vermilion, bluish		
		violet and black (bf)	15	10
		a. Bright vermilion omitted	£1500	
		b. Booklet stamp with margins.		
		Glazed, ordinary paper	20	20
		ba. Ditto. Chalk-surfaced paper (f)	20	20
49	**8**	3p. gold, pale greenish yellow,		
		orange-red and black (bf)	20	20
50	**14**	3½p. mult (glazed, ordinary paper) (b)	20	20
51	**7**	4p. multicoloured (b)	20	20
52	**5**	5p. turquoise-green and black (ll) (b)	20	20
53	**11**	6p. gold, pale greenish yellow, lt		
		bronze-green and black (b)	20	20
54	**13**	7½p. gold, brt verm, bistre and blk (b)	30	35
55	**12**	9p. gold, brt red, crimson and blk (b)	75	75
56	**34**	10p. bright reddish violet and blk (a)	1·90	1·90
		a. Ordinary paper. Bright reddish		
		violet and deep black (d)	1·50	1·50
57	**16**	20p. mult (glazed, ordinary paper) (ag)	70	70
		a. Shade* (e)	85	85
58	**17**	50p. mult (glazed, ordinary paper) (aeh)	1·50	1·50
44/58	*Set of 15*		6·00	6·00
First Day Covers (2)				9·00
44/58, 28a *Presentation Packs (3)*			11·00	
44/56 *Set of 13 Gutter Pairs*			18·00	

*No. 57 has the sky in a pale turquoise-blue; on No. 57a it is pale turquoise-green.
Printings: (a) 6.1.71; (b) 15.2.71; (c). 3.72; (d) 1.9.72; (e) 25.1.73; (f) 2.4.73; (g) 10.74; (h) 7.75.
Cylinder Nos.: ½p., 1p., 1½p., 5p., 10p. 1A–1A, 1B–1B; 2p., 3½p. 1A, 1B (each×5); 2½p., 3p., 4p., 6p., 7½p., 9p. 1A, 1B (each×4); 20p none; 50p. 21–22–23–24. Sheets from ptg (g) have an additional S99 (reversed).
On the 3½p. only four '1A' Nos. are shown in the margin, the black '1A' being omitted in error.
Sheets: 50 (2 panes 5×5) ½p to 10p.; 30 (5×6) others.
Imprint: Central, bottom margin (½p. to 10p.).
Quantities sold: ½p. 980,959; 1p. 568,509; 1½p. 559,576; 2p.2,512,903; 2½p. 4,469,578; 3p. 2,245,564; 3½p. 317,523; 4p. 527,696; 5p. 511,742; 6p. 346,255; 7½p. 322,905; 9p. 349,211; 10p. 538,153;20p 630,888; 50p 258,150.
In addition to the 10p.–£1 pack, a 10p.–50p. Presentation pack also exists.
Withdrawn: 1.4.75 ½p. to 10p. (½p., 9p. 10p. and *Presentation Pack*s sold out by 5.74); 31.3.76 20p., 50p.

35 Hong Kong 2c. of 1862

36 Great Britain 4d. of 1855–7

37 Italy 5c. of 1862

38 Confederate States 5c. of 1862

Thomas de la Rue Commemoration

(Des and recess DLR)

1971 (2 June). P 14×13½ (C).

59	**35**	2p. dull purple to brown-purple*	35	15
60	**36**	2½p. carmine-red	35	15
61	**37**	4p. deep bluish green	1·10	1·10
62	**38**	7½p. deep blue	1·40	1·40
59/62	*Set of 4*		2·75	2·75
First Day Cover				4·00
Presentation Pack			4·50	

*These colours represent the extreme range of shades of this value. The majority of the printing, however, is an intermediate shade.
Plate Nos.: 1A, 1B each.
Sheets: 25 (5×5).
Imprint: Central, bottom margin.
Quantities sold: 2p. 897,742; 2½p. 1,404,085; 4p. 210,691; 7½p. 199,424.
Withdrawn: 1.6.72.

39 Ebenezer Church, St. Peter Port

40 Church of St. Pierre du Bois

41 St. Joseph's Church, St. Peter Port

42 Church of St. Phillipe de Toteval

Christmas. Guernsey Churches (2nd series)

(Des and photo Courvoisier)

1971 (27 Oct). Granite paper. P 11½ (C).

63	**39**	2p. multicoloured	20	10
64	**40**	2½p. multicoloured	20	10
65	**41**	5p. multicoloured	1·10	1·10
66	**42**	7½p. multicoloured	1·40	1·40
63/6 Set of 4			2·50	2·40
First Day Cover				3·00
Presentation Pack			4·00	
Set of 4 Gutter Pairs			16·00	

Cylinder Nos: A1–1–1–1, B1–1–1–1, C1–1–1–1, D1–1–1–1 (all values).
Sheets: 50 (2 panes 5×5).
Imprint: central, bottom margin (2p., 2½p.) or left-hand corner, bottom margin (5p., 7½p.).
Quantities sold: 2p. 991,155; 2½p. 916,004; 5p. 223,412; 7½p. 215,768.
Withdrawn: 26.10.72.

43 Earl of Chesterfield (1794)

44 Dasher (1827)

45 Ibex (1891)

46 Alberta (1900)

Mail Packet Boats (1st series)

(Des and photo Courvoisier)

1972 (10 Feb). Granite paper. P 11 (C).

67	**43**	2p. multicoloured	15	10
68	**44**	2½p. multicoloured	15	10
69	**45**	7½p. multicoloured	40	35
70	**46**	9p. multicoloured	60	50
67/70 Set of 4			1·20	95
First Day Cover				3·00
Presentation Pack			3·00	

See also Nos. 80/3.
Cylinder Nos.: A1–1–1–1 or B1–1–1–1 (all values).
Sheets: 25 (5×5).
Imprint: Central, bottom margin.
Quantities sold: 2p. 973,503; 2½p. 954,263; 7½p. 288,929; 9p. 289,340.
Withdrawn: 9.2.73.

47 Guernsey Bull

World Conference of Guernsey Breeders, Guernsey

(Photo Courvoisier)

1972 (22 May). Granite paper. P 11½ (C).

71	**47**	5p. multicoloured	45	40
First Day Cover*				2·50
Gutter Pair			4·50	

*Prepared by the Royal Guernsey Agricultural and Horticultural Society.
Cylinder Nos.: A1–1–1–1, B1–1–1–1.
Sheets: 50 (2 panes 5×5).

48 Bermuda Buttercup   **49** Heath Spotted Orchid

50 Kaffir Fig   **51** Scarlet Pimpernel

Wild Flowers

(Des and photo Courvoisier)

1972 (24 May). Granite paper. P 11½ (C).

72	**48**	2p. multicoloured	10	10
73	**49**	2½p. multicoloured	10	10
74	**50**	7½p. multicoloured	50	50
75	**51**	9p. multicoloured	60	60
72/5 Set of 4			1·00	1·00
First Day Cover				2·50
Presentation Pack			3·25	
Set of 4 Gutter Pairs			4·00	

Cylinder Nos.: A1–1–1–1, B1–1–1–1, C1–1–1–1, D1–1–1–1 (all values).
Sheets: 50 (2 panes 5×5).
Imprint: 2p., 7½p. Central, bottom margin, others left-hand corner, bottom margin.
Quantities sold: 2p. 1,006,041; 2½p. 1,028,826; 7½p. 249,471; 9p. 244,839.
Withdrawn: 23.5.73.

52 Angels adoring Christ   **53** The Epiphany

54 The Virgin Mary   **55** Christ

Royal Silver Wedding and Christmas

(Des and photo Courvoisier)

1972 (20 Nov). Designs show stained glass windows from Guernsey Churches. Granite paper. P 11½ (C).

76	**52**	2p. multicoloured	20	20
77	**53**	2½p. multicoloured	20	20
78	**54**	7½p. multicoloured	30	30
79	**55**	9p. multicoloured	45	45
76/9 *Set of 4*			1·00	1·00
First Day Cover				1·10
Presentation Pack			1·90	
Set of 4 Gutter Pairs			2·50	

Cylinder Nos.: A1-1-1-1-1, B1-1-1-1-1 each.
Sheets: 50 (2 panes 5×5).
Imprint: Central, bottom margin of each pane.
Quantities sold: 2p. 878.893; 2½p. 1,037,387; 7½p. 314,972; 9p 313,367.
Sold out: By 31.3.73.

56 *St. Julien* (1925)

57 *Isle of Guernsey* (1930)

58 *St. Patrick* (1947)

59 *Sarnia* (1961)

Mail Packet Boats (2nd series)

(Des and photo Courvoisier)

1973 (9 Mar). Granite paper. P 11½ (C).

80	**56**	2½p. multicoloured	10	10
81	**57**	3p. multicoloured	20	20
82	**58**	7½p. multicoloured	40	40
83	**59**	9p. multicoloured	45	45
80/3 *Set of 4*			1·10	1·00
First Day Cover				1·40
Presentation Pack			2·00	
Set of 4 Gutter Pairs			5·00	

Cylinder Nos.: All values A1-1-1-1, B1-1-1-1, C1-1-1-1, D1-1-1-1.
Sheets: 50 (2 panes 5×5).
Imprint: Central, bottom margin of each pane.
Quantities sold: 2½p. 947,888; 3p. 1,274,699; 7½p. 278,998; 9p 263,569.
Withdrawn: 8.3.74. (3p. and *Presentation Pack* sold out earlier).

60 Supermarine Sea Eagle

61 Westland Wessex Trimotor

62 de Havilland DH.89 Dragon Rapide

63 Douglas DC-3

64 Vickers Viscount 800 *Anne Marie*

50th Anniversary of Air Service

(Des and photo Courvoisier)

1973 (4 July). Granite paper. P 11½ (C).

84	**60**	2½p. multicoloured	10	10
85	**61**	3p. multicoloured	10	10
86	**62**	5p. multicoloured	25	25
87	**63**	7½p. multicoloured	35	30
88	**64**	9p. multicoloured	45	45
84/8 *Set of 5*			1·10	1·00
First Day Cover				1·50
Presentation Pack			2·00	
Set of 5 Gutter Pairs			4·00	

Cylinder Nos.: A1-1-1-1, B1-1-1-1 each.
Sheets: 50 (2 panes (5×5).
Imprint: Central, bottom margin of each pane.
Quantities sold: 2½p. 918,953; 3p. 1,285,890; 5p. 313,882; 7½p. 294,369; 9p. 288,225.
Withdrawn: 3.7.74. (5p. and *Presentation Pack* sold out earlier).

65 'The Good Shepherd'

66 Christ at the Well of Samaria

67 St. Dominic

68 Mary and the Child Jesus

Christmas

(Des and photo Courvoisier)

1973 (24 Oct). Designs show stained glass windows from Guernsey Churches. Granite paper. P 11½ (C).

89	**65**	2½p. multicoloured	20	20
90	**66**	3p. multicoloured	20	20
91	**67**	7½p. multicoloured	40	40
92	**68**	20p. multicoloured	50	50
89/92 *Set of 4*			1·10	1·10
First Day Cover				1·25
Presentation Pack			1·50	
Set of 4 Gutter Pairs			2·50	

Cylinder Nos.: A1–1–1–1, B1–1–1–1 each.
Sheets: 50 (2 panes 5×5).
Imprint: Central, bottom margin of each pane.
Quantities sold: 2½p. 1,284,342; 3p. 1,285,851; 7½p. 367,714; 20p. 367,625.
Withdrawn: 23.10.74.

69 Princess Anne and Capt. Mark Phillips

Royal Wedding

(Des G. Anderson. Photo Courvoisier)

1973 (14 Nov). Granite paper. P 11½ (C).

93	**69**	25p. multicoloured	75	55
First Day Cover				75
Presentation Pack			90	
Gutter Pair			1·50	

Cylinder Nos.: A1–1–1–1, B1–1–1–1.
Sheets: 50 (2 panes 5×5).
Imprint: Central, bottom margin of each pane.
Quantity sold: 392,767.
Withdrawn: 13.11.74.

70 *John Lockett*, 1875

71 *Arthur Lionel*, 1912

72 *Euphrosyne Kendal*, 1954

73 *Arun*, 1972

150th Anniversary of Royal National Life-boat Institution

(Des and photo Courvoisier)

1974 (15 Jan). Granite paper. P 11½ (C).

94	**70**	2½p. multicoloured	15	15
95	**71**	3p. multicoloured	15	15
96	**72**	8p. multicoloured	30	30
97	**73**	10p. multicoloured	40	40
94/7 *Set of 4*			90	90
First Day Cover				1·00
Presentation Pack			1·60	
Set of 4 Gutter Pairs			1·50	

Cylinder Nos.: A1–1–1–1, B1–1–1–1 each.
Sheets: 50 (2 panes 5×5).
Imprint: Central, bottom margin of each pane.
Quantities sold: 2½p. 1,016,058; 3p. 1,162,020; 8p. 393,660; 10p. 393,668.
Withdrawn: 14.1.75 (8p., 10p. and *Presentation Pack* sold out earlier).

74 Private, East Regt., 1815

75 Officer, 2nd North Regt., 1825

76 Gunner, Guernsey Artillery, 1787

77 Gunner, Guernsey Artillery, 1815

78 Corporal, Royal Guernsey Artillery, 1868

79 Field Officer, Royal Guernsey Artillery, 1895

80 Sergeant, 3rd Regt., 1867

81 Officer, East Regt., 1822

82 Field Officer, Royal Guernsey Artillery, 1895

83 Colour-Sergeant of Grenadiers, 1833

84 Officer, North Regt., 1832

85 Officer, East Regt., 1822

86 Field Officer, Rifle Company, 1868

87 Private, 4th West Regt., 1785

88 Field Officer, 4th West Regt., 1824

89 Driver, Field Battery, Royal Guernsey Artillery, 1848

90 Officer, Field Battery, Royal Guernsey Artillery, 1868

91 Cavalry Trooper, Light Dragoons, 1814

Guernsey Militia

(Photo Courvoisier (½p to 10p.), Delrieu (others))

1974 (2 Apr)–**78**. Granite paper (½p. to 10p.). P 11½ (½p. to 10p.), 13×13½ (20, 50p.) or 13½×13 (£1), all comb.

98	**74**	½p. multicoloured (ak)	10	10
		a. Booklet strip of 8 (98×5 and 102×3) †	35	
		b. Booklet pane of 16 (98×4, 102×6 and 103×6) †	75	
99	**75**	1p. multicoloured (acj)	10	10
		a. Booklet strip of 8 (99×4, 103, 105×2 and 105a) (8.2.77) †	55	
		b. Booklet strip of 4 (99, 101×2, and 105a) (7.2.78) †	35	
100	**76**	1½p. multicoloured (a)	10	10
101	**77**	2p. multicoloured (al)	10	10
102	**78**	2½p. multicoloured (a)	10	10
103	**79**	3p. multicoloured (a)	10	10
104	**80**	3½p. multicoloured (a)	10	10
105	**81**	4p. multicoloured (abc)	10	10
105a	**82**	5p. multicoloured (f)	15	15
106	**83**	5½p. multicoloured (a)	15	15
107	**84**	6p. multicoloured (ae)	15	15
107a	**85**	7p. multicoloured (f)	30	30
108	**86**	8p. multicoloured (ah)	25	25
109	**87**	9p. multicoloured (am)	25	25
110	**88**	10p. multicoloured (ai)	30	30
111	**89**	20p. multicoloured (d)	60	60
112	**90**	50p. multicoloured (d)	1·75	1·60
113	**91**	£1 multicoloured (d)	2·50	2·00
98/113 Set of 18			5·50	5·50
First Day Covers (3)				5·75
Presentation Packs (4)			5·75	
Set of 15 Gutter Pairs (Nos. 98/110)			3·50	

†Nos. 98a/b come from a special booklet sheet of 88 (8×11), and Nos. 99a/b from booklet sheets of 80 (two panes 8×5). These sheets were put on sale in addition to the normal sheets. The strips and panes have the left-hand selvedge stuck into booklet covers, except for No. 99b which had the strip loose, and then folded and supplied in plastic wallets.

Printings: (a) 2.4.74; (b) 10.74; (c). 12.74; (d) 1.4.75; (e) 12.75; (f) 29.5.76; (g) 6.76; (h) 7.76; (i) 11.76; (j) 8.2.77; (k) 7.77; (l) 12.77; (m) 8.12.78.

Plate Nos.: 20p to £1 none; A1–1–1–1, B1–1–1–1–1 1½p., 2p., 6p.; A1–1–1–1, B1–1–1–1 others.

Sheets: 20p to £1, 25 (5×5); others, 100 (2 panes 10×5).

Imprint: Central, bottom margin of each page.

Quantities sold: ½p. 1,173,560; 1p. 1,367,828; 1½p. 525,248; 2p. 1,098,053; 2½p. 1,124,091; 3p. 1,953,796; 3½p. 1,891,493; 4p. 3,435, 614; 5p. 2, 920,246; 5½p. 634,870; 6p. 2,006,983; 7p. 3,103, 925; 8p. 811, 418; 9p. 717,815; 10p. 1,133, 141; 20p. 788, 840; 50p 570,505; £1 464,428.

Withdrawn: 12.2.80 ½p. to 20p; 4.2.81 50p, £1.

92 Badge of Guernsey and U.P.U. Emblem

93 Map of Guernsey

94 U.P.U. Building, Berne, and Guernsey Flag

95 'Salles des Etats'

Centenary of Universal Postal Union

(Photo Courvoisier)

1974 (7 June). Granite paper. P 11½ (C).

114	**92**	2½p. multicoloured	15	15
115	**93**	3p. multicoloured	15	15
116	**94**	8p. multicoloured	25	25
117	**95**	10p. multicoloured	30	30
114/17 Set of 4			75	75
First Day Cover				90
Presentation Pack			1·10	
Set of 4 Gutter Pairs			1·50	

Cylinder Nos.: 2½p., 8p. A1–1–1, B1–1–1; 3p. A1–1–1–1, B1–1–1–1; 10p. A1–1–1–1–1, B1–1–1–1–1.

Sheets: 50 (2 panes 5×5).

Imprint: Central, bottom margin.

Quantities sold: 2½p. 1,231,657; 3p. 1,839,674; 8p. 345,271; 10p. 356,501.

Withdrawn: 6.6.75.

96 'Cradle Rock'

97 'La Baie de Moulin Huet'

98 'Au Bord de la Mer'   **99** Self-portrait

Renoir Paintings

(Des and photo Delrieu)

1974 (21 Sept). P 13 (C).

118	**96**	3p. multicoloured	20	20
119	**97**	5½p. multicoloured	20	20
120	**98**	8p. multicoloured	40	40
121	**99**	10p. multicoloured	40	40
118/21 Set of 4			1·00	1·00
First Day Cover				1·25
Presentation Pack			2·00	

     Sheets: 25 (5×5).
     Imprint: Right-hand corner, top margin (3p. and 5½p.), and bottom corner, right-hand margin (others).
     Quantities sold: 3p. 670,648; 5p. 422,677; 8p. 377,615; 10p. 391,095.
     Withdrawn: 20.9.75.

100 Guernsey   **101** Guernsey
Spleenwort   Quillwort

102 Guernsey Fern   **103** Least Adder's
                              Tongue

Guernsey Ferns

(Des and photo Courvoisier)

1975 (7 Jan). Granite paper. P 11½ (C).

122	**100**	3½p. multicoloured	20	20
123	**101**	4p. multicoloured	20	20
124	**102**	8p. multicoloured	40	40
125	**103**	10p. multicoloured	40	40
122/5 Set of 4			1·00	1·00
First Day Cover				1·25
Presentation Pack			2·00	
Set of 4 Gutter Pairs			2·00	

     Cylinder Nos.: 3½p., 4p., 8p. each A1–1–1–1, B1–1–1–1, C1–1–1–1, D1–1–1–1; 10p. A1–1–1–1–1, B1–1–1–1–1, C1–1–1–1–1, D1–1–1–1–1.
     Sheets: 50 (2 panes 5×5).
     Imprint: Central, bottom margin.
     Quantities sold: 3½p. 1,089,142; 4p. 1,370,743; 8p. 430,672; 10p. 443,636.
     Withdrawn: 6.1.76.

104 Victor Hugo House   **105** Candie Gardens

106 United Europe   **107** Tapestry Room, Hauteville
Oak, Hauteville

Victor Hugo's Exile in Guernsey

(Des and photo Courvoisier)

1975 (6 June). Granite paper. P 11½ (C).

126	**104**	3½p. multicoloured	20	20
127	**105**	4p. multicoloured	20	20
128	**106**	8p. multicoloured	40	40
129	**107**	10p. multicoloured	40	40
126/9 Set of 4			1·00	1·00
First Day Cover				1·25
Presentation Pack			1·90	
MS130 114×143 mm Nos. 126/9			1·00	1·00
First Day Cover				6·50

     Cylinder Nos.: A1–1–1–1, B1–1–1–1 each.
     Sheets: 50 (5×10) 3½p., 10p.; (10×5) others.
     Imprint: Central, left-hand margin (3½p., 10p.) or central, bottom margin (4p., 8p.).
     Quantities sold: 3½p. 810,327; 4p. 1,346,628; 8p. 377,637; 10p. 369,282; miniature sheet 269,217.
     Withdrawn: 5.6.76.

108 Globe and Seal of   **109** Globe and
Bailiwick   Guernsey Flag

110 Globe, Guernsey Flag and
Alderney Shield

111 Globe, Guernsey Flag and
Sark Shield

Christmas

(Des and photo Delrieu)

1975 (7 Oct). P 13 (C).

131	**108**	4p. multicoloured		20	20
132	**109**	6p. multicoloured		20	20
133	**110**	10p. multicoloured		40	40
134	**111**	12p. multicoloured		40	40
131/4		*Set of 4*		1·00	1·00
		First Day Cover			1·25
		Presentation Pack		1·50	

Sheets: 25 (5×5).
Imprint: Central, left-hand margin (4p., 6p.); central, bottom margin (10p., 12p.).
Quantities sold: 4p., 678,619; 6p. 667,413; 10p. 392,529; 12p. 361,548.
Withdrawn: 6.10.76.

112 Les Hanois

113 Les Casquets

114 Quesnard

115 Point Robert

Lighthouses

(Des and photo Courvoisier)

1976 (10 Feb). Granite paper. P 11½ (C).

135	**112**	4p. multicoloured		20	20
136	**113**	6p. multicoloured		20	20
137	**114**	11p. multicoloured		40	40
138	**115**	13p. multicoloured		40	40
135/8		*Set of 4*		1·00	1·00
		First Day Cover			1·25
		Presentation Pack		1·50	
		Set of 4 Gutter Pairs		2·00	

Cylinder Nos.: A1–1–1–1, B1–1–1–1 each.
Sheets: 50 (2 panes 5×5).
Quantities sold: 4p. 846,362; 6p. 900,899; 11p. 366,468; 13p. 348,358.
Withdrawn: 9.2.77.

116 Milk Can

117 Christening Cup

Europa. Handicrafts

(Des and photo Courvoisier)

1976 (29 May). Granite paper. P 11½ (C).

139	**116**	10p. brown and green		35	35
140	**117**	25p. grey and blue		70	70
139/40		*Set of 2*		90	90
		First Day Cover			1·10
		Presentation Pack		1·25	

Sheets: 9 (3×3).
Quantities sold: 1,185,014 of each.
Sold out: 4.6.76.

118 Pine Forest, Guernsey

119 Herm and Jethou

120 Grand Greve Bay,   **121** Trois Vaux Bay,
Sark   Alderney

Views

(Des and photo Courvoisier)

1976 (3 Aug). Granite paper. P 11½ (C).

141	**118**	5p. multicoloured		20	20
142	**119**	7p. multicoloured		20	20
143	**120**	11p. multicoloured		40	40
144	**121**	13p. multicoloured		40	40
141/4		*Set of 4*		1·00	1·00
		First Day Cover			1·25
		Presentation Pack		1·50	
		Set of 4 Gutter Pairs		2·00	

Cylinder Nos.: A1–1–1–1, B1–1–1–1 each.
Sheets: 50 (2 panes 5×5).
Quantities sold: 5p. 661,771; 7p. 1,016,350; 11p. 349,773; 13p. 336,027.
Withdrawn: 2.8.77.

122 Royal Court House, Guernsey

123 Elizabeth College, Guernsey

124 La Seigneurie, Sark

125 Island Hall, Alderney

Christmas. Buildings

(Des and photo Courvoisier)

1976 (14 Oct). Granite paper. P 11½ (C).

145	**122**	5p. multicoloured	20	20
146	**123**	7p. multicoloured	20	20
147	**124**	11p. multicoloured	40	40
148	**125**	13p. multicoloured	40	40
145/8	*Set of 4*		1·00	1·00
First Day Cover				1·25
Presentation Pack			1·50	
Set of 4 Gutter Pairs			2·00	

Cylinder Nos.: A1–1–1–1, B1–1–1–1 each.
Sheets: 50 (2 panes 5×5).
Imprint: Central, bottom margin.
Quantities sold: 5p. 1,097,445; 7p. 1,051,184; 11p. 371,155; 13p. 352,347.
Withdrawn: 13.10.77.

126 Queen Elizabeth II

127 Queen Elizabeth II

Silver Jubilee

(Des R. Granger Barrett. Photo Courvoisier)

1977 (8 Feb). Granite Paper. P 11½ (C).

149	**126**	7p. multicoloured	30	30
150	**127**	35p. multicoloured	1·00	1·00
149/50	*Set of 2*		1·10	1·10
First Day Cover				1·25
Presentation Pack			1·50	

Cylinder Nos.: 7p. A1–1–1–1, B1–1–1–1; 35p. A1–1–1–1–1.
Sheets: 25 (5×5).
Imprint: Central, bottom margin.
Quantities sold: 7p. 1,004,250; 35p. 536,971.
Withdrawn: 7.2.78.

128 Woodland, Talbot's Valley

129 Pastureland, Talbot's Valley

Europa. Landscapes

(Des and photo Courvoisier)

1977 (17 May). Granite paper. P 11½ (C).

151	**128**	7p. multicoloured	40	40
152	**129**	25p. multicoloured	70	70
151/2	*Set of 2*		1·00	1·00
First Day Cover				1·25
Presentation Pack			1·50	
Set of 2 Gutter Pairs			2·00	

Cylinder Nos.: A1–1–1–1, B1–1–1–1 each.
Sheets: 50 (2 panes 5×5).
Imprint: Right-hand corner, bottom margin.
Quantities sold: 7p. 1,371,463; 25p. 598,453.
Withdrawn: 16.5.78.

130 Statue-menhir, Castel

131 Megalithic Tomb, St. Saviour

132 Cist, Tourgis

133 Statue-menhir, St. Martin

Prehistoric Monuments

(Des and photo Courvoisier)

1977 (2 Aug). Granite paper. P 11½ (C).

153	**130**	5p. multicoloured	20	20
154	**131**	7p. multicoloured	20	20
155	**132**	11p. multicoloured	40	40
156	**133**	13p. multicoloured	40	40
153/6	*Set of 4*		1·00	1·00
First Day Cover				1·25
Presentation Pack			1·50	
Set of 4 Gutter Pairs			2·00	

Cylinder Nos.: A1–1–1–1, B1–1–1–1 each.
Sheets: 50 (2 panes 5×5).
Imprint: Central, right-hand margin (5p. and 13p.); Central, bottom margin (others).
Quantities sold: 5p. 747,236; 7p. 1,077,714; 11p. 390,927; 13p. 373,063.
Withdrawn: 1.8.78.

134 Mobile First Aid Unit

135 Mobile Radar Unit

136 Marine Ambulance *Flying Christine II*　　**137** Cliff Rescue

Christmas. St. John Ambulance Centenary

(Des P. Slade and M. Horder. Photo Courvoisier)

1977 (25 Oct). Granite paper. P 11½ (C).

157	**134**	5p. multicoloured	20	20
158	**135**	7p. multicoloured	20	20
159	**136**	11p. multicoloured	40	40
160	**137**	13p. multicoloured	40	40
157/60	*Set of 4*		1·00	1·00
	First Day Cover			1·25
	Presentation Pack		1·50	
	Set of 4 Gutter Pairs		2·00	

Cylinder Nos.: 5p. A1–1–1–1–1, B1–1–1–1–1; others A1–1–1–1, B1–1–1–1.
Sheets: 50 (2 panes 5×5).
Imprint: Right-hand corner, bottom margin (7p. and 11p.); top, right-hand margin (others).
Quantities sold: 5p. 1,218,293; 7p. 1,155,448; 11p. 406,244; 13p. 383,489.
Withdrawn: 24.10.78.

138 View from Clifton, c. 1830

139 Market Square, St. Peter Port, c. 1838

140 Petit-Bo Bay, c. 1839

141 The Quay, St. Peter Port, c. 1830

Old Guernsey Prints (1st series)

(Des, recess and litho DLR)

1978 (7 Feb). P 14×13½ (C).

161	**138**	5p. black and light stone	20	20
162	**139**	7p. black and cream	20	20
163	**140**	11p. black and light pink	40	40
164	**141**	13p. black and light azure	40	40
161/4	*Set of 4*		1·00	1·00
	First Day Cover			1·25
	Presentation Pack		1·50	
	Set of 4 Gutter Pairs		2·00	

See also Nos. 249/52.
Plate Nos.: All values 1A–1A, 1B–1B, 1C–1C, 1D.–1D.
Sheets: 50 (2 panes 5×5).
Imprint: Left-hand corner, bottom margin.
Quantities sold: 5p. 858,816; 7p. 930,955; 11p. 442,009; 13p. 338,163.
Withdrawn: 6.2.79.

142 Prosperity Memorial　　**143** Victoria Monument

Europa. Monuments

(Des R. Granger Barrett. Litho Questa)

1978 (2 May). P 14½ (C).

165	**142**	5p. multicoloured	20	20
		a. Imperf between stamp and right margin		
166	**143**	7p. multicoloured	35	35
165/6	*Set of 2*		50	50
	First Day Cover			70
	Presentation Pack		90	

Sheets: 20 (5p. 5×4; 7p. 4×5).
Quantities sold: 5p. 2,581,345; 7p. 2,370,766.
Withdrawn: 1.5.79.

144 Queen Elizabeth　　**145** Queen Elizabeth

25th Anniversary of Coronation

(Des R. Granger Barrett from bust by Arnold Machin.
Photo Courvoisier)

1978 (2 May). Granite paper. P 11½ (C).

167	**144**	20p. black, grey and bright blue.............	55	55
First Day Cover				60
Presentation Pack..			60	
Gutter Pair..			90	

Cylinder Nos.: A1–1–1, B1–1–1.
Sheets: 50 (2 panes 5×5).
Imprint: Right-hand corner, bottom margin.
Quantity sold: 488,466.
Withdrawn: 1.5.79.

Royal Visit.

(Des R. Granger Barrett from bust by Arnold Machin.
Photo Courvoisier)

1978 (28 June). Granite paper. P 11½ (C).

168	**145**	7p. black, grey and bright green...........	30	30
First Day Cover				45
Presentation Pack..			50	
Gutter Pair..			60	

Cylinder Nos.: A1–1–1, B1–1–1.
Sheets: 50 (2 panes 5×5).
Imprint: Top corner, right-hand margin.
Quantity sold: 1,149,768.
Withdrawn: 27.6.79.

146 Northern Gannet   **147** Firecrest

148 Dartford Warbler   **149** Spotted Redshank

Birds

(Des John Waddington Ltd. Photo Courvoisier)

1978 (29 Aug). Granite paper. P 11½ (C).

169	**146**	5p. multicoloured................................	10	10
170	**147**	7p. multicoloured................................	20	15
171	**148**	11p. multicoloured..............................	30	20
172	**149**	13p. multicoloured..............................	40	30
169/72	*Set of 4*		85	70
First Day Cover..				1·00
Presentation Pack..			1·25	
Set of 4 Gutter Pairs..			1·70	

Cylinder Nos.: All values A1–1–1–1, B1–1–1–1, C1–1–1–1,
D1–1–1–1.
Sheets: 50 (2 panes 5×5).
Imprint: Right-hand corner, bottom margin.
Quantities sold: 5p. 750,011; 7p. 924,627; 11p. 442,395; 13p.
432,106.
Withdrawn: 28.8.79.

150 Solanum

151 Christmas Rose

152 Holly   **153** Mistletoe

Christmas

(Des and photo Courvoisier)

1978 (31 Oct). Granite paper. P 11½ (C).

173	**150**	5p. multicoloured................................	20	20
174	**151**	7p. multicoloured................................	20	20
175	**152**	11p. multicoloured..............................	40	40
176	**153**	13p. deep blue-green, grey and greenish yellow	40	40
173/6	*Set of 4*		1·00	1·00
First Day Cover..				1·25
Presentation Pack..			1·50	
Set of 4 Gutter pairs..			2·00	

Cylinder Nos.: 13p. A1–1–1, B1–1–1; others A1–1–1–1, B1–1–1–1.
Sheets: 50 (2 panes 5×5).
Imprint: 5, 7p. central, bottom margin; others central, right-hand
margin.
Quantities sold: 5p. 1,222,140; 7p. 1,246,260; 11p. 409,168; 13p. 372,991.
Withdrawn: 30.10.79.

154 One Double,   **155** Two Doubles,   **156** Four Doubles,
1830   1899   1902

157 Eight Doubles,   **158** Three Pence,   **159** Five New
1959   1956   pence, 1968

160 Fifty New   **161** Ten New   **162** Half New
pence, 1969   pence, 1970   Penny, 1974

163 One New   **164** Two New   **165** Half Penny,
Penny, 1971   Pence, 1971   1979

166 One Penny, 1977

167 Two Pence, 1977

168 Five Pence, 1977

169 Ten pence, 1977

170 Twenty-five Pence, 1972

171 Ten Shillings Wiliam I Commem, 1966

172 Silver Jubilee Commemorative Crown, 1977

173 Royal Silver Wedding Commemorative Crown, 1972

174 Seal of the Bailiwick

Coins

(Des R. Reed and Courvoisier (£5). Photo Courvoisier)

1979 (13 Feb)–**83**. Granite paper. P 11½ (C).

177	**154**	½p. multicoloured (a)	10	10
		a. Booklet pane. Nos. 177×2, 178×3, 179×2, 181, 183 and 187 (C)	70	
		b. Booklet pane. Nos. 177×2, 178, 179×2, and 187×3 (C)	90	
178	**155**	1p. multicoloured (al)	10	10
		a. Booklet strip of 4. Nos. 178×2, 179 and 182	40	
179	**156**	2p. multicoloured (a)	10	10
		a. Booklet strip of 5. Nos. 179, 182×2 and 184×2	90	
180	**157**	4p. multicoloured (a)	10	10
		a. Booklet pane of 10. Nos. 180 and 184, each×5 (d)	1·20	
		b. Booklet pane of 15. Nos. 180, 184 and 190, each×5(d)	2·50	
		c. Booklet pane of 10. Nos. 180×2, 185×3 and 191×5 (k)	1·90	
		d. Booklet pane of 15. Nos. 180, 185 and 191, each×5 (k)	2·20	
181	**158**	5p. grey-black, silver and chestnut (a)	10	10
		a. Grey-black, silver and yellowish brown (f)	30	40
		b. Booklet pane of 10. Nos. 181a×5, 184×4 and 191 (f)	1·70	

		c. Booklet pane of 15. Nos. 181a, 184 and 191, each×5 (f)	2·20	
182	**159**	6p. grey-black, silver and brown-red (a)	15	10
183	**160**	7p. grey-black, silver and grn (a)	20	15
184	**161**	8p. grey-blk, silver and brn (agij)	25	15
185	**162**	9p. multicoloured (a)	25	15
186	**163**	10p. mult (green background) (a)	30	25
187		10p. mult (orge background) (b)	30	15
188	**164**	11p. multicoloured (a)	30	15
189	**165**	11½p. multicoloured (b)	30	15
190	**166**	12p. multicoloured (a)	30	15
191	**167**	13p. multicoloured (ah)	30	20
192	**168**	14p. grey-blk, silver and dull bl (a)	35	20
193	**169**	15p. grey-blk, silver and bistre (a)	35	25
194	**170**	20p. grey-black, silver and dull brown (a)	60	50
195	**171**	50p. grey-black, orange-red and silver (b)	1·50	1·00
196	**172**	£1 grey-black, yellowish green and silver (b)	2·25	1·50
197	**173**	£2 grey-black, new blue and silver (b)	4·50	3·00
198	**174**	£5 multicoloured (e)	9·00	9·00
177/98 *Set of 22*			19·00	15·00
First Day Covers (4)				17·00
Presentation Packs (4)			19·00	
Set of 22 Gutter Pairs			38·00	

Nos. 177a/b, 178a, 179a, 180a/d and 181b/c come from special booklet sheets of 40 (8×5) (Nos. 177a and 178a), 30 (6×5) (Nos. 177b, 180a/b, 180d and 181b/c), 25 (5×5) (No. 179a) or 20 (4×5) (No. 180c). These were put on sale as complete sheets or separated into strips, folded and either affixed by the selvedge to booklet covers or supplied loose in plastic wallets.

The booklet sheets containing Nos. 177a/b show either four (No. 177a) or three (No. 177b) different arrangements of the same stamps.

Printings: (a) 13.2.79; (b) 5.2.80; (c) 6.5.80; (d) 24.2.81; (e) 22.5.81; (f) 2.2.82; (g) 4.82; (h) 5.82; (i) 7.82; (j) 11.82; (k) 14.3.83; (l) 6.83.

Cylinder Nos.: 5, 6, 7, 8, 14, 15, 20, 50p., £1, £2 A1–1–1, B1–1–1; others A1–1–1–1, B1–1–1–1. 1p. (6.83) A2–1–1–1, B2–1–1–1.

Sheets: ½ to 20p. 100 (2 panes 10×5); 50p. to £5.50 (2 panes 5×5).

Imprint: 50p. top corner, left-hand margin; £1, £2 right-hand corner, bottom margin; £5 bottom corner, right-hand margin; others central margin.

Quantities sold: ½p. 1,285,162; 1p. 1,888,850; 2p. 1,249,506; 4p. 650,195; 5p. 1,110,783; 6p. 1,678,775; 7p. 1,683,430; 8p. 3,059,366; 9p. 1,952,892; 10p. (No. 186) 484,956; 10p. (No. 187) 1,751,126; 11p. 711,268; 11½p. 351,422; 12p. 957,197; 13p. 1,459,086; 14p. 595,744; 15p. 677,289; 20p. 960,124; 50p. 863,760; £1 537,871; £2 375,786.

Withdrawn: 4.2.81 10p. (No. 186); 22.7.85 (all other values except £5); 31.12.98 £5.

175 Pillar Box and Postmark, 1853, Mail Van and Postmark, 1979

176 Telephone, 1897 and Telex Machine, 1979

Europa. Communications

(Des R. Granger Barrett. Photo Courvoisier)

1979 (8 May). Granite paper. P 11½ (C).

201	**175**	6p. multicoloured	20	20
202	**176**	8p. multicoloured	35	35
201/2 *Set of 2*			50	50
First Day Cover				70
Presentation Pack			90	

Cylinder Nos.: Both values A1–1–1–1–1, B1–1–1–1–1.

Sheets: 20 (5×4).

Quantities sold: 6p. 1,863,564; 8p. 2,293,379.

Withdrawn: 7.5.80.

177 Steam Tram, 1879

178 Electric Tram, 1896

179 Motor Bus, 1911

180 Motor Bus, 1979

History of Public Transport

(Photo Courvoisier)

1979 (7 Aug). Granite paper. P 11½ (C).

203	**177**	6p. multicoloured	30	30
204	**178**	8p. multicoloured	15	15
205	**179**	11p. multicoloured	40	40
206	**180**	13p. multicoloured	40	40
203/6 *Set of 4*			1·00	1·00
First Day Cover				1·25
Presentation Pack			1·50	
Set of 4 Gutter Pairs			2·00	

Cylinder Nos.: 6p. A1–1–1–1–1, B1–1–1–1–1; others A1–1–1–1, B1–1–1–1.
Sheets: 50 (2 panes 5×5).
Imprint: Central, bottom margin.
Quantities sold: 6p. 676,046; 8p. 981,431; 11p. 384,701; 13p. 371,882.
Withdrawn: 6.8.80.

181 Bureau and Postal Headquarters

182 'Mails and Telegrams'

183 'Parcels'

184 'Philately'

Tenth Anniversary of Guernsey Postal Administration

(Des R. Granger Barrett. Photo Courvoisier)

1979 (1 Oct). Granite paper. P 11½ (C).

207	**181**	6p. multicoloured	20	20
208	**182**	8p. multicoloured	25	25
209	**183**	13p. multicoloured	40	40
210	**184**	15p. multicoloured	45	40
207/10 *Set of 4*			1·10	1·10
First Day Cover				1·25
Presentation Pack			1·50	
Set of 4 Gutter Pairs			2·20	
MS211 120×80 mm. Nos. 207/10			1·10	1·10
First Day Cover				1·40

One copy of a pre-release sample as No. 210, but with a face value of 11p., is known. Such stamps were not sold for postal purposes.
Cylinder Nos.: All values A1–1–1–1, B1–1–1–1.
Sheets: 50 (2 panes 5×5).
Imprint: Central, bottom margin.
Quantities sold: 6p. 1,254,914; 8p. 1,376,682; 13p. 389,524; 15p. 386,234; miniature sheet 398,443.
Withdrawn: 30.9.80.

185 Major-General   **186** Admiral Lord
Le Marchant   de Saumarez

Europa. Personalities

(Des and photo Courvoisier)

1980 (6 May). Granite paper. P 11½ (C).

212	**185**	10p. multicoloured	20	20
213	**186**	13½p. multicoloured	40	40
212/13 *Set of 2*			55	55
First Day Cover				70
Presentation Pack			90	

Cylinder Nos.: Both values A1–1–1–1–1, B1–1–1–1–1, C1–1–1–1–1, D1–1–1–1–1.
Sheets: 20 (5×4).
Quantities sold: 10p. 2,794,871; 13½p. 1,715,880.
Withdrawn: 5.5.81.

187 Policewoman with Lost Child

188 Police Motorcyclist escorting Lorry

189 Police Dog-handler

60th Anniversary of Guernsey Police Force

(Litho John Waddington Ltd)

1980 (6 May). P 13½×14 (C).
214	**187**	7p. multicoloured	30	30
215	**188**	15p. multicoloured	40	40
216	**189**	17½p. multicoloured	45	45
214/16	*Set of 3*		1·10	1·10
First Day Cover				1·25
Presentation Pack			1·50	
Set of 3 Gutter Pairs			2·20	

Plate Nos: All values 1A, 1B, 1C, 1D. (each×4).
Sheets: 50 (2 panes 5×5).
Imprint: Central, bottom margin.
Quantities sold: 7p. 907,714; 15p. 352,802; 17½p. 337,551.
Withdrawn: 5.5.81.

190 Golden Guernsey Goat

191 Golden Guernsey Goat

192 Golden Guernsey Goat

193 Golden Guernsey Goats

Golden Guernsey Goats

(Des P. Lambert. Photo Delrieu)

1980 (5 Aug). P 13 (C).
217	**190**	7p. multicoloured	20	20
218	**191**	10p. multicoloured	20	20
219	**192**	15p. multicoloured	40	40
220	**193**	17½p. multicoloured	45	45
217/20	*Set of 4*		1·10	1·10
First Day Cover				1·25
Presentation Pack			1·50	
Set of 4 Gutter Pairs			2·20	

Cylinder Nos: 7p. 598–599–600–601–602–603; 10p. 578–580–581–583; 15p. 605–606–607–608–609–610; 17½p. 621–622–623–624–625–626.
Sheets: 50 (2 panes 5×5).
Imprint: Bottom margin.
Quantities sold: 7p. 779,424; 10p. 931,214; 15p. 364,917; 17½p. 329,133.
Withdrawn: 4.4.81.

194 'Sark Cottage'

195 'Moulin Huet'

196 'Boats at Sea'

197 'Cow Lane'   **198** 'Peter Le Lievre'

Christmas. Peter le Lievre Paintings

(Photo Courvoisier)

1980 (15 Nov). Granite paper. P 11½ (C).
221	**194**	7p. multicoloured	20	20
222	**195**	10p. multicoloured	25	25
223	**196**	13½p. multicoloured	35	35
224	**197**	15p. multicoloured	35	35
225	**198**	17½p. multicoloured	40	40
221/5	*Set of 5*		1·40	1·40
First Day Cover				1·60
Presentation Pack			2·00	
Stamp-cards (set of 5)			2·00	4·00
Set of 5 Gutter Pairs			2·75	

Cylinder Nos.: All values A1–1–1–1, B1–1–1–1.
Sheets: 50 (2 panes 5×5).
Imprint: 15, 17½p. top corner, right-hand margin; others right-hand corner, bottom margin.
Quantities sold: 7p. 1,199,280; 10p. 1,159,622; 13½p. 397,812; 15p. 432,182; 17½p. 359,116.
Withdrawn: 14.11.81.

199 *Polyommatus icarus*

200 *Vanessa atalanta*

201 *Aglais urticae*

202 *Lasiommata megera*

Butterflies

(Photo Harrison)

1981 (24 Feb). P 14 (C).
226	**199**	8p. multicoloured	20	20
227	**200**	12p. multicoloured	30	30
228	**201**	22p. multicoloured	50	50
229	**202**	25p. multicoloured	60	60
226/9 *Set of 4*			1·40	1·40
First Day Cover				2·20
Presentation Pack			1·70	
Set of 4 Gutter Pairs			2·75	

Cylinder Nos.: All values 1A, 1B (each×5).
Sheets: 50 (2 panes 5×5).
Imprint: Right-hand corner, bottom margin.
Quantities sold: 8p. 986,229; 12p. 971,801; 22p. 438,478; 25p. 438,575.
Withdrawn: 23.2.82.

203 Sailors paying
respect to 'Le Petit
Bonhomme Andriou'
(rock resembling
head of a man)

204 Fairies and
Guernsey Lily

Europa. Folklore

(Des C. Abbott. Litho Questa)

1981 (22 May). P 14½ (C).
230	**203**	12p. gold, red-brown and cinnamon	50	50
231	**204**	18p. gold, indigo and azure	60	60
230/1 *Set of 2*			1·00	1·00
First Day Cover				1·10
Presentation Pack			1·50	
Set of 2 Gutter Pairs			2·00	

Plate Nos.: 12p. 1B, 1F, 1G, 1H (each×3); 18p. 1B, 1D., 1F, 1G, 1H (each×3).
Sheets: 20 (2 panes 5×2).
Imprint: Central, left-hand margin.
Quantities sold: 12p. 2,516,514; 18p. 1,937,023.
Withdrawn: 21.5.82.

205 Prince Charles

206 Prince Charles
and Lady Diana
Spencer

207 Lady Diana

208 Royal Family

Royal Wedding

(Des C. Abbott. Litho Questa)

1981 (29 July). P 14½ (C).
232	**205**	8p. multicoloured	20	20
		a. Strip of 3. Nos. 232/4	75	75
233	**206**	8p. multicoloured	20	20
234	**207**	8p. multicoloured	20	20
235	**205**	12p. multicoloured	30	30
		a. Strip of 3. Nos. 235/7	1·10	1·10
236	**206**	12p. multicoloured	30	30
237	**207**	12p. multicoloured	30	30
238	**208**	25p. multicoloured	65	65
232/8 *Set of 7*			2·25	2·25
First Day Cover				3·25
Presentation Pack			3·25	
Stamp-cards (set of 7)			2·00	7·00
MS239 104×127 mm. Nos. 232/8. P 14 (C)			2·50	2·50
First Day Cover				4·00

Plate Nos.: 8p. 1A, 1C (each×6); 12p. 1B (×6); 25p. 1A (×6).
Sheets: 8p., 12p. 60 (6×10) each value in strips of 3 across sheet, 25p. 30 (3×10).
Imprint: Bottom corner, right-hand side margin.
Quantities sold: 8p. 2,115,103; 12p. 2,235,005; 25p. 510,608; miniature sheet 432,743.
Withdrawn: 28.7.82.

209 Sark Launch

210 Britten Norman 'short nose'
Trislander Airplane

211 Hydrofoil

212 Herm Catamaran

213 *Sea Trent* (coaster)

Inter-island Transport

(Des and photo Courvoisier)

1981 (25 Aug). Granite paper. P 11½ (C).

240	**209**	8p. multicoloured	20	20
241	**210**	12p. multicoloured	30	30
242	**211**	18p. multicoloured	40	40
243	**212**	22p. multicoloured	60	65
244	**213**	25p. multicoloured	75	75
240/4 *Set of 5*			2·00	2·00
First Day Cover				2·25
Presentation Pack			2·50	
Set of 5 Gutter Pairs			4·00	

Cylinder Nos.: All values A1–1–1–1, B1–1–1–1.
Sheets: 50 (2 panes 5×5).
Imprint: Right-hand corner, bottom margin.
Quantities sold: 8p. 790,215; 12p. 785,488; 18p. 457,763; 22p. 469,315; 25p. 466,112.
Withdrawn: 24.8.82.

214 Rifle Shooting   215 Riding

216 Swimming   217 Circuit Construction

International Year for Disabled Persons

(Des P. le Vasseur. Litho Questa)

1981 (17 Nov). P 14½ (C).

245	**214**	8p. multicoloured	25	25
246	**215**	12p. multicoloured	30	30
247	**216**	22p. multicoloured	60	60
248	**217**	25p. multicoloured	75	75
245/8 *Set of 4*			1·75	1·75
First Day Cover				2·00
Presentation Pack			2·25	
Set of 4 Gutter Pairs			3·50	

Plate Nos.: All values 1A, 1B, 1C, 1D, 1E, 1F, 1G, 1H (each×4).
Sheets: 50 (2 panes 5×5).
Imprint: Foot of right-hand margin on each pane.
Quantities sold: 8p. 912,908; 12p. 910,614; 22p. 280,882; 25p. 287,725.
Withdrawn: 16.11.82.

218 Jethou

219 Fermain Bay

220 The Terres

221 St. Peter Port

Old Guernsey Prints (2nd series). Sketches by T. Compton

(Des, recess and litho DLR)

1982 (2 Feb). P 14×13½ (C).

249	**218**	8p. black and pale blue	30	30
250	**219**	12p. black and pale turquoise-grn	30	30
251	**220**	22p. black and pale yellow-brown	60	60
252	**221**	25p. black and pale rose-lilac	70	70
249/52 *Set of 4*			1·70	1·70
First Day Cover				2·00
Presentation Pack			2·25	
Set of 4 Gutter Pairs			3·40	

Plate Nos.: All values 1A–1A, 1B–1B, 1C–1C, 1D.–1D.
Sheets: 50 (2 panes 5×5).
Imprint: Left-hand corner, bottom margin.
Quantities sold: 8p. 350,198; 12p. 346,515; 22p. 346,661; 25p. 244,669.
Withdrawn: 1.2.83.

222 Sir Edgar MacCulloch (founder-president) and Guille-Allés Library, St. Peter Port

223 Norman Invasion Fleet crossing English Channel, 1066 ('history')

224 H.M.S. *Crescent*, 1793 ('history')

225 Dragonfly ('entomology')

226 Common Snipe caught for Ringing ('ornithology')

227 Samian Bowl 160–200 A.D. ('archaeology')

Centenary of La Société Guernesiaise

(Des G. Drummond. Photo Courvoisier)

1982 (28 Apr). Granite paper. P 11½ (C).

253	**222**	8p. multicoloured	20	20
254	**223**	13p. multicoloured	35	35
255	**224**	20p. multicoloured	50	50
256	**225**	24p. multicoloured	60	60
257	**226**	26p. multicoloured	70	70
258	**227**	29p. multicoloured	80	80
253/8 *Set of 6*			2·80	2·80
First Day Cover				3·00
First Day Cover (Nos. 254/5)				1·00
Presentation Pack			3·50	

Presentation Pack (Nos. 254/5).. 1·70
Stamp-cards (set of 6).. 2·00   4·00
     The 13p. and 20p. (Nos. 254/5) also include the Europa C.E.P.T. emblem in the designs.
     Cylinder Nos.: 24p. A1–1–1–1, B1–1–1–1, C1–1–1–1, D1–1–1–1; others A1–1–1–1–1, B1–1–1–1–1, C1–1–1–1–1, D1–1–1–1–1.
     Sheets: 20 (5×4).
     Quantities sold: 8p. 921,095; 13p. 2,820,311; 20p. 1,491,351; 24p. 315,735; 26p. 309,919; 29p. 298,761.
     Withdrawn: 27.4.83.

228 Sea Scouts

229 Scouts

230 Cub Scouts

231 Air Scouts

75th Anniversary of Boy Scout Movement

(Des W.L.G. Creative Services Ltd. Litho Questa)

1982 (13 July). P 14½×14 (C).

259	**228**	8p. multicoloured	25	25
260	**229**	13p. multicoloured	30	30
261	**230**	26p. multicoloured	75	75
262	**231**	29p. multicoloured	90	90
259/62 Set of 4			2·00	2·00
First Day Cover				2·20
Presentation Pack			2·50	
Set of 4 Gutter Pairs			4·00	

     Plate Nos.: 8p. 1A, 1B, 1C, 1D. (each×6); others 1A, 1B, 1C, 1D. (each×7).
     Sheets: 50 (2 panes 5×5).
     Imprint: Bottom corner, right-hand margin.
     Quantities sold: 8p. 796,018; 13p. 930,924; 26p. 237,958; 29p. 233,204.
     Withdrawn: 12.7.83.

232 Midnight Mass

233 Exchanging Gifts

234 Christmas Meal

235 Exchanging Cards

236 Queens Christmas Message

Christmas

(Des Lynette Hammant. Photo Harrison)

1982 (12 Oct). P 14½ (C).

263	**232**	8p. multicoloured	20	20
		a. Black (Queen's head, value and inscr) omitted	£2750	
264	**233**	13p. multicoloured	40	40
265	**234**	24p. multicoloured	65	65
266	**235**	26p. multicoloured	65	65
267	**236**	29p. multicoloured	80	80
263/7 Set of 5			2·50	2·50
First Day Cover				2·75
Presentation Pack			3·00	
Set of 5 Gutter Pairs			5·00	

     Cylinder Nos.: All values 1A, 1B (each×5).
     Sheets: 50 (2 panes 5×5).
     Imprint: Right-hand corner, bottom margin.
     Quantities sold: 8p. 944,560; 13p. 927,844; 24p. 227,145; 26p. 249,110; 29p. 232,323.
     Withdrawn: 11.10.83.

237 Flute Player and Boats

238 Cymbal Player and Tug 'o' war

239 Trumpet Player and Bible Class

240 Drummer and Cadets marching

241 Boys Brigade Band

Centenary of Boys – Brigade

(Des Sally Stiff. Photo Harrison)

1983 (18 Jan). P 14 (C).

268	**237**	8p. multicoloured	30	30
269	**238**	13p. multicoloured	40	40
270	**239**	24p. multicoloured	65	65
271	**240**	26p. multicoloured	70	70
272	**241**	29p. multicoloured	80	80
268/72 Set of 5			2·60	2·60
First Day Cover				2·75
Presentation Pack			3·00	
Set of 5 Gutter Pairs			5·00	

     Cylinder Nos.: All values 1A, 1B (each×5).
     Sheets: 50 (2 panes 5×5).
     Imprint: Bottom margin, right-hand corner.
     Quantities sold: 8p. 671,921; 13p. 538,257; 24p. 223,069; 26p. 234,482; 29p. 214,723.
     Withdrawn: 17.1.84.

242 Building Albert Pier Extension, 1850s

243 St. Peter Port Harbour, 1983

244 St. Peter Port, 1680   **245** Artists Impression of Future Development Scheme

Europa. Great Works of Human Genius. Development of St. Peter Port Harbour

(Des J. Larrivière. Artwork C. Abbott. Photo Courvoisier)

1983 (14 Mar). Granite paper. P 11½ (C).

273	**242**	13p. multicoloured	40	30
		a. Horiz. pair. Nos. 273/4	75	75
274	**243**	13p. multicoloured	40	30
275	**244**	20p. multicoloured	50	50
		a. Horiz. pair. Nos. 275/6	1·10	1·10
276	**245**	20p. multicoloured	50	50
273/6	*Set of 4*		1·60	1·50
First Day Cover				1·75
Presentation Pack			2·20	

Cylinder Nos.: Both values A1–1–1–1–1, B1–1–1–1–1.
Sheets: 20 (4×5). The two designs of each value were printed together, *se-tenant*, in horizontal pairs throughout.
Quantities sold: 13p. 1,884,714; 20p. 1,676,250.
Withdrawn: 13.3.84.

246 'View at Guernsey'   **247** 'Children on the Seashore'

248 'Marine, Guernsey'   **249** 'La Baie du Moulin Huet à travers les Arbres'

250 'Brouillard à Guernesey'

Centenary of Renoir's visit to Guernsey

(Des and photo Courvoisier)

1983 (6 Sept). Granite paper. P 11×11½ (13p.) or 11½ (others), all comb.

277	**246**	9p. multicoloured	20	15
278	**247**	13p. multicoloured	30	30
279	**248**	26p. multicoloured	70	70
280	**249**	28p. multicoloured	85	80
281	**250**	31p. multicoloured	90	90
277/81	*Set of 5*		2·60	2·60
First Day Cover				3·00
Presentation Pack			3·25	
Stamp-cards (set of 5)			1·50	4·00
Set of 5 Gutter Pairs			5·00	

Cylinder Nos.: 13p. A1–1–1–1–1, B1–1–1–1–1, C1–1–1–1–1, D1–1–1–1–1; others A1–1–1–1–1, B1–1–1–1–1.
Sheets: 40 (2 panes 4×5).
Quantities sold: 9p. 547,148; 13p. 757,838; 26p. 185,045; 28p. 219,830; 31p. 305,219.
Withdrawn: 5.9.84.

251 Launching *Star of the West*, 1869, and Capt. J. Lenfestey   **252** Leaving St. Peter Port

253 Off Rio Grande Bar   **254** Off St. Lucia

255 Map of 1879–80 Voyage

Guernsey Shipping (1st series). *Star of the West* **(brigantine)**

(Des R. Granger Barrett. Litho Questa)

1983 (15 Nov). P 14 (C).

282	**251**	9p. multicoloured	20	20
283	**252**	13p. multicoloured	30	30
284	**253**	26p. multicoloured	70	70
285	**254**	28p. multicoloured	85	85
286	**255**	31p. multicoloured	95	95
282/6	*Set of 5*		2·75	2·75
First Day Cover				3·00
Presentation Pack			3·25	
Set of 5 Gutter Pairs			5·50	

See also Nos. 415/19.
Plate Nos.: 26p., 31p. 1C, 1D. (each×5); others 1A, 1B (each×5).
Sheets: 50 (2 panes 5×5).
Imprint: Bottom corner, right-hand margin.
Quantities sold: 9p. 706,809; 13p. 974,736; 26p. 236,974; 28p. 216,279; 31p. 218,647.
Withdrawn: 14.11.84.

256 Dame of Sark as Young Woman

257 German Occupation, 1940–45

258 Royal Visit, 1957

259 Chief Pleas

260 'Dame of Sark' Rose

Birth Centenary of Sibyl Hathaway, Dame of Sark

(Des Jennifer Toombs. Litho Questa)

1984 (7 Feb). P 14½ (C).

287	**256**	9p. multicoloured	20	20
288	**257**	13p. multicoloured	30	15
289	**258**	26p. multicoloured	70	65
290	**259**	28p. multicoloured	75	70
291	**260**	31p. multicoloured	80	75
287/91	*Set of 5*		2·50	2·25
First Day Cover				2·50
Presentation Pack			3·00	
Set of 5 Gutter Pairs			5·00	

Plate Nos.: 13p. 1A, 1B, 1C, 1D. (each×5); others 1A, 1B, 1C, 1D., (each×7).
Sheets: 50 (2 panes 5×5).
Imprint: Bottom corner, right-hand margin.
Quantities sold: 9p. 637,566; 13p. 836,270; 26p. 315,561; 28p. 293,716; 31p. 270,742.
Withdrawn: 6.2.85.

261 C.E.P.T. 25th Anniversary Logo

Europa

(Des J. Larrivière. Litho Questa)

1984 (10 Apr). P 15×14½ (C).

292	**261**	13p. cobalt, dull ultramarine and blk.....	40	40
293		20½p. emerald, deep dull grn and blk......	75	75
292/3	*Set of 2*		1·00	1·00
First Day Cover				1·20
Presentation Pack			1·50	

Plate Nos.: Both values 1A, 1B, 1C, 1D (each×3).
Sheets: 20 (4×5).
Imprint: Bottom corner, right-hand margin.
Quantities sold: 13p. 1,680,033; 20½p. 903,972.
Withdrawn: 9.4.85.

262 The Royal Court and St. George's Flag

263 Castle Cornet and Union Flag

Links with the Commonwealth

(Des C. Abbott. Litho Questa)

1984 (10 Apr). P 14×14½ (C).

294	**262**	9p. multicoloured	20	15
295	**263**	31p. multicoloured	85	85
294/5	*Set of 2*		1·00	95
First Day Cover				1·20
Presentation Pack			1·50	

Plate Nos.: Both values 1A, 1B, 1C, 1D. (each×6).
Sheets: 20 (4×5).
Imprint: Bottom corner, right-hand margin.
Quantities sold: 9p. 1,419,845, 31p. 285,099.
Withdrawn: 9.4.85.

GUERNSEY 1ᴾ
264 Little Chapel

GUERNSEY 2ᴾ
265 Fort Grey

GUERNSEY 3ᴾ
266 Chapel St. Apolline

GUERNSEY 4ᴾ
267 Petit Port

GUERNSEY 5ᴾ
268 Little Russel

GUERNSEY 6ᴾ
269 The Harbour, Herm

GUERNSEY 7ᴾ
270 Saints

GUERNSEY 8ᴾ
271 St. Saviour

GUERNSEY 9ᴾ
272 New Jetty (inscr 'Cambridge Berth')

GUERNSEY 10ᴾ
273 Belvoir, Herm

GUERNSEY 11ᴾ
274 La Seigneurie, Sark

GUERNSEY 13ᴾ
276 St. Saviour's Reservoir

GUERNSEY 12ᴾ
275 Petit Bot

GUERNSEY 14ᴾ
277 St. Peter Port

GUERNSEY 15ᴾ
278 Havelet

GUERNSEY 16ᴾ
279 Hostel of St. John

GUERNSEY 18ᴾ
280 Le Variouf

GUERNSEY 20ᴾ
281 La Coupee, Sark

GUERNSEY 21ᴾ
282 King's Mills

GUERNSEY 26ᴾ
283 Town Church

GUERNSEY 30ᴾ
284 Grandes Rocques

GUERNSEY 40ᴾ
285 Torteval Church

GUERNSEY 50ᴾ
286 Bordeaux

GUERNSEY £1
287 Albecq

GUERNSEY £2
288 L'Ancresse

Bailiwick Views

(Des C. Abbott. Litho Questa)

1984 (18 Sept)–**91**. P 14½ (C).

296	**264**	1p. multicoloured (c)	10	10
297	**265**	2p. multicoloured (c)	10	10
		a. Booklet pane. Nos. 297×2, 299×4, 300×2 and 305×2 (d)	1·60	
298	**266**	3p. multicoloured (a)	10	10
		a. Booklet pane. Nos. 298, 299×2, 306×4 and 309×3 (f)	2·00	
299	**267**	4p. multicoloured (a)	10	10
		a. Booklet pane. Nos. 299×2, 304×3 and 307×5	2·50	
		b. Booklet pane. Nos. 299, 304 and 307, each×5	2·50	
		c. Booklet pane. Nos. 299×4, 306b×3 and 309c×3 (g)	2·75	
		d. Booklet pane. Nos. 299, 301, 306 b×3 and 309d×3 (h)	3·25	
		e. Black ptg double	£1500	
300	**268**	5p. multicoloured (c)	15	10
		a. Booklet pane. Nos. 300×2, 301×2, 309×3 and 310b×3 (j)	3·75	
301	**269**	6p. multicoloured (c)	15	15
		a. Booklet pane. Nos. 301×4, 308×4 and 310×2 (i)	3·25	
		b. Uncoated paper		
		c. Black ptg double	£1500	

302	**270**	7p. multicoloured (c)	15	15
303	**271**	8p. multicoloured (c)	20	15
304	**272**	9p. multicoloured (a)	20	10
		a. Booklet pane. Nos. 304×4 and 308×6 (b)	2·50	
		b. Booklet pane. Nos. 304×2 and 308×8 (b)	2·50	
		c. Black ptg double		
305	**273**	10p. multicoloured (a)	25	15
		a. Booklet pane. Nos. 305 and 308, each×5 (e)	3·00	
306	**274**	11p. multicoloured (c)	30	15
		a. Booklet pane. Nos. 306 and 309, each×5 (f)	3·25	
306b	**275**	12p. multicoloured (g)	35	15
		ba. Booklet pane. Nos. 306b and 309c, each×5	3·00	
		bb. Booklet pane. Nos. 306b and 309d, each×4 (h)	3·50	
		bc. Black ptg double	£950	
307	**276**	13p. multicoloured (a)	30	25
308	**277**	14p. multicoloured (a)	30	20
		a. Booklet pane. Nos. 308 and 310, each×5 (i)	3·75	
		b. Uncoated paper	£900	
309	**278**	15p. multicoloured (C)	35	35
		a. Booklet pane. Nos. 309 and 310b, each×5 (j)	5·50	
		b. Imperf at sides and foot (horiz pair)	£1500	
309c	**279**	16p. multicoloured (g)	40	35
		ca. Black and red ptgs double		
309d	**280**	18p. multicoloured (h)	35	35
		da. Black ptg double	£950	
310	**281**	20p. multicoloured (a)	50	50
		a. Uncoated paper	£900	
310b	**282**	21p. multicoloured (j)	55	55
310c	**283**	26p. multicoloured (j)	1·00	1·00
		ca. Imperf at sides and foot (horiz pair)	£1500	
311	**284**	30p. multicoloured (c)	1·00	1·00
312	**285**	40p. multicoloured (a)	1·00	1·00
313	**286**	50p. multicoloured (a)	1·25	1·25
314	**287**	£1 multicoloured (a)	2·10	2·10
315	**288**	£2 multicoloured (c)	4·00	4·00
296/315	Set of 25		15·00	15·00
First Day Covers (5)				16·00
Presentation Packs (3)			17·00	
Stamp-cards (set of 25)			7·00	22·00
Set of 25 Gutter Pairs			30·00	

For 11p, 12p, 15p. and 16p. stamps in a smaller size see Nos. 398/9a.

Booklet panes Nos. 297a, 298a, 299a/c, 304a/b, 305a, 306a and 306ba have margins all round and were issued, folded and loose, within the booklet covers. Booklet panes Nos. 299d, 300a, 306bb, 308a and 309a have the outer edges imperforate on three sides and were also issued loose within the booklet covers.

Nos. 299e, 301c, 306bc and 309da come from an example of booklet pane No. 299d.

Nos. 301b, 308b and 310a come from examples of booklet panes Nos. 301a and 308a.

Unfolded booklet panes (with and without margins) were also available from the Philatelic Bureau and Head Post Office.

In addition to the presentation packs listed, there was a Tourists Definitive Pack containing the original set of 20, selling price £5.50.

Printings: (a) 18.9.84; (b) 19.3.85; (c). 23.7.85; (d) 2.12.85; (e) 1.4.86; (f) 30.3.87; (g) 28.3.88; (h) 28.2.89; (i) 27.12.89; (j) 2.4.91.

Plate Nos.: All values 1A, 1B, 1C, 1D. (each×5).

Sheets: 1p., 3p., 8p., 12p., 14p., 15p., 18p., 26p., 40p., 100 (2 panes 10×5); others 100 (2 panes 5×10).

Imprint: Bottom, right-hand margin of each pane.

Quantities sold: 1p. 1,397,906; 2p. 1,240,037; 3p. 460,949; 4p. 478,679; 5p. 690,128; 6p. 560,950; 7p. 302,367; 8p. 425,421; 9p. 1,959,119; 10p. 1,692,125; 11p. 1,510,077; 12p. 2,837,219; 13p. 730,405; 14p. 3,925,313; 15p. 2,631,599; 16p. 1,322,353; 18p. 1,398,065; 20p. 2,149,053; 21p. 1,675,329; 26p. 210,575; 30p. 790,261; 40p. 604,514; 50p 765,831; £1 647,055; £2 666,177. Withdrawn: 21.5.93.

289 'A Partridge in a Pear Tree'

290 'Two Turtle Doves'

291 'Three French Hens'

292 'Four Colly Birds'　　**293** 'Five Gold Rings'　　**294** 'Six Geese a-laying'

295 'Seven Swans a-swimming'　　**296** 'Eight Maids a-milking'　　**297** 'Nine Drummers drumming'

298 'Ten Pipers piping'　　**299** 'Eleven Ladies dancing'　　**300** 'Twelve Lords a-leaping'

Christmas. 'The Twelve Days of Christmas'

(Des R. Downer. Litho Questa)

1984 (20 Nov). P 14½ (C).

316	**289**	5p. multicoloured	15	15
		a. Sheetlet of 12. Nos. 316/27	2·00	2·00
317	**290**	5p. multicoloured	15	15
318	**291**	5p. multicoloured	15	15
319	**292**	5p. multicoloured	15	15
320	**293**	5p. multicoloured	15	15
321	**294**	5p. multicoloured	15	15
322	**295**	5p. multicoloured	15	15
323	**296**	5p. multicoloured	15	15
324	**297**	5p. multicoloured	15	15
325	**298**	5p. multicoloured	15	15
326	**299**	5p. multicoloured	15	15
327	**300**	5p. multicoloured	15	15
316/27	*Set of 12*		2·00	2·00
First Day Cover				2·25
Presentation Pack			2·50	

Sheets: 12 (4×3) containing Nos. 316/27 se-tenant. Imprint: Bottom, left-hand margin.
Quantity sold: 271,168 sheetlets.
Withdrawn: 19.11.85.

301 Sir John Doyle and Coat of Arms　　**302** Battle of Germantown, 1777

303 Reclaiming Braye du Valle, 1806　　**304** Mail for Alderney, 1812

150th Death Anniversary of Lieutenant-General Sir John Doyle

(Des E. Stemp. Photo Courvoisier)

1984 (20 Nov). Granite paper. P 11½ (C).

328	**301**	13p. multicoloured	30	30
329	**302**	29p. multicoloured	75	75
330	**303**	31p. multicoloured	75	75
331	**304**	34p. multicoloured	90	90
328/31	*Set of 4*		2·50	2·50
First Day Cover				2·75
Presentation Pack			3·25	
Set of 4 Gutter Pairs			5·00	

Cylinder Nos.: All values A1–1–1–1–1, B1–1–1–1–1, C1–1–1–1–1, D1–1–1–1–1.
Sheets: 50 (2 panes 5×5).
Quantities sold: 13p. 642,178; 29p. 460,535; 31p. 450,051; 34p. 465,982.
Withdrawn: 19.11.85.

Yearbook 1984

1984 (1 Dec). Comprises Nos. 287/95, 298/9, 304/5, 307/8, 310, 312/14, 316/31 and A13/17 (price £9.95).

Yearbook		35·00

Withdrawn: 29.3.86.

305 Cuckoo Wrasse　　**306** Red Gurnard

307 Red Mullet　　**308** Mackerel

309 Oceanic Sunfish

Fish

(Des P. Barrett. Photo Courvoisier)

1985 (22 Jan). Granite paper. P 11½ (C).

332	**305**	9p. multicoloured	30	30
333	**306**	13p. multicoloured	40	40
334	**307**	29p. multicoloured	90	90
335	**308**	31p. multicoloured	1·00	1·00
336	**309**	34p. multicoloured	1·00	1·00
332/6	*Set of 5*		3·25	3·25
First Day Cover				3·50
Presentation Pack			4·00	
Set of 5 Gutter Pairs			6·50	

Cylinder Nos.: 13p., 29p. A1–1–1–1–1, B1–1–1–1–1, C1–1–1–1–1, D1–1–1–1; others A1–1–1–1, B1–1–1–1, C1–1–1–1, D1–1–1–1.
Sheets: 50 (2 panes 5×5).
Quantities sold: 9p. 465,322; 13p. 724,941; 29p. 221,392; 31p. 174,948; 34p. 157,422.
Withdrawn: 21.1.86.

310 Dove

40th Anniversary of Peace in Europe

(Des C. Abbott. Litho Questa)

1985 (9 May). P 14×14½ (C).
337	**310**	22p. multicoloured		75	75
		First Day Cover			90
		Presentation Pack		1·20	
		Gutter Pair		1·50	

Plate Nos.: 1A, 1B, 1C, 1D. (each×4).
Sheets: 50 (2 panes 5×5).
Imprint: Bottom, right-hand margin of each pane.
Quantity sold: 246,024.
Withdrawn: 8.5.86.

311 I.Y.Y. Emblem and Young People of Different Races

312 Girl Guides cooking over Campfire

International Youth Year

(Des Suzanne Brehaut (9p.), Mary Harrison (31p.). Litho Questa)

1985 (14 May). P 14 (C).
338	**311**	9p. multicoloured		25	25
339	**312**	31p. multicoloured		80	80
338/9	Set of 2			1·00	1·00
		First Day Cover			1·20
		Presentation Pack (with No. 342)		3·00	

Plate Nos.: Both values 1A, 1B, 1C, 1D., 1E, 1F (each×6).
Sheets: 20 (5×4).
Imprint: Bottom, right-hand margin.
Quantities sold: 9p. 1,246,421; 31p. 264,938.
Withdrawn: 13.5.86.

313 Stave of Music enclosing Flags

314 Stave of Music and Musical Instruments

Europa. European Music Year

(Des Fiona Sloan (14p.), Katie Lillington (22p.). Litho Questa)

1985 (14 May). P 14×14½ (C).
340	**313**	14p. multicoloured		35	35
341	**314**	22p. multicoloured		60	55
340/1	Set of 2			90	90
		First Day Cover			1·10
		Presentation Pack		1·40	

Plate Nos.: Both values 1A, 1B, 1C, 1D., 1E, 1F (each×6).
Sheets: 20 (4×5).
Imprint: Bottom, right-hand margin.
Quantities sold: 14p. 1,742,651; 22p. 879,421.
Withdrawn: 13.5.86.

315 Guide Leader, Girl Guide and Brownie

75th Anniversary of Girl Guide Movement

(Des Karon Mahy. Litho Questa)

1985 (14 May). P 14 (C).
342	**315**	34p. multicoloured		1·00	1·10
		First Day Cover			1·40

Plate Nos.: 1A, 1B, 1C, 1D. (each×6).
Sheets: 20 (5×4).
Imprint: Bottom, right-hand margin.
Quantity sold: 182,426.
Withdrawn: 13.5.86.

316 Santa Claus

317 Lussibruden (Sweden)

318 King Balthazar

319 Saint Nicholas (Netherlands)

320 La Befana (Italy)

321 Julenisse (Denmark)

322 Christkind (Germany)

323 King Wenceslas (Czechoslovakia)

324 Shepherd of Les Baux (France)

325 King Caspar

326 Baboushka (Russia)

327 King Melchior

Christmas. Gift-bearers

(Des C. Abbott. Photo Courvoisier)

1985 (19 Nov). Granite paper. P 12½ (C).
343	**316**	5p. multicoloured		25	25
		a. Sheetlet of 12. Nos. 343/54		3·00	3·00
344	**317**	5p. multicoloured		25	25
345	**318**	5p. multicoloured		25	25
346	**319**	5p. multicoloured		25	25
347	**320**	5p. multicoloured		25	25
348	**321**	5p. multicoloured		25	25
349	**322**	5p. multicoloured		25	25
350	**323**	5p. multicoloured		25	25
351	**324**	5p. multicoloured		25	25
352	**325**	5p. multicoloured		25	25
353	**326**	5p. multicoloured		25	25
354	**327**	5p. multicoloured		25	25
343/54	Set of 12			3·00	3·00
		First Day Cover			3·50
		Presentation Pack		3·75	

Sheets: 12 (4×3) containing Nos. 343/54 se-tenant.
Imprint: Central, bottom margin.
Quantity sold: 236,937 sheetlets.
Withdrawn: 18.11.86.

328 'Vraicing'

329 'Castle Cornet'

330 'Rocquaine Bay'

331 'Little Russel'

332 'Seaweed-gatherers'

Paintings by Paul Jacob Naftel

(Des and photo Harrison)

1985 (19 Nov). P 15×14 (C).

355	**328**	9p. multicoloured	20	20
356	**329**	14p. multicoloured	35	35
357	**330**	22p. multicoloured	65	65
358	**331**	31p. multicoloured	1·10	1·10
359	**332**	34p. multicoloured	1·40	1·40
355/9	*Set of 5*		3·25	3·25
First Day Cover				3·75
Presentation Pack			4·00	
Set of 5 Gutter Pairs			6·50	

Cylinder Nos.: All values 1A, 1B (each×5).
Sheets: 50 (2 panes 5×5).
Imprint: Left-hand margin of each pane.
Quantities sold: 9p. 398,472; 14p. 452,728; 22p. 164,922; 31p. 197,422; 34p. 173,428.
Withdrawn: 18.11.86.

Yearbook 1985

1985 (Dec). Comprises Nos. 296/7, 300/3, 306, 309, 311, 315, 332/59 and A18/27 (price £10.50).

Yearbook		55·00

Withdrawn: 31.12.86.

333 Squadron off Nargue Island, 1809

334 Battle of the Nile, 1798

335 Battle of St. Vincent, 1797

336 H.M.S. *Crescent* off Cherbourg, 1793

337 Battle of the Saints, 1782

150th Death Anniversary of Admiral Lord De Saumarez

(Des T. Thompson. Photo Courvoisier)

1986 (4 Feb). Granite paper. P 11½ (C).

360	**333**	9p. multicoloured	35	25
361	**334**	14p. multicoloured	45	30
362	**335**	29p. multicoloured	80	70
363	**336**	31p. multicoloured	1·25	95
364	**337**	34p. multicoloured	1·25	1·00
360/4	*Set of 5*		3·50	3·00
First Day Cover				3·25
Presentation Pack			3·25	
Set of 5 Gutter Pairs			7·00	

Cylinder Nos.: All values A1-1-1-1-1, B1-1-1-1-1.
Sheets: 40 (2 panes 5×4).
Quantities sold: 9p. 456,518; 14p. 706,727; 29p. 157,693; 31p. 163,612; 34p. 160,724.
Withdrawn: 3.2.87.

338 Profile of Queen Elizabeth II
(after R. Maklouf)

60th Birthday of Queen Elizabeth II

(Des C. Abbott. Litho Questa)

1986 (21 Apr). P 14 (C).

365	**338**	60p. multicoloured	1·50	1·50
First Day Cover				1·80
Presentation Pack			2·50	
Gutter Pair			3·00	

Plate Nos.: 1A, 1B, 1C, 1D. (each×4).
Sheets: 40 (2 panes 5×4).
Imprint: Bottom, right-hand margin of each pane.
Quantity sold: 169,661.
Withdrawn: 20.4.87.

339 Northern Gannet and Nylon Net (Operation Gannet')

340 Whitsun Orchid

341 Guernsey Elm

Europa. Nature and Environmental Protection

(Des P. Newcombe. Photo Courvoisier)

1986 (22 May). Granite paper. P 11½ (C).

366	**339**	10p. multicoloured	35	35
367	**340**	14p. multicoloured	45	45
368	**341**	22p. multicoloured	80	80
366/8 *Set of 3*			1·50	1·50
First Day Cover				1·90
Presentation Pack			2·00	

Cylinder Nos.: All values A1–1–1–1–1, B1–1–1–1–1, C1–1–1–1–1, D1–1–1–1–1.
Sheets: 20 (4×5).
Quantities sold: 10p. 977,212; 14p. 995,123; 22p. 662,565.
Withdrawn: 21.5.87.

342 Prince Andrew and Miss Sarah Ferguson

343 Prince Andrew and Miss Sarah Ferguson

Royal Wedding

(Des C. Abbott. Litho Questa)

1986 (23 July). P 14 (14p.) or 13½×14 (34p.), both comb.

369	**342**	14p. multicoloured	40	40
370	**343**	34p. multicoloured	1·00	1·00
369/70 *Set of 2*			1·30	1·30
First Day Cover				1·50
Presentation Pack			2·00	
Set of 2 Gutter Pairs			2·50	

Plate Nos.: Both values 1A, 1B, 1C, 1D., 1E, 1F (each×5).
Sheets: 50 (2 panes 5×5).
Imprint: Bottom, right-hand margin of each pane.
Quantities sold: 14p. 292,018; 34p. 199,297.
Withdrawn: 22.7.87.

344 Bowls

345 Cricket

346 Squash

347 Hockey

348 Swimming

349 Shooting

Sport in Guernsey

(Des R. Goldsmith. Litho Questa)

1986 (24 July). P 14½ (C).

371	**344**	10p. multicoloured	25	20
372	**345**	14p. multicoloured	35	20
		a. Black (face value, inscr etc.) printed treble	£275	
373	**346**	22p. multicoloured	50	45
		a. Black (face value, inscr etc.) printed treble		
374	**347**	29p. multicoloured	90	80
375	**348**	31p. multicoloured	90	80
376	**349**	34p. multicoloured	1·00	90
371/6 *Set of 6*			3·50	3·00
First Day Cover				3·25
Presentation Pack			4·00	
Set of 4 Gutter Pairs			7·00	

Plate Nos.: All values 1A, 1B, 1C, 1D. (each×4).
Sheets: 50 (2 panes 5×5).
Imprint: Bottom, right-hand margin of each pane.
Quantities sold: 10p. 399,897; 14p. 985,699; 22p. 212,203; 29p. 141,882; 31p 157,751; 34p. 156,164.
Withdrawn: 23.7.87.

350 Guernsey Museum and Art Gallery, Candie Gardens

351 Fort Grey Maritime Museum

352 Castle Cornet

353 National Trust of Guernsey Folk Museum

Centenary of Guernsey Museums

(Des Sir Hugh Casson. Litho Questa)

1986 (18 Nov). P 14 (C).

377	**350**	14p. multicoloured	30	30
378	**351**	29p. multicoloured	85	85
379	**352**	31p. multicoloured	85	85
380	**353**	34p. multicoloured	1·00	1·00
377/80 *Set of 4*			2·75	2·75
First Day Cover				3·00
Presentation Pack			3·25	
Set of 4 Gutter Pairs			5·50	

Plate Nos.: All values 1A, 1B, 1C, 1D. (each×5).
Sheets: 50 (2 panes 5×5).
Imprint: Bottom, right-hand margin of each pane.
Quantities sold: 14p. 796,879; 29p. 141,974; 31p. 159,326; 34p. 144,074.
Withdrawn: 17.11.87.

354 'While Shepherds watched their Flocks by Night'

355 'In the Bleak Mid-Winter'

356 'O Little Town of Bethlehem'

357 'The Holly and the Ivy'

358 'O Little Christmas Tree'

359 'Away in a Manger'

360 'Good King Wenceslas'

361 'We Three Kings of Orient Are'

362 'Hark the Herald Angels Sing'

363 'I saw Three Ships'

364 'Little Donkey'

365 'Jingle Bells'

Christmas. Carols

(Des Wendy Bramall. Photo Courvoisier)

1986 (18 Nov). Granite paper. P 12½ (C).

381	**354**	6p. multicoloured	30	30
		a. Sheetlet of 12. Nos. 381/92	3·00	3·00
382	**355**	6p. multicoloured	30	30
383	**356**	6p. multicoloured	30	30
384	**357**	6p. multicoloured	30	30
385	**358**	6p. multicoloured	30	30
386	**359**	6p. multicoloured	30	30
387	**360**	6p. multicoloured	30	30
388	**361**	6p. multicoloured	30	30
389	**362**	6p. multicoloured	30	30
390	**363**	6p. multicoloured	30	30
391	**364**	6p. multicoloured	30	30
392	**365**	6p. multicoloured	30	30
381/92 *Set of 12*			3·00	3·00
First Day Cover				3·25
Presentation Pack			3·50	

Sheets: 12 (4×3) containing Nos. 381/92 *se-tenant*.
Imprint: Central, bottom margin.
Quantity sold: 226,119 sheetlets.
Withdrawn: 17.11.87.

Yearbook 1986

1986 (Dec). Comprises Nos. 360/92 and A28/31 (price £9.95).

Yearbook		36·00

Withdrawn: 31.12.87

366 Duke of Richmond and Map of 1787
(*Illustration reduced size. Actual size 134×103 mm*)

Bicentenary of Duke of Richmond's Survey of Guernsey

(Des J. Cooter. Litho Questa)

1987 (10 Feb). P 14½×14 (C).

MS393	134×103 mm **366** 14p., 29p., 31p., 34p. multicoloured	3·50	3·75
First Day Cover			4·50
Presentation Pack		4·50	

Quantity sold: 176,655.
Withdrawn: 9.2.88.

367 Post Office Headquarters

368 Architect's Elevation of Post Office Headquarters

369 Guernsey Grammar School

370 Architect's Elevation of Grammar School

Europa. Modern Architecture

(Des R. Reed. Litho Cartor)

1987 (5 May). P 13×13½ (C).

394	**367**	15p. multicoloured	35	30
		a. Horiz pair. Nos. 394/5	75	80
395	**368**	15p. multicoloured	35	30
396	**369**	22p. multicoloured	50	50
		a. Horiz pair. Nos. 396/7	1·20	1·30
397	**370**	22p. multicoloured	50	50
394/7 *Set of 4*			1·90	1·90
First Day Cover				2·20
Presentation Pack			2·50	

Plate Nos.: Both values 1A, 1B, 1C, 1D. (each×4).
Sheets: 20 (4×5), the two designs for each value printed together, *se-tenant*, in horizontal pairs throughout the sheets.
Quantities sold: 15p. 595,661 pairs; 22p. 434,886 pairs.
Withdrawn: 4.5.88.

Coil Stamps

(Photo Harrison)

1987 (15 May)–**88**. As Nos. 306, 306b, 309 and 309c, but smaller., 22×18 mm (11p., 16p.) or 18×22 mm (12p., 15p.). P 14×14½ (11p., 16p.) or 14½×14 (12p., 15p.), all comb.

398	**274**	11p. multicoloured (a)	50	50
398a	**275**	12p. multicoloured (b)	40	40
399	**278**	15p. multicoloured (a)	60	60
399a	**279**	16p. multicoloured (b)	50	50
398/9a *Set of 4*			1·80	1·80
First Day Covers (2)				12·00

Printings: (a) 15.5.87; (b) 28.3.88.
Coils: Rolls of 1000 (a) or 500 (b).
Withdrawn: 26.12.89 11p., 15p.; 22.5.92 12p., 16p.

371 Sir Edmund Andros and La Plaiderie, Guernsey

372 Governor's Palace, Virginia

373 Governor Andros in Boston

374 Map of New Amsterdam (New York), 1661

350th Birth Anniversary of Sir Edmund Andros (colonial administrator)

(Des B. Sanders. Photo Courvoisier)

1987 (7 July). Granite paper. P 12 (C).

400	**371**	15p. multicoloured	35	35
401	**372**	29p. multicoloured	1·00	1·00
402	**373**	31p. multicoloured	1·00	1·00
403	**374**	34p. multicoloured	1·40	1·40
400/3	*Set of 4*		3·25	3·25
First Day Cover				3·50
Presentation Pack			3·50	
Set of 4 Gutter Pairs			6·50	

Cylinder Nos.: All values A1–1–1–1–1, B1–1–1–1–1.
Sheets: 40 (2 panes 5×4).
Quantites sold: 15p. 707,843; 29p. 129,462; 31p. 136,308; 34p. 129,527.
Withdrawn: 6.7.88.

375 The Jester's warning to Young William

376 Hastings Battlefield

377 Norman Soldier with Pennant

378 William the Conqueror

379 Queen Matilda and Abbaye aux Dames, Caen

380 William's Coronation Regalia and Halley's Comet

900th Death Anniversary of William the Conqueror

(Des P. le Vasseur. Litho Cartor)

1987 (9 Sept). P 13½×14 (C).

404	**375**	11p. multicoloured	30	30
405	**376**	15p. multicoloured	40	35
		a. Horiz pair. Nos. 405/6	80	90
406	**377**	15p. multicoloured	40	35
407	**378**	22p. multicoloured	60	60
		a. Horiz pair. Nos. 407/8	1·20	1·20
408	**379**	22p. multicoloured	60	60
409	**380**	34p. multicoloured	90	1·10
404/9	*Set of 6*		3·00	3·25
First Day Cover				3·50
Presentation Pack			3·75	
Set of 4 Gutter Pairs			6·00	

Plate Nos.: All values 1A, 1B, 1C, 1D. (each×4).
Sheets: 40 (2 panes 4×5), the two designs for the 15p. and 22p. values were printed together, *se-tenant*, in horizontal pairs throughout the sheets.
Imprint: Bottom, left-hand margin.
Quantities sold: 11p. 639,904; 15p. 241,572 pairs; 22p. 142,718 pairs; 34p. 131,655.
Withdrawn: 8.9.88.

381 John Wesley preaching on the Quay, Alderney

382 Preaching at Mon Plaisir, St. Peter Port

383 Preaching at Assembly Rooms

384 Wesley and La Ville Baudu (early Methodist meeting place)

385 Wesley and first Methodist Chapel, St. Peter Port

Bicentenary of John Wesley's Visit to Guernsey

(Des R. Geary. Litho Questa)

1987 (17 Nov). P 14½ (C).

410	**381**	7p. multicoloured	20	20
411	**382**	15p. multicoloured	40	40
412	**383**	29p. multicoloured	80	80
413	**384**	31p. multicoloured	85	85
414	**385**	34p. multicoloured	1·00	1·00
410/14	*Set of 5*		3·00	3·00
First Day Cover				3·25
Presentation Pack			3·75	
Set of 5 Gutter Pairs			6·00	

Plate Nos.: All values 1A, 1B, 1C, 1D. (each×4).
Sheets: 50 (2 panes 5×5).
Imprint: Bottom, right-hand margin of each pane.
Quantities sold: 7p. 762,772; 15p. 887,797; 29p. 122,322; 31p. 126,591; 34p. 125,863.
Withdrawn: 16.11.88.

Yearbook 1987

1987 (Dec). Comprises Nos. **MS**393/7, 400/14 and A32/6 (price £9.95).

Yearbook		38·00

Withdrawn: 31.12.88.

386 *Golden Spur* off St. Sampson's Harbour

387 Entering Hong Kong Harbour

388 Anchored off Macao

389 In China Tea Race

390 *Golden Spur* and Map showing Voyage of 1872–74

Guernsey Shipping (2nd series). *Golden Spur* **(full-rigged ship)**

(Des R. Granger Barrett. Litho BDT)

1988 (9 Feb). P 13½ (C).

415	**386**	11p. multicoloured	50	50
416	**387**	15p. multicoloured	50	50
417	**388**	29p. multicoloured	1·00	1·00
418	**389**	31p. multicoloured	1·00	1·00
419	**390**	34p. multicoloured	1·25	1·25
415/19	*Set of 5*		3·50	3·50
First Day Cover				3·75
Presentation Pack			4·00	
Set of 5 Gutter Pairs			7·00	

Plate Nos.: All values 1A, 1B, 1C, 1D. (each×4).
Sheets: 50 (2 panes 5×5).
Imprint: Central, side margins of each pane.
Quantities sold: 11p. 213,291; 15p. 214,048; 29p. 136,246; 31p. 143,815; 34p. 141,177.
Withdrawn: 8.2.89.

391 Rowing Boat and Bedford 'Rascal' Mail Van

392 Rowing Boat and Vickers Viscount 800 Mail Plane

393 Postman on Bicycle and Horse-drawn Carriages, Sark

394 Postmen on Bicycles and Carriage

Europa. Transport and Communications

(Des C. Abbott. Litho Questa)

1988 (10 May). P 14½ (C).

420	**391**	16p. multicoloured	40	35
		a. Horiz pair. Nos. 420/1	80	90
421	**392**	16p. multicoloured	40	35
422	**393**	22p. multicoloured	70	70
		a. Horiz pair. Nos. 422/3	1·40	1·40
423	**394**	22p. multicoloured	70	70
420/3	*Set of 4*		2·00	2·10
First Day Cover				2·25
Presentation Pack			2·50	

Plate Nos.: Both values 1A, 1B, 1C, 1D. (each×5).
Sheets: 20 (4×5), the two designs for each value printed together, *se-tenant*, in horizontal pairs throughout the sheets.
Imprint: Top, right-hand margin.
Quantities sold: 16p. 387,699 pairs; 22p. 359,634 pairs.
Withdrawn: 9.5.89.

395 Frederick Corbin Lukis and Lukis House, St. Peter Port

396 Natural History Books and Reconstructed Pot

397 Lukis directing Excavation of Le Creux ès Faies and Prehistoric Beaker

398 Lukis House Observatory and Garden

399 Prehistoric Artifacts

Birth Bicentenary of Frederick Corbin Lukis (archaeologist)

(Des Wendy Bramall, Photo Courvoisier)

1988 (12 July). Granite paper. P 12½ (C).

424	**395**	12p. multicoloured	30	25
425	**396**	16p. multicoloured	35	25
426	**397**	29p. multicoloured	80	85
427	**398**	31p. multicoloured	90	85
428	**399**	34p. multicoloured	90	90
424/8	*Set of 5*		3·00	2·50
First Day Cover				3·00
Presentation Pack			3·50	
Set of 5 Gutter Pairs			6·00	

Cylinder Nos.: 29p., 34p. A1–1–1, B1–1–1, C1–1–1, D1–1–1; others A1–1–1–1, B1–1–1–1, C1–1–1–1, D1–1–1–1.
Sheets: 40 (2 panes 5×4).
Quantities sold: 12p. 634,056; 16p. 510,713; 29p. 120,538; 31p. 114,192; 34p. 134,358.
Withdrawn: 11.7.89.

400 *Cougar* , *Rocky* and *Annabella* (power-boats) and Westland Wessex Rescue Helicopter off Jethou

401 *Paul Picot* and other Powerboats in Gouliot Passage

402 Start of Race at St. Peter Port

403 Admirality Chart showing Course

World Offshore Powerboat Championships

(Des and photo Courvoisier)

1988 (6 Sept). Granite paper. P 12 (C).

429	**400**	16p. multicoloured	35	35
430	**401**	30p. multicoloured	1·10	1·10
431	**402**	32p. multicoloured	1·20	1·20
432	**403**	35p. multicoloured	1·25	1·25

429/32 Set of 4 .... 3·50 3·50
First Day Cover .... 3·75
Presentation Pack .... 4·00
Set of 4 Gutter Pairs .... 7·00

Cylinder Nos.: 16p., 32p. A1–1–1–1, B1–1–1–1; 30p., 35p. C1–1–1–1, D1–1–1–1.
Sheets: 40 (2 panes 5×4) 16p., 30p. or (2 panes 4×5) others.
Quantities sold: 16p. 582,190; 30p. 127,183; 32p. 166,804; 35p. 128,552.
Withdrawn: 5.9.89.

404 Joshua Gosselin and Herbarium

405 Hares-tail Grass

406 Dried Hares-tail Grass

407 Variegated Catchfly

408 Dried Variegated Catchfly

409 Rock Sea Lavender

Bicentenary of Joshua Gosselin's *Flora Sarniensis*

(Des M. Oxenham. Litho Cartor)

1988 (15 Nov). P 13½×14 (C).

433	**404**	12p. multicoloured	25	25
434	**405**	16p. multicoloured	35	35
		a. Horiz pair. Nos. 434/5	85	85
435	**406**	16p. multicoloured	35	35
436	**407**	23p. multicoloured	60	60
		a. Horiz pair. Nos. 436/7	1·20	1·40
437	**408**	23p. multicoloured	60	60
438	**409**	35p. multicoloured	1·20	1·20

433/8 Set of 6 .... 3·25 3·50
First Day Cover .... 4·00
Presentation Pack .... 4·25
Set of 4 Gutter Pairs .... 6·50

Plate Nos.: All values 1A, 1B, 1C, 1D. (each×4).
Sheets: 40 (2 panes 4×5), the two designs for the 16p. and 23p. values printed together, *se-tenant*, in horizontal pairs throughout the sheets.
Imprint: Bottom, left-hand margin.
Quantities sold: 12p. 562,702; 16p. 378,679 pairs; 23p. 141,152 pairs; 35p. 133,205.
Withdrawn: 14.11.89.

410 Coutances Cathedral, France

411 Interior of Notre Dame du Rosaire Church, Guernsey

412 Stained Glass, St. Sampson's Church, Guernsey

413 Dol-de-Bretagne Cathedral, France

414 Bishops Throne, Town Church, Guernsey

415 Winchester Cathedral

416 St. John's Cathedral, Portsmouth

417 High Altar St. Joseph's Church, Guernsey

418 Mont Saint–Michel, France

419 Chancel, Vale Church, Guernsey

420 Lychgate, Forest Church, Guernsey

421 Marmoutier Abbey, France

Christmas. Ecclesiastical Links

(Des R. Downer. Litho Questa)

1988 (15 Nov). P 14½ (C).

439	**410**	8p. multicoloured	30	30
		a. Sheetlet of 12. Nos. 439/50	3·00	3·00
440	**411**	8p. multicoloured	30	30
441	**412**	8p. multicoloured	30	30
442	**413**	8p. multicoloured	30	30
443	**414**	8p. multicoloured	30	30
444	**415**	8p. multicoloured	30	30
445	**416**	8p. multicoloured	30	30
446	**417**	8p. multicoloured	30	30
447	**418**	8p. multicoloured	30	30
448	**419**	8p. multicoloured	30	30
449	**420**	8p. multicoloured	30	30
450	**421**	8p. multicoloured	30	30

439/50 Set of 12 .... 3·00 3·00
First Day Cover .... 3·25
Presentation Pack .... 3·50

Sheets : 12 (4×3) containing Nos. 439/50 *se-tenant*.
Imprint: Bottom, left-hand margin.
Quantity sold: 185,939 sheetlets.
Withdrawn: 14.11.89.

Yearbook 1988

1988 (Dec). Comprises Nos. 306b, 309c and 415/50 (price £10.95).
Yearbook .... 37·00
Withdrawn: 31.12.89.

422 Lé (Tip Cat)

423 Girl with Cobo Alice Doll

424 Lé Colimachaön (hopscotch)

Europa. Children's Toys and Games

(Des P. le Vasseur. Litho Cartor)

1989 (28 Feb). P 13½ (C).
451	422	12p. multicoloured	30	20
452	423	16p. multicoloured	40	40
453	424	23p. multicoloured	75	85
451/3	*Set of 3*		1·20	1·20
	First Day Cover			1·60
	Presentation Pack		1·90	

Plate Nos.: All values 1A, 1B, 1C (each×4).
Sheets: 20 (4×5).
Imprint: Top, right-hand margin.
Quantities sold: 12p. 839,111; 16p. 829,156; 23p. 448,761.
Withdrawn: 27.2.90.

425 Outline
Map of Guernsey

Coil Stamps

(Photo Harrison)

1989 (3 Apr–27 Dec). No value expressed. P 14½×14 (C).
454	425	(14p.) ultramarine (b)	90	90
455		(18p.) emerald (a)	90	90
454/5	*Set of 2*		1·60	1·60
	First Day Covers (2)			18·00

No. 454 is inscribed 'MINIMUM BAILIWICK POSTAGE PAID' and
No. 455 'MINIMUM FIRST CLASS POSTAGE TO UK PAID'. They were
originally sold at 14p. and 18p., but this was changed in line with
postage rate rises.
Printings: (a) 3.4.89; (b) 27.12.89.
Coils: Rolls of 500, numbered on the reverse of every fifth stamp.
Withdrawn: 30.6.96.

426 Guernsey Airways de
Havilland DH.86 Dragon Express
and Mail Van

427 Supermarine Southampton
II Flying Boat at mooring

428 B.E.A. de Havilland DH.89
Dragon Rapide

429 Short S.25 Sunderland Mk V
Flying Boat taking off

430 Air U.K. British Aerospace
BAe 146

431 Avro Shackleton M.R.3

**50th Anniversaries of Guernsey Airport (Nos. 456, 458 and 460)
and 201 Squadron's Affiliation with Guernsey
(Nos. 457, 459 and 461)**

(Des N. Foggo. Litho BDT)

1989 (5 May). P 13½ (C).
456	426	12p. multicoloured	35	30
		a. Booklet pane. No. 456×6	2·00	
457	427	12p. multicoloured	35	30
458	428	18p. multicoloured	50	75
		a. Booklet pane. No. 458×6	3·00	
459	429	18p. multicoloured	50	75
460	430	35p. multicoloured	1·00	1·00
		a. Booklet pane. No. 460×6	6·00	
461	431	35p. multicoloured	1·00	1·30
456/61	*Set of 6*		3·25	3·75
	First Day Cover			5·50
	Presentation Pack		4·50	
	Set of 4 Gutter Pairs		6·50	

Each booklet pane has margins all round with text printed at the
foot.
Plate Nos.: All values 1A, 1B (each×4).
Sheets: 50 (2 panes 5×5).
Imprint: Central, side margins of each pane.
Quantities sold: No. 456, 461,080; No. 457, 362,154; No. 458,
436,134; No. 459, 388,274; No. 460, 172,574; No. 461, 149,134.
Withdrawn: 4.5.90.

432 Queen Elizabeth II
(June Mendoza)

Royal Visit

(Des A. Theobald. Lithio BDT)

1989 (23 May). P 15×14.
462	432	30p. multicoloured	75	80
	First Day Cover			1·70
	Presentation Pack		2·00	

Plate Nos.: 1A (×5).
Sheets: 20 (5×4).
Imprint: Top, right-hand margin.
Quantity sold: 180,900.
Withdrawn: 22.5.90.

433 *Ibex* at G.W.R. Terminal,
St. Peter Port

434 *Great Western* (paddle-
steamer) in Little Russel

435 *St. Julien* passing Casquets
Light

436 *Roebuck* off Portland

437 *Antelope* and Boat Train on
Weymouth Quay

Centenary of Great Western Railway Steamer Service to Channel Islands

(Des C. Jaques. Litho BDT)

1989 (5 Sept). P 13½ (C).

463	**433**	12p. multicoloured	30	30
464	**434**	18p. multicoloured	40	40
465	**435**	29p. multicoloured	80	80
466	**436**	34p. multicoloured	1·00	95
467	**437**	37p. multicoloured	1·20	1·10
463/7 Set of 5			3·25	3·25
First Day Cover				4·00
Presentation Pack			5·00	
Set of 5 Gutter Pairs			6·50	
MS468 115×117 mm. Nos. 463/7			4·00	4·25
First Day Cover				7·00

Plate Nos.: All values 1A, 1B (each×4).
Sheets: 50 (2 panes (5×5).
Imprint: Central, side margins of each pane.
Quantities sold: 12p. 741,870; 18p. 666,520; 29p. 223,570; 34p. 202,570; 37p. 209,020; miniature sheet 74,127.
Withdrawn 4.9.90.

438 Two-toed Sloth   **439** Capuchin Monkey   **440** White-lipped Tamarin

441 Common Squirrel-Monkey   **442** Common Gibbon

Tenth Anniversary of Guernsey Zoological Trust. Animals of the Rainforest

(Des Anne Farncombe. Litho Cartor)

1989 (17 Nov). P 13½×14 (C).

469	**438**	18p. multicoloured	90	90
		a. Strip of 5. Nos. 469/73	4·00	4·00
470	**439**	29p. multicoloured	90	90
471	**440**	32p. multicoloured	90	90
472	**441**	34p. multicoloured	90	90
473	**442**	37p. multicoloured	90	90
469/73 Set of 5			4·00	4·00
First Day Cover				4·25
Presentation Pack			4·50	
Stamp-cards (Set of 5)			2·00	7·00

Plate Nos.: 1B (×4).
Sheets: 20 (5×4). Nos. 469/73 were printed in se-tenant strips of five across the sheet.
Imprint: Top, right-hand margin.
Quantities sold: 148,505 of each value.
Withdrawn: 16.11.90.

443 Star   **444** Fairy   **445** Candles

446 Bird   **447** Present   **448** Carol-singer

449 Christmas Cracker   **450** Bauble   **451** Christmas Stocking

452 Bell   **453** Fawn   **454** Church

Christmas. Christmas Tree Decorations

(Des Wendy Bramall. Litho BDT)

1989 (17 Nov). P 13 (C).

474	**443**	10p. multicoloured	35	35
		a. Sheetlet of 12. Nos. 474/85	3·75	3·75
475	**444**	10p. multicoloured	35	35
476	**445**	10p. multicoloured	35	35
477	**446**	10p. multicoloured	35	35
478	**447**	10p. multicoloured	35	35
479	**448**	10p. multicoloured	35	35
480	**449**	10p. multicoloured	35	35
481	**450**	10p. multicoloured	35	35
482	**451**	10p. multicoloured	35	35
483	**452**	10p. multicoloured	35	35
484	**453**	10p. multicoloured	35	35
485	**454**	10p. multicoloured	35	35
474/85 Set of 12			3·75	3·75
First Day Cover				4·50
Presentation Pack			4·75	

Sheets: 12 (3×4) containing Nos. 474/85 se-tenant.
Imprint: Central, left-hand margin.
Quantity sold: 229,000 sheetlets.
Withdrawn: 16.11.90.

Yearbook 1989

1989 (17 Nov). Comprises Nos. 309d, 451/3, 456/62. **MS**468/85 and A37/41 (price £11.75).

Yearbook		35·00

Withdrawn: 31.12.90.

455 Sark Post Office, c. 1890

456 Sark Post Office, 1990

457 Arcade Post Office Counter,
St. Peter Port, c. 1840

458 Arcade Post Office Counter,
St. Peter Port, 1990

Europa. Post Office Buildings

(Des C. Abbott. Litho Enschedé)

1990 (27 Feb). P 13½×14 (C).

486	**455**	20p. blackish brown, sepia and pale		
		cinnamon	45	45
487	**456**	20p. multicoloured	45	45
488	**457**	24p. blackish brown, sepia and pale		
		cinnamon	60	65
489	**458**	24p. multicoloured	60	65
486/9 *Set of 4*			1·90	2·00
First Day Cover				2·40
Presentation Pack			2·50	

Plate Nos.: Nos. 486 and 488 1A, 1B (each×3); Nos. 487 and 489
1A, 1B (each×4).
Sheets: 20 (4×5).
Imprint: Central, side margins.
Quantities sold: No. 486, 498,819; No. 487, 398,759; No. 488,
495,039; No. 489, 397,759.
Withdrawn: 26.2.91.

459 Penny Black and Mail
Steamer off St. Peter Port, 1840

460 Penny Red, 1841, and Pillar
Box of 1853

461 Bisected 2d., 1940, and
German Army Band

462 Regional 3d., 1958, and
Guernsey Emblems

463 Independent Postal
Administration 1½d., 1969, and
Queue at Main Post Office

150th Anniversary of the Penny Black

(Des Jennifer Toombs. Litho Questa)

1990 (3 May). P 14 (C).

490	**459**	14p. multicoloured	45	45
491	**460**	20p. multicoloured	60	60
492	**461**	32p. multicoloured	90	90
493	**462**	34p. multicoloured	1·00	1·00
494	**463**	37p. multicoloured	1·10	1·10
490/4 *Set of 5*			3·50	3·50
First Day Cover				4·00

Presentation Pack		5·50
Set of 5 Gutter Pairs		7·00
MS495 151×116 mm. Nos. 490/4	3·75	3·75
First Day Cover		15·00

No. **MS**495 also commemorates 'Stamp World London 90'
International Stamp Exhibition. It was reissued on 24 August 1990
overprinted for 'NEW ZEALAND 1990' and sold at this international
stamp exhibition in Auckland. (*Price £15 unused, £15 used, £30 on first
day cover*).
Plate Nos.: 14p., 32p. 1A, 1B (each×4); 20p., 34p. 1C, 1D. (each×4);
37p. 1A, 1B, 1C, 1D. (each×4).
Sheets: 50 (2 panes 5×5).
Imprint: Bottom corner, right-hand margin of each pane.
Quantities sold: 14p. 687,850; 20p. 662,800; 32p. 155,960; 34p.
143,850; 37p. 174,830; miniature sheet 92,701.
Withdrawn: 4.5.91.

464 Lt. Philip Saumarez writing
Log Book

465 Anson's Squadron leaving
Portsmouth, 1740

466 Ships at St. Catherine's Island,
Brazil

467 H.M.S. *Tryal* (sloop) dismasted,
Cape Horn, 1741

468 Crew of H.M.S. *Centurion* on Juan
Fernandez

250th Anniversary of Anson's Circumnavigation

(Des R. Granger Barrett. Litho Enschedé)

1990 (26 July). P 13½×14 (C).

496	**464**	14p. multicoloured	35	35
497	**465**	20p. multicoloured	50	50
498	**466**	29p. multicoloured	80	80
499	**467**	34p. multicoloured	1·00	1·00
500	**468**	37p. multicoloured	1·10	1·10
496/500 *Set of 5*			3·50	3·50
First Day Cover				3·75

Presentation Pack.....................................	4·00		
Stamp-cards (Set of 5)..............................	2·00	6·00	
Set of 5 Gutter Pairs................................	7·00		

Plate Nos.: 14p., 20p., 29p. 1A, 1B, 1C, 1D. (each×4);
34p., 37p. 1A, 1B (each×4).
Sheets: 50 (2 panes 5×5).
Imprint: Central, side margins of each pane.
Quantities sold: 14p. 985,850; 20p. 481,400; 29p. 162,800; 34p. 143,500; 37p. 138,450.
Withdrawn: 25.7.91.

469 Grey Seal and Pup   **470** Bottle-nosed Dolphin

471 Basking Shark   **472** Common Porpoise

World Wide Fund for Nature (Marine Life)

(Des Jennifer Toombs. Litho Questa)

1990 (16 Oct). P 14½ (C).

501	469	20p. multicoloured....................		50	50
502	470	26p. multicoloured....................		1·10	1·10
503	471	31p. multicoloured....................		1·25	1·25
504	472	37p. multicoloured....................		1·40	1·40
501/4 Set of 4				3·75	3·75
First Day Cover					4·25
Presentation Pack				4·50	
Set of 4 Gutter Pairs				6·50	

Plate Nos.: 20p., 31p. 1A, 1B (each×4); 26p., 37p. 1C, 1D. (each×4).
Sheets: 50 (2 panes 5×5).
Imprint: Top, right-hand margin of each pane.
Quantities sold: 20p. 973,900; 26p. 478,200; 31p. 328,650; 37p. 303,600.
Withdrawn: 15.10.91.

473 Blue Tit and Great Tit   **474** Snow Bunting   **475** Common Kestrel

476 Common Starling   **477** Western Greenfinch   **478** European Robin

479 Winter Wren   **480** Barn Owl   **481** Mistle Thrush

482 Grey Heron   **483** Chaffinch   **484** Common Kingfisher

Christmas. Winter Birds

(Des Wendy Bramall. Litho BDT)

1990 (16 Oct). P 13 (C).

505	473	10p. multicoloured....................		35	40
		a. Sheetlet of 12. Nos. 505/16....		3·50	3·75
506	474	10p. multicoloured....................		35	40
507	475	10p. multicoloured....................		35	40
508	476	10p. multicoloured....................		35	40
509	477	10p. multicoloured....................		35	40
510	478	10p. multicoloured....................		35	40
511	479	10p. multicoloured....................		35	40
512	480	10p. multicoloured....................		35	40
513	481	10p. multicoloured....................		35	40
514	482	10p. multicoloured....................		35	40
515	483	10p. multicoloured....................		35	40
516	484	10p. multicoloured....................		35	40
505/16 Set of 12				3·50	3·75
First Day Cover					4·00
Presentation Pack				3·75	

Sheets: 12 (3×4) containing Nos. 505/16 se-tenant.
Imprint: Central, left-hand margin.
Quantity sold: 237,602 sheetlets.
Withdrawn: 15.10.91.

Yearbook 1990

1990 (1 Nov). Comprises Nos. 486/9, **MS**495, 496/516, A12a and A42/6 (price £12.25).

Yearbook..	35·00	

Withdrawn: 31.12.91.

485 Air Raid and 1941 ½d. Stamp   **486** 1941 1d. Stamp

487 1944 2½d. Stamp

50th Anniversary of First Guernsey Stamps

(Des C. Abbott. Litho BDT)

1991 (18 Feb). P 13½ (C).

517	485	37p. multicoloured....................		1·10	1·10
		a. Booklet pane. Nos. 517/19......		4·00	
518	486	53p. multicoloured....................		1·50	1·50
519	487	57p. multicoloured....................		1·50	1·50
517/19 Set of 3				3·75	3·75
First Day Cover					4·00
Presentation Pack				4·25	
Set of 3 Gutter Pairs				6·50	

Booklet pane No. 517a exists in three versions, which differ in the order of the stamps from left to right and in the information printed on the pane margins.
Plate Nos.: 37p., 53p. 1A, 1B (each×4); 57p. 1A, 1B, 1C, 1D. (each×4).
Sheets: 40 (2 panes 5×4).
Imprint: Central, side margins.
Quantities sold: 37p. 260,015; 53p. 250,536; 57p. 250,219.
Withdrawn: 17.2.92.

488 Visit of Queen Victoria to Guernsey, and Discovery of Neptune, 1846

489 Visit of Queen Elizabeth II and Prince Philip to Sark, and Flight of 'Sputnik' (1st artificial satellite, 1957)

490 Maiden Voyage of *Sarnia* (ferry), and 'Vostok 1' (first manned space flight), 1961

491 Cancelling Guernsey Stamps, and First Manned Landing on Moon, 1969

Europa. Europe in Space

(Des Jennifer Toombs. Litho Enschedé)

1991 (30 Apr). P 13½×14 (C).

520	**488**	21p. multicoloured	55	55
521	**489**	21p. multicoloured	55	55
522	**490**	26p. multicoloured	75	75
523	**491**	26p. multicoloured	75	75
520/3 *Set of 4*			2·25	2·25
First Day Cover				2·50
Presentation Pack			2·75	

Plate Nos.: Both values 1A, 1B (each×5).
Sheets: 20 (4×5).
Imprint: Central, side margins.
Quantities sold: No. 520, 390,924; No. 521, 390,834; No. 522, 369,404; No. 523, 370,244.
Withdrawn: 29.4.92.

492 Children in Guernsey Sailing Trust 'GP14' Dinghy

493 Guernsey Regatta

494 Lombard Channel Islands' Challenge Race

495 Rolex Swan Regatta

496 Old Gaffers' Association Gaff-rigged Yacht

Centenary of Guernsey Yacht Club

(Des C. Abbott. Litho BDT)

1991 (2 July). P 14 (C).

524	**492**	15p. multicoloured	45	25
525	**493**	21p. multicoloured	70	40
526	**494**	26p. multicoloured	80	80
527	**495**	31p. multicoloured	90	1·10
528	**496**	37p. multicoloured	1·00	1·40
524/8 *Set of 5*			3·50	3·75
First Day Cover				4·25
Presentation Pack			5·00	
Set 5 Gutter Pairs			7·00	
MS529 163×75 mm. Nos. 524/8			4·00	4·25
First Day Cover				10·00

Stamps from No. **MS**529 show 'GUERNSEY' and the face value in yellow.
Plate Nos.: 37p. 1C, 1D. (each×5); others 1A, 1B (each×5).
Sheets: 50 (2 panes 5×5).
Imprint: Top corner, right-hand margin of each pane.
Quantities sold: 15p. 711,043; 21p. 708,743; 26p. 188,894; 31p. 158,938; 37p. 138.543; miniature sheet 81,012.
Withdrawn: 1.7.92.

497 Pair of Oystercatchers

498 Three Ruddy Turnstones

499 Dunlins and Ruddy Turnstones

500 Curlew and Ruddy Turnstones

501 Ringed Plover with Chicks

502 Black-headed Gull, Sea Campion and Sea Radish

503 Yellow Horned Poppy

504 Pair of Common Stonechats, Hare's Foot Clover and Fennel

505 Hare's Foot Clover, Fennel and Slender Oat

506 Ruddy Turnstone and Sea Kale on Shore

Nature Conservation. L'Eree Shingle Bank Reserve

(Des Wendy Bramall. Litho Questa)

1991 (15 Oct). P 14½ (C).

530	**497**	15p. multicoloured	35	20
		a. Horiz strip of 5. Nos. 530/4	2·75	2·50
531	**498**	15p. multicoloured	35	20
532	**499**	15p. multicoloured	35	20
533	**500**	15p. multicoloured	35	20
534	**501**	15p. multicoloured	35	20
535	**502**	21p. multicoloured	35	20
		a. Horiz strip of 5. Nos. 535/9	2·75	2·50
536	**503**	21p. multicoloured	35	20

537	**504**	21p. multicoloured	35	20
538	**505**	21p. multicoloured	35	20
539	**506**	21p. multicoloured	35	20

530/9 *Set of 10* .... 4·50 4·00
First Day Cover .... 5·00
Presentation Pack .... 5·00
Stamp-cards (Set of 10) .... 4·00 10·00

Plate Nos.: Both values 1A, 1B, 1C, 1D. (each×4).
Sheets: 20 (5×4), the five designs for each value printed together, *se-tenant*, in horizontal strips throughout the sheets.
Imprint: Bottom, left-hand margin.
Quantities sold: 15p. 270,830 strips; 21p. 272,198 strips.
Withdrawn: 14.10.92.

507 'Rudolph the Red-nosed Reindeer' (Melanie Sharpe)
508 'Christmas Pudding' (James Quinn)
509 'Snowman' (Lisa Guille)

510 'Snowman in Top Hat' (Jessica Ede-Golightly)
511 'Robins and Christmas Tree' (Sharon Le Page)
512 'Shepherds and Angels' (Anna Coquelin)

513 'Nativity' (Claudine Lithou)
514 'Three Wise Men' (Johnathan Le Noury)
515 'Star of Bethlehem and Angels' (Marcia Mahy)

516 'Christmas Tree' (Laurel Garfield)
517 'Santa Claus' (Rebecca Driscoll)
518 'Snowman and Star' (Ian Lowe)

Christmas. Children's Paintings

(Litho BDT)

1991 (15 Oct). P 13½×13 (C).

540	**507**	12p. multicoloured	30	15
		a. Sheetlet of 12. Nos. 540/51	3·25	3·25
541	**508**	12p. multicoloured	30	15
542	**509**	12p. multicoloured	30	15
543	**510**	12p. multicoloured	30	15
544	**511**	12p. multicoloured	30	15
545	**512**	12p. multicoloured	30	15
546	**513**	12p. multicoloured	30	15
547	**514**	12p. multicoloured	30	15
548	**515**	12p. multicoloured	30	15
549	**516**	12p. multicoloured	30	15
550	**517**	12p. multicoloured	30	15
551	**518**	12p. multicoloured	30	15

540/51 *Set of 12* .... 3·25 3·25
First Day Cover .... 3·50
Presentation Pack .... 3·75

Sheets: 12 (3×4) containing Nos. 540/51 *se-tenant*.
Imprint: Central, left-hand margin.
Quantity sold: 192,203 sheetlets.
Withdrawn: 14.10.92.

Yearbook 1991

1991 (1 Nov). Comprises Nos. 310*b/c*, 517/51, A12*b* and A47/51 (price £14).
Yearbook .... 35·00
Withdrawn: 31.12.92.

519 Queen Elizabeth II, in 1952
520 In 1977

521 In 1986
522 In 1991

40th Anniversary of Accession

(Des C. Abbott. Litho Questa)

1992 (6 Feb). P 14 (C).

552	**519**	23p. multicoloured	50	50
553	**520**	28p. multicoloured	65	65
554	**521**	33p. multicoloured	90	90
555	**522**	39p. multicoloured	1·10	1·10

552/5 *Set of 4* .... 2·75 2·75
First Day Cover .... 3·25
Presentation Pack .... 3·25
Set of 4 Gutter Pairs .... 5·50

Plate Nos.: All values 1A, 1B (each×6).
Sheets: 50 (2 panes 5×5).
Quantities sold: 23p. 773,200; 28p. 479,095; 33p. 212,446; 39p. 219,900.
Withdrawn: 5.2.93.

523 Christopher Columbus

524 Examples of Columbus's Signature

525 *Santa Maria*

526 Map of First Voyage

Europa. 500th Anniversary of Discovery of America by Columbus

(Des R. Ollington. Litho Walsall)

1992 (6 Feb). P 13½×14 (C).

556	**523**	23p. multicoloured	65	60
557	**524**	23p. multicoloured	65	60
558	**525**	28p. multicoloured	1·20	1·20
559	**526**	28p. multicoloured	1·20	1·20
556/9 *Set of 4*			3·25	3·25
First Day Cover				3·75
Presentation Pack			3·75	
MS560 157×77 mm. Nos. 556/9			4·50	5·00
First Day Cover				7·00

No. **MS**560 was reissued on 22 May 1992 overprinted for 'WORLD COLUMBIAN STAMP EXPO 92' and sold at this international stamp exhibition in Chicago. (*Price £5 unused, £6 used, £9 on first day cover*).

Plate Nos.: All values 1A, 1B, 1C (each×4).

Sheets: 20 (4×5).

Imprint: Bottom, right-hand margin.

Quantities sold: No. 556, 543,672; No. 557, 575,663; No. 558, 363,124; No. 559, 364,684; miniature sheet 157,166.

Withdrawn: 5.2.93.

527 Guernsey Calves (*Illustration reduced. Actual size 93×71 mm*)

150th Anniversary of Royal Guernsey Agricultural and Horticultural Society

(Des R. Goldsmith. Litho Questa)

1992 (22 May). Sheet 93×71 mm. P 14 (C).

MS561 **527** multicoloured		2·50	2·50
First Day Cover			3·25
Presentation Pack		2·75	

Quantity sold: 142,549.

Withdrawn: 21.5.93.

GUERNSEY
528 Stephanotis floribunda

GUERNSEY
529 Potted Hydrangea

GUERNSEY
530 Stock

GUERNSEY
531 Anemones

GUERNSEY
532 Gladiolus

GUERNSEY
533 Asparagus plumosus, Gypsophilia Paniculata

GUERNSEY
534 Guernsey Lily

GUERNSEY
535 Enchantment Lily

GUERNSEY
536 Clematis 'Freckles'

GUERNSEY
537 Alstromeria

GUERNSEY 16p
538 Standard Carnation

GUERNSEY
539 Standard Rose

GUERNSEY
540 Spray Rose

GUERNSEY 23p
541 Mixed Freesia

GUERNSEY 24p
542 Standard Rose

GUERNSEY 25p
543 Iris 'Ideal'

GUERNSEY 26p
544 Freesia 'Pink Glow'

GUERNSEY 28p
545 Lisianthus

GUERNSEY 30p
546 Spray Chrysanthemum

GUERNSEY
547 Spray Carnation

GUERNSEY 50p
548 Single Freesia

GUERNSEY £1
549 Floral Arrangement

GUERNSEY £2
550 Chelsea Flower Show Exhibit

GUERNSEY £3
551 'Floral Fantasia' (exhibit)

Guernsey Flowers

(Des R. Gorringe. Litho Walsall (Nos. 572a, 572ba, 574a, 575a, 576b and 577a), Questa (No. 576a), Cartor (No. 582a) or BDT (others))

1992 (22 May)–**97**. P 14 (£1, £2) or 13 (others), all comb.

562	**528**	1p. multicoloured (b)	10	10
563	**529**	2p. multicoloured (b)	10	10
564	**530**	3p. multicoloured (a)	10	10
565	**531**	4p. multicoloured (a)	15	15
566	**532**	5p. multicoloured (a)	15	15
567	**533**	6p. multicoloured (b)	15	15
568	**534**	7p. multicoloured (b)	20	20
569	**535**	8p. multicoloured (b)	20	20
570	**536**	9p. multicoloured (b)	20	25
571	**537**	10p. multicoloured (a)	25	25
572	**538**	16p. multicoloured (a)	50	35
		a. Perf 14 (ab)	60	50
		ab. Lavender ptg double	£850	
		ac. Booklet pane. Nos. 572a×5 and 574a×3 (a)	4·00	
		ad. Booklet pane of 8 (b)	3·25	
572b	**539**	18p. multicoloured (e)	55	45
		ba. Perf 14	55	45
		bb. Booklet pane of 8	4·00	
573	**540**	20p. multicoloured (a)	60	50
574	**541**	23p. multicoloured (a)	60	55
		a. Perf 14	80	60
		ab. Brownish grey ptg double	£850	
		ac. Booklet pane of 8	6·00	
575	**542**	24p. multicoloured (b)	70	60
		a. Perf 14	80	60
		ab. Booklet pane of 8	6·00	
576	**543**	25p. multicoloured (c)	70	60
		a. Perf 14½×15	80	60
		ab. Booklet pane of 4	3·75	
576b	**544**	26p. multicoloured (e)	70	60
		ba. Perf 14	80	60
		bb. Booklet pane of 4	3·75	
577	**545**	28p. multicoloured (b)	80	65
		a. Perf 14	1·10	65
		ab. Booklet pane of 4	3·50	
578	**546**	30p. multicoloured (b)	80	70
579	**547**	40p. multicoloured (a)	1·00	1·00
580	**548**	50p. multicoloured (a)	1·20	1·00
581	**549**	£1 multicoloured (a)	2·50	2·00
582	**550**	£2 multicoloured (b)	5·00	4·00
582a	**551**	£3 multicoloured (d)	7·00	6·00
562/82a Set of 24			22·00	18·00
First Day Covers (5)				25·00
Presentation Packs (3)			25·00	
Pack Stamp-cards (Set of 24)			5·00	27·00
Set of 24 Gutter Pairs			40·00	

Nos. 572a, 572ba, 574a, 575a, 576a, 576ba and 577a were only issued in booklets with the upper and lower edges of the panes imperforate and in unfolded booklet panes, available from the Philatelic Bureau and Head Post Office.

For No. 581 in miniature sheets see Nos. **MS**644 (with imprint date '1994') and **MS**681 (with imprint date '1995').

Printings: (a) 22.5.92; (b) 2.3.93; (c). 18.2.94; (d) 24.1.96; (e) 2.1.97, each with appropriate imprint date.

Plate Nos.: £1 1A, 1B (each×8); £3 1A, 1B, 1C, 1D. (each×5); others 1A, 1B, 1C, 1D. (each×6).

Sheets: 1p., 2p., 3p., 4p., 5p., 6p., 7p., 8p., 9p., 10p., 18p., 20p., 40p. 100 (2 panes 10×5); 16p., 23p., 24p., 25p., 26p., 28p., 30p., 50p. (2 panes 5×10); £1, £2, £3 50 (2 panes 5×5).

Imprints: 1p., 2p., 3p., 4p., 5p., 6p., 7p., 8p., 9p., 10p., 18p., 20p., 40p., £1, £2 left-hand corner, top and bottom margin; £3 central, side margins; others top of side margin.

Withdrawn: 31.8.99 1p to £2; 31.8.2003 £3.

552 Building the Ship

553 Loading the Cargo

554 Ship at Sea

555 Ship under Attack

556 Crew swimming Ashore

'Operation Asterix' (excavation of Roman ship)

(Des Studio Legrain. Litho Cartor)

1992 (18 Sept). P 13 (C).

583	**552**	16p. multicoloured	45	35
		a. Booklet pane. Nos. 583/7 plus label	3·50	
584	**553**	23p. multicoloured	60	50
585	**554**	28p. multicoloured	80	90
586	**555**	33p. multicoloured	95	95
587	**556**	39p. multicoloured	1·10	1·10
583/7 Set of 5			3·50	3·50
First Day Cover				4·25
Presentation Pack			4·25	
Set of 5 Gutter Pairs			7·00	

Booklet pane No. 583a has margins all round and exists with marginal inscriptions in either English, French, Italian or German.

Plate Nos.: All values 1A, 1B, 1C, 1D. (each×4).

Sheets: 50 (2 panes 5×5).

Imprint: Central, side margins.

Quantities sold: 16p. 904,428; 23p. 743,228; 28p. 308,091; 33p. 281,941; 39p. 291,841.

Withdrawn: 17.9.93.

557 Tram No. 10 decorated for Battle of Flowers

558 Tram No. 10 passing Hougue a la Perre

559 Tram No. 1 at St. Sampsons

560 First Steam Tram at St. Peter Port, 1879

561 Last Electric Tram, 1934

Guernsey Trams

(Des A. Peck. Litho Enschedé)

1992 (17 Nov). P 13½ (C).

588	**557**	16p. multicoloured	45	30
589	**558**	23p. multicoloured	60	35
590	**559**	28p. multicoloured	75	80
591	**560**	33p. multicoloured	90	1·00
592	**561**	39p. multicoloured	1·10	1·10
588/92	*Set of 5*		3·50	3·25
First Day Cover				4·25
Presentation Pack			4·75	
Set of 5 Gutter Pairs			7·50	

Plate Nos.: 39p., 1A, 1B, 1C, 1D. (each×6); others 1A, 1B (each×6).
Sheets: 50 (2 panes 5×5).
Imprint: Central, side margins of each pane.
Quantities sold: 16p. 366,400; 23p. 282,520; 28p. 181,670; 33p 130,920; 39p. 156,170.
Withdrawn: 16.11.93.

562 Man in Party Hat　　**563** Girl and Christmas Tree　　**564** Woman and Balloons

565 Mince Pies and Champagne　　**566** Roast Turkey　　**567** Christmas Pudding

568 Christmas Cake　　**569** Fancy Cakes　　**570** Cheese

571 Nuts　　**572** Ham　　**573** Chocolate Log

Christmas. Seasonal Fayre

(Des Wendy Bramall. Litho BDT)

1992 (17 Nov). P 13 (C).

593	**562**	13p. multicoloured	45	45
		a. Sheetlet of 12. Nos. 593/604	4·75	4·75
		ab. Gold ptg double		
594	**563**	13p. multicoloured	45	45
595	**564**	13p. multicoloured	45	45
596	**565**	13p. multicoloured	45	45
597	**566**	13p. multicoloured	45	45
598	**567**	13p. multicoloured	45	45
599	**568**	13p. multicoloured	45	45
600	**569**	13p. multicoloured	45	45
601	**570**	13p. multicoloured	45	45
602	**571**	13p. multicoloured	45	45
603	**572**	13p. multicoloured	45	45
604	**573**	13p. multicoloured	45	45
593/604	*Set of 12*		4·75	4·75
First Day Cover				5·00
Presentation Pack			4·50	

Sheets: 12 (3×4) containing Nos. 593/604 *se-tenant*, forming a composite design showing family during Christmas meal.
Imprint: Central, left-hand margin.
Quantity sold: 183,550 sheetlets.
Withdrawn: 16.11.93.

Yearbook 1992

1992 (18 Nov). Comprises Nos. 552/61, 564/6, 571/4, 579/81, 583/604, A12c and A52/5 (price £16.25).

Yearbook	35·00

Withdrawn: 31.12.93.

574 Rupert Bear, Bingo and Dog

574a Rupert and Friends (*Illustration reduced. Actual size 116×97 mm*)

Rupert Bear and Friends (cartoon characters created by Mary and Herbert Tourtel)

(Des J. Harold. Litho Walsall)

1993 (2 Feb). P 13½×13 (C).

605	**574**	24p. multicoloured	75	75
First Day Cover				2·00
Gutter Pair			1·50	
MS606	116×97 mm. **574a** 16p. Airplane and castle; 16p. Professor's servant and Autumn Elf; 16p. Algy Pug; 16p. Baby Badger on sledge; 24p. Bill Badger, Willie Mouse, Reggie Rabbit and Podgy playing in snow; 24p. Type **574**; 24p. The Balloonist avoiding Gregory on toboggan; 24p. Tiger Lily and Edward Trunk			5·75	5·50
	a. Black ptg double			
First Day Cover				4·50
Presentation Pack (605 and **MS**606)			6·00	

The 24p. values in No. **MS**606 are as Type **574**; the 16p. designs are smaller, each 25½×26 mm.
Plate Nos.: 24p 1A, 1B (each×4).
Sheets: 50 (2 panes 5×5).
Imprint: Top left-hand margin of each pane.
Quantities sold: 24p. 523,690; miniature sheet 107,258.
Withdrawn: 1.2.94.

575 Tapestry by Kelly Fletcher　　**576** 'Le Marchi a Passion' (etching and aquatint, Sally Reed)

577 'Red Abstract' (painting, Molly Harris)

578 'Dress Shop, King's Road, (painting, Damon Bell)

Europa. Contemporary Art

(Des B. Bell. Litho Enschedé)

1993 (7 May). P 13½×14 (C).

607	**575**	24p. multicoloured	70	70
608	**576**	24p. multicoloured	70	70
609	**577**	28p. multicoloured	80	80
610	**578**	28p. multicoloured	80	80
607/10 Set of 4			2·75	2·75
First Day Cover				3·00
Presentation Pack			3·00	

Plate Nos.: 24p. (No. 607) 1A, 1B, 1C, 1D. (each×5); others 1A, 1B (each×5).
Sheets: 20 (4×5).
Imprint: Central, side margins.
Quantities sold: No. 607, 289,838; No. 608, 292,450; No. 609, 283,627; No. 610, 280,150.
Withdrawn: 6.5.94.

579 Arrest of Guernsey Parliamentarians, Fermain Bay

580 Parliamentary Ships attacking Castle Cornet

581 Parliamentary Captives escaping

582 Castle Cannon firing at St. Peter Port

583 Surrender of Castle Cornet, 19 December 1651

350th Anniversary of Siege of Castle Cornet

(Des C. Abbott. Litho Questa)

1993 (7 May). P 14½×14 (C).

611	**579**	16p. multicoloured	35	35
612	**580**	24p. multicoloured	60	60
613	**581**	28p. multicoloured	75	75
614	**582**	33p. multicoloured	85	85
615	**583**	39p. multicoloured	90	90
611/15 Set of 5			3·00	3·00
First Day Cover				3·75
Presentation Pack			3·75	
Set of 5 Gutter Pairs			6·00	
MS616 203×75 mm. Nos. 611/15			3·25	4·00
First Day Cover				10·00

Plate Nos.: All values 1A, 1B (each×5).
Sheets: 40 (2 panes 4×5).
Imprint: Central, right-hand margin.
Quantities sold: 16p. 253,310; 24p. 289,408; 28p. 125,877; 33p 124,981; 39p. 125,761; miniature sheet 184,308.
Withdrawn: 6.5.94.

584 Playing Cards **585** Fountain Pens **586** Envelope–folding Machine

587 Great Britain 1855 4d. Stamp

588 Thomas de la Rue and Mauritius £1 Banknote

Birth Bicentenary of Thomas de la Rue (printer)

(Des J. Stephenson. Litho (16, 24, 28p.) or recess (33, 39p.) Enschedé)

1993 (27 July). P 13½ (C).

617	**584**	16p. multicoloured	40	45
		a. Booklet pane of 4 with margins all round	1·50	
618	**585**	24p. multicoloured	65	65
		a. Booklet pane of 4 with margins all round	2·20	
619	**586**	28p. multicoloured	80	80
		a. Booklet pane of 4 with margins all round	3·00	
620	**587**	33p. carmine-lake	95	95
		a. Booklet pane of 4 with margins all round	3·25	
621	**588**	39p. blackish green	1·10	1·10
		a. Booklet pane of 4 with margins all round	3·75	
617/21 Set of 5			3·50	3·50
First Day Cover				3·75
Presentation Pack			4·00	
Set of 5 Gutter Pairs			7·25	

Plate Nos.: 16p., 24p. 1A×4; 28p. 1A, 1B (each×4); 33p., 39p. 1A.
Sheets: 50 (2 panes 5×5).
Imprint: Central, side margins of each pane.
Quantities sold: 16p. 465,736; 24p. 452,982; 28p. 111,030; 33p. 113,299; 39p. 119,548.
Withdrawn: 26.7.94.

589 'The Twelve Pearls'

590 'Healing Rays'

591 'Hand of God over the Holy City'

592 'Wing and Seabirds' (facing left)

593 'Christ the Healer'

594 'Wing and Seabirds' (facing right)

595 'The Young Jesus in the Temple'

596 'The Raising of Jarius' 'Daughter'

597 'Suffer Little Children to come unto Me'

598 'Pilgrim's Progress'

599 'The Light of the World'

600 'Raphael, Archangel of Healing, with Tobias'

Christmas. Stained Glass Windows by Mary-Eily de Putron from Chapel of Christ the Healer

(Des Jennifer Toombs. Litho BDT)

1993 (2 Nov). P 13 (C).

622	**589**	13p. multicoloured	30	15
		a. Sheetlet of 12. Nos. 622/33	3·50	3·25
623	**590**	13p. multicoloured	30	15
624	**591**	13p. multicoloured	30	15
625	**592**	13p. multicoloured	30	15
626	**593**	13p. multicoloured	30	15
627	**594**	13p. multicoloured	30	15
628	**595**	13p. multicoloured	30	15
629	**596**	13p. multicoloured	30	15
630	**597**	13p. multicoloured	30	15
631	**598**	13p. multicoloured	30	15
632	**599**	13p. multicoloured	30	15
633	**600**	13p. multicoloured	30	15
622/33		Set of 12	3·50	3·25
First Day Cover				4·00
Presentation Pack			4·00	

Sheets: 12 (3×4) containing Nos. 622/33 *se-tenant*.
Imprint: Central, left-hand margin.
Quantity sold: 150,594 sheetlets.
Withdrawn: 1.11.94.

Yearbook 1993

1993 (2 Nov). Comprises Nos. 562/3, 567/70, 575, 577/8, 582, 605/33, A12d/e and A56/9 (price £17).

Yearbook		35·00

Withdrawn: 30.12.94.

601 Les Fouaillages (ancient burial ground)

602 Mounted Celtic Warrior

603 Jars, Arrow Heads and Stone Axe from Les Fouaillages

604 Sword, Spear Head and Torque from King's Road Burial

Europa. Archaeological Discoveries

(Des Miranda Schofield. Litho Cartor)

1994 (18 Feb). P 13½ (C).

634	**601**	24p. multicoloured	55	55
635	**602**	24p. multicoloured	55	55
636	**603**	30p. multicoloured	80	75
637	**604**	30p. multicoloured	80	75
634/7		Set of 4	2·40	2·20
First Day Cover				2·75
Presentation Pack			2·75	

Some sheets of No. 635 were overprinted with the 'Hong Kong '94' emblem on the left margin for sale at this philatelic exhibition. The Hong Kong '94 sheet was supplied within a souvenir folder, cost £2·40.
Plate Nos.: All values 1A.
Sheets: 10 (2×5) with large inscribed margin at left.
Quantities sold: No. 634, 241,910; No. 635, 241,943; No. 636, 237,126; No. 637, 232,797; 'Hong Kong '94' margin opt 31,124 sheets.
Withdrawn: 17.2.95.

605 Canadian Supermarine Spitfires Mk V over Normandy Beaches (*Illustration reduced. Actual size 93×71 mm*)

50th Anniversary of D-Day

(Des N. Trudgian. Litho BDT)

1994 (6 June). Sheet 93×71 mm. P 14 (C).

MS638	**605**	£2 multicoloured	5·00	5·50
First Day Cover				6·50
Presentation Pack			5·00	

Quantity sold: 156,793.
Withdrawn: 5.6.95.

606 Peugeot 'Type 3', 1984

607 Mercedes 'Simplex', 1903

608 Humber Tourer, 1906

609 Bentley Sports Tourer, 1936

610 MG TC Midget, 1948

Centenary of First Car in Guernsey

(Des R. Ollington. Litho BDT)

1994 (19 July). P 14½×14 (C).

639	**606**	16p. multicoloured	40	40
		a. Booklet pane of 4 with margins all round	1·70	
640	**607**	24p. multicoloured	60	45
		a. Booklet pane of 4 with margins all round	2·75	
641	**608**	35p. multicoloured	90	1·00
		a. Booklet pane of 4 with margins all round	4·00	
642	**609**	41p. multicoloured	1·00	1·00
		a. Booklet pane of 4 with margins all round	4·25	
643	**610**	60p. multicoloured	1·50	1·40
		a. Booklet pane of 4 with margins all round	6·50	
639/43		Set of 5	4·00	3·75
		First Day Cover		4·25
		Presentation Pack	4·75	
		Set of 5 Gutter Pairs	8·50	

Plate Nos.: 60p. 1A, 1B, 1C, 1D. (each×5); others 1A, 1B (each×5).
Sheets: 50 (2 panes 5×5).
Imprint: Central, side margins of each pane.
Quantities sold: 16p. 279,325; 24p. 238,478; 35p. 114,668; 41p. 116,567; 60p. 117,435.
Withdrawn: 18.7.95.

610a Floral Arrangement (*Illustration reduced. Actual size 110×90 mm*)

'Philakorea '94' International Stamp Exhibition, Seoul

(Des R. Gorringe and M. Whyte. Litho Cartor)

1994 (16 Aug). Sheet 110×90 mm containing stamp as No. 581 with changed imprint date. P 13 (C).

MS644	**610a**	£1 multicoloured	3·25	3·00
		First Day Cover		5·50
		Presentation Pack	4·50	

Quantity sold: 78,679.
Withdrawn: 15.8.95.

611 *Trident* (Herm Ferry)

612 Handley Page HPR-7 Super Dart Herald of Channel Express

613 Britten Norman Trislander G-JOEY Aurigny Air Services

614 *Bon Marin de Serk* (Sark Ferry)

615 Map of Bailiwick

25th Anniversary of Guernsey Postal Administration

(Des A. Copp. Litho Questa)

1994 (1 Oct). P 14 (C).

645	**611**	16p. multicoloured	35	30
646	**612**	24p. multicoloured	55	50
647	**613**	35p. multicoloured	85	75
648	**614**	41p. multicoloured	1·00	85
649	**615**	60p. multicoloured	1·40	1·20
645/9		Set of 5	3·75	3·25
		First Day Cover		3·75
		Presentation Pack	4·50	
		Stamp-cards (set of 5)	1·60	5·50
MS650		150×100 mm. Nos. 645/9	6·75	7·00
		First Day Cover		5·50

Plate Nos.: All values 1A (×5).
Sheets: 20 (5×4).
Imprint: Central, left-hand margin.
Quantities sold: 16p. 218,779; 24p. 188,946; 35p. 129,318; 41p. 139,622; 60p. 140,855; miniature sheet 63,283.
Withdrawn: 30.9.95.

616 Dolls' House

617 Doll

618 Teddy in Bassinette

619 Sweets in Pillar Box and Playing Cards

620 Spinning Top

621 Building Blocks

622 Rocking Horse

623 Teddy Bear

624 Tricycle

625 Wooden Duck

626 Hornby Toy Lococmotive

627 Ludo Game

Christmas. Bygone Toys

(Des A. Peck. Litho BDT)

1994 (1 Oct). P 13 (C).

651	**616**	13p. multicoloured	40	15
		a. Sheetlet of 6. Nos. 651/6	2·00	2·20
652	**617**	13p. multicoloured	40	15
653	**618**	13p. multicoloured	40	15
654	**619**	13p. multicoloured	40	15
655	**620**	13p. multicoloured	40	15
656	**621**	13p. multicoloured	40	15
657	**622**	24p. multicoloured	75	30
		a. Sheetlet of 6. Nos. 657/62	3·50	4·00

658	**623**	24p. multicoloured	75	30
659	**624**	24p. multicoloured	75	30
660	**625**	24p. multicoloured	75	30
661	**626**	24p. multicoloured	75	30
662	**627**	24p. multicoloured	75	30
651/62	*Set of 12*		5·00	5·50
First Day Covers (2)				6·50
Presentation Pack			5·75	

Sheets: 6 (3×2) containing Nos. 650/5 or 656/61 *se-tenant*.
Imprint: Bottom, left-hand margin.
Quantities sold: 13p. 192,937 sheetlets; 24p 133,416 sheetlets.
Withdrawn: 30.9.95.

Yearbook 1994

1994 (1 Oct) Comprises Nos. 576, 634/62, A60/76. Softback (price
£19). Hardback (price £30).

Yearbook (softback)		40·00
Yearbook (hardback)		65·00

Withdrawn: 29.12.95.

The welcoming face of
GUERNSEY 24
628 Seafood 'Face'

629 Buckets and
Spade 'Face'

The welcoming face of
GUERNSEY 24
630 Flowers 'Face'

The welcoming face of
GUERNSEY 24
631 Fruit and
Vegetables 'Face'

632 Sea Shells and
Seaweed 'Face'

The welcoming face of
GUERNSEY 24
633 Anchor and Life
Belts 'Face'

The welcoming face of
GUERNSEY 24
634 Glasses, Cork and
Cutlery 'Face'

The welcoming face of
GUERNSEY 24
635 Butterflies and
Caterpillars 'Face'

Greetings Stamps. 'The Welcoming Face of Guernsey'

(Des R. Ollington. Litho Questa)

1995 (28 Feb). P 14 (C).

663	**628**	24p. multicoloured	60	55
664	**629**	24p. multicoloured	60	55
665	**630**	24p. multicoloured	60	55
666	**631**	24p. multicoloured	60	55
667	**632**	24p. multicoloured	60	55
668	**633**	24p. multicoloured	60	55
669	**634**	24p. multicoloured	60	55
670	**635**	24p. multicoloured	60	55
663/70	*Set of 8*		4·25	4·00
First Day Cover				5·00
Presentation Pack			5·00	
Stamp-cards (set of 8)			1·70	6·00
Set of 8 Gutter Pairs			8·50	
MS671 137×109 mm. Nos. 663/70			4·25	4·25
First Day Cover				8·00

MS671 was used for the make up of stamp booklet SB54.

Plate Nos.: All values 1A, 1B (each×5).
Sheets: 50 (2 panes 5×5).
Imprint: Central, left-hand margin.
Quantities sold: No. 663, 138,328; No. 664, 113,568; No. 665,
138,555; No. 666, 138,474; No. 667, 113,520; No. 668, 113,568;
No. 669, 113,573; No. 670, 113,580; miniature sheet 128,702.
Withdrawn: 27.2.96.

636 Winston Churchill and
Wireless

637 Union Jack and Royal
Navy Ships off St. Peter Port

638 Royal Arms and Military
Band

639 *Vega* (Red Cross supply
ship)

640 Rejoicing Crowd

50th Anniversary of Liberation

(Des M. Whyte. Litho Enschedé)

1995 (9 May). P 13½×14 (C).

672	**636**	16p. multicoloured	45	30
673	**637**	24p. multicoloured	60	50
674	**638**	35p. multicoloured	90	90
675	**639**	41p. multicoloured	90	90
676	**640**	60p. multicoloured	1·50	1·20
672/6	*Set of 5*		4·00	3·50
First Day Cover				4·50
Presentation Pack			5·50	
Set of 5 Gutter Pairs			8·00	
MS677 189×75 mm. Nos. 672/6			4·50	4·75
First Day Cover				6·00

Plate Nos.: 60p. 1A, 1B, 1C, 1D. (each×4); others 1A, 1B (each×4).
Sheets: 50 (2 panes 5×5).
Imprint: Central, side margins.
Quantities sold: 16p. 558,373; 24p. 410,244; 35p 130,472; 41p.
158,351; 60p. 159,394; miniature sheet 86,502.
Withdrawn: 8.5.96.

641 Silhouette of Doves on Ground

642 Silhouette of Doves in Flight

Europa. Peace and Freedom

(Des K. Bassford. Litho Walsall)

1995 (9 May). P 14 (C).
678	**641**	25p. multicoloured	90	90
679	**642**	30p. multicoloured	1·10	1·10
678/9	*Set of 2*		1·75	1·75
	First Day Cover			2·00
	Presentation Pack		2·10	

The designs of Nos. 678/9 each provide a stereogram or hidden three-dimensional image of a single dove designed by D. Burder.
Plate Nos.: Both values 1A, 1B, 1C (each×4).
Sheets: 10 (2×5).
Imprint: Central, bottom margin.
Quantities sold: 25p. 219,750; 30p. 171,902.
Withdrawn: 8.5.96.

643 Prince Charles, Castle Cornet and Bailiwick Arms

Royal Visit

(Des C. Abbott. Litho Questa)

1995 (9 May). P 14 (C).
680	**643**	£1.50 multicoloured	4·50	4·50
	First Day Cover			4·75
	Presentation Pack		4·00	
	Gutter Pair		7·00	

Plate Nos.: 1A, 1B, 1C, 1D. (each×5).
Sheets: 40 (2 panes 5×4).
Imprint: Central, left-hand margin.
Quantity sold: 140,954.
Withdrawn: 8.5.96.

643a (*Illustration reduced. Actual size 110×90 mm*)

'Singapore '95' International Stamp Exhibition

(Des R. Gorringe and M. Whyte. Litho Cartor)

1995 (1 Sept). Sheet 110×90 mm containing stamp as No. 581 with changed imprint date. P 13 (C).
MS681 **643a** £1 multicoloured	3·75	3·75	
First Day Cover		4·50	
Presentation Pack	3·75		

Quantity sold: 64,768.
Withdrawn: 31.8.96.

644   **645**

646   **647**

50th Anniversary of United Nations

(Des K. Bassford. Litho and embossed Enschedé)

1995 (24 Oct). P 14×13½ (C).
682	**644**	50p. pale new blue and gold	1·10	1·10
		a. Block of 4. Nos. 682/5	4·25	4·25
683	**645**	50p. pale new blue and gold	1·10	1·10
684	**646**	50p. pale new blue and gold	1·10	1·10
685	**647**	50p. pale new blue and gold	1·10	1·10
682/5	*Set of 4*		4·00	4·25
	First Day Cover			5·00
	Presentation Pack		5·00	

Plate Nos.: 1A–1A.
Sheets: 36 (6×6). Nos. 682/5 were printed together, *se-tenant*, throughout the sheet with each block of four showing the complete United Nations emblem.
Imprint: Central, side margins.
Quantity sold: 448,348.
Withdrawn: 23.10.96.

648 'Christmas Trees for Sale in Bern' (Cornelia **649** Nussbrum-Weibel)

650 'Evening Snowfall' (Katerina Mertikas) **651**

652 'It came upon a Midnight Clear' **653** (Georgia Guback)

654 'Children of the World' **655**

Christmas. 50th Anniversary of U.N.I.C.E.F.

(Adapted M. Whyte from U.N.I.C.E.F. Christmas Cards. Litho BDT)

1995 (16 Nov). P 13 (C).
686	**648**	13p. multicoloured	40	15
		a. Horiz pair. Nos. 686/7	80	70
687	**649**	13p. multicoloured	40	15
688	**650**	13p. +1p. multicoloured	40	20
		a. Horiz pair. Nos. 688/9	80	90
689	**651**	13p. +1p. multicoloured	40	20
690	**652**	24p. multicoloured	70	30
		a. Horiz pair. Nos. 690/1	1·40	1·40
691	**653**	24p. multicoloured	70	30
692	**654**	24p. +2p. multicoloured	70	30
		a. Horiz pair. Nos. 692/3	1·40	1·40
693	**655**	24p. +2p. multicoloured	70	30

686/93 *Set of 8*...			4·00	4·00
First Day Cover				5·00
Presentation Pack..			5·00	

Sheets: 12 (4×3), the two designs for each value printed together, *se-tenant*, in horizontal pairs throughout the sheets, each pair forming a composite design.

Quantities sold: Nos. 686/7, 540,858; Nos. 688/9, 352,684; Nos. 690/1, 365,098; Nos. 692/3, 365,740.

Withdrawn: 15.11.96.

Yearbook 1995

1995 (1 Dec). Comprises Nos. 663/93 and A77/84 (price £23).

Yearbook		50·00

Withdrawn: 31.12.97.

656 Princess Anne (President, Save the Children Fund) and Children　**657** Queen Elizabeth II and people of the Commonwealth

Europa. Famous Women

(Des D. Miller. Litho BDT)

1996 (21 Apr). P 14 (C).

694	**656**	25p. multicoloured	55	50
695	**657**	30p. multicoloured	70	75
694/5 *Set of 2*			1·20	1·20
First Day Cover				2·00
Presentation Pack..			2·00	

The background designs of Nos. 694/5 continue on to the vertical sheet margins.

Plate Nos.: Both values 1A, 1B (each×4).

Sheets: 10 (2×5).

Quantities sold: 25p. 224,821; 30p. 268,410.

Withdrawn: 20.4.97.

658 England v U.S.S.R., 1968　**659**

660 Italy v Belgium, 1972　**661**

662 Ireland v Netherlands, 1988　**663**

664 Denmark v Germany, 1992 Final　**665**

Final European Football Championship, England

(Des M. Whyte. Litho Questa)

1996 (25 Apr). P 14½×14 (C).

696	**658**	16p. multicoloured	55	20
		a. Horiz pair. Nos. 696/7......................	1·20	1·10
697	**659**	16p. multicoloured	55	20
698	**660**	24p. multicoloured	75	25
		a. Horiz pair. Nos. 698/9......................	1·50	1·50
699	**661**	24p. multicoloured	75	25
700	**662**	35p. multicoloured	80	40
		a. Horiz pair. Nos. 700/1......................	1·60	1·60
701	**663**	35p. multicoloured	80	40
702	**664**	41p. multicoloured	95	45
		a. Horiz pair. Nos. 702/3......................	2·00	1·90
703	**665**	41p. multicoloured	95	45
696/703 *Set of 8*			6·00	5·50
First Day Cover				6·00
Presentation Pack...			6·00	
Souvenir Folder (complete sheets).....................			24·00	

Plate Nos.: All values 1A (×4).

Sheets: 8 (2×4), the two designs for each value printed together, *se-tenant*, in horizontal pairs throughout sheets with illustrated margins, each pair forming a composite design.

Quantities sold: 16p. 386,746; 24p. 369,805; 35p 360,860; 41p. 364,757.

Withdrawn: 24.4.97.

666 Maj-Gen. Brock meeting Tecumseh (Indian Chief) (24p.); Maj-Gen. Isaac Brock on Horseback, 1812 (£1)
(*Illustration reduced. Actual size 110×90 mm*)

'CAPEX '96' International Stamp Exhibition, Toronto

(Des A. Peck. Litho Enschedé)

1996 (8 June). Sheet 110×90 mm. P 13½ (C).

MS704 **666**	24p. £1 multicoloured	3·00	2·75
First Day Cover			4·00
Presentation Pack..		3·75	

Quantity sold: 93,054.

Withdrawn: 7.6.97.

667 Runner　　**668** Throwing the Javelin　　**669** Throwing the Discus

670 Wrestling　　**671** Jumping

Centenary of Modern Olympic Games. Ancient Greek Athletes

(Des K. Bassford. Litho Questa)

1996 (19 July). P 14 (C).

705	**667**	16p. black, orange-yellow and orge......	50	40
706	**668**	24p. black, orange-yellow and orge......	95	90
707	**669**	41p. black, orange-yellow and orge......	1·10	1·20
708	**670**	55p. black, orange-yellow and orge......	1·40	1·50
709	**671**	60p. black, orange-yellow and orge......	1·60	1·70
705/9 *Set of 5*			4·50	4·75
First Day Cover				5·00
Presentation Pack			5·00	
Set of 5 Gutter Pairs			9·00	
MS710 192×75 mm. Nos. 705/9			4·50	4·75
First Day Cover				5·75

No. 708 also includes the 'OLYMPHILEX '96' International Stamp Exhibition, Atlanta, logo.

Plate Nos.: All values 1A, 1B (each×3).
Sheets: 55p 50 (2 panes 5×5); others 100 (2 panes 10×5).
Imprint: Central, right-hand margin of top pane.
Quantities sold: 16p. 337,288; 24p. 305,309; 41p. 132,730; 55p. 122,263; 60p. 141,372; miniature sheet 87,045.
Withdrawn: 18.7.97.

672 Humphrey Bogart as Philip Marlowe

673 Peter Sellers as Inspector Clouseau

674 Basil Rathbone as Sherlock Holmes

675 Margaret Rutherford as Miss Marple

676 Warner Oland as Charlie Chan

Centenary of Cinema. Screen Detectives

(Des R. Ollington. Litho Enschedé)

1996 (6 Nov). P 15×14 (C).

711	**672**	16p. multicoloured	40	40
		a. Booklet pane. No. 711×3 with margins all round	1·40	
		b. Booklet pane. Nos. 711/15 with margins all round	4·50	
712	**673**	24p. multicoloured	60	60
		a. Booklet pane. No. 712×3 with margins all round	2·30	
713	**674**	35p. multicoloured	85	85
		a. Booklet pane. No. 713×3 with margins all round	2·75	
714	**675**	41p. multicoloured	90	90
		a. Booklet pane. No. 714×3 with margins all round	3·00	
715	**676**	60p. multicoloured	1·40	1·40
		a. Booklet pane. No. 715×3 with margins all round	4·50	
711/15 *Set of 5*			3·75	3·75
First Day Cover				4·75
Presentation Pack			4·75	
Set of 5 Gutter Pairs			7·50	

Plate Nos.: All values 1A, 1B (each×4).
Sheets: 50 (2 panes 5×5).
Imprint: Central, side margins.
Quantities sold: 16p. 140,740; 24p. 141,567; 35p. 141,953; 41p. 139,648; 60p. 138,363.
Withdrawn: 5.11.97.

677 The Annunciation

678 Journey to Bethlehem

679 Arrival at the Inn

680 Angel and Shepherds

681 Mary, Joseph and Jesus in Stable

682 Shepherds worshipping Jesus

683 Three Kings following Star

684 Three Kings with Gifts

685 The Presentation in the Temple

686 Mary and Jesus

687 Joseph warned by Angel

688 The Flight into Egypt

689 Mary cradling Jesus

690 The Nativity

Christmas

(Des P. le Vasseur. Litho BDT)

1996 (6 Nov). P 13 (C).

716	**677**	13p. multicoloured	40	40
		a. Sheetlet of 12. Nos. 716/27	4·50	4·50
717	**678**	13p. multicoloured	40	40
718	**679**	13p. multicoloured	40	40
719	**680**	13p. multicoloured	40	40
720	**681**	13p. multicoloured	40	40
721	**682**	13p. multicoloured	40	40
722	**683**	13p. multicoloured	40	40
723	**684**	13p. multicoloured	40	40
724	**685**	13p. multicoloured	40	40
725	**686**	13p. multicoloured	40	40
726	**687**	13p. multicoloured	40	40
727	**688**	13p. multicoloured	40	40
728	**689**	24p. multicoloured	40	40
729	**690**	25p. multicoloured	40	40
716/29 *Set of 14*			5·25	5·25
First Day Cover				5·00
Presentation Pack			5·00	
Set of 2 Gutter Pairs (24, 25p.)			2·40	

Plate Nos.: 24p, 25p 1A, 1B (each×4).
Sheets: 13p. 12 (4×3) containing Nos. 716/27 *se-tenant*; 24p., 25p. 100 (2 panes 5×10).
Imprint: 13p. bottom, left-hand margin; 24p., 25p. central, side margins.
Quantities sold: 13p. 1,212,144 sheetlets; 24p. 416,811; 25p. 121,820.
Withdrawn: 5.11.97.

Yearbook 1996

1996 (1 Dec). Comprises Nos. 582a, 694/729 and A85/95 (price £25).
Yearbook .... 60·00
    Sold out: 6.99.

691 Holly Blue (*Celastrina argiolus*)

692 Hummingbird Hawk-moth (*Macroglossum stellatarum*)

693 Emperor Moth (*Saturnia pavonia*)

694 Brimstone (*Gonepteryx rhamni*)

695 Painted Lady (*Cynthia cardui*)
(*Illustration reduced. Actual size 92×68 mm*)

Endangered Species. Butterflies and Moths

(Des A. Peck. Litho BDT)

1997 (12 Feb). P 14 (C).

730	**691**	18p. multicoloured	55	50
731	**692**	25p. multicoloured	65	60
732	**693**	26p. multicoloured	85	85
733	**694**	37p. multicoloured	1·10	1·10
730/3 Set of 4			2·75	2·75
First Day Cover				3·25
Presentation Pack			3·25	
Souvenir Folder (complete sheets)			25·00	
MS734 92×68 mm. **695** £1 multicoloured. P 13½ (c)...			3·00	2·50
First Day Cover				3·75
Presentation Pack			3·50	

No. **MS**734 includes the 'HONG KONG '97' International Stamp Exhibition logo on the sheet margin.
Plate Nos.: All values 1A, 1B (each×4).
Sheets: 10 (2×5) with designs extending into side margins.
Quantities sold: 18p. 244,917; 25p. 244,899; 26p. 168,917; 37p. 169,909; miniature sheet 147,990.
Withdrawn: 11.2.98.

696 Gilliatt fighting Octopus

697 Gilliatt grieving on Rock

Europa. Tales and Legends. Scenes from *Les Travailleurs de la Mer* by Victor Hugo

(Des M. Wilkinson. Litho Cartor)

1997 (24 Apr). P 13½ (C).

735	**696**	26p. multicoloured	70	70
736	**697**	31p. multicoloured	1·00	1·10
735/6 Set of 2			1·50	1·50
First Day Cover				2·10
Presentation Pack			2·10	

Plate Nos.: Both values 1A, 1B (each×4).
Sheets: 10 (2×5) with enlarged inscribed margins at left.
Quantities sold: 26p. 246,098; 31p. 246,080.
Withdrawn: 23.4.98.

698 Shell Beach, Herm   **699** La Seigneurie, Sark   **700** Castle Cornet, Guernsey

Island Treasures (1st series)

(Des Guernsey P.O. Litho BDT)

1997 (24 Apr). Self-adhesive. P 9½ (diecut).

737	**698**	18p. multicoloured	60	30
		a. Booklet pane of 8.............................	5·00	
738	**699**	25p. multicoloured	70	60
		a. Booklet pane of 8.............................	6·00	
739	**700**	26p. multicoloured	80	75
		a. Booklet pane of 4.............................	4·75	
737/9 Set of 3			1·90	1·50
First Day Cover				3·00
Presentation Pack			3·00	

Nos. 737/9 were issued in stamp booklets or as rolls of 100 (18p. and 25p.).
See also Nos. 770/3.
Quantities sold: 18p. 2,789,925; 25p. 2,788,039; 26p. 415,882.
Withdrawn: 31.3.98.

701 19th-century Shipyard, St. Peter Port (30p.); *Costa Rica Packet* (barque) (£1) (*Illustration reduced. Actual size 110×90 mm*)

'PACIFIC '97' World Philatelic Exhibition, San Francisco

(Des C. Abbott. Litho Questa)

1997 (29 May). Sheet 110×90 mm. P 14 (C).

MS740 **701** 30p. brn-olive and gold; £1 mult..............	4·00	4·00
First Day Cover		4·50
Presentation Pack	4·50	

Quantity sold: 86,711.
Withdrawn: 28.5.98.

702 Transistor Radio, Microphone and Radio Logos

703 Television, Video Camera and Satellite Dish

704 Fax Machine, Telephones and Mobile Phone

705 Printing Press, Newspaper and Type

706 Stamp, Coding Machine and Postbox

707 C.D., Computer and Disk

Methods of Communication

(Des Miranda Schofield. Litho Cartor)

1997 (21 Aug). P 13½×13 (C).

741	**702**	18p. multicoloured	60	60
742	**703**	25p. multicoloured	75	75
743	**704**	26p. multicoloured	75	75
744	**705**	37p. multicoloured	1·00	1·00
745	**706**	43p. multicoloured	1·40	1·50
746	**707**	63p. multicoloured	1·60	1·75
741/6	*Set of 6*		5·50	5·75
First Day Cover				5·50
Presentation Pack			5·25	
Set of 6 Gutter Pairs			9·00	

Plate Nos.: All values 1A, 1B (each×4).
Sheets: 50 (2 panes 5×5).
Imprint: Central, side margins.
Quantities sold: 18p 193,539; 25p. 144,558; 26p. 143,542; 37p. 140,565; 43p. 143,565; 63p. 193,524.
Withdrawn: 20.8.98.

708 Teddy Bear making Cake

709 Teddy Bears decorating Christmas Tree

710 Two Teddy Bears in Armchair

711 Teddy Bear as Father Christmas

712 Teddy Bears unwrapping Presents

713 Teddy Bears eating Christmas Dinner

Christmas. Teddy Bears

(Des Sally Diamond. Litho Walsall)

1997 (6 Nov). P 14½×14 (C).

747	**708**	15p. multicoloured	45	45
748	**709**	25p. multicoloured	70	70
749	**710**	26p. multicoloured	70	70
750	**711**	37p. multicoloured	1·00	1·00
751	**712**	43p. multicoloured	1·10	1·10
752	**713**	63p. multicoloured	1·60	1·60
747/52	*Set of 6*		5·00	5·00
First Day Cover				5·50
Presentation Pack			5·25	
Set of 6 Gutter Pairs			10·00	
MS753 123×107 mm. Nos. 747/52.			6·00	6·00
First Day Cover				5·75

Plate Nos.: All values 1A, 1B (each×4).
Sheets: 50 (2 panes 5×5).
Imprint: Central, right-hand margin.
Quantities sold: 15p. 1,793,893; 25p. 443,027; 26p. 143,322; 37p. 118,980; 43p. 119,090; 63p. 118,894; miniature sheet 86,125.
Withdrawn: 5.11.98.

714 Visiting Guernsey, 1957

715 Coronation Day, 1953 (inscr '1947')

716 Royal Family, 1957

717 On Royal Yacht, 1972

718 Queen Elizabeth and Prince Philip at Trooping the Colour, 1987

719 Queen Elizabeth and Prince Philip, 1997

Golden Wedding of Queen Elizabeth and Prince Philip

(Des M. Whyte. Litho Questa)

1997 (20 Nov). P 14½ (C).

754	**714**	18p. multicoloured	50	50
		a. Booklet pane. Nos. 754/5, each×3.	3·25	
		b. Booklet pane. Nos. 754/9	5·50	
755	**715**	25p. multicoloured	75	75
756	**716**	26p. multicoloured	75	75
		a. Booklet pane. Nos. 756/7, each×3.	5·00	
757	**717**	37p. multicoloured	1·10	1·10
758	**718**	43p. multicoloured	1·25	1·25
		a. Booklet pane. Nos. 758/9, each×3.	8·75	
759	**719**	63p. multicoloured	1·75	1·75
754/9 *Set of 6*			5·50	5·50
First Day Cover				5·50
Presentation Pack			5·25	
Set of 6 Gutter Pairs			9·00	

Plate Nos.: All values 1A, 1B (each×6).
Sheets: 50 (2 panes 5×5).
Imprint: Central, right-hand margin.
Quantities sold: 18p. 220,866; 25p. 218,707; 26p. 218,240; 37p. 216,772; 43p. 217,837; 63p. 216,874.
Withdrawn: 19.11.98.

Yearbook 1997

1997 (1 Dec). Comprises Nos. 572*b*, 576*b*, 730/59, A70*b*, A72*b/c* and A96/109 (price £25).

Yearbook		55·00

Sold out: 9.99.

720 11th-century (St. Martin)

721 12th-century (St. Saviour)

722 13th-century (Vale)

723 14th-century (St. Sampson)

724 15th-century (Torteval)

725 16th-century (Castel)

726 17th-century (St. Andrew)

727 18th-century (Forest)

728 19th-century (St. Pierre du Bois)

729 20th-century (St. Peter Port)

The Millennium Tapestries Project

(Des Sally Diamond. Litho Questa)

1998 (10 Feb). P 15×14½ (C).

760	**720**	25p. multicoloured	70	70
		a. Horiz strip of 10 or two strips of 5. Nos. 760/9	6·50	6·50
		b. Booklet pane. Nos. 760/1, each×2, and 762/3 with margins all round	4·00	
		c. Booklet pane. Nos. 760/1 and 768/9, each×2 with margins all round	3·50	
761	**721**	25p. multicoloured	70	70
762	**722**	25p. multicoloured	70	70
		a. Booklet pane. Nos. 762/3, each×2, and 764/5 with margins all round..	4·00	
763	**723**	25p. multicoloured	70	70
764	**724**	25p. multicoloured	70	70
		a. Booklet pane. Nos. 764/5, each×2, and 766/7 with margins all round..	4·00	
765	**725**	25p. multicoloured	70	70
766	**726**	25p. multicoloured	70	70
		a. Booklet pane. Nos. 766/7, each×2, and 768/9 with margins all round..	4·00	
767	**727**	25p. multicoloured	70	70
768	**728**	25p. multicoloured	70	70
769	**729**	25p. multicoloured	70	70
760/9 *Set of 10*			6·50	6·50
First Day Cover				6·25
Presentation Pack			6·00	

Plate Nos.: 1A, 1B (each×4).
Sheets: 50 (10×5); the ten designs printed together, *se-tenant*, in horizontal strips throughout the sheet.
Imprint: Central, side margins.
Withdrawn: 9.2.99.

730 Fort Grey

731 Grand Havre

732 Little Chapel

733 Guernsey Cow

Island Treasures (2nd series)

(Des Joanna Brehaut. Litho BDT)

1998 (25 Mar). Self-adhesive. P 9½ (diecut).

770	**730**	(20p.) multicoloured	1·20	1·20
		a. Horiz pair. Nos. 770/1	2·50	2·50
		b. Booklet pane. Nos. 770/1, each×4 with margins all round	6·00	
771	**731**	(20p.) multicoloured	1·20	1·20
772	**732**	(25p.) multicoloured	1·50	1·50
		a. Horiz pair. Nos. 772/3	3·00	3·00
		b. Booklet pane. Nos. 772/3, each×4 with margins all round	6·00	
773	**733**	(25p.) multicoloured	1·50	1·50
770/3	*Set of 4*		5·00	5·00
First Day Cover				3·00
Presentation Pack			3·00	

Nos. 770/1 are inscribed 'Bailiwick Minimum Postage Paid' and were initially sold at 20p. Nos. 772/3 are inscribed 'UK Minimum Postage Paid' and were initially sold at 25p.

Nos. 770/3 were issued in stamp booklets or as rolls of 100, each roll containing two designs.

Sold out: 6.2001.

734 Fairey IIIC, Balloon, Sopwith Camel and Avro 504

735 Fairey Swordfish, Tiger Moth, Supermarine Walrus and Gloster Gladiator

736 Hawker Hurricane, Supermarine Spitfire, Vickers Wellington, Short Sunderland (flying boat), Westland Lysander and Bristol Blenheim

737 de Havilland Mosquito, Avro Lancaster, Auster III, Gloster Meteor and Horsa Glider

738 Canberra, Hawker Sea Fury, Bristol Sycamore, Hawker Hunter, Handley Page Victor and BAe Lightning

739 Panavia Tornado GR1, BAe Hawk, BAe Sea Harrier, Westland Lynx (helicopter) and Hawker Siddeley Nimrod

80th Anniversary of the Royal Air Force

(Des C. Abbott. Litho Cartor)

1998 (7 May). P 13½×13 (C).

774	**734**	20p. multicoloured	50	50
775	**735**	25p. multicoloured	60	60
776	**736**	30p. multicoloured	70	70
777	**737**	37p. multicoloured	90	85
778	**738**	43p. multicoloured	1·00	1·20
779	**739**	63p. multicoloured	1·40	1·50
774/9	*Set of 6*		5·00	5·00
First Day Cover				5·75
Presentation Pack			5·25	

Plate Nos.: All values 1A (×5).
Sheets: 50 (5×10).
Imprint: Central, side margins.
Withdrawn: 6.5.99.

740 Jules Rimet (first President of FIFA) (30p.); Bobby Moore and Queen Elizabeth II, 1966 (£1.75) (*Illustration reduced. Actual size 110×90 mm*)

150th Anniversary of the Cambridge Rules for Football

(Des A. Peck. Litho Enschedé)

1998 (7 May). Sheet 110×90 mm. P 13½×14 (C).

MS780	**740**	30p., £1.75 multicoloured	5·50	5·50
First Day Cover				5·75
Presentation Pack			5·25	

Withdrawn: 6.5.99.

741 Girls in Traditional Costume watching Sheep Display, West Show

742 Marching Band and 'Battle of Flowers' Exhibit, North Show

743 Prince Charles, Monument and Tank, Liberation Day

744 Goat, Dahlias and Show-jumping, South Show

Europa. National Festivals

(Des Sally Diamond. Litho Enschedé)

1998 (11 Aug). P 13½ (C).

781	**741**	20p. multicoloured	70	70
782	**742**	25p. multicoloured	80	80
783	**743**	30p. multicoloured	90	90
784	**744**	37p. multicoloured	1·00	1·00
781/4 *Set of 4*			3·25	3·25
First Day Cover				3·75
Presentation Pack			3·50	

Plate Nos.: All values 1A, 1B, 1C (each×4).
Sheets: 10 (2×5) with enlarged inscribed margin at left.
Imprint: Central, right-hand margin.
Withdrawn: 10.8.99.
The 25p. and 30p. values include the 'EUROPA' emblem.

745 Outboard Motorboat

746 St. John Ambulance Inshore Rescue Dinghy

747 Pilot Boat, St. Peter Port

748 *Flying Christine III* (St. John Ambulance launch)

749 Crab-fishing Boat

750 Herm Island Ferry

751 *Sarnia* (St. Peter Port Harbour Authority launch)

752 *Leopardess* (States' fisheries protection launch)

753 Trawler

754 Powerboat

755 Dart 18 Racing Catamaran

756 30ft Bermuda-rigged Sloop

757 Motor Cruiser

758 Ocean-going Sailing Yacht

759 Motor Yacht, Beaucette Marina

760 *Queen Elizabeth 2* (liner)

761 *Oriana* (liner)

762 *Queen Mary 2* (liner)

763 Royal Yacht *Britannia*

Maritime Heritage

(Des M. Wilkinson. Litho Walsall (1p to 75p), litho and embossed Walsall (£1, £3) BDT (£4) or Questa (£5))

1998 (11 Aug)–**2005**. P 14 (1p. to 9p.), 14½×14 (10p. to 75p.), 14×14½ (£1, £3), 13½ (£4) or 15×14½ (£5), all comb.

785	**745**	1p. multicoloured (b)	10	10
786	**746**	2p. multicoloured (b)	10	10
787	**747**	3p. multicoloured (b)	10	10
788	**748**	4p. multicoloured (b)	10	10
789	**749**	5p. multicoloured (b)	10	10
790	**750**	6p. multicoloured (b)	10	10
791	**751**	7p. multicoloured (b)	15	20
792	**752**	8p. multicoloured (b)	15	20
793	**753**	9p. multicoloured (b)	20	25
794	**754**	10p. multicoloured (b)	20	25
795	**755**	20p. multicoloured (c)	40	45
796	**756**	30p. multicoloured (c)	60	65
797	**757**	40p. multicoloured (b)	80	85
798	**758**	50p. multicoloured (b)	1·00	1·10
799	**759**	75p. multicoloured (b)	1·50	1·30
800	**760**	£1 multicoloured (b)	2·00	1·80
801	**761**	£3 multicoloured (c)	6·00	5·50
802	**762**	£4 multicoloured (d)	9·00	9·00
803	**763**	£5 multicoloured (a)	13·00	10·00
785/803 *Set of 19*			32·00	29·00
First Day Covers (4)				35·00
Presentation Packs (4)			34·00	
Set of 17 Gutter Pairs (1p. to £3)			25·00	

Printings: (a) 11.8.98; (b) 27.7.99; (c). 4.8.2000; (d) 9.5.2005.
Plate Nos.: £5 1A, 1B, 1C, 1d. (each×5); £4 1A (×4); others 1A, 1B (each×4).

Sheets: 1p. to £3.50 (2 panes 5×5); £4 10 (2×5); £5 10 (5×2).
Imprint: Side margins (£5) or centre, left-hand margin (others).
Sold out: 11.2002 (£5).
Withdrawn: 3.2008 (except 20p., 30p., £3, withdrawn 12.2008, and £4 withdrawn 10.2014).

Nos. 804/9, T **764/8** are vacant.

769 Modern Tree, Teletubby Po and Playstation

770 1960s Tinsel Tree, Toy Bus and Doll

771 1930s Gold Foil Tree, Panda and Toy Tank

772 1920s Tree, Model of *Bluebird* and Doll

773 1900s Tree, Teddy Bear and Toy Train

774 1950s Tree, Wooden Doll and Spinning Top

150th Anniversary of the Introduction of the Christmas Tree

(Des R. Ollington. Litho BDT)

1998 (10 Nov). P 13½ (C).

810	**769**	17p. multicoloured	1·00	1·00
811	**770**	25p. multicoloured	1·00	1·00
812	**771**	30p. multicoloured	1·00	1·00
813	**772**	37p. multicoloured	1·25	1·25
814	**773**	43p. multicoloured	1·25	1·25
815	**774**	63p. multicoloured	1·75	1·75
810/15 Set of 6			6·50	6·50
First Day Cover				5·50
MS816 160×94 mm. Nos. 810/15			7·00	7·00
First Day Cover				6·00
Presentation Pack			5·50	

Plate Nos.: 17p., 25p. 1A, 1B (each×4); others 1A (×4).
Sheets: 50 (5×10).
Imprint: Central, side margins.
Withdrawn: 9.11.99.

Yearbook 1998

1998 (1 Dec). Comprises Nos. 760/84, 802, 810/16 and A110/23 (price £27).

Yearbook	55·00	

Sold out: 4.2001.

775 Elizabeth Bowes–Lyon, 1907   **776** On Wedding Day, 1923   **777** Holding Princess Elizabeth, 1926

778 At Coronation, 1937   **779** Visiting Bombed Areas of London, 1940   **780** Fishing near Auckland, New Zealand, 1966

781 At Guernsey Function, 1963   **782** Receiving Flowers on Birthday, 1992

783 Presenting Trophy, Sandown Park Races, 1989   **784** Opening Royal Norfolk Regimental Museum, Norwich, 1990

Life and Times of Queen Elizabeth the Queen Mother

(Des R. Ollington. Litho Cartor)

1999 (4 Feb). P 13 (C).

817	**775**	25p. multicoloured	70	30
		a. Horiz strip of 10 or two strips of 5. Nos. 817/26	6·50	6·50
		b. Booklet pane. Nos. 817/18, each×2, and 819/20, with margins all round	4·00	
		c. Booklet pane. Nos. 817/18 and 825/6, each×2, with margins all round	4·00	

818	**776**	25p. multicoloured		70	30
819	**777**	25p. multicoloured		70	30
		b. Booklet pane. Nos. 819/20, each×2, and 821/2, with margins all round	4·00		
820	**778**	25p. multicoloured		70	30
821	**779**	25p. multicoloured		70	30
		b. Booklet pane. Nos. 821/2, each×2, and 823/4, with margins all round	4·00		
822	**780**	25p. multicoloured		70	30
823	**781**	25p. multicoloured		70	30
		b. Booklet pane. Nos. 823/4, each×2, and 825/6, with margins all round	4·00		
824	**782**	25p. multicoloured		70	30
825	**783**	25p. multicoloured		70	30
826	**784**	25p. multicoloured		70	30
817/26	*Set of 10*			6·50	6·50
First Day Cover					6·75
Presentation Pack				6·75	

Plate Nos.: 1A, 1B (each×5).
Sheets: 50 (10×5), the ten designs printed together, *se-tenant*, as horizontal strips throughout the sheets.
Imprint: Central, side margins.
Withdrawn: 3.2.2000.

785 *Spirit of Guernsey*, 1995

786 *Sir William Arnold*, 1973

787 *Euphrosyne Kendal*, 1954

788 *Queen Victoria*, 1929

789 *Arthur Lionel*, 1912

790 *Vincent Kirk Ella*, 1888

175th Anniversary of Royal National Lifeboat Institution

(Des K. Wisdom. Litho Cartor)

1999 (27 Apr). P 13½×13 (C).

827	**785**	20p. multicoloured		50	50
828	**786**	25p. multicoloured		60	60
829	**787**	30p. multicoloured		70	70
830	**788**	38p. multicoloured		90	90
831	**789**	44p. multicoloured		1·10	1·10
832	**790**	64p. multicoloured		1·50	1·50
827/32	*Set of 6*			5·00	4·75
First Day Cover					6·00
Presentation Pack				5·75	

Plate Nos.: All values 1A (×5).
Sheets: 50 (5×10).
Imprint: Central, side margins.
Withdrawn: 26.4.2000.

791 Burnet Rose and Local Carriage Label

792 Atlantic Puffin

793 Small Heath Butterfly

794 Shells on Shell Beach

Europa. Parks and Gardens. Herm Island

(Des Colleen Corlett. Litho Walsall)

1999 (27 Apr). P 13½×13 (C).

833	**791**	20p. multicoloured		50	50
834	**792**	25p. multicoloured		85	85
835	**793**	30p. multicoloured		90	90
836	**794**	38p. multicoloured		1·30	1·30
833/6	*Set of 4*			3·50	3·50
First Day Cover					4·00
Presentation Pack				3·50	

Plate Nos.: All values 1A, 1B (each×4).
Sheets: 10 (2×5) with enlarged illustrated margin at left (20, 30p.) or right (25, 38p.).
Imprint: Central right (20, 30p.) or left (25, 38p.) margin.
Withdrawn: 26.4.2000.
The 30p. value includes the 'EUROPA' emblem.

795 Prince Edward and Miss Sophie Rhys-Jones
(*Illustraion reduced. Actual size* 93×70 mm)

Royal Wedding

(Des Sally Diamond. Litho BDT)

1999 (19 June). Sheet 93×70 mm. P 13 (C).

MS837 795	£1 multicoloured		3·25	3·00
First Day Cover				5·00
Presentation Pack			3·50	

Withdrawn: 18.6.2000.

796 Major-General Le Marchant (founder) and Cadet at Sword Drill

797 Duke of York (official sponsor) and Cadet on Horseback

798 Field-Marshal Earl Haig and Cadets on Parade

799 Field-Marshal Viscount Montgomery and Bridging Exercise

800 David Niven (actor) and Rifle Practice

801 Sir Winston Churchill and Tank

Bicentenary of The Royal Military Academy, Sandhurst

(Des R. Ollington. Litho BDT)

1999 (27 July). P 14 (C).

838	**796**	20p. multicoloured	60	60
839	**797**	25p. multicoloured	65	55
840	**798**	30p. multicoloured	90	90
841	**799**	38p. multicoloured	1·25	1·25
842	**800**	44p. multicoloured	1·50	1·50
843	**801**	64p. multicoloured	1·90	1·90
838/43 *Set of 6*			6·25	6·50
First Day Cover				7·25
Presentation Pack			6·00	

Plate Nos.: All values 1A (×4).
Sheets: 50 (5×10).
Imprint: Lower side margins.
Withdrawn: 26.7.2000.

802 The Nativity

803 Virgin Mary and Child

804 Holy Family

805 Cattle around Manger

806 Adoration of the Shepherds

807 Adoration of the Magi

Christmas. Wood Carvings by Denis Brehaut from Notre Dame Church

(Des Sally Diamond. Litho Questa)

1999 (19 Oct). P 14×14½ (C).

844	**802**	17p. multicoloured	45	40
845	**803**	25p. multicoloured	60	55
846	**804**	30p. multicoloured	75	70
847	**805**	38p. multicoloured	90	85
848	**806**	44p. multicoloured	1·10	1·20
849	**807**	64p. multicoloured	1·50	1·70
844/9 *Set of 6*			4·75	5·00
First Day Cover				6·00
Presentation Pack			5·75	
MS850 159×86 mm. Nos. 844/9			5·50	5·50
First Day Cover				6·00

Plate Nos.: All values 1A, 1B, 1C (each×4).
Sheets: 50 (5×10.).
Imprint: Bottom, right-hand margin.
Withdrawn: 18.10.2000.

Yearbook 1999

1999 (1 Dec). Comprises Nos. 785/94, 797/800, 817/50 and **MS**A124/39 (price £28).

Yearbook .... 55·00
Sold out: By 12.2002.

808 'Space Bus' (Fallon Ephgrave)

809 'Children holding Hands' (Abigail Downing)

810 'No Captivity' (Laura Martin)

811 'Post Office of the Future' (Sarah Haddow)

812 'Solar-powered Car' (Sophie Medland)

813 'Woman flying' (Danielle McIver)

New Millennium. 'Stampin' the Future' (children's stamp design competition)

(Litho Questa)

2000 (1 Jan). P 14×14½ (C).

851	**808**	20p. multicoloured	60	45
852	**809**	25p. multicoloured	60	55
853	**810**	30p. multicoloured	70	65
854	**811**	38p. multicoloured	90	80
855	**812**	44p. multicoloured	1·20	1·50
856	**813**	64p. multicoloured	1·50	1·75
851/6 *Set of 6*			5·00	5·00
First Day Cover				5·50
Presentation Pack			5·50	

Plate Nos.: All values 1A, 1B (each×5).
Sheets: 50 (5×10).
Imprint: Lower right-hand margin.
Withdrawn: 31.12.2000.

814 Bristol Blenheim

815 Hawker Hurricane

816 Boulton Paul Defiant II

817 Gloster Gladiator

818 Bristol Beaufighter IF

819 Supermarine Spitfire IIc

60th Anniversary of Battle of Britain. R.A.F. Aircraft

(Des R. Ollington. Litho Cartor)

2000 (28 Apr.) P 13½×13 (C).

857	814	21p. multicoloured	60	50
		a. Booklet pane. Nos. 857 and 859/61	3·50	
		b. Booklet pane. Nos. 857/8, 860 and 862	3·50	
		c. Booklet pane. Nos. 857/9 and 861	3·00	
858	815	26p. multicoloured	70	55
		a. Booklet pane. Nos. 858/61	3·50	
859	816	36p. multicoloured	1·10	85
860	817	40p. multicoloured	1·25	95
861	818	45p. multicoloured	1·40	1·20
862	819	65p. multicoloured	1·75	1·50
		a. Booklet pane. No. 862×2	3·00	
857/62 Set of 6			6·00	5·50
First Day Cover				5·50
Presentation Pack			6·50	

Plate Nos.: All values 1A (×5).
Sheets: 50 (5×10).
Imprint: Central, side margins.
Withdrawn: 27.4.2001.

820 Guernsey Flag on Kite and '2000'

821 Stylized Sails bearing National Flowers

822 'Building Europe'

823 Rainbow and Three Doves

Europa

(Des J.-P. Cousin (36p.), KWL (others). Litho BDT)

2000 (9 May). P 13 (C).

863	820	21p. multicoloured	50	45
864	821	26p. multicoloured	60	55
865	822	36p. multicoloured	1·00	1·00
866	823	65p. multicoloured	1·60	1·75
863/6 Set of 4			3·50	3·50
First Day Cover				4·00
Presentation Pack			4·00	

Plate Nos.: All values 1A (×4).
Sheets: 10 (2×5) with enlarged inscribed margin at left.
Imprint: Centre, right-hand margin.
Withdrawn: 8.5.2001.
The 36p. value includes the 'EUROPA' emblem.

824 Iris Stylosa

825 Watsonia

826 Richardia maculata

827 Narcissus bulbocodium

828 Triteleia laxa

829 Tigridia pavonia

830 Agapanthus umbellatus

831 Sparaxis

832 *Pancratium maritimum*

833 *Nerine sarniensis*

'A Botanist's Sketchbook'. Restoration of Candie Gardens, St. Peter Port

(Des Petula Stone. Litho Enschedé)

2000 (4 Aug). P 13½×13 (C).

867	**824**	26p. multicoloured	70	70
		a. Horiz strip of 10 or two strips of 5.		
		Nos. 867/76	6·50	6·00
868	**825**	26p. multicoloured	70	70
869	**826**	26p. multicoloured	70	70
870	**827**	26p. multicoloured	70	70
871	**828**	26p. multicoloured	70	70
872	**829**	26p. multicoloured	70	70
873	**830**	26p. multicoloured	70	70
874	**831**	26p. multicoloured	70	70
875	**832**	26p. multicoloured	70	70
876	**833**	26p. multicoloured	70	70

867/76 Set of 10 .... 6·50 6·00
First Day Cover .... 7·75
Presentation Pack .... 6·50

Plate Nos.: All values 1A, 1B (each×5).
Sheets: 50 (10×5). Nos. 867/76 were printed together, *se-tenant*, in horizontal strips of ten throughout the sheet.
Imprint: Upper side margins.
Withdrawn: 3.8.2001.

834 Town Church, St. Peter Port

835 Children leaving St. Sampson's Church

836 Flying Kite by Vale Church

837 Carol singing outside St. Pierre du Bois Church

838 Building Snowman near St. Martin's Church

839 Street Scene including St. John's Church, St. Peter Port

Christmas. Guernsey Churches

(Des Gill Brown. Litho Questa)

2000 (19 Oct). P 14½×14 (C).

877	**834**	18p. multicoloured	40	40
878	**835**	26p. multicoloured	60	55
879	**836**	36p. multicoloured	90	85
880	**837**	40p. multicoloured	95	1·00
881	**838**	45p. multicoloured	1·10	1·40
882	**839**	65p. multicoloured	1·50	1·75

877/82 Set of 6 .... 5·00 5·00
First Day Cover .... 7·00

Presentation Pack .... 6·00
MS883 160×86 mm. Nos. 877/82 .... 6·00 6·00
First Day Cover .... 8·00

Plate Nos.: All values 1A (×5).
Sheets: 50 (5×10).
Imprint: Bottom, right-hand margin.
Withdrawn: 18.10.2001.

Yearbook 2000

2000 (1 Dec). Comprises Nos. 795/6, 801, 851/83 and A140/61 (price £29.95).
Yearbook .... 65·00
Sold out: By 12.2002.

840 Queen Victoria and Diamond Jubilee Statue

841 Letter of Thanks to Guernsey, 1846

842 Statues of Queen Victoria and Prince Albert

843 Stone commemorating 1846 Visit

844 Statue of Prince Albert

845 Victoria Tower, 1848

Death Centenary of Queen Victoria

(Des A. Fothergill. Litho Questa)

2001 (22 Jan). P 15×14½ (C).

884	**840**	21p. multicoloured	50	50
885	**841**	26p. multicoloured	60	55
886	**842**	36p. multicoloured	90	85
887	**843**	40p. multicoloured	95	95
888	**844**	45p. multicoloured	1·10	1·10
889	**845**	65p. multicoloured	1·50	1·50

884/9 Set of 6 .... 5·00 5·00
First Day Cover .... 6·00
Presentation Pack .... 6·00
MS890 165×80 mm. Nos. 884/9. P 14½ (C) .... 6·00 7·00
a. Imperf £750
First Day Cover .... 7·50

No. **MS**890 includes the logo of the 'Hong Kong 2001' Stamp Exhibition on the sheet margin.
Plate Nos.: All values 1A (×4).
Sheets: 50 (10×5).
Imprint: Central, left-hand margin.
Withdrawn: 21.1.2002.

846 River Kingfisher

847 Garganey

848 Little Egret

849 Little Ringed Plover

Europa. Water, a Natural Treasure. Water Birds

(Des Wendy Bramall. Litho BDT)

2001 (1 Feb). P 14×15 (C).

891	**846**	21p. multicoloured	1·25	1·25
892	**847**	26p. multicoloured	1·25	1·25
893	**848**	36p. multicoloured	1·50	1·50
894	**849**	65p. multicoloured	2·00	2·00
891/4 *Set of 4*			6·00	6·00
First Day Cover				4·50
Presentation Pack			5·00	

　　Plate Nos.: All values 1A (×4).
　　Sheets: 10 (2×5) with enlarged inscribed margins at left.
　　Imprint: Central, right-hand margin.
　　Withdrawn: 31.1.2002.
　　The 26p. and 36p. values include the 'EUROPA' emblem.

850 Cavalier King Charles Spaniel　**851** Miniature Schnauzer　**852** German Shepherd Dog

853 Cocker Spaniel　**854** West Highland White Terrier　**855** Dachshund

Centenary of Guernsey Dog Club

(Des A. Peck. Litho BDT)

2001 (26 Apr). P 13 (C).

895	**850**	22p. multicoloured	55	50
896	**851**	27p. multicoloured	65	60
897	**852**	36p. multicoloured	90	85
898	**853**	40p. multicoloured	95	95
899	**854**	45p. multicoloured	1·10	1·10
900	**855**	65p. multicoloured	1·50	1·50
895/900 *Set of 6*			5·00	5·00
First Day Cover				6·00
Presentation Pack			6·00	

　　Plate Nos.: All values 1A (×4).
　　Sheets: 50 (10×5).
　　Imprint: Upper right-hand margin.
　　Withdrawn: 25.4.2002.

856 La Corbiére Sunset　**857** Rue des Hougues　**858** St. Saviour's Reservoir

859 Shell Beach, Herm　**860** Telegraph Bay, Alderney　**861** Alderney Railway

862 Vazon Bay　　　　　**863** La Coupeé, Sark

864 Les Hanois Lighthouse　　**865** Albecq Beach

Island Colours

(Des Sally Diamond)

2001 (26 Apr). Self-adhesive. P 14 (die-cut).

　　(a) Litho Enschedé (from sheetlets of 10 and booklets)

901	**856**	(22p.) multicoloured	45	50
		a. Sheetlet of 10. Nos. 901/10	8·00	8·50
		b. Booklet pane. Nos. 901/5, each×2.	6·00	
902	**857**	(22p.) multicoloured	45	50
903	**858**	(22p.) multicoloured	45	50
904	**859**	(22p.) multicoloured	45	50
905	**860**	(22p.) multicoloured	45	50
906	**861**	(27p.) multicoloured	55	60
		b. Booklet pane. Nos. 906/10, each×2.	9·00	
907	**862**	(27p.) multicoloured	55	60
908	**863**	(27p.) multicoloured	55	60
909	**864**	(27p.) multicoloured	55	60
910	**865**	(27p.) multicoloured	55	60
901/10 *Set of 10*			8·00	8·80
First Day Cover				8·50
Presentation Pack			9·00	

　　(b) Photo Enschedé (from rolls of 100)

911	**856**	(22p.) multicoloured	45	50
		a. Strip of 5. Nos. 911/15	7·00	7·50
912	**857**	(22p.) multicoloured	45	50
913	**858**	(22p.) multicoloured	45	50
914	**859**	(22p.) multicoloured	45	50
915	**860**	(22p.) multicoloured	45	50
916	**861**	(27p.) multicoloured	55	60
		a. Strip of 5. Nos. 916/20	7·00	7·50
917	**862**	(27p.) multicoloured	55	60
918	**863**	(27p.) multicoloured	55	60
919	**864**	(27p.) multicoloured	55	60
920	**865**	(27p.) multicoloured	55	60
911/20 *Set of 10*			14·00	15·00

　　Nos. 901/5 and 911/15 were intended for postage within the Bailiwick and are inscribed 'GY'. They were each initially sold at 22p. Nos. 906/10 and 916/20 were intended for postage to Great Britain and are inscribed 'UK'. They were each initially sold at 27p.
　　Sheets: Nos. 901/10 were printed in sheetlets of ten (5×2) or in booklets with the surplus self-adhesive paper around each stamp retained. Nos. 911/20 were printed in rolls of 100, one for each rate, and have the surplus self-adhesive paper removed. The photogravure printing can be identified by the lack of outlines around the inscriptions.
　　Sold out: By 7.2004 booklets and rolls of 100; by 5.2007 sheetlets.

866 Droplets of Water on Leaf ('Vision')

867 Ruby-throated Hummingbird ('Understanding')

868 Butterfly's Wing ('Individuality')

869 Sea Shell ('Strength')

870 Honeycomb ('Community')

871 Dandelion ('Maturity')

Incorporation of Guernsey Post Ltd

(Des Charlotte Barnes. Litho Walsall)

2001 (1 Aug).

(a) P 13½×13 (C)

921	866	22p. multicoloured	45	50
		a. Booklet pane of 3	1·20	
922	867	27p. multicoloured	55	60
		a. Booklet pane of 3	1·60	
923	868	36p. multicoloured	70	75
		a. Booklet pane of 3	2·10	
924	869	40p. multicoloured	80	85
		a. Booklet pane of 3	2·40	
925	870	45p. multicoloured	90	95
		a. Booklet pane of 3	2·50	
926	871	65p. multicoloured	1·20	1·40
		a. Booklet pane of 3	3·75	
921/6 Set of 6			4·50	5·00
First Day Cover				5·75
Presentation Pack (includes 927a, no stitching)			5·75	

(b) Design as No. 28 (1969 £1), but redrawn and printed in litho. P 14×14½ (C)

927	18	£1 multicoloured	5·00	5·50
		a. Booklet pane of 1	5·00	

No. 927 was only sold as part of a £8.05 stamp booklet but loose panes (without stitch holes) were provided free to regular Guernsey Philatelic Bureau customers. In addition to the change of printing process, No. 927 differs from the original 1969 stamp by showing the Queen's portrait without a tiara and by having 'GUERNSEY BAILIWICK' in white instead of grey.
Plate Nos.: All values 1A (×4).
Sheets: 50 (5×10).
Imprint: Upper right-hand margin.
Withdrawn: 31.7.2002.

872 'Tree of Joy', St. Peter Port

873 Cross, Les Cotils Christian Centre

874 Les Ruettes Cottage, St. Saviour's

875 Farmhouse, Le Preel, Castel

876 Sark Post Office

877 High Street, St. Peter Port

Christmas. Festive Lights

(Des Sally Diamond. Litho Questa)

2001 (16 Oct). P 14×14½ (C).

928	872	19p. multicoloured	40	45
929	873	27p. multicoloured	55	60
930	874	36p. multicoloured	75	80
931	875	40p. multicoloured	1·00	1·10
932	876	45p. multicoloured	1·10	1·20
933	877	65p. multicoloured	1·50	1·60
928/33 Set of 6			5·00	5·50
First Day Cover				5·75
Presentation Pack			5·75	
MS934 150×100 mm. Nos. 928/33			6·00	6·50
First Day Cover				5·75

No. **MS934** includes the 'Hafnia 01' International Stamp Exhibition logo on the sheet margin.
Plate Nos.: 19p., 27p. 1A, 1B, 1C, 1D. (each×4); others 1A (×4).
Sheets: 50 (5×10).
Imprint: Upper right-hand margin.
Withdrawn: 15.10.2002.

Yearbook 2001

2001 (1 Dec). Comprises Nos. 884/910, 921/6, 928/34 and A162/83 (price £29.95).

Yearbook		65·00

Sold out: By 4.2003.

878 Victor Hugo and St. Peter Port

879 Cosette

880 Valjean

881 Inspector Javert

882 Cosette and Marius

883 Novel and Score for Les Misérables (musical by Alain Boublil and Claude-Michel Schönberg)

Birth Bicentenary of Victor Hugo (French author).
Les Misérables (novel)

(Des R. Ollington. Litho Cartor)

2002 (6 Feb). P 13½×13 (C).

935	**878**	22p. multicoloured	45	50
936	**879**	27p. multicoloured	55	60
937	**880**	36p. multicoloured	75	80
938	**881**	40p. multicoloured	90	95
939	**882**	45p. multicoloured	1·10	1·10
940	**883**	65p. multicoloured	1·50	1·60
935/40 *Set of 6*			5·00	5·75
First Day Cover				5·75
Presentation Pack			5·75	
MS941 150×100 mm. Nos. 935/40			5·50	6·00
First Day Cover				7·00

The 27p. value reproduces the main image from promotional material for Cameron Mackintosh's musical production.

Plate Nos.: All values 1A (×4).
Sheets: 50 (5×10).
Imprint: Central, side margins.
Withdrawn: 5.2.2003.

884 Juggling   **885** Clowns   **886** Trapeze Artists

887 Knife Thrower   **888** Acrobat   **889** High-wire Cyclist

Europa. The Circus

(Des R. Carter. Litho Questa)

2002 (6 Feb). P 14½ (C).

942	**884**	22p. multicoloured	45	50
943	**885**	27p. multicoloured	55	60
944	**886**	36p. multicoloured	70	75
945	**887**	40p. multicoloured	80	90
946	**888**	45p. multicoloured	90	95
947	**889**	65p. multicoloured	1·20	1·40
942/7 *Set of 6*			4·50	5·00
First Day Cover				6·50
Presentation Pack			5·75	

Plate Nos.: All values 1A (×4).
Sheets: 10 (2×5) with enlarged illustrated margins at right.
Imprint: Central, left-hand margin.
Withdrawn 5.2.2003.
The 27p. and 36p. values include the 'EUROPA' emblem.

890 Queen Elizabeth and Crowd

891 Queen Elizabeth at St. Peter Port

892 Queen Elizabeth and Prince Philip at St. Anne's School, Alderney

893 Queen Elizabeth and La Seigneurie, Sark

894 At Millennium Stone, L'Ancresse

895 In Evening Dress, and Floodlit Castle Cornet

Golden Jubilee

(Des Sarah Thomas. Litho BDT)

2002 (30 Apr). P 13½ (C).

948	**890**	22p. multicoloured	45	50
		a. Booklet pane. Nos. 948 and 951/3 with margins all round	4·50	
		b. Booklet pane. Nos. 948/50 and 953 with margins all round	3·00	
		c. Booklet pane. Nos. 948/53 with margins all round	4·50	
949	**891**	27p. multicoloured	55	60
		a. Booklet pane. Nos. 949/52 with margins all round	3·00	
950	**892**	36p. multicoloured	70	75
951	**893**	40p. multicoloured	80	85
952	**894**	45p. multicoloured	90	95
953	**895**	65p. multicoloured	1·20	1·40
948/53 *Set of 6*			4·50	5·00
First Day Cover				5·75
Presentation Pack			5·75	

Plate Nos.: All values 1A (×4).
Sheets: 50 (10×5).
Imprint: Upper right-hand margin.
Withdrawn: 29.4.2003.

896 Original Pillar Box, Union Street

150th Anniversary of First Pillar Box

(Des Sally Diamond. Litho Questa)

2002 (30 Apr). Sheet 55×90 mm. P 14½×14 (C).

MS954 **896** £1.75 multicoloured	6·50	6·75
First Day Cover		7·00
Presentation Pack	5·00	

Withdrawn: 29.4.2003.

For a full range of Stanley Gibbons catalogues, please visit **www.stanleygibbons.com**

897 Family and Ferry, La Maseline

898 Passenger Tractors

899 Campsite

900 Cyclists at La Coupée

901 Swimming in Venus Pool

902 La Seigneurie Gardens

903 Posting Cards

904 Carriage Ride

905 Tea at a Café

906 On the Beach at Creux Harbour

Holidays on Sark

(Des M. Remphry. Litho BDT)

2002 (30 July). P 13 (C).

955	**897**	27p. multicoloured	45	30
		a. Block of 10 of two horiz strips of		
		5. Nos. 955/64	6·00	6·00
956	**898**	27p. multicoloured	45	30
957	**899**	27p. multicoloured	45	30
958	**900**	27p. multicoloured	45	30
959	**901**	27p. multicoloured	45	30
960	**902**	27p. multicoloured	45	30
961	**903**	27p. multicoloured	45	30
962	**904**	27p. multicoloured	45	30
963	**905**	27p. multicoloured	45	30
964	**906**	27p. multicoloured	45	30
955/64		Set of 10	6·00	6·00
		First Day Cover		6·50
		Presentation Pack	6·50	

Plate Nos.: 1A (×4).
Sheets: 50 (5×10). Nos. 955/64 were printed together, *se-tenant*, in blocks of ten throughout the sheet.
Imprint: Upper side margins.
Withdrawn: 29.7.2003.

907 Elizabeth College and Cadet Corps Parade, 1934

908 Captain Le Patourel in Action, Tunisia, 1942, and V.C.

909 Captain Le Patourel and Nurse, 1943

910 Award Ceremony, Cairo, 1943

911 Major Le Patourel welcomed Home to Guernsey, 1948

912 Herbert Le Patourel carrying the King's Colour, 1968

60th Anniversary of Herbert Le Patourel's Victoria Cross

(Des A. Theobald. Litho Cartor)

2002 (30 July). P 13½×13 (C).

965	**907**	22p. multicoloured	45	50
966	**908**	27p. multicoloured	55	60
967	**909**	36p. multicoloured	70	75
968	**910**	40p. multicoloured	80	85
969	**911**	45p. multicoloured	90	95
970	**912**	65p. multicoloured	1·20	1·40
965/70		Set of 6	4·50	5·00
		First Day Cover		5·75
		Presentation Pack	5·75	

Plate Nos.: All values 1A (×4).
Sheets: 50 (5×10).
Imprint: Central, side margins.
Withdrawn: 29.7.2003.

913 Queen Elizabeth the Queen Mother and Bouquet
(*Illustration reduced. Actual size 140×98 mm*)

Queen Elizabeth the Queen Mother Commemoration

(Des M. Whyte. Litho and die-stamped Enschedé)

2002 (4 Aug). Sheet 140×98 mm. P 13½ (C).

MS971 **913**	£2 multicoloured	5·00	5·00
	First Day Cover		5·75
	Presentation Pack	5·00	

Withdrawn: 3.8.2003.

914 Mary and Jesus

915 Mary, Joseph and Jesus in the Stable

916 Angel appearing to Shepherds

917 Shepherds with Mary and Jesus

918 Three Wise Men

919 Stable with Star Overhead

Christmas

(Des Petula Stone. Litho Cartor)

2002 (17 Oct). P 13 (C).

972	**914**	22p. multicoloured		50	50
973	**915**	27p. multicoloured		70	70
974	**916**	36p. multicoloured		1·10	1·10
975	**917**	40p. multicoloured		1·25	1·25
976	**918**	45p. multicoloured		1·50	1·50
977	**919**	65p. multicoloured		1·75	1·75
972/7		Set of 6		6·50	6·50
		First Day Cover			6·75
		Presentation Pack		6·00	
MS978		130×102 mm. Nos. 972/7		5·00	5·00
		First Day Cover			5·75

Plate Nos.: All values 1A (×5).
Sheets: 50 (5×10).
Imprint: Central, side margins.
Withdrawn: 16.10.2003.

Yearbook 2002

2002 (1 Dec). Comprises Nos. 935/78 and **MS**A184/202 (price £33.90).

Yearbook		65·00

Sold out: 6.2005.

920 Lancaster Bomber and Crew

921 Flight of Lancaster bombers crossing English coast

922 Lancaster bombers in enemy searchlights

923 Dropping bouncing bombs

924 H.M.S. *Charybdis* (cruiser) and H.M.S. *Limbourne* (destroyer)

Memories of the Second World War (1st series). 60th Anniversary of Operation Tunnel (£1.50) and Dambusters Raid (others).

(Des N. Watton. Litho Questa)

2003 (30 Jan). P 14½ (£1.50) or 14 (others) (both comb.).

979	**920**	22p. multicoloured		75	50
980	**921**	27p. multicoloured		75	60
981	**922**	36p. multicoloured		1·00	75
982	**923**	40p. multicoloured		1·00	85
983	**924**	£1.50 multicoloured		3·50	3·25
979/83		Set of 5		6·50	5·75

First Day Cover		6·50
Presentation Pack	7·00	

See also Nos. 1027/31 and 1060/4.
Plate Nos.: All values 1A (×5).
Sheets: 50 (5×10).
Imprint: Upper right-hand margin.
Withdrawn: 29.1.2004.

925 Hurdling

926 Cycling

927 Gymnastics

928 Sailing

929 Golf

930 Running

Island Games, Guernsey

(Des Charlotte Barnes. Litho Cartor)

2003 (30 Jan). P 12½ (C).

984	**925**	22p. multicoloured		45	50
985	**926**	27p. multicoloured		55	60
986	**927**	36p. multicoloured		75	80
987	**928**	40p. multicoloured		80	85
988	**929**	45p. multicoloured		90	95
989	**930**	65p. multicoloured		1·20	1·40
984/9		Set of 6		4·50	5·00
		First Day Cover			5·75
		Presentation Pack		5·75	
MS990		140×75 mm. Nos. 984/9		5·00	5·00
		First Day Cover			5·75

Plate Nos.: All values 1A (×4).
Sheets: 50 (5×10).
Imprint: Central, side margins.
Withdrawn: 29.1.2004.

931 St. Peter Port Harbour ('Naturally Guernsey', 2003)

932 Motor-cruiser off Guernsey ('The islands of Guernsey', 1995)

933 'Children on the Seashore' (Renoir) ('Holiday Guernsey', 1988)

934 St. Peter Port Harbour ('Bailiwick of Guernsey', 1978)

935 St. Peter Port and Cliffs ('Guernsey - The Charming Channel Island', 1968)

936 Secluded Bay ('Guernsey', 1956)

Europa. Poster Art

(Des M. Quéru. Litho DLR)

2003 (10 Apr). P 14½ (C).

991	**931**	22p. multicoloured	45	50
992	**932**	27p. multicoloured	55	60
993	**933**	36p. multicoloured	75	80
994	**934**	40p. multicoloured	80	85
995	**935**	45p. multicoloured	90	95
996	**936**	65p. multicoloured	1·20	1·40
991/6	*Set of 6*		5·00	5·00
First Day Cover				5·75
Presentation Pack			5·75	

Sheets: 10 (2×5) with enlarged illustrated margin at right.
Imprint: Central, left-hand margin.
Withdrawn: 9.4.2004.
The 27p. and 36p. values include the 'EUROPA' emblem.

937 H.M.S. Guernsey (*Illustration reduced. Actual size 117×84 mm*)

Decommissioning of H.M.S. *Guernsey* (fishery protection patrol vessel)

(Des K. Taylor. Litho DLR)

2003 (10 Apr). Sheet 117×84 mm. P 13½×14 (C).

MS997 **937** £1.50 multicoloured		4·50	4·00
First Day Cover			4·50
Presentation Pack		4·75	

Withdrawn: 9.4.2004.

938 Princess Diana and Baby Prince William

939 Prince William aged 3, with Prince Charles and Prince Harry at Kensington Palace

940 Aged 4, in Parachute Regiment Uniform

941 Aged 7, with Prince Harry on his First Day at Wetherby School

942 Aged 8, with Prince Charles at Guards Polo

943 Aged 9, on Ski Slopes with Princess Diana

944 On First Day at Eton, 1995

945 With Prince Charles and Prince Harry at Balmoral, 1997

946 Wearing Hard Hat during Community Project in Chile, 2000

947 Playing Polo, 2002

21st Birthday of Prince William of Wales

(Des Sally Diamond. Litho Enschedé)

2003 (21 June). P 13½×13 (C).

998	**938**	27p. multicoloured	55	30
		a. Horiz strip of 10. Nos. 998/1007	9·00	7·00
		b. Perf 13½×14	55	30
		ba. Booklet pane. Nos. 998b, 1000b, 1003b/4b and 1006b/7b with margins all round	5·00	
		bb. Booklet pane. Nos. 998b, 1001b, 1003b/5b and 1007b with margins all round	5·00	
		bc. Booklet pane. Nos. 998b/1000b, 1002b, 1005b and 1007b with margins all round	5·00	
999	**939**	27p. multicoloured	55	30
		b. Perf 13½×14	55	30
		ba. Booklet pane. Nos. 999b/1002b and 1005b/6b with margins all round	5·00	
		bb. Booklet pane. Nos. 999b, 1001b/1004b and 1006b with margins all round	5·00	
1000	**940**	27p. multicoloured	55	30
		b. Perf 13½×14	55	30
1001	**941**	27p. multicoloured	55	30
		b. Perf 13½×14	55	30
1002	**942**	27p. multicoloured	55	30
		b. Perf 13½×14	55	30
1003	**943**	27p. multicoloured	55	30
		b. Perf 13½×14	55	30
1004	**944**	27p. multicoloured	55	30
		b. Perf 13½×14	55	30
1005	**945**	27p. multicoloured	55	30
		b. Perf 13½×14	55	30
1006	**946**	27p. multicoloured	55	30
		b. Perf 13½×14	55	30
1007	**947**	27p. multicoloured	55	30
		b. Perf 13½×14	55	30
998/1007	*Set of 10*		9·00	7·00

First Day Cover.. 6·50
Presentation Pack.. 10·00
    Nos. 998b/1007b were only issued in £8.10 booklets, No. SB72.
      Plate Nos.: 1A (×4).
      Sheets: 50 (10×5). Nos. 998/1007 were printed together, *se-tenant*, in horizontal strips of ten throughout the sheet.
      Imprint: Upper side margins.
      Withdrawn: 20.6.2004.

948 Letters of Alphabet

Letters on a Stamp on a Letter

(Des A. Fothergill. Litho and die-stamped Enschedé)

2003 (3 July). P 13½ (C).
1008   **948**   £5 pale orange, royal blue and silver.   10·00   10·50
First Day Cover.. 11·00
Presentation Pack.. 11·00
    The alphabet letters are printed in thermochromic ink which fades from pale orange to white when exposed to heat.
    No. 1008 was retained in use as a definitive stamp.
      Sheets: 4 (4×1).

949 Sleeping Boy and Christmas Tree   **950** Boy opening Shutter to see Santa's Sleigh

951 Santa on Roof with Reindeer   **952** Santa with Presents

953 Santa leaving Presents under Christmas Tree   **954** Santa in Sleigh

Christmas. Scenes from Poem 'Twas the Night before Christmas' by Clement Clarke Moore

(Des Petula Stone. Litho DLR)

2003 (16 Oct). P 14×14½ (C).
1009   **949**   10p. multicoloured.................................... 20   25
1010   **950**   27p. multicoloured.................................... 55   60
1011   **951**   36p. multicoloured.................................... 70   75
1012   **952**   40p. multicoloured.................................... 80   85
1013   **953**   45p. multicoloured.................................... 1·20   1·30
1014   **954**   65p. multicoloured.................................... 1·50   1·70
1009/14 Set of 6.. 4·75   5·00
First Day Cover.. 5·75
Presentation Pack.. 5·75
MS1015 130×104 mm. Nos. 1009/14 .... 4·75   4·75
First Day Cover.. 5·75
      Plate Nos.: All values 1A (×4).
      Sheets: 50 (5×10).
      Imprint: Upper right-hand margin.
      Withdrawn: 15.10.2004.

Yearbook 2003

2003 (1 Dec). Comprises Nos. 979/**MS**1015 and **MS**A203/22 (price £34.86).
Yearbook.. 70·00
    Sold out: By 3.2007.

955 Golden Snub-nosed Monkey (*Illustration reduced. Actual size 120×85 mm*)

Endangered Species (1st series). Golden Snub-nosed Monkey (*Pygathrix roxellana*)

(Des J. Kirk. Litho DLR)

2004 (29 Jan). Sheet 120×85 mm. P 14 (C).
MS1016 **955** £2 multicoloured.................................... 6·50   6·50
First Day Cover.. 8·50
Presentation Pack.. 8·50
    See also Nos. **MS**1085, **MS**1096, **MS**1173, **MS**1266, **MS**1320, **MS**1368, **MS**1406 and **MS**1449
      Withdrawn: 28.1.2005.

956 'Rosemoor'   **957** 'Arctic Queen'   **958** 'Harlow Carr'

959 'Guernsey Cream'   **960** 'Josephine'   **961** ' Blue Moon'

962 'Wisley'   **963** 'Liberation'

964 'Royal Velvet'   **965** 'Hyde Hall'

Raymond Evison's Guernsey Clematis

(Des R. Evison. Litho Cartor)

2004 (29 Jan). Self-adhesive. P 12½ (die-cut).
1017   **956**   (22p.) multicoloured............................... 75   75
    a. Sheetlet. Nos. 1017/26...................... 8·00
    b. Booklet pane with information panel. Nos. 1017/21, each×2 .... 7·00
    c. Booklet pane. Nos. 1017/21, each×2 7·00
1018   **957**   (22p.) multicoloured............................... 75   75
1019   **958**   (22p.) multicoloured............................... 75   75
1020   **959**   (22p.) multicoloured............................... 75   75
1021   **960**   (22p.) multicoloured............................... 75   75
1022   **961**   (27p.) multicoloured............................... 85   85
    a. Booklet pane with information panel. Nos. 1022/6, each×2.............. 8·75

b. Booklet pane. Nos. 1022/6, each×2 .... 8·75

1023	**962**	(27p.) multicoloured	85	85
1024	**963**	(27p.) multicoloured	85	85
1025	**964**	(27p.) multicoloured	85	85
1026	**965**	(27p.) multicoloured	85	85

1017/26 *Set of 10*.. 8·00   8·00
First Day Cover..   9·00
Presentation Pack.. 9·00

Nos. 1017/21 were intended for postage within the Bailiwick and are inscribed "GY". They were each initially sold at 22p. Nos. 1022/6 were intended for postage to Great Britain and are inscribed "UK". They were each initially sold at 27p.

Sheets: 10 (5×2). Nos. 1017/26 were printed in sheetlets of ten containing Nos. 1017/26 and in booklets of ten or 100, all with the surplus self-adhesive paper around each stamp retained. The booklets of ten contain either Nos. 1017/21×2 (pane No. 1017b) or Nos. 1022/6×2 (pane No. 1022a), and the stamps are peeled directly from the cover in two blocks 3×2 and 2×2, the blocks separated by a gutter containing text. The booklets of 100 contain ten panes of either Nos. 1017/21×2 (pane No. 1017c) or Nos. 1022/6×2 (pane No. 1022b). These panes have the stamps in one block 5×2, on plain white backing paper, the panes being separated from the booklet by a line of rouletting.

Loose single booklet panes of ten (1017c and 1022b) were also available from the Philatelic Bureau.

966 Supermarine Spitfire

967 Landing Craft and Ship

968 Troops going Ashore at Gold Beach

969 Troops in Water

970 *Vega* (Red Cross supply ship)

Memories of the Second World War (2nd series).
60th Anniv of D-Day Landings

(Des N. Watton. Litho BDT)

2004 (12 May). P 15×14 (£1.50) or 14 (others) (both comb).

1027	**966**	26p. multicoloured	85	85
1028	**967**	32p. multicoloured	1·00	1·00
1029	**968**	36p. multicoloured	1·20	1·20
1030	**969**	40p. multicoloured	1·30	1·30
1031	**970**	£1.50 multicoloured	5·00	5·00

1027/31 *Set of 5*... 9·25   9·25
First Day Cover..   11·50
Presentation Pack.. 11·50

Plate Nos.: All values 1A (×4).
Sheets: 50 (5×10).
Imprint: Upper side margins.
Withdrawn: 11.5.2005.

971 Sandcastle, Rider, Bucket and Spade, Deckchair and Canoeist

972 Pathway Sign, Walking Trails, Bench and Guernsey Landscapes

973 Lighthouse and Yachts in Marina, St. Peter Port

974 Glasses of Red Wine and Meals on Table

975 Statue-menhir at Castel and Loop Holed Tower, Le Gran'mere Statue-menhir, Little Chapel and Victor Hugo Statue

976 Guernsey Lily, Wildflowers and Robin

Europa. Holidays

(Des P. Furness. Litho BDT)

2004 (12 May). P 13½ (C).

1032	**971**	26p. multicoloured	85	85
1033	**972**	32p. multicoloured	1·10	1·10
1034	**973**	36p. multicoloured	1·20	1·20
1035	**974**	40p. multicoloured	1·30	1·30
1036	**975**	45p. multicoloured	1·50	1·50
1037	**976**	65p. multicoloured	2·10	2·10

1032/7 *Set of 6*... 8·00   8·00
First Day Cover..   10·00
Presentation Pack.. 10·00

Sheets: 10 (2×5) with enlarged illustrated margins at right.
Imprint: Central, left-hand margin.
Withdrawn: 11.5.2005.
The 32p. and 36p. values include the 'EUROPA' emblem.

977 Three Crowns (Loyalty)

978 Three Ships (Trade)

979 Knotted Rope (Unity)

980 Three Castle Turrets (Protection)

981 Three Scrolls (Justice)

982 Three Leaping Fish (Industry)

800th Anniv of Allegiance to England – Celebration 800

(Des Charlotte Barnes. Litho Enschedé)

2004 (24 June). P 13½×14 (C).

1038	**977**	26p. multicoloured	85	85
1039	**978**	32p. multicoloured	1·10	1·10
1040	**979**	36p. multicoloured	1·20	1·20
1041	**980**	40p. multicoloured	1·30	1·30
1042	**981**	45p. multicoloured	1·50	1·50
1043	**982**	65p. multicoloured	2·10	2·10
1038/43 *Set of 6*			8·00	8·00
First Day Cover				10·00
Presentation Pack			10·00	
MS1044 140×80 mm. Nos. 1038/43. P 14×13½			8·00	8·00
First Day Cover				10·00

Plate Nos.: All values 1A (×5).
Sheets: 50 (10×5).
Imprint: Upper side margins.
Withdrawn: 23.6.2005.

983 Discus Thrower

984 Javelin Thrower

985 Runners

986 Wrestlers

987 Olympic Sports (*Illustration reduced. Actual size 152×98 mm*)

Olympic Games, Athens, Greece

(Des A. Fothergill. Litho BDT)

2004 (29 July). P 13½ (C).

1045	**983**	32p. multicoloured	1·00	1·00
		a. Booklet pane. No. 1045×2 and Nos. 1046/7 with margins all round	4·75	
		b. Booklet pane. No. 1045, No. 1047×2 and No. 1048 with margins all round	6·00	
		c. Booklet pane. Nos. 1045/6 and 1048×2 with margins all round	6·50	
		d. Booklet pane. Nos. 1045/8 with margins all round	5·75	
1046	**984**	36p. multicoloured	1·20	1·20
		a. Booklet pane. No. 1046×2 and Nos. 1047/8 with margins all round	6·00	
1047	**985**	45p. multicoloured	1·50	1·50
1048	**986**	65p. multicoloured	2·10	2·10
1045/8 *Set of 4*			5·75	5·75
First Day Cover				7·75
Presentation Pack			5·25	
MS1049 152×98 mm. **987** £1 multicoloured. P 15×14 (C)			4·75	4·75
		a. Booklet pane. As No. **MS**1049, but with line of roulettes at left	3·50	
First Day Cover				5·25
Presentation Pack			7·75	

Plate Nos.: All values 1A (×4).
Sheets: 50 (10×5).
Imprint: Upper side margins.
Withdrawn: 28.7.2005.
MS1049 also commemorates Olymphilex 2004.

988 'Little Donkey'

989 'While Shepherds Watched'

990 'Away in a Manger'

991 'Unto Us a Child is Born'

992 'We Three Kings'

993 Angels Wings

994 Bauble

995 Holly

996 Detail of Snowman

997 Star atop Tree

'The Innocence of Christmas'

(Des J. Almer. Litho Cartor)

2004 (28 Oct). P 13 (C).

1050	**988**	20p. multicoloured	65	25
		a. Horiz strip of 5. Nos. 1050/4	3·25	3·50
1051	**989**	20p. multicoloured	65	25
1052	**990**	20p. multicoloured	65	25
1053	**991**	20p. multicoloured	65	25
1054	**992**	20p. multicoloured	65	25
1055	**993**	32p. multicoloured	1·10	1·10
1056	**994**	36p. multicoloured	1·20	1·20
1057	**995**	40p. multicoloured	1·30	1·30
1058	**996**	45p. multicoloured	1·50	1·50
1059	**997**	65p. multicoloured	2·20	2·20
1050/9		Set of 10	150	150
		First Day Covers (2)		14·50
		Presentation Pack	13·50	

Plate Nos.: All values 1A (×4).
Sheets: 50 (5×10). The 20p. values were printed together, *se-tenant*, in horizontal strips of five with the backgrounds forming a composite design.
Imprint: Upper and lower side margins.
Withdrawn: 27.10.2005.

Yearbook 2004

2004 (1 Dec). Comprises Nos. **MS**1016/59 and A223/47 (price £33·13).
Yearbook .... 65·00

998 British Soldiers in Landrover and welcoming Crowd

999 Guernsey Woman waving and Liberty Sign and Flags on Building

1000 Parents and Children reunited

1001 Return of Local Men from Hampshire Regiment

1002 Winston Churchill

Memories of the Second World War (3rd series).
60th Anniv of Liberation

(Des N. Watton. Litho BDT)

2005 (3 Feb). P 15×14½ (£1.50) or 14½ (others) (both comb).

1060	**998**	26p. multicoloured	50	55
1061	**999**	32p. multicoloured	65	70
1062	**1000**	36p. multicoloured	70	75
1063	**1001**	40p. multicoloured	80	85
1064	**1002**	£1.50 multicoloured	3·00	3·25
1060/4		Set of 5	5·50	6·00
		First Day Cover		7·00
		Presentation Pack	7·00	

Plate Nos.: All values 1A (×4).
Sheets: 50 (5×10).
Imprint: Upper left-hand margin.
Withdrawn: 2.2.2006.

1003 Iris 'Dorothea' and 'Royal'

1004 Nerine Fothergilli 'Major'

1005 Iris 'Garnet'

1006 Narcissus 'Sir Watkin'

1007 Narcissus 'Rip van Winkle'

1008 Narcissus 'Sulphur Pheonix'

Birth Centenary of William J. Caparne (artist and iris breeder).
Watercolour Paintings of Flowers

(Litho Enschedé)

2005 (3 Feb). P 13½ (C).

1065	**1003**	26p. multicoloured	50	55
1066	**1004**	32p. multicoloured	65	70
1067	**1005**	36p. multicoloured	70	95
1068	**1006**	40p. multicoloured	85	1·00
1069	**1007**	45p. multicoloured	1·00	1·10
1070	**1008**	65p. multicoloured	1·50	1·50
1065/70		Set of 6	5·00	5·00
		First Day Cover		6·00
		Presentation Pack	6·00	
MS1071		140×85 mm. Nos. 1065/70	5·00	5·50
		First Day Cover		6·00

Plate Nos.: All values 1A (×4).
Sheets: 50 (10×5).
Imprint: Upper left-hand margin.
Withdrawn: 2.2.2006.

1009 Spider Crab

1010 Seared Red Mullet and Crab Cake

1011 Lobster Salad

1012 Brill on Spinach with Local Moules

1013 Prawn Salad

1014 Salmon Wrapped in Spinach with Local Moules

Europa. Gastronomy. Seafood and Coastal Scenes

(Des P. Furness. Litho Enschedé)

2005 (9 May). P 14×13½ (C).

1072	**1009**	26p. multicoloured	50	55
1073	**1010**	32p. multicoloured	65	70
1074	**1011**	36p. multicoloured	70	75
1075	**1012**	40p. multicoloured	80	85
1076	**1013**	45p. multicoloured	90	95
1077	**1014**	65p. multicoloured	1·30	1·40
1072/7 *Set of 6*			4·75	5·00
First Day Cover				6·25
Presentation Pack			6·25	

Plate Nos.: All values 1A (×4).
Sheets: 10 (2×5) with enlarged illustrated right-hand margins.
Imprint: Lower left-hand margin.
Withdrawn: 8.5.2006.
The 32p. and 36p. values include the 'EUROPA' emblem.

1015 King George VI   **1016** Queen Elizabeth II

60th Anniv of Liberation of Guernsey

(Des Keren Le Patourel. Litho and embossed BDT)

2005 (9 May). P 15×14½ (C).

1078	**1015**	£1 multicoloured	2·75	2·75
		a. Horiz pair. Nos. 1078/9	5·00	5·00
1079	**1016**	£1 multicoloured	2·75	2·75
1078/9 *Set of 2*			5·00	5·00
First Day Cover				5·50
Presentation Pack			5·50	

Nos. 1078/9 were retained in use as definitive stamps.
Plate Nos.: 1A (×5).
Sheets: 20 (4×5); the two designs printed together, *se-tenant*, in horizontal pairs throughout the sheet, each pair forming a composite background design.
Imprint: Central, side margins.

1017 Fishing Boat

1018 Yacht off Herm Harbour

1019 Windsurfer

1020 Sea Angler on Rocks at Albecq

1021 Horse and Rider on Beach, Vazon Bay

'Sea Guernsey' (1st series)

(Des Sally Diamond. Litho Enschedé)

2005 (21 July). P 13½×14 (C).

1080	**1017**	26p. multicoloured	50	55
		a. Booklet pane. Nos. 1080/1, each×2, with margins all round	2·30	
		b. Booklet pane. Nos. 1080 and 1084, each×2, with margins all round	3·50	
1081	**1018**	32p. multicoloured	65	70
		a. Booklet pane. Nos. 1081/2, each×2, with margins all round	2·75	
		b. Booklet pane. Nos. 1081/4 with margins all round	3·50	
1082	**1019**	36p. multicoloured	70	75
		a. Booklet pane. Nos. 1082/3, each×2, with margins all round	3·00	
1083	**1020**	40p. multicoloured	80	85
		a. Booklet pane. Nos. 1083/4, each×2, with margins all round	4·50	
1084	**1021**	65p. multicoloured	1·50	1·40
1080/4 *Set of 5*			4·00	4·00
First Day Cover				5·25
Presentation Pack			5·25	

See also Nos. 1180/5, 1302/7 and 1388/93.
Plate Nos.: All values 1A (×4).
Sheets: 10 (2×5).
Imprint: Lower right-hand margin.
Withdrawn: 20.7.2006.

1022 Basking Shark (*Illustration reduced. Actual size 185×65 mm*)

Endangered Species (2nd series). Basking Shark (*Centorhinus maximas*)

(Des J. Kirk. Litho BDT)

2005 (21 July). Sheet 185×65 mm. P 13½ (C).

MS1085	**1022**	£2 multicoloured	5·00	5·00
First Day Cover				6·00
Presentation Pack			6·00	

Withdrawn: 20.7.2006.

1023 Christ holding Guernsey Flag, St. Pierre du Bois   **1024** Madonna and Child, St. Saviour   **1025** John baptising Christ, St. Martin

1026 Christ the Light of the World, Torteval   **1027** Madonna and Child, St. Sampson   **1028** Madonna and Child, Vale

1029 Three Kings, Castel

1030 St. Nicholas, Alderney

1031 Madonna and Child, St. Andrew

1032 St. Marguerite Forest

Christmas. Stained-glass Windows from Guernsey and Alderney Parish Churches

(Des K. Taylor. Litho Austrian State Ptg Wks, Vienna)

2005 (27 Oct). P 14×14½ (C).

1086	**1023**	20p. multicoloured	40	45
		a. Horiz strip of 5. Nos. 1086/90	2·00	2·20
1087	**1024**	20p. multicoloured	40	45
1088	**1025**	20p. multicoloured	40	45
1089	**1026**	20p. multicoloured	40	45
1090	**1027**	20p. multicoloured	40	45
1091	**1028**	32p. multicoloured	65	70
1092	**1029**	36p. multicoloured	70	75
1093	**1030**	40p. multicoloured	80	85
1094	**1031**	45p. multicoloured	90	95
1095	**1032**	65p. multicoloured	1·30	1·40
1086/95 Set of 10			6·25	6·75
First Day Covers (2)				9·00
Presentation Pack			7·75	

Plate Nos.: All values 1A (×4).
Sheets: 50 (10×5). The 20p. values were printed together, *se-tenant*, in horizontal strips of five with the backgrounds forming a composite design.
Imprint: Lower side margins.
Withdrawn: 26.10.2006.

Yearbook 2005

2005 (1 Dec). Comprises Nos. 802, 1060/95 and A248/**MS**A266 (price £34·64).

Yearbook		65·00

1033 Atlantic Leatherback Turtle; American Wood Ibis
(*Illustration reduced. Actual size* 110×90 *mm*)

Endangered Species (3rd series). Florida Everglades

(Des J. Kirk. Litho BDT)

2006 (16 Feb). Sheet 110×90 mm. P 14×15 (C).

MS1096 **1033** £1, £1.50 multicoloured	6·50	6·00
First Day Cover			7·00
Presentation Pack		7·00	

Withdrawn: 15.2.2007.

1034 Iraq Conflict, 2004

1035 Falklands War, 1982

1036 Battle of El Alamein, 1942

1037 Gallipoli Campaign, 1915

1038 Battle of Rorke's Drift, 1879

1039 Charge of the Light Brigade, 1854

150th Anniversary of the Victoria Cross

(Des M. Hargreaves. Litho Austrian State Ptg Wks, Vienna)

2006 (16 Feb). P 14×13½ (C).

1097	**1034**	29p. multicoloured	60	65
1098	**1035**	34p. multicoloured	70	75
1099	**1036**	38p. multicoloured	75	80
1100	**1037**	42p. multicoloured	85	90
1101	**1038**	47p. multicoloured	95	1·00
1102	**1039**	68p. multicoloured	1·40	1·50
1097/102 Set of 6			5·25	5·50
First Day Cover				6·50
Presentation Pack			6·50	

Plate Nos.: All values 1A (×4).
Sheets: 50 (5×10).
Imprint: Upper left-hand margin.
Withdrawn: 15.2.2007.

1040 Pilbeam MP58, British Speed Hill Climb Championship, 1995

1041 Renault Spider Cup, 1999

1042 British Formula 3, 2001

1043 FIA European Touring Car Championship, 2004

1044 Nürburgring, Germany, 2005

1045 FIA World Touring Car Championship, 2005

Andy Priaulx's Motor Racing Victories

(Des P. Furness. Litho BDT)

2006 (20 May). P 13½ (C).

1103	**1040**	29p. multicoloured	70	70
1104	**1041**	34p. multicoloured	1·00	1·00
1105	**1042**	42p. multicoloured	1·00	1·00
1106	**1043**	45p. multicoloured	1·15	1·15
1107	**1044**	47p. multicoloured	1·60	1·60
1108	**1045**	68p. multicoloured	1·90	1·90
1103/8	*Set of 6*		6·75	7·00
First Day Cover				7·00
Presentation Pack			6·50	
MS1109 160×100 mm. Nos. 1103/8			6·00	6·00
First Day Cover				7·00

Plate Nos.: All values 1A (×4).
Sheets: 10 (2×5) with enlarged illustrated right margins.
Imprint: Central, left-hand margin.
Withdrawn: 19.5.2007.

1046 Brunel and Mailbags at Paddington Station

1047 Duke Class Locomotive No. 3258 *King Arthur* at Paddington Station

1048 *King Arthur* on Wharncliffe Viaduct

1049 Loading Mail from Train onto *Ibex* at Weymouth Harbour

1050 Weymouth & Channel Island Steam Packet *Ibex*

1051 Unloading Mail from *Ibex* at St. Peter Port Harbour

Birth Bicentenary of Isambard Kingdom Brunel (engineer)

(Des N. Watton. Litho Cartor)

2006 (20 May). P 13½×13 (C).

1110	**1046**	29p. multicoloured	60	65
		a. Booklet pane. Nos. 1110/13	3·00	
		b. Booklet pane. Nos. 1110 and 1113/15	3·75	
		c. Booklet pane. Nos. 1110/11 and 1114/15	5·00	
		d. Booklet pane. Nos. 1110/12 and 1115	4·00	
1111	**1047**	34p. multicoloured	70	75
		a. Booklet pane. Nos. 1111/14	4·00	
1112	**1048**	42p. multicoloured	85	90
		a. Booklet pane. Nos. 1112/15	5·00	
1113	**1049**	45p. multicoloured	90	95
1114	**1050**	47p. multicoloured	1·20	1·20
1115	**1051**	68p. multicoloured	1·70	1·70
1110/15	*Set of 6*		5·75	6·00
First Day Cover				7·00
Presentation Pack			7·00	

Plate Nos.: All values 1A (×4).
Sheets: 50 (5×10).
Imprint: Upper and lower left-hand margins.
Withdrawn: 19.5.2007.

1052 Student working as Waiter in Paris

1053 Sphinx, Egypt

1054 Great Wall of China

1055 Student and Aborigines at Ayers Rock, Australia

1056 Head of Statue of Liberty, New York

1057 Students at Taj Mahal, India

Europa. Integration. Student's Gap Year Travels

(Des R. Carter. Litho Cartor)

2006 (20 May). P 13½×14 (C).

1116	**1052**	29p. multicoloured	70	70
1117	**1053**	34p. multicoloured	1·00	1·00
1118	**1054**	42p. multicoloured	1·00	1·00
1119	**1055**	45p. multicoloured	1·15	1·15
1120	**1056**	47p. multicoloured	1·60	1·60
1121	**1057**	68p. multicoloured	1·90	1·90
1116/21	*Set of 6*		6·75	7·00
First Day Cover				6·50
Presentation Pack			6·50	

Plate Nos.: All values 1A (×4).
Sheets: 10 (2×5) with enlarged illustrated margins at right and foot.
Imprint: Lower left-hand margin.
Withdrawn: 19.5.2007.
The 34p. and 42p. values include the 'EUROPA' emblem.

1058 Queen Elizabeth II

80th Birthday of Queen Elizabeth II

(Des P. Furness. Litho and embossed Cartor)

2006 (17 June). P 14½ (C).

1122	**1058**	£10 multicoloured	22·00	22·00
First Day Cover				24·00
Presentation Pack			24·00	
Souvenir Folder (No. 1122 & complete sheets of				
Nos. A274/81)			65·00	

Sheets: 5 (5×1).
Imprint: Top, right-hand margin.
No. 1122 was retained in use as a definitive stamp.

1059 Grey Seal

1060 Ormer

1061 Common Blenny

1062 Le Creux és Faies (Neolithic grave)

1063 Yellow Horned Poppy

1064 Oystercatcher

Designation of L'Erée Wetland as Ramsar Site

(Des Wendy Bramall. Litho Enschedé)

2006 (27 July). P 14×13½ (C).

1123	**1059**	29p. multicoloured	60	65
1124	**1060**	34p. multicoloured	70	75
1125	**1061**	42p. multicoloured	85	90
1126	**1062**	45p. multicoloured	1·00	95
1127	**1063**	47p. multicoloured	1·20	1·00
1128	**1064**	68p. multicoloured	1·50	1·50
1123/8	*Set of 6*		5·50	5·75
First Day Cover				6·50
Presentation Pack			6·50	
MS1129	140×95 mm. Nos. 1123/8		6·50	5·75
First Day Cover				6·50

Plate Nos.: All values 1A (×4).
Sheets: 10 (2×5) with enlarged illustrated margins at right and foot.
Imprint: Central, left-hand margin.
Withdrawn: 26.7.2007.

1065 A Partridge in a Pear Tree

1066 Two Turtle Doves

1067 Three French Hens

1068 Four Calling Birds

1069 Five Gold Rings

1070 Six Geese a-laying

1071 Seven Swans a-swimming

1072 Eight Maids a-milking

1073 Nine Ladies Dancing

1074 Ten Lords a-leaping

1075 Eleven Pipers Piping

1076 Twelve Drummers Drumming

Christmas. *'The Twelve Days of Christmas'* (carol)

(Des M. Wilkinson. Litho Austrian State Ptg Wks, Vienna)

2006 (2 Nov). P 15 (C).

1130	**1065**	22p. multicoloured	45	50
		a. Horiz strip of 6. Nos. 1130/5	2·50	
1131	**1066**	22p. multicoloured	45	50
1132	**1067**	22p. multicoloured	45	50
1133	**1068**	22p. multicoloured	45	50
1134	**1069**	22p. multicoloured	45	50
1135	**1070**	22p. multicoloured	45	50
1136	**1071**	29p. multicoloured	60	65
1137	**1072**	34p. multicoloured	70	75
1138	**1073**	42p. multicoloured	85	90
1139	**1074**	45p. multicoloured	90	95
1140	**1075**	47p. multicoloured	95	1·00
1141	**1076**	68p. multicoloured	1·40	1·50
1130/41	*Set of 12*		8·00	8·75
First Day Covers (2)				11·00
Presentation Pack			9·25	

Plate Nos.: All values 1A (×4).
Sheets: 22p. 60 (6×10); 29p. to 68p. 50 (10×5). The 22p. values were printed together, *se-tenant*, in horizontal strips of six.
Imprint: Upper side margins.
Withdrawn: 1.11.2007.

Yearbook 2006.

2006 (1 Dec). Comprises Nos. **MS**1096/141, A267/97 and A306/7 (price £49·31).

Yearbook £100

1077 Departure of Troops on *Queen Elizabeth 2*, Southampton

1078 Troops landing at San Carlos Bay

1079 Sea Harriers flying over SS *Canberra*

1080 Lt. Col. H. Jones firing Machine Gun

1081 Helicopter and H.M.S. *Invincible*

1082 Troops marching with Union Jack towards Port Stanley

25th Anniversary of the Battle for the Falklands

(Des R. Carter. Litho BDT)

2007 (8 Mar). P 13½ (C).

1142	**1077**	32p. multicoloured	75	75
1143	**1078**	37p. multicoloured	90	90
1144	**1079**	45p. multicoloured	1·10	1·10
1145	**1080**	48p. multicoloured	1·10	1·10
1146	**1081**	50p. multicoloured	1·20	1·50
1147	**1082**	71p. multicoloured	1·70	2·00
1142/7	*Set of 6*		6·75	7·00
First Day Cover				8·50
Presentation Pack			8·00	
MS1148 150×100 mm. Nos. 1142/7			6·75	7·00
First Day Cover				8·50

Plate Nos.: All values 1A (×4).
Sheets: 10 (2×5) with enlarged illustrated margins at right and foot.
Imprint: Central, left-hand margin.
Withdrawn: 7.3.2008.

1083 Rocks at Albecq

1084 Ivy Bee

1085 Vale Church

1086 Common Frog

1087 Parasol Mushroom

1088 Southern Marsh Orchid

1089 Shore Crab

1090 Alderney Blonde Hedgehog

1091 Barn Owl

1092 Le Trépied Dolmen

125th Anniversary of La Société Guernesiaise

(Des A. Wallace. Litho Cartor)

2007 (8 Mar). Self-adhesive. P 12½ (die-cut).

1149	**1083**	(32p.) multicoloured	80	80
		a. Sheetlet. Nos. 1149/58	8·00	
		b. Booklet pane with information panel. Nos. 1149/53, each×2	7·50	
		c. Booklet pane. Nos. 1149/53 each×2	7·50	
1150	**1084**	(32p.) multicoloured	80	80
1151	**1085**	(32p.) multicoloured	80	80
1152	**1086**	(32p.) multicoloured	80	80
1153	**1087**	(32p.) multicoloured	80	80
1154	**1088**	(37p.) multicoloured	80	80
		a. Booklet pane with information panel. Nos. 1154/8, each×2	8·75	
		b. Booklet pane. Nos. 1154/8, each×2	8·75	
1155	**1089**	(37p.) multicoloured	80	80
1156	**1090**	(37p.) multicoloured	80	80
1157	**1091**	(37p.) multicoloured	80	80
1158	**1092**	(37p.) multicoloured	80	80
1149/58 Set of 10			8·00	8·00
First Day Cover				9·00
Presentation Pack			9·00	

Nos. 1149/53 were intended for postage within the Bailiwick, are inscribed "GY" and sold for 32p. each. Nos. 1154/8 were intended for postage to Great Britain, are inscribed "UK" and sold for 37p. each.

Sheets: 10 (5×2). Nos. 1149/58 were printed in sheetlets of ten containing Nos. 1149/58 and in booklets of ten or 100, all with the surplus self-adhesive paper around each stamp retained. The booklets of ten contain either Nos. 1149/53×2 (pane No. 1149b) or Nos. 1154/8×2 (pane No. 1154a), and the stamps are peeled directly from the cover in two blocks 3×2 and 2×2, the blocks separated by a gutter containing text. The booklets of 100 contain ten panes of either Nos. 1149/53×2 (pane No. 1149c) or Nos. 1154/8×2 (pane No. 1154b). These panes have the stamps in one block 5×2, on plain white backing paper.

Loose single booklet panes of ten (1149c and 1154b) were also available from the Philatelic Bureau.

1093 Scouts camping, 1907

1094 Scout sailing, 1924

1095 Two Scouts fishing from Rocks, 1947

1096 Scouts making and flying Model Aircraft, 1968

1097 Scouts on Caving Expedition, 1990

1098 Scouts rollerblading, Cambridge Park, St. Peter Port, 2007

Europa. Centenary of Scouting

(Des Björn Von Schlippe. Litho Cartor)

2007 (24 May). P 13½ (C).

1159	**1093**	32p. multicoloured	75	75
1160	**1094**	37p. multicoloured	90	90
1161	**1095**	45p. multicoloured	1·10	1·10
1162	**1096**	48p. multicoloured	1·10	1·10
1163	**1097**	50p. multicoloured	1·50	1·20
1164	**1098**	71p. multicoloured	2·00	1·70
1159/64 Set of 6			7·00	6·75
First Day Cover				8·50
Presentation Pack			8·50	

Nos. 1160/1 include the Europa emblem.

Sheets: 10 (2×5) with enlarged illustrated margins at right and foot. Imprint: Central, left-hand margin.

Withdrawn: 23.5.2008.

1099 Mike Hawthorn, 1958

1100 Jackie Stewart, 1971

1101 Graham Hill, 1962

1102 James Hunt, 1976

1103 Jim Clark, 1963

1104 Nigel Mansell, 1992

1105 John Surtees, 1964

1106 Damon Hill, 1996

British Formula One World Champions (1st series)

(Des Chris Griffiths. Litho Austrian State Ptg Wks, Vienna)

2007 (24 May). P 14 (C).

1165	**1099**	32p. multicoloured	75	75
1166	**1100**	32p. multicoloured	75	75
1167	**1101**	37p. multicoloured	85	85
1168	**1102**	37p. multicoloured	85	85
1169	**1103**	45p. multicoloured	1·20	1·10
1170	**1104**	48p. multicoloured	1·50	1·10
1171	**1105**	50p. multicoloured	1·70	1·20
1172	**1106**	71p. multicoloured	2·50	1·70
1165/72 *Set of 8*			9·00	8·25
First Day Cover				10·00
Presentation Pack			10·50	

See also Nos. 1401/4.

Plate Nos.: All values 1A (×4).
Sheets: 10 (2×5) with enlarged illustrated margins at left and foot.
Imprint: Lower right-hand margin.
Withdrawn: 23.5.2008.

1107 Mountain Gorillas (*Illustration reduced. Actual size 118×84 mm*)

Endangered Species (4th series). Mountain Gorilla (*Gorilla beringei beringei*)

(Des Joel Kirk. Litho Austrian State Ptg Wks, Vienna)

2007 (2 Aug). Sheet 118×84 mm. P 14 (C).

MS1173 **1107** £2.50 multicoloured			7·00	7·00
First Day Cover				7·75
Presentation Pack			7·75	

Withdrawn: 1.8.2008.

1108 Engagement, 1947

1109 With Baby Princess Anne

1110 Off-duty

1111 On Tour

1112 With Princes William and Harry

1113 In Recent Years

Diamond Wedding of Queen Elizabeth II and Duke of Edinburgh

(Des Mark Whyte. Litho Enschedé)

2007 (2 Aug). P 13½×14 (C).

1174	**1108**	32p. multicoloured	75	75
		a. Booklet pane. Nos. 1174/5, each×2, with margins all round	3·25	
		b. Booklet pane. Nos. 1174 and 1179, each×2, with margins all round	5·00	
1175	**1109**	37p. multicoloured	90	90
		a. Booklet pane. Nos. 1175/6, each×2, with margins all round	4·00	
1176	**1110**	45p. multicoloured	1·10	1·10
		a. Booklet pane. Nos. 1176/7, each×2, with margins all round	4·50	
1177	**1111**	48p. multicoloured	1·10	1·10
		a. Booklet pane. Nos. 1177/8, each×2, with margins all round	4·50	

1178	**1112**	50p. multicoloured	1·20	1·50
		a. Booklet pane. Nos. 1178/9,		
		each×2, with margins all round ..	5·75	
1179	**1113**	71p. multicoloured	1·70	1·90
1174/9 Set of 6			6·75	7·00
First Day Cover				8·50
Presentation Pack			8·50	

Plate Nos.: All values 1A (×4).
Sheets: 10 (2×5) with enlarged illustrated margins at right and foot.
Imprint: Central, left-hand margin.
Withdrawn: 1.8.2008.

1114 St. Peter Port Harbour

1115 Fort Grey, Rocquaine Bay

1116 Point Robert Lighthouse, Sark

1117 Brecqhou seen from Sark

1118 Vazon Bay

1119 Fontenelle Bay

Sea Guernsey (2nd series) (Sepac)

(Litho Austrian State Ptg Wks, Vienna)

2007 (1 Oct)–**10**. P 14×13½ (C).

1180	**1114**	32p. multicoloured (a)	75	75
1181	**1115**	37p. multicoloured (a)	90	90
1182	**1116**	45p. multicoloured (a)	1·10	1·10
1183	**1117**	48p. multicoloured (a)	1·10	1·10
1184	**1118**	50p. multicoloured (a)	1·50	1·50
1184a	**1116**	55p. multicoloured (b)	1·50	1·50
1185	**1119**	71p. multicoloured (a)	2·00	1·90
1180/5 Set of 7			8·00	8·00
First Day Covers (2)				11·00
Presentation Pack (1180/4, 1185)			8·50	

The 45p. value includes the 'Sepac' emblem. This value was also available in a souvenir folder with ten other 'Sepac' logo stamps issued by other participating postal administrations, original selling price £10.75.
Nos. 1180/4 and 1185 have no imprint date.
No. 1184a has an imprint date of '2010'.
Printings: (a) 1.10.2007; (b) 18.6.2010.
Plate Nos.: All values 1A (×4).
Sheets: 50 (5×10).
Imprint: Upper side margins.
Withdrawn: 30.9.2008 (except 55p.).

1120 Crystal Angel   **1121** Crystal Decoration   **1122** Pine Cone

1123 Bauble   **1124** Snowflake   **1125** Decoration with Star

1126 Gold Bauble   **1127** Candles   **1128** Gold Bell

1129 Wrapped   **1130** Spiky Star   **1131** Fairy Present

Christmas. Decorations

(Litho Austrian State Ptg Wks, Vienna)

2007 (25 Oct). P 14½×15 (C).

1186	**1120**	27p. multicoloured	60	60
1187	**1121**	27p. multicoloured	60	60
1188	**1122**	27p. multicoloured	60	60
1189	**1123**	27p. multicoloured	60	60
1190	**1124**	27p. multicoloured	60	60
1191	**1125**	27p. multicoloured	60	60
1192	**1126**	32p. multicoloured	75	75
1193	**1127**	37p. multicoloured	90	90
1194	**1128**	45p. multicoloured	1·10	1·10
1195	**1129**	48p. multicoloured	1·10	1·10
1196	**1130**	50p. multicoloured	1·20	1·20
1197	**1131**	71p. multicoloured	1·70	1·70
1186/97 Set of 12			10·00	10·00
First Day Cover				11·50
Presentation Pack			11·50	

Plate Nos.: All values 1A (×4).
Sheets: 50 (10×5).
Imprint: Upper side margins.
Withdrawn: 24.10.2008.

Yearbook 2007

2007 (1 Dec). Comprises Nos. 1142/97, A298, A301, A304, A308 and A309/28 (price £47.32).

| Yearbook | | | | 85·00 |

1132 World Touring Car Championship, 2005; 2006; 2007 (*Illustration reduced. Actual size 140×95 mm*)

Andy Priaulx Triple World Touring Car Champion 2005–2007

(Des Chris Griffiths. Litho Walsall)

2008 (18 Jan). Sheet 140×95 mm. P 14×14½ (C).
MS1198 **1132** £1×3 multicoloured...................................... 7·00   7·50
First Day Cover...   8·75
Presentation Pack.. 8·75
    Withdrawn: 17.1.2009.

1133 Beadlet Anemones   **1134** Sand Crocus

1135 Fulmar   **1136** Sheep's-bit

1137 Thick-lipped Grey Mullet   **1138** Light Bulb Sea-Squirt

Designation of Gouliot Headland and Caves, Sark as RAMSAR Site

(Des Wendy Bramall. Litho BDT)

2008 (28 Feb). P 13½ (C).
1199	**1133**	34p. multicoloured	80	80
1200	**1134**	40p. multicoloured	95	95
1201	**1135**	48p. multicoloured	1·10	1·10
1202	**1136**	51p. multicoloured	1·20	1·20
1203	**1137**	53p. multicoloured	1·30	1·30
1204	**1138**	74p. multicoloured	1·70	1·70

1199/204 Set of 6... 7·00   7·00
First Day Cover ....   8·75
Presentation Pack.. 8·75
MS1205 140×95 mm. Nos. 1199/204....................... 7·00   7·00
First Day Cover ....   8·75
    Plate Nos.: All values 1A (×4).
    Sheets: 10 (2×5) with enlarged illustrated margins at right and foot.
    Imprint: Central, left-hand margin.
    Withdrawn: 27.2.2009.

Nos. 1206/10 are vacant.

1139 Red Campion   **1140** Great Bindweed   **1141** Spear Thistle

1142 Greater Bird's-foot Trefoil   **1143** Sheep's-bit

1144 Marguerite   **1145** Sea Campion

Raymond Evison's Wild Flora (1st series)

(Litho (£1, £2 also embossed) Austrian State Ptg Wks)

2008 (28 Feb). P 14 (C).
1211	**1139**	10p. multicoloured	25	25
1212	**1140**	20p. multicoloured	45	45
1213	**1141**	30p. multicoloured	70	70
1214	**1142**	40p. multicoloured	95	95
1215	**1143**	50p. multicoloured	1·20	1·20
1216	**1144**	£1 multicoloured	2·30	2·30
1217	**1145**	£2 multicoloured	4·75	4·75

1211/17 Set of 7... 10·50   10·50
First Day Cover ....   14·00
Presentation Pack.. 12·50
Set of 7 Gutter Pairs... 21·00
    See also Nos. 1274/83.
    Plate Nos.: All values 1A (×4).
    Sheets: 50 (2 panes 5×5).
    Imprint: Upper side margins.

Nos. 1218/19 and T **1146/52** are vacant.

1153 'À la perchôine' ('Till the next time')

1154 'Banjour' ('Hello')

1155 'Oh! Té v'là' ('Oh! There you are')

1156 'Mais oy-ous!' ('Good gracious!')

1157 'Cor chapin!' ('Gor blimey!')

1158 'L'affaire va-t-alle?'
('How are things?')

Europa. The Letter. Quotations in Guernsiasis (Guernsey French) and their English Translations

(Des Chris Griffiths. Litho Cartor)

2008 (15 May). P 13½×13 (C).

1220	**1153**	34p. multicoloured	80	80
1221	**1154**	40p. multicoloured	95	95
1222	**1155**	48p. multicoloured	1·10	1·10
1223	**1156**	51p. multicoloured	1·20	1·20
1224	**1157**	53p. multicoloured	1·30	1·30
1225	**1158**	74p. multicoloured	1·70	1·70
1220/5 Set of 6			7·00	7·00
First Day Cover				8·75
Presentation Pack			8·75	

The new blue plate number/colour dab on the sheet margin of the 40p. value is invisible because of the matching background colour.
The 40p. and 48p. values include the 'EUROPA' emblem.
Plate Nos.: All values 1A (×4).
Sheets: 10 (2×5) with enlarged illustrated left margins.
Imprint: Upper right-hand margin.
Withdrawn: 14.5.2009.

1159 Mr. Happy

1160 Mr. Bump

1161 Little Miss Naughty

1162 Mr. Greedy

1163 Mr. Strong

1164 Mr. Tickle

Mr. Men and Little Miss Series of Children's Books by Roger Hargreaves

(Des Andrew Fothergill. Litho Enschedé)

2008 (15 May). P 14×13½ (C).

1226	**1159**	34p. Type **242**	80	80
1227	**1160**	40p. Mr. Bump	95	95
1228	**1161**	48p. Little Miss Naughty	1·10	1·10
1229	**1162**	51p. Mr. Greedy	1·20	1·20
1230	**1163**	53p. Mr. Strong	1·30	1·30
1231	**1164**	74p. Mr. Tickle	1·70	1·70
1226/31 Set of 6			7·00	7·00

First Day Cover		8·75
Presentation Pack	8·75	

Plate Nos.: All values 1A (×4).
Sheets: 10 (2×5) with enlarged illustrated margins at left and foot.
Imprint: Lower right-hand margin.
Withdrawn: 14.5.2009.

1165 Pleimont Point

1166 Saint's Harbour

1167 Rocks at Albecq

1168 Groynes at Vazon Bay

1169 La Bette Bay

1170 Bordeaux Harbour

1171 St. Saviour's Reservoir

1172 Vazon Bay

1173 St. Peter Port Lighthouse

1174 Petit Port

'Abstract Guernsey' (1st series). Photographs of Guernsey Coastline

(Litho Walsall)

2008 (9 June). Self-adhesive. P 12½ (die-cut).

1232	**1165**	(34p.) multicoloured	80	80
		a. Sheetlet of 10. Nos. 1232/41	8·75	
		b. Booklet pane with information pane. Nos. 1232/6, each×2	9·00	
		c. Booklet pane. Nos. 1232/6, each×2	9·00	
1233	**1166**	(34p.) multicoloured	80	80
1234	**1167**	(34p.) multicoloured	80	80
1235	**1168**	(34p.) multicoloured	80	80
1236	**1169**	(34p.) multicoloured	80	80
1237	**1170**	(40p.) multicoloured	95	95
		a. Booklet pane with information pane. Nos. 1237/41, each×2	11·00	
		b. Booklet pane. Nos. 1237/41, each×2	11·00	
1238	**1171**	(40p.) multicoloured	95	95
1239	**1172**	(40p.) multicoloured	95	95
1240	**1173**	(40p.) multicoloured	95	95
1241	**1174**	(40p.) multicoloured	95	95
1232/41 Set of 10			8·75	8·75
First Day Cover				10·50
Presentation Pack			10·50	

See also No.s 1321/32.
Nos. 1232/6 were intended for postage within the Bailiwick and are inscribed 'GY'. They were each initially sold at 34p. Nos. 1237/41 were intended for postage to Great Britain and are inscribed 'UK'. They were each initially sold at 40p.
Stamps from the sheetlet 1232a measure 12.4 all round, but stamps from booklet panes have a slightly different perforation, 12.4×12.7.
Sheets: (5×2) were printed in sheetlets of ten containing Nos. 1232/41 (available only from the Philatelic Bureau) and also in booklets of ten or 100, all with the surplus self-adhesive paper around each stamp retained. The booklets of ten contain either Nos. 1232/6 (pane no. 1232b) or Nos. 1237/41 (pane No. 1237a), and the stamps are peeled directly from the cover in two blocks 3×2 and 2×2, the blocks separated by a gutter containing text. The booklets of 100 contain ten panes of either Nos. 1232/6×2 (pane No. 1232c) or 1237/41×2 (pane No. 1237b). These panes have the stamps in one block 5×2, with plain white backing paper and are stitched at left.
Loose single booklet panes of ten (1232c and 1237b) were also available from the Philatelic Bureau.

1175 Ford Model T Touring Car, 1913

1176 Delivery Van, 1912

1177 Pick-up, 1925

1178 Couplet, 1917

1179 First World War Army Ambulance

1180 Roadster, 1912

Centenary of the Model T Ford

(Des Robin Carter. Litho BDT)

2008 (31 July). P 13½ (C).

1242	**1175**	34p. multicoloured	80	80
		a. Booklet pane. Nos. 1242/5 with margins all round	4·00	
		b. Booklet pane. Nos. 1242/3 and 1246/7 with margins all round	4·75	
		c. Booklet pane. Nos. 1242, 1244/5 and 1247 with margins all round	4·75	
		d. Booklet pane. Nos. 1242/3 and 1245/6 with margins all round	4·25	
1243	**1176**	40p. multicoloured	95	95
		a. Booklet pane. Nos. 1243/4 and 1246/7 with margins all round	5·00	
1244	**1177**	48p. multicoloured	1·10	1·10
		a. Booklet pane. Nos. 1244/7 with margins all round	5·25	
1245	**1178**	51p. multicoloured	1·20	1·20
1246	**1179**	53p. multicoloured	1·30	1·30
1247	**1180**	74p. multicoloured	1·70	1·70
1242/7 *Set of 6*			7·00	7·00
First Day Cover				8·75
Presentation Pack			8·75	

Plate Nos.: All values 1A (×4).
Sheets: 10 (2×5) with enlarged illustrated margins at right and foot.
Imprint: Central, left-hand margin.
Withdrawn: 30.7.2009.

1181 Early Drawing of St. Paul's Cathedral

1182 Cathedral and River Thames, 1860s

1183 Cathedral during World War II Blitz

1184 Cathedral illuminated at Night

1185 Close-up of St. Paul's Cathedral

1186 Cathedral seen from Millennium Bridge

Guernsey Granite at St. Paul's Cathedral, London

(Des Mark Whyte. Litho Cartor)

2008 (31 Oct). P 13½ (C).

1248	**1181**	34p. multicoloured	80	80
1249	**1182**	40p. multicoloured	95	95
1250	**1183**	48p. multicoloured	1·10	1·10
1251	**1184**	51p. multicoloured	1·20	1·20
1252	**1185**	53p. multicoloured	1·30	1·30
1253	**1186**	74p. multicoloured	1·70	1·70
1248/53 *Set of 6*			7·00	7·00
First Day Cover				8·75
Presentation Pack			8·75	

Nos. 1248/53 commemorate the 300th anniversary of St. Paul's Cathedral.
They all have powdered Guernsey granite applied to the value tablets.
Plate Nos.: All values 1A (×4).
Sheets: 25 (5×5).
Imprint: Upper left margin.
Withdrawn: 29.10.2009.

1187 Spruce

1188 Christmas Cactus

1189 Ivy

1190 Cyclamen

1191 Mistletoe

1192 Butchers Broom

1193 Holly

1194 Poinsettia

1195 Bracken

1196 Hawthorn

1197 Clematis 'Peppermint'

1198 Pyracantha

Christmas. Festive Foliage

(Des Andrew Fothergill. Litho Enschedé)

2008 (31 Oct). P 14×13½ (C).

1254	**1187**	29p. multicoloured	70	70
1255	**1188**	29p. multicoloured	70	70
1256	**1189**	29p. multicoloured	70	70
1257	**1190**	29p. multicoloured	70	70
1258	**1191**	29p. multicoloured	70	70
1259	**1192**	29p. multicoloured	70	70
1260	**1193**	34p. multicoloured	80	80
1261	**1194**	40p. multicoloured	95	95
1262	**1195**	48p. multicoloured	1·10	1·10
1263	**1196**	51p. multicoloured	1·20	1·20
1264	**1197**	53p. multicoloured	1·20	1·20
1265	**1198**	74p. multicoloured	1·70	1·70
1254/65 *Set of 12*			11·00	11·00
First Day Cover				14·50
Presentation Pack			13·00	

Plate Nos.: All value 1A (×4).
Sheets: 50 (10×5).
Imprint: Upper side margins.
Withdrawn: 29.10.2009.

Yearbook 2008

2008 (1 Dec). Comprises Nos. 1199/265 and A329/55 (price £56.94).
Yearbook £110

1199 Amur Leopard (*Illustration reduced. Actual size 116×84 mm*)

Endangered Species (5th series). Amur Leopard (*Panthera pardus orientalis*)

(Des Joel Kirk. Litho Enschedé)

2009 (26 Feb). Sheet 116×84 mm. P 13½×14 (C).

MS1266 **1199** £3 multicoloured			8·50	8·50
First Day Cover				8·75
Presentation Pack			8·75	

Withdrawn: 27.2.2010.

1200 Land Iguana

1201 Wallaby

1202 Giant Tortoise

1203 Marine Iguana

1204 Guanaco

1205 Komodo Dragon

'Darwin's Discoveries'

(Des Andrew Fothergill. Litho Austrian State Ptg Wks, Vienna)

2009 (26 Feb). P 14 (C).

1267	**1200**	36p. multicoloured	85	85
1268	**1201**	43p. multicoloured	1·00	1·00
1269	**1202**	51p. multicoloured	1·25	1·25
1270	**1203**	54p. multicoloured	1·25	1·25
1271	**1204**	56p. multicoloured	1·25	1·25
1272	**1205**	77p. multicoloured	1·75	1·75
1267/72 *Set of 6*			7·25	7·25
First Day Cover				9·25
Presentation Pack			9·25	
MS1273 144×80 mm. Nos. 1267/72			7·50	7·50
First Day Cover				9·25

Nos. 1267/72 commemorate the birth bicentenary of Charles Darwin.

Plate Nos.: All values 1A (×4).
Sheets: 10 (2×5) with enlarged illustrated left margins.
Imprint: Lower right-hand margin.
Withdrawn: 27.2.2010.

1206 Stinking Onion

1207 Common Mallow

1208 Primrose

1209 Loose-flowered Orchid

1210 Common Centaury

1211 Yellow Horned-poppy

1212 Sea Kale

1213 Bluebell

1214 Sea Bindweed

1215 Common Poppy

Raymond Evison's Wild Flora (2nd series)

(Des Raymond Evison. Litho (£3 also embossed) Cartor)

2009 (28 May). P 13½ (C).

1274	**1206**	1p. multicoloured	10	10
1275	**1207**	2p. multicoloured	10	10
1276	**1208**	3p. multicoloured	10	10
1277	**1209**	4p. multicoloured	10	10
1278	**1210**	5p. multicoloured	10	10

1279	**1211**	6p. multicoloured	15	15
1280	**1212**	7p. multicoloured	20	20
1281	**1213**	8p. multicoloured	25	25
1282	**1214**	9p. multicoloured	25	25
1283	**1215**	£3 multicoloured	8·50	8·50

1274/83 *Set of 10*.. 8·50   8·50
First Day Cover.. 9·75
Presentation Pack.. 9·75

    Plate Nos.: All values 1A (each×4).
    Sheets: 50 1p. to 9p. (5×10) £3 (10×5).

1216 Quasar (digital enhancement)

1217 Asteroid (digital enhancement)

1218 Satellite View of Sunrays falling on the Earth's Surface

1219 Jupiter, Sun in Background (digital composite)

1220 The Moon touches the Sun before a Total Eclipse

1221 Solar Eruption from the Sun (satellite image)

Europa. Astronomy. 400th Anniversary of the Telescope

              (Des Mark Totty. Litho Enschedé)

2009 (28 May). P 13 (C).

1284	**1216**	36p. multicoloured	85	85
1285	**1217**	43p. multicoloured	1·00	1·00
1286	**1218**	51p. multicoloured	1·25	1·25
1287	**1219**	54p. multicoloured	1·25	1·25
1288	**1220**	56p. multicoloured	1·40	1·40
1289	**1221**	77p. multicoloured	1·75	1·75

1283/8 *Set of 6*.. 7·25   7·25
First Day Cover.. 9·00
Presentation Pack.. 9·00

    The 43p. and 51p. values include the 'EUROPA' emblem.
    Plate Nos.: All values 1A (each×4).
    Sheets: 10 (2×5) with enlarged illustrated right margins.
    Imprint: Central, left-hand margin.
    Withdrawn: 27.5.2010.

1222 Henry VIII as Young Man

1223 Coronation of Henry VIII and Katherine of Aragon, 1509

1224 Meeting of Henry VIII and Francis I, Field of the Cloth of Gold, 1520

1225 Thomas Wolsey presenting Hampton Court Palace to Henry VIII

1226 Henry VIII dancing with Anne Boleyn

1227 Henry VIII watching his Navy as *Mary Rose* sinks, 1545

500th Anniversary of the Coronation of King Henry VIII

              (Des Gail Armstrong. Litho BDT)

2009 (30 July). P 13 (C).

1290	**1222**	36p. multicoloured	85	85
		a. Booklet pane. No. 1290×4 with margins all round	3·25	
1291	**1223**	43p. multicoloured	1·00	1·00
		a. Booklet pane. No. 1291×4 with margins all round	4·00	
1292	**1224**	51p. multicoloured	1·25	1·25
		a. Booklet pane. No. 1292×4 with margins all round	4·75	
1293	**1225**	54p. multicoloured	1·25	1·25
		a. Booklet pane. No. 1293×4 with margins all round	5·00	
1294	**1226**	56p. multicoloured	1·40	1·40
		a. Booklet pane. No. 1294×4 with margins all round	5·00	
1295	**1227**	77p. multicoloured	1·75	1·75
		a. Booklet pane. No. 1295×4 with margins all round	7·00	

1290/5 *Set of 6*.. 7·25   7·25
First Day Cover.. 9·00
Presentation Pack.. 9·00

    Plate Nos.: All values 1A (×4).
    Sheets: 10 (2×5) with enlarged illustrated right margins.
    Imprint: Central, left-hand margin.
    Withdrawn: 29.7.2010.

1228 'The Psychedelic 60's'

1229 'God Save the 70's'

1230 'The POPular 80's'

1231 'The Urban 90's'

1232 'The Seductive 00's'

1233 'Looking to the Future'

40th Anniversary of Postal Independence

(Des Paul Mason-Barney. Litho Cartor)

2009 (30 July). P 14×13½ (C).

1296	**1228**	36p. multicoloured	85	85
1297	**1229**	43p. multicoloured	1·00	1·00
1298	**1230**	51p. multicoloured	1·25	1·25
1299	**1231**	54p. multicoloured	1·25	1·25
1300	**1232**	56p. multicoloured	1·40	1·40
1301	**1233**	77p. multicoloured	1·75	1·75
1296/301 Set of 6			7·25	7·25
First Day Cover				9·00
Presentation Pack			9·00	

Plate Nos.: All values 1A (each×4).
Sheets: 10 (5×2).
Imprint: Central, top margin.
Withdrawn: 29.7.2010.

1234 Jerbourg Point

1235 Vazon Bay

1236 Saints Bay Moorings

1237 Le Jaonnet Bay

1238 Rocquaine Bay

1239 Bordeaux Harbour

Sea Guernsey (3rd series) (Sepac)

(Litho Enschedé)

2009 (16 Sept). P 13½ (C).

1302	**1234**	36p. multicoloured	85	85
1303	**1235**	43p. multicoloured	1·00	1·00
1304	**1236**	51p. multicoloured	1·25	1·25
1305	**1237**	54p. multicoloured	1·25	1·25
1306	**1238**	56p. multicoloured	1·40	1·40
1307	**1239**	77p. multicoloured	1·75	1·75
1302/7 Set of 6			7·25	7·25
First Day Cover				9·00
Presentation Pack			9·00	

The 51p. value includes the 'Sepac' emblem. This value was available in a souvenir folder with 12 other 'Sepac' logo stamps issued by other participating postal administrations, original selling price £14.75.
Plate Nos.: All values 1A (×4).
Sheets: 50 (5×10).
Imprint: Upper side margins.
Withdrawn: 15.9.2010.

1240 Castel Church

1241 Torteval Church

1242 St. Martin's Church

1243 St. John's Church

1244 St. Sampson's Church

1245 St. Peter Port Church

1246 St. Mathew's Church

1247 St. Saviour's Church

1248 Forest Church

1249 St. Andrew's Church

1250 Vale Church

1251 St. Peter's Church

Christmas. Churches

(Litho BDT)

2009 (29 Oct). P 13½ (C).

1308	**1240**	31p. multicoloured	75	75
1309	**1241**	31p. multicoloured	75	75
1310	**1242**	31p. multicoloured	75	75
1311	**1243**	31p. multicoloured	75	75
1312	**1244**	31p. multicoloured	75	75
1313	**1245**	31p. multicoloured	75	75

1314	**1246**	36p. multicoloured	85	85
1315	**1247**	43p. multicoloured	1·00	1·00
1316	**1248**	51p. multicoloured	1·25	1·25
1317	**1249**	54p. multicoloured	1·25	1·25
1318	**1250**	56p. multicoloured	1·40	1·40
1319	**1251**	77p. multicoloured	1·75	1·75
1308/19 Set of 12			11·50	11·50
First Day Covers (2)				15·00
Presentation Pack			13·50	

Plate Nos.: All values 1A (×4).
Sheets: 50 (5×10).
Imprint: Central, bottom margin.
Withdrawn: 28.10.2010.

Yearbook 2009

2009 (1 Dec). Comprises Nos. **MS**1266/319 *and* A356/80 (price £46.35).
Yearbook .... 90·00

1252 Asian Elephant (*Illustration reduced. Actual size 118×84 mm*)

Endangered Species (6th series). Asian Elephant (*Elephas maximus*)

(Des Joel Kirk. Litho Austrian State Ptg Wks, Vienna)

2010 (25 Feb). Sheet 118×84 mm. P 14 (C).

MS1320	**1252**	£3.07 multicoloured	7·25	7·25
First Day Cover				9·00
Presentation Pack			9·00	

Withdrawn: 24.2.2011.

1253 Port à la Jument, Sark

1254 The Dog and Lion Rocks

1255 Fort Grey

1256 Sunset on West Coast of Guernsey

1257 Slipway at Havelet Bay at Sunrise

1258 Castle Cornet

Abstract Guernsey (2nd series). Photographs of Guernsey Coastline

(Litho Cartor)

2010 (18 Mar).

(a) Ordinary gum. P 13 (C)

1321	**1253**	(48p.) multicoloured		1·10	1·10
		a. Pair. Nos. 1321/2		2·25	2·25
1322	**1254**	(48p.) multicoloured		1·10	1·10
1323	**1255**	(50p.) multicoloured		1·25	1·25
1324	**1256**	(58p.) multicoloured		1·40	1·40
		a. Pair. Nos. 1324/5		2·75	2·75
1325	**1257**	(58p.) multicoloured		1·40	1·40
1326	**1258**	(80p.) multicoloured		1·90	1·90
1321/6 Set of 6				8·00	8·00
First Day Cover					10·00

(b) Self-adhesive. P 12½ (die-cut)

1327	**1253**	(48p.) multicoloured		1·10	1·10
		a. Sheetlet of 6. Nos. 1327/32		8·00	
		b. Booklet pane. Nos. 1327/8, each×2		4·50	
		c. Booklet pane. Nos. 1327/8, each×5		10·00	
1328	**1254**	(48p.) multicoloured		1·10	1·10
1329	**1255**	(50p.) multicoloured		1·25	1·25
1330	**1256**	(58p.) multicoloured		1·40	1·40
		a. Booklet pane. Nos. 1330/1, each×2		5·50	
		b. Booklet pane. Nos. 1330/1, each×5		12·00	
1331	**1257**	(58p.) multicoloured		1·40	1·40
1332	**1258**	(80p.) multicoloured		1·90	1·90
1327/32 Set of 6				8·00	8·00
First Day Cover					10·00
Presentation Pack (1321/32)				17·00	

Nos. 1321/2 and 1327/8 were intended for postage within the Bailiwick and are inscribed 'GY LARGE'. They were each initially sold at 48p.

Nos. 1324/5 and 1330/1 were intended for postage to Great Britain and are inscribed 'UK LARGE'. They were each initially sold at 58p.

Loose single booklet panes of ten (1327c and 1330b) were also available from the Philatelic Bureau.

Nos. 1323 and 1329 for postage to Europe are inscribed 'EUR' and were initially sold at 50p. each.

Nos. 1326 and 1332 for postage to rest of world are inscribed 'ROW' and were initially sold at 80p. each.

For operational reasons this set was charged at the new rates which did not change officially until 1 April 2010.

Nos. 1327/32 were printed together in sheetlets of six (3×2). Nos. 1327/8 and 1330/1 were also available from booklets of four, Nos. SB91/2, originally sold at £1.92 and £2.32, and booklets of 50, Nos. SB93/4, originally sold at £24 and £29.

Plate Nos.: All values 1A (each×4).
Sheets: 20 (5×4). Nos. 1321/2 and 1324/5 (the GY LARGE and UK LARGE values) were each printed together, *se-tenant*, in vertical pairs throughout the sheets.
Imprint: Top margin at left.

1259 Penny the Postie and Pirate Captain Titch in Boat made from Wooden Chest

1260 Captain Titch spies enemy Captain Bullybones

1261 Captain Titch reclaiming his Stolen Ship

Europa. Children's Books. *The Adventures of Penny the Postie* by Keith Robinson

(Des Keith Robinson. Litho BDT)

2010 (4 May). P 13 (45p.) or 14 (50p., £2) (both comb).

1333	**1259**	45p multicoloured		1·00	1·00
1334	**1260**	50p multicoloured		1·25	1·25
1335	**1261**	£2 multicoloured		4·50	4·50
1333/5 Set of 3				6·75	6·75
First Day Cover					9·50
Presentation Pack				8·50	
Souvenir Book				10·00	
MS1336 149×96 mm. Nos. 1333/5				6·75	6·75
First Day Cover					9.50

No. **MS**1336 is cut around in the shape of a scroll.
In addition to the Presentation Pack a souvenir book containing **MS**1336 was issued (price £4.95).
Nos. 1333/4 include the Europa emblem.
Plate Nos.: All values 1A (each×4).
Sheets: 10 (5×2).
Imprint: Top margin at left.
Withdrawn: 3.5.2011.

1262 Guide kayaking ('Outdoor Activities')

1263 Spitfire crossing Searchlights ('Help during WW1&2')

1264 Crystal Palace Maze (renovated to celebrate Centenary)

1265 Agnes Baden-Powell (founder) wearing First Guide Uniform

1266 Mount Everest (Guide trek to base camp, 2009)

1267 Queen's Guide Award

Centenary of Girl Guiding. Embroidered Badges

(Des Paul Mason-Barney. Litho Enschedé)

2010 (27 May). P 13½ (C).

1337	**1262**	36p multicoloured		80	80
1338	**1263**	45p multicoloured		1·00	1·00
1339	**1264**	48p multicoloured		1·10	1·10
1340	**1265**	50p multicoloured		1·25	1·25
1341	**1266**	58p multicoloured		1·40	1·40
1342	**1267**	80p multicoloured		1·75	1·75
1337/42 Set of 6				7·25	7·25
First Day Cover					10·00
Presentation Pack				17·00	

Plate Nos.: All values 1A (each×4).
Sheets: 10 (5×2).
Imprint: Top margin at left.
Withdrawn: 26.5.2011.

1268 26 Cornet Street, St. Peter Port

1269 Field of Daffodils at Jerbourg

1270 Martello Tower at Fermain Bay, St. Peter Port

1271 Ivy Gates, La Rohais, St. Peter Port

1272 Pleinmont Headland

1273 La Moulin de Quanteraine

50th Anniv of the National Trust for Guernsey

(Des Andrew Robinson. Litho Enschedé)

2010 (5 July). P 13½ (C).

1343	**1268**	36p. multicoloured	80	80
1344	**1269**	45p. multicoloured	1·00	1·00
1345	**1270**	48p. multicoloured	1·10	1·10
1346	**1271**	50p. multicoloured	1·25	1·25
1347	**1272**	58p. multicoloured	1·40	1·40
1348	**1273**	80p. multicoloured	1·75	1·75
1343/8 *Set of 6*			7·25	
First Day Cover				10·00
Presentation Pack			9·00	

Plate Nos.: All values 1A (each×4).
Sheets: 10 (2×5) with enlarged illustrated margins at right.
Imprint: Central, left-hand margins.
Withdrawn: 4.7.2011.

1274 Loading Gas Masks onto Truck, 1939

1275 Guernsey Children waiting to Leave, 1940

1276 German Soldiers leaving Guernsey, 1945

1277 Evacuees returning to Guernsey, 1945

1278 Queen Elizabeth with Guernsey Children, June 1945

1279 Liberation Day, 1946

70th Anniv of the Guernsey Evacuation

(Des Mark Totty. Litho BDT)

2010 (29 July). P 13½ (C).

1349	**1274**	36p. multicoloured	80	80
1350	**1275**	45p. multicoloured	1·00	1·00
1351	**1276**	48p. multicoloured	1·10	1·10
1352	**1277**	50p. multicoloured	1·25	1·25
1353	**1278**	58p. multicoloured	1·40	1·40
1354	**1279**	80p. multicoloured	1·75	1·75
1349/54 *Set of 6*			7·25	7·25
First Day Cover				10·00
Presentation Pack			9·00	

Plate Nos.: All values 1A (each×4).
Sheets: 10 (2×5) with enlarged illustrated margins at right and foot.
Imprint: Central, left-hand margins.
Withdrawn: 28.7.2011.

1280 Tennis

1281 Bowls

1282 Shooting

1283 Swimming

1284 Athletics

1285 Cycling

29th Commonwealth Games, Delhi, India

(Des Andrew Robinson. Litho BDT)

2010 (23 Sept). P 13½ (C).

1355	**1280**	36p. multicoloured	80	80
		a. Booklet pane. Nos. 1355×4 with		
		margins all round	3·25	
1356	**1281**	45p. multicoloured	1·00	1·00
		a. Booklet pane. Nos. 1356×4 with		
		margins all round	4·25	
1357	**1282**	48p. multicoloured	1·10	1·10
		a. Booklet pane. Nos. 1357×4 with		
		margins all round	4·50	
1358	**1283**	50p. multicoloured	1·25	1·25
		a. Booklet pane. Nos. 1358×4 with		
		margins all round	4·50	
1359	**1284**	58p. multicoloured	1·40	1·40
		a. Booklet pane. Nos. 1359×4 with		
		margins all round	5·25	
1360	**1285**	80p. multicoloured	1·75	1·75
		a. Booklet pane. Nos. 1360×4 with		
		margins all round	7·25	
1355/60 *Set of 6*			7·25	7·25
First Day Cover				10·00
Presentation Pack			9·00	

Nos. 1355/60 commemorate the 40th anniv of Guernsey's participation in the Commonwealth Games.

They were issued in separate sheetlets of ten stamps (2×5) with enlarged illustrated margins.

Plate Nos.: All values 1A (each×4).
Sheets: 10 (2×5) with enlarged illustrated margins at right and foot.
Imprint: Lower left-hand margins.
Withdrawn: 23.9.2011.

1286 'The Holly and the Ivy'

1287 'Little Donkey'

1288 'Silent Night'

1289 'I Saw Three Ships'

1290 'Joy to the World'

1291 'Ding Dong Merrily on High'

1292 'We Three Kings'

Christmas Carols

(Des Two Degrees North. Litho Enschedé)

2010 (4 Nov). P 13½×14 (C).

1361	**1286**	31p. multicoloured	75	75
1362	**1287**	36p. multicoloured	80	80
1363	**1288**	45p. multicoloured	1·00	1·00
1364	**1289**	48p. multicoloured	1·10	1·10
1365	**1290**	50p. multicoloured	1·25	1·25
1366	**1291**	58p. multicoloured	1·40	1·40
1367	**1292**	80p. multicoloured	1·75	1·75
1361/6 *Set of 7*			8·00	8·00
First Day Cover				10·50
Presentation Pack			9·75	

Plate Nos.: All values 1A (each×4).
Sheets: 50 (10×5).
Imprint: Central, bottom margin.
Withdrawn: 4.11.2011.

Yearbook 2010

2010 (1 Dec). Comprises Nos. 1184a, **MS**1320/67, A346a and A381/414 (price £58.28).

Yearbook		£115

1293 Blue Whale (*Illustration reduced. Actual size 118×83 mm*)

Endangered Species. (7th series) Blue Whale (*Balaenoptera musculus*)

(Des Joel Kirk. Litho Southern Colour Print, New Zealand)

2011 (23 Feb). Sheet 118×83 mm. P 13 (C).

MS1368 **1293**	£3 multicoloured		7·00	7·00
First Day Cover				9·00
Presentation Pack			9·00	

Withdrawn: 23.2.2012.

1294 Air Raid Precautions Messenger Boy and Boy Evacuee ('Hope')

1295 Royal Navy Veteran Christopher Walsh ('Reflection')

1296 World War II Soldiers ('Comradeship')

1297 Soldier of 12th Battalion, Hampshire Regiment, training in a Smoke Screen ('Selflessness')

1298 Nurse Joyce Collier and Navy Commando ('Service')

1299 Soldier receiving Medal ('Dedication')

90th Anniv of the Royal British Legion

(Des Two Degrees North. Litho Cartor)

2011 (23 Feb). P 13½×13 (C).

1369	**1294**	36p. multicoloured	80	80
1370	**1295**	45p. multicoloured	1·00	1·00
1371	**1296**	52p. multicoloured	1·10	1·10
1372	**1297**	58p. multicoloured	1·25	1·25
1373	**1298**	65p. multicoloured	1·25	1·25
1374	**1299**	70p. multicoloured	1·60	1·60
1369/74 Set of 6			7·00	
First Day Cover				10·00
Presentation Pack			9·50	
MS1375 140×100 mm. Nos. 1369/74			7·00	7·00
First Day Cover				10·00

Plate Nos.: All values 1A (each×4).
Sheets: 10 (2×5) with enlarged illustrated right-hand margins.
Imprint: Top left margin.
Withdrawn: 23.2.2012.

1300 Acorns and Oak Leaves

1301 Hazelnuts and Hazel Leaves

1302 Conker and Horse Chestnut Leaves

Europa. Forests

(Des Keith Robinson. Litho and spot varnish Enschedé)

2011 (4 May). P 13½ (C).

1376	**1300**	45p. multicoloured	1·10	1·10
1377	**1301**	52p. multicoloured	1·50	1·50
1378	**1302**	£2 multicoloured	4·75	4·75
1376/8 Set of 3			7·25	
First Day Cover				10·00
Presentation Pack			9·25	
MS1379 133×85 mm. Nos. 1376/8			7·25	7·25
First Day Cover				10·00

No. MS1379 is cut around in the shape of a pile of leaves.
Plate Nos.: All values 1A (each×4).
Sheets: 10 (5×2) with enlarged illustrated lower margins.
Imprint: Top left margin.
Withdrawn: 3.5.2012.
The 45p. and 52p. values include the 'EUROPA' emblem.

1303 Engagement of Prince William to Miss Catherine Middleton, 16 November 2010

1304 Wedding of Prince William and Miss Catherine Middleton

Royal Wedding

(Des The Potting Shed. Litho Southern Colour Print, New Zealand)

2011 (2 June). Two sheets, each 110×55 mm. P 14 (C).

MS1380	**1303**	£2 multicoloured	4·75	4·75
MS1381	**1304**	£2 multicoloured	4·75	4·75
First Day Covers (2)				15·00
Presentation Pack			12·50	

Withdrawn: 2.6.2012.

1305 How to Roast your Pig

1306 Literary Society Bookshelf

1307 Arrival of Juliet Ashton at St. Peter Port wearing Red Cloak

1308 View through Elizabeth McKenna's Cottage Window

1309 Juliet Ashton and Dawsey Adams looking over Moonlit Sea

1310 Isola Pribby's Parrot Zenobia

The Guernsey Literary and Potato Peel Pie Society
(book by Mary Ann Shaffer and Annie Barrows)

(Des Charlotte Burns. Litho BDT)

2011 (28 July). P 13 (C).

1382	**1305**	36p. multicoloured	85	85
1383	**1306**	47p. multicoloured	1·10	1·10
1384	**1307**	48p. multicoloured	1·25	1·25
1385	**1308**	52p. multicoloured	1·25	1·25
1386	**1309**	61p. multicoloured	1·50	1·50
1387	**1310**	65p. multicoloured	1·60	1·60
1382/7 *Set of 6*			7·50	7·50
First Day Cover				10·50
Presentation Pack			9·50	

Plate Nos.: All values 1A (each×4).
Sheets: 10 (5×2) with enlarged inscribed lower margins.
Imprint: Top left margins.
Withdrawn: 27.7.2012.

1311 Victoria Marina, St. Peter Port

1312 L'Ancresse Bay

1313 Bordeaux Harbour Slipway

1314 South Coast Sunset

1315 Salerie Harbour

1316 Petit Port

Sea Guernsey (4th series) (Sepac)

(Litho Southern Colour Print, New Zealand)

2011 (28 Sept). P 14 (C).

1388	**1311**	36p. multicoloured	90	90
1389	**1312**	45p. multicoloured	1·10	1·10
1390	**1313**	52p. multicoloured	1·25	1·25
1391	**1314**	58p. multicoloured	1·40	1·40
1392	**1315**	65p. multicoloured	1·60	1·60
1393	**1316**	70p. multicoloured	1·75	1·75
1388/93 *Set of 6*			8·00	8·00
First Day Cover				10·50
Presentation Pack			10·00	

The 52p. value includes the 'Sepac' emblem. This value was available in a souvenir folder with 13 other 'Sepac' logo stamps issued by other participating postal administrations, original selling price £14.68.

Plate Nos.: All values 1A (each×4).
Sheets: 50 (5×10).
Imprint: Upper right-hand margins.
Withdrawn: 27.9.2011.

1317 Forest Church (John Shakerley)   **1318** L'Ancresse Common (Nigel Byrom)

1319 Guernsey Cows (Sarah Plumley)   **1320** St. Peter Port (Karen Millard)

1321 La Coupée, Sark (Sue Daly)   **1322** St. Peter's Church (Jason Bishop)

1323 Cobo (Eric Ferbrache)

Christmas. 'Winter Wonderland'. Winning Entries from Photography Competition

(Des The Potting Shed. Litho Southern Colour Print, New Zealand)

2011 (27 Oct). P 13½×13 (C).

1394	**1317**	31p. multicoloured	80	80
1395	**1318**	36p. multicoloured	90	90
1396	**1319**	47p. multicoloured	1·10	1·10
1397	**1320**	48p. multicoloured	1·10	1·10
1398	**1321**	52p. multicoloured	1·25	1·25
1399	**1322**	61p. multicoloured	1·50	1·50
1400	**1323**	65p. multicoloured	1·60	1·60
1394/400 *Set of 7*			8·00	8·00
First Day Cover				10·50
Presentation Pack			10·00	

Plate Nos.: All values 1A (each×5).
Sheets: 50 (5×10).
Imprint: Upper side margin.
Withdrawn: 26.10.2012.

1374 Male Cuckoo Wrasse

1375 John Dory

1376 Black-face Blenny Marine Life (*Illustration reduced. Actual size 140×100 mm*)

Guernsey Marine Life

(Des Bridget Yabsley. Litho Lowe-Martin)

2013 (20 Feb). P 12½ (1450/5) or 13½ (**MS**1456) (both comb).

1450	**1370**	39p. multicoloured	95	95
1451	**1371**	52p. multicoloured	1·25	1·25
1452	**1372**	53p. multicoloured	1·25	1·25
1453	**1373**	59p. multicoloured	1·40	1·40
1454	**1374**	69p. multicoloured	1·75	1·75
1455	**1375**	74p. multicoloured	1·75	1·75
1450/5	*Set of 6*		8·00	8·00
First Day Cover				11·00
Presentation Pack			10·50	
MS1456 140×100 mm. **1376** £5 multicoloured			8·00	8·00
First Day Cover				14·50
Presentation Pack			14·00	

Plate Nos. All values 1A (each×4).
Sheets: 10 (5×2).
Imprint: Top margin at right.

1377 Guernsey Post Daihatsu Hijet Van

1378 La Poste Citroen 2CV Van

1379 Royal Mail Morris 6cwt O-Type Van in Lake District

1380 Deutsche Bundespost VW Beetle Van

1381 Posten AB Kalmar Tjorven (DAF)

1382 U.S. Mail Studebaker Zip Van

Europa. Post Office Vehicles

(Des Robin Carter. Litho Cartor)

2013 (8 May). P 13 (C).

1457	**1377**	(40p.) multicoloured	95	95
1458	**1378**	(53p.) multicoloured	1·25	1·25
1459	**1379**	(55p.) multicoloured	1·25	1·25
1460	**1380**	(63p.) multicoloured	1·40	1·40
1461	**1381**	(71p.) multicoloured	1·75	1·75
1462	**1382**	(79p.) multicoloured	1·75	1·75
1457/62	*Set of 6*		8·00	8·00
First Day Cover				11·50
MS1463 140×100 mm. Nos. 1457/62			8·00	8·00
Presentation Pack			10·50	

No. 1457 was inscr 'GY LETTER', No. 1458 'GY LARGE LETTER', No. 1459 'UK LETTER', No. 1460 'INT LETTER 20G', No. 1761 'UK LARGE LETTER' and No. 1762 'INT LETTER 40G' and they were originally sold for 40p., 53p., 55p., 63p., 71p. and 79p. respectively.

First Day Cover		11·50

Nos. 1459/60 include the Europa emblem.
Plate Nos.: All values 1A (each×4).
Sheets: 10 (2×5).
Imprint: Lower left-hand margins.

1383 Sign of the Mermaid Tavern

1384 Shell Beach

1385 Belvoir Bay

1386 Herm Harbour Moorings

1387 Fisherman's Beach

1388 Gift Shop

Herm Island

(Des Bridget Yabsley. Litho Lowe-Martin Group)

2013 (29 May). P 13×12½ (C).

1464	**1383**	40p. multicoloured	95	95
1465	**1384**	53p. multicoloured	1·25	1·25
1466	**1385**	55p. multicoloured	1·25	1·25
1467	**1386**	63p. multicoloured	1·40	1·40
1468	**1387**	71p. multicoloured	1·75	1·75
1469	**1388**	79p. multicoloured	1·75	1·75
1464/9	*Set of 6*		8·00	8·00
First Day Cover				11·50
Presentation Pack			10·50	

Plate Nos.: All values 1A (each×4).
Sheets: 10 (5×2).
Imprint: Top margin at right.

1389 'In presenting to a generous public a Prospectus of *The Star*, or Guernsey Weekly Advertiser', 29 June 1813

1390 'The Queen's Diamond Jubilee A Glorious and Wonderful Pageant, *The Star*, 24 June 1897

1391 'Orders of the Commandant' (Evening Press, 1 July 1940) and 1941 1/2d. Stamp printed by *The Guernsey Press*

1392 'Serving the islands for 200 years', *Guernsey Press*, 29 June 2013

1393 'Live Live her Gracious Majesty Queen Elizabeth II', *Evening Press*, 2 June 1953

1394 'Peace and Liberation', *Evening Press*, 9 May 1945

Bicentenary of the Guernsey Press and Star

(Des Charlotte Barnes. Litho Lowe-Martin)

2013 (31 July). P 12½ (C).

1470	**1389**	40p. black and grey	95	95
1471	**1390**	53p. black and grey	1·25	1·25
1472	**1391**	55p. black and grey	1·25	1·25
1473	**1392**	63p. black and grey	1·40	1·40
1474	**1393**	71p. black and grey	1·75	1·75
1475	**1394**	79p. black and grey	1·75	1·75
1470/5 Set of 6			8·00	8·00
First Day Cover				11·50
Presentation Pack			10·50	

Plate Nos. All values 1A (each×5).
Sheets: 10 (5×2).
Imprint: Central, bottom margin.

1395 Tractor and Hay-kicker

1396 Prizewinning Produce

1397 Shire Horses pulling Brewery Dray

1398 Guernsey Cows

1399 Steam Tractor Engine

1400 Haymaking in Traditional Dress

Centenary of the West Show (Sepac)

(Des Joel Kirk. Litho Lowe-Martin)

2013 (24 Sept). P 13 (C).

1476	**1395**	40p. multicoloured	95	95
1477	**1396**	53p. multicoloured	1·25	1·25
1478	**1397**	55p. multicoloured	1·25	1·25
1479	**1398**	63p. multicoloured	1·40	1·40
1480	**1399**	71p. multicoloured	1·75	1·75
1481	**1400**	79p. multicoloured	1·75	1·75
1476/81 Set of 6			8·00	8·00
First Day Cover				11·50
Presentation Pack			10·50	

Plate Nos.: All values 1A (each×4).
Sheets: 50 (5×10).
Imprint: Upper side margins.
No. 1479 includes the 'Sepac' emblem. This value was also available in a souvenir folder with 11 other 'Sepac' logo stamps issued by other participating postal administrations. Original selling price £14.68.

1401 Duke and Duchess of Cambridge and Prince George (*Illustration reduced. Actual size 110×55 mm*)

Birth of Prince George of Cambridge

(Des Bridget Yabsley. Litho Lowe-Martin)

2013 (24 Sept). Sheet 110×55 mm. P 12½ (C).

MS1482 **1401** £3 multicoloured		7·00	7·00
First Day Cover		10·00	
Presentation Pack		9·25	

1402 Clematis 'Samaritan Jo'

1403 Clematis 'Anna Louise'

1404 Clematis 'Chelsea'

1405 Clematis 'Edda'

1406 Clematis 'The Countess of Wessex'

1407 Clematis 'Giselle'

'Raymond Evison 25 Years of Gold'. Clematis

(Des Two Degrees North. Litho BDT)

2013 (13 Nov). P 13½ (C).

1483	**1402**	40p. multicoloured	95	95
		a. Booklet pane. No. 1483×4 with margins all round	3·75	
1484	**1403**	53p. multicoloured	1·25	1·25
		a. Booklet pane. No. 1484×4 with margins all round	5·00	
1485	**1404**	55p. multicoloured	1·25	1·25
		a. Booklet pane. No. 1485×4 with margins all round	5·00	
1486	**1405**	63p. multicoloured	1·40	1·40
		a. Booklet pane. No. 1486×4 with margins all round	5·50	
1487	**1406**	71p. multicoloured	1·75	1·75
		a. Booklet pane. No. 1487×4 with margins all round	6·75	
1488	**1407**	79p. multicoloured	1·75	1·75
		a. Booklet pane. No. 1488×4 with margins all round	7·00	
1483/8 *Set of 6*			8·00	8·00
First Day Cover				11·50
Presentation Pack			10·50	

Nos. 1483/8 commemorate clematis producer Raymond Evison's 25th gold medal at Chelsea Flower Show.

Plate Nos. All values 1A (each ×4).
Sheets: 10 (2×5).
Imprint: Central, right-hand margin.

1408 Santa's Sleigh passing Window

1409 Santa on Roof

1410 Santa stuck in Chimney

1411 Children pulling Santa out of Chimney

1412 Santa sneezing

1413 Santa leaving Presents

1414 Santa leaving in his Sleigh

Christmas. When Santa got Stuck up the Chimney

(Des Nick Watton. Litho Cartor)

2013 (13 Nov). P 13×13½ (C).

1489	**1408**	35p. multicoloured	85	85
1490	**1409**	40p. multicoloured	95	95
1491	**1410**	53p. multicoloured	1·25	1·25
1492	**1411**	55p. multicoloured	1·25	1·25
1493	**1412**	63p. multicoloured	1·40	1·40
1494	**1413**	71p. multicoloured	1·75	1·75
1495	**1414**	79p. multicoloured	1·75	1·75
1489/95 *Set of 7*			9·00	9·00
First Day Cover				12·00
Presentation Pack			11·50	

Plate Nos.: All values 1A (each ×4).
Sheets: 50 (5×10).
Imprint: Upper side margins.

Yearbook 2013

2013 (1 Dec). Comprises Nos. 1449/95 and A481/507 (price £62.79).

	Yearbook	£125

1415 Horse

1416 Cantering Horse

1417 Horse kicking

1418 Horse

1419 Horse rearing

1420 Eight Horses

Chinese New Year. Year of the Horse

(Des Chrissy Lau. Litho Lowe-Martin)

2014 (8 Jan). P 13 (C).

1496	**1415**	40p. multicoloured	95	95
1497	**1416**	53p. multicoloured	1·25	1·25
1498	**1417**	55p. multicoloured	1·25	1·25
1499	**1418**	63p. multicoloured	1·40	1·40
1500	**1419**	71p. multicoloured	1·75	1·75
1501	**1420**	79p. multicoloured	1·75	1·75
1496/501 *Set of 6*			7·50	7·50
First Day Cover				9·75
Presentation Pack			9·25	
MS1502 140×100 mm. Nos. 1496/501			8·00	8·00
First Day Cover				9·75

Plate Nos.: All values 1A (each ×2)
Sheets: 10 (2×5)
Imprint: Central, left-hand margin

1421 Sumatran Orangutan

Endangered Species (10th series). Sumatran Orangutan (*Pongo abelii*).

(Des Joel Kirk. Litho Cartor)

2014 (12 Feb). Sheet 118×84 mm. P 14 (C).
MS1503 1421 £3 multicoloured		7·00	7·00
First Day Cover			8·75
Presentation Pack		8·00	

1422 Keys and Wheel

1423 Crank, Tirants and Wheel

1424 Wheel and Strings

1425 Bridge, Wheel, Strings and Keys

1426 Crank, Tirants, Wheel, Tangents and Keys

1427 Chifournie

Europa. National Musical Instruments. The Chifournie (hurdy gurdy).

(Des The Potting Shed. Litho Lowe Martin)

2014 (8 May). P 13 (C).
1504	1422	40p. multicoloured	95	95
1505	1423	53p. multicoloured	1·25	1·25
1506	1424	55p. multicoloured	1·25	1·25
1507	1425	63p. multicoloured	1·40	1·40
1508	1426	71p. multicoloured	1·75	1·75
1509	1427	79p. multicoloured	1·75	1·75
1504/9 Set of 6			7·50	7·50
First Day Cover				9·75

Presentation Pack	9·25	
MS1510 140×100 mm. Nos. 1504/9	8·00	8·00
First Day Cover		9·75

Plate Nos.: All values 1A (each×4).
Sheets: 10 (5×2).
Imprint: Top margin.

Nos. 1504/**MS**1510 have an augmented reality Sepac or Lowe-Martin app showing the chifournie being played which can be downloaded onto a smartphone or tablet.

1428 St. Peter Port Marina

1429 White House View, Herm

1430 Mermaid Tavern, Herm

1431 St. Pierre du Bois

1432 St. Martin's Church

1433 Albion Tavern, St. Peter Port

50th Anniversary of Britain in Bloom

(Des Andrew Robinson. Litho BDT)

2014 (28 May). P 13½ (C).
1511	1428	(41p.) multicoloured	95	95
1512	1429	(54p.) multicoloured	1·25	1·25
1513	1430	(55p.) multicoloured	1·25	1·25
1514	1431	(66p.) multicoloured	1·50	1·50
1515	1432	(74p.) multicoloured	1·75	1·75
1516	1433	(83p.) multicoloured	1·75	1·75
1511/16 Set of 6			7·50	7·50
First Day Cover				10·00
Presentation Pack			9·50	

Nos. 1511/16 were inscr 'GY LETTER', 'GY LARGE LETTER', 'INT LETTER 20g', 'UK LARGE LETTER' and 'INT LETTER 40g' and were originally sold for 41p., 54p., 55p., 66p., 74p. or 83p.
No. 1514 was inscr 'sepac'.
Plate Nos.: All values 1A (each×4).
Sheets: 10 (2×5).
Imprint: Central, left-hand margin.

1434 Map of Guernsey Cartoon Character

Postcrossing (connecting people worldwide through postcards)

(Des Bridget Yabsley. Litho BDT)

2014 (28 May). P 13 (C).
1517	1434	(66p.) multicoloured	1·50	1·50
PHQ Card			1·10	2·50

No. 1517 was inscr 'INT LETTER 20g' and originally sold for 66p.
Plate Nos.: All values 1A (each×4).
Sheets: 50 (5×10).
Imprint: Top right-hand margin.

1435 Chancre (Edible Crab)

1436 Lobster

1437 Velvet Swimming Crab

1438 Hermit Crab

1439 Squat Lobster

1440 Spider Crab

1441 Anemone Shrimp

Marine Life (2nd series)

(Des Bridget Yabsley. Litho Lowe-Martin)

2014 (30 July). P 13×13½ (**MS**1524) or 12½ (others) (both comb.).

1518	**1435**	41p. multicoloured	95	95
1519	**1436**	54p. multicoloured	1·25	1·25
1520	**1437**	55p. multicoloured	1·25	1·25
1521	**1438**	66p. multicoloured	1·50	1·50
1522	**1439**	74p. multicoloured	1·75	1·75
1523	**1440**	83p. multicoloured	1·90	1·90

1518/23 Set of 6 .... 7·75   7·75
First Day Cover ....   10·00
Presentation Pack .... 9·50

MS1524   141×100 mm. **1441** £3 multicoloured
(48×66 mm) .... 7·00   7·00
First Day Cover ....   8·75
Presentation Pack .... 8·00

   Plate Nos.: All values 1A (each ×4).
   Sheets: 10 (5×2).
   Imprint: Upper right-hand margin.

1442 Guernsey Cow, The Little Chapel

1443 Rowing boat, Bec du Nez

1444 Tortval Church

1445 Coastline, Moulin Huet

1446 St. Peter Port Harbour

1447 Fisherman's Beach, Herm

1448 Creux Harbour, Sark

1449 Fort Essex, Alderney

1450 Vazon Bay, Guernsey

1451 Petit Bois, Guernsey

'Love the Bailiwick'

(Des Mark Totty. Litho Walsall)

2014 (30 July). P 12½ (die-cut).

1525	**1442**	(41p.) multicoloured	95	95
		a. Sheetlet. Nos. 1525/34	11·00	
		b. Booklet pane with information pane. Nos. 1525/9, each ×2	9·50	
		c. Booklet pane. Nos. 1525/9, each ×2	9·50	
1526	**1443**	(41p.) multicoloured	95	95
1527	**1444**	(41p.) multicoloured	95	95
1528	**1445**	(41p.) multicoloured	95	95
1529	**1446**	(41p.) multicoloured	95	95
1530	**1447**	(55p.) multicoloured	1·25	1·25
		b. Booklet pane with information pane. Nos. 1530/4, each ×2	12·50	
		c. Booklet pane. Nos. 1530/4, each ×2	12·50	
1531	**1448**	(55p.) multicoloured	1·25	1·25
1532	**1449**	(55p.) multicoloured	1·25	1·25
1533	**1450**	(55p.) multicoloured	1·25	1·25
1534	**1451**	(55p.) multicoloured	1·25	1·25

1525/34 Set of 10 .... 11·00   11·00
First Day Cover ....   12·50
Presentation Pack ....   12·00

   Nos. 1525/9 were intended for postage within the Bailiwick, were inscr 'GY' and sold for 41p. each.

   Nos. 1530/4 were intended for postage to Great Britain, were inscr 'UK' and sold for 55p.

   Sheets: Nos. 1525/34 were printed in sheetlets of ten containing Nos. 1525/34 (available only from the Philatelic Bureau), and also in booklets of ten or 100. The booklets of ten contain either Nos. 1525/9 (1525b) or 1530/4 (1530b), and the stamps are peeled directly from the cover in two blocks 3×2 and 2×2, the blocks separated by a gutter containing text. The booklets of 100 contain ten panes of either Nos. 1525/9 (1525c) or 1530/4 (1530c). These panes have the stamps in one block 5×2, with plain white backing paper and are stitched at left. Loose single booklet panes of ten (1525c and 1530c) were also available from the Philatelic Bureau.

   Stamps from the sheetlet 1525a measure 12.5×12.4, from the booklets of ten (1525b, 1530b) measure 12.5×12.6 and from booklets of 100 (1525c, 1530c) measure 12.5×12.7.

1452 Rudolf the Red-nosed Reindeer (Katka Devon)

1453 Robins on Branches, Snowman and Father Christmas (Patience Ogier)

1454 Rudolf and Present (Georgia Winstanley)

1455 Father Christmas (Mali Chatterton)

1456 Robin wearing Hat (Ruby Parker)

1457 Snowman (Giselle Fuller)

1458 Robin on top of Chimney (Keone Hardy)

Christmas. 'What Christmas Means'. Winning Designs in Children's Painting Competition.

(Litho Cartor)

2014 (6 Nov). Self-adhesive. P 8 (die-cut around design).

1535	**1452**	36p. multicoloured	85	85
1536	**1453**	41p. multi-coloured	95	95
1537	**1454**	54p. multicoloured	1·25	1·25
1538	**1455**	55p. multicoloured	1·25	1·25
1539	**1456**	66p. multicoloured	1·50	1·50
1540	**1457**	74p. multicoloured	1·75	1·75
1541	**1458**	83p. multicoloured	1·90	1·90
1535/41 *Set of 7*			8·50	8·50
First Day Cover				11·00
Presentation Pack				10·50

The perforations around Nos. 1535/41 follow the shape of the design.
Plate Nos.: All values 1A (each ×4).
Sheets: 9 (3×6).
Imprint: Central, left-hand margin.

1459 Pte Yves Cataroche

1460 Major George Le Page

1461 Dorothy Nicolls

1462 Lt. Frank Lané

1463 Ada Le Poidevin

1464 Pte Latimer Le Poidevin

Stories from the Great War (1st issue)

(Des Charlotte Barnes. Litho BDT)

2014 (11 Nov). P 14×14½ (C).

1542	**1459**	41p. multicoloured	95	95
		a. Booklet pane. No. 1542×4 with margins all round	3·75	
1543	**1460**	54p. multicoloured	1·25	1·25
		a. Booklet pane. No. 1543×4 with margins all round	5·00	
1544	**1461**	55p. multicoloured	1·25	1·25
		a. Booklet pane. No. 1544×4 with margins all round	5·00	
1545	**1462**	66p. multicoloured	1·50	1·50
		a. Booklet pane. No. 1545×4 with margins all round	6·00	
1546	**1463**	74p. multicoloured	1·75	1·75
		a. Booklet pane. No. 1546×4 with margins all round	7·00	
1547	**1464**	83p. multicoloured	1·90	1·90
		a. Booklet pane. No. 1547×4 with margins all round	7·50	
1542/7 *Set of 6*			7·75	7·75
First Day Cover				10·00
Presentation Pack			9·50	

Plate Nos.: All values 1A (each ×4).
Sheets: 10 (5×2).
Imprint: Lower right-hand margin.

Yearbook 2014

2014. Comprises Nos. 1496/547 and A508/37 (£62·84)

Yearbook		£125

1465 Winston Churchill, 'A Born Orator'; Painting at Chartwell; On VE Day

50th Death Anniversary of Winston Churchill

(Des Two Degrees North. Litho Lowe-Martin)

2015 (22 Jan). Sheet 140×95 mm. P 13 (C).

MS1548 **1465** £1×3 multicoloured		7·00	7·00
First Day Cover			8·75
Presentation Pack		8·00	

1466 Goat with Peony Pattern

1467 Goat with Chinese Ceramic Pattern

1468 Goat with traditional Chinese pattern

1469 Goat with Chrysanthemum pattern

1470 Goat with lotus pattern

1471 Three goats with spring blossom patterns

Chinese New Year. Year of the Goat

(Des Chrissy Lau. Litho Lowe-Martin)

2015 (28 Jan). P 13 (C).

1549	**1466**	41p. deep carmine and gold	95	95
1550	**1467**	54p. deep carmine and gold	1·25	1·25
1551	**1468**	55p. deep carmine and gold	1·25	1·25
1552	**1469**	66p. deep carmine and gold	1·50	1·50
1553	**1470**	74p. deep carmine and gold	1·75	1·75
1554	**1471**	83p. deep carmine and gold	1·90	1·90
1549/54 *Set of 6*			8·00	8·00
First Day Cover				10·00
Presentation Pack			9·50	
MS1555 140×100 mm. Nos. 1549/54			8·50	8·50
First Day Cover				10·00

Plate Nos.: All values 1A (each ×2).
Sheets: 10 (2×5).
Imprint: Central, left-hand margin.

1472 Prince George's Rocking Horse, c. 2013

1473 Princess Victoria's Wooden Dolls, c. 1831

1474 Prince Charles' Toy Car, c. 1950

1475 Teddy from the Royal Nursery

1476 Princess Elizabeth's Mini Bakers Wagon, c. 1930

1477 Silver Rattles, c. 1774, 1763, 2003

Europa. Old Toys

(Des Robin Carter. Litho BDT)

2015 (1 May). P 13½ (C).

1556	**1472**	41p. multicoloured	95	95
1557	**1473**	54p. multicoloured	1·25	1·25
1558	**1474**	55p. multicoloured	1·25	1·25
1559	**1475**	66p. multicoloured	1·50	1·50
1560	**1476**	74p. multicoloured	1·75	1·75
1561	**1477**	83p. multicoloured	1·90	1·90
1556/61 *Set of 6*			8·00	8·00
First Day Cover				10·00
Presentation Pack			9·50	
MS1562 140×100 mm. Nos. 1556/61			8·50	8·50
First Day Cover				10·00

Nos. 1558/9 include the 'EUROPA' emblem.
Plate Nos.: All values 1A (each ×4).
Sheets: 10 (2×5).
Imprint: Central, left-hand margin.

1478 Two Boys tasting Chocolate for the First Time

1479 Col. H. R. Power tours St. Peter Port Seafront

1480 The Duke of Cornwall's Light Infantry Band

1481 Petty Officer J. D. Langlois

1482 Royal Visit of King George VI and Queen Elizabeth

1483 US 516 docks in St. Peter Port Harbour

70th Anniversary of Liberation

(Des Bridget Yabsley. Litho Cartor)

2015 (1 May). P 13 (C).

1563	**1478**	(42p.) multicoloured	95	95
		a. Booklet pane. No. 1563×4 with margins all round	3·75	
1564	**1479**	(56p.) multicoloured	1·25	1·25
		a. Booklet pane. No. 1564×4 with margins all round	5·00	
1565	**1480**	(57p.) multicoloured	1·25	1·25
		a. Booklet pane. No. 1565×4 with margins all round	5·00	
1566	**1481**	(62p.) multicoloured	1·50	1·50
		a. Booklet pane. No. 1566×4 with margins all round	6·00	
1567	**1482**	(68p.) multicoloured	1·75	1·75
		a. Booklet pane. No. 1567×4 with margins all round	7·00	
1568	**1483**	(77p.) multicoloured	1·90	1·90
		a. Booklet pane. No. 1568×4 with margins all round	7·50	
1563/8 *Set of 6*			8·00	8·00
First Day Cover				10·00
Presentation Pack			9·25	

Nos. 1563/8 were inscr 'GY' Letter, 'UK Letter', 'GY Large Letter', 'EUR Letter', 'UK Large Letter' and 'ROW Letter'.

Although the above rates were not introduced until a month after the stamps were issued, we understand that Nos. 1563/8 were only sold at the revised prices.

Plate Nos.: All values 1A (each×4).
Sheets: 10 (2×5).
Imprint: Lower left-hand margin.

1484 Penny Black

175th Anniversary of the Penny Black

(Des Keith Robinson. Litho Lowe-Martin)

2015 (1 May). Sheet 110×70 mm. P 12½ (C).

MS1569 **1484** £2 multicoloured		4·75	4·75
First Day Cover			6·75
Presentation Pack		6·00	

1485 Moulin Huet Bay (John Paul Jacob Naftel) **1486** La Moye Harbour, Le Gouffre (Peter Le Lievre)

1487 Cradle Rock and Pea Stacks (William John Caparne) **1488** La Saignée, Sark (William A. Toplis)

1489 Grande Rocques Old Fort (Ethel Cheeswright) **1490** Moulin Huet Bay (Pierre-Auguste Renoir)

Artists of Guernsey

(Des Andrew Robinson. Litho BDT)

2015 (22 July). P 14 (C).

1570	**1485**	42p. multicoloured	95	95
1571	**1486**	56p. multicoloured	1·25	1·25
1572	**1487**	57p. multicoloured	1·40	1·40
1573	**1488**	62p. multicoloured	1·40	1·40
1574	**1489**	68p. multicoloured	1·50	1·50
1575	**1490**	77p. multicoloured	1·75	1·75
1570/5 *Set of 6*			7·50	7·50
First Day Cover				10·00
Presentation Pack			9·50	

The 62p. value includes the 'sepac' emblem.
Plate Nos.: All values 1A (each×4).
Sheets: 10 (2×5).
Imprint: Central right-hand margin.

1491 St. Magloire, Patron Saint of Sark **1492** 15th-century Sark

1493 French Invasion of Sark **1494** Le Manoir, home of Sark's First Seigneur

1495 19th-century Silver and Copper Mining on Little Sark

1496 Elizabethan Bronze Cannon presented to Helier de Carteret, First Seigneur, by Queen Elizabeth I in 1572 (£1); Queen Elizabeth I (£2)

450th Anniversary of Sark as a Fief to the Crown

(Des Nick Shewring. Litho Lowe-Martin)

2015 (22 July). P 12½ (£2) or 13 (others) (both comb).

1576	**1491**	42p. multicoloured	95	95
1577	**1492**	57p. multicoloured	1·40	1·40
1578	**1493**	62p. multicoloured	1·40	1·40
1579	**1494**	68p. multicoloured	1·50	1·50
1580	**1495**	77p. multicoloured	1·75	1·75
1576/80 *Set of 5*			6·50	6·50
First Day Cover				8·75
Presentation Pack			8·25	
MS1581 110×80 mm. **1496** £1 multicoloured; £2				
multicoloured			7·00	7·00
First Day Cover				8·75
Presentation Pack			8·00	

  Plate Nos.: All values 1A (each ×4).
  Sheets: 10 (2×5).
  Imprint: Central, left-hand margin.

1497 Adoration of the Magi

1498 The Annunciation

1499 Angels sitting above the Kingdom

1500 The Crucifixion

1501 Twelve Apostles (detail)

1502 Kingdom of Heaven

1503 God in Majesty

Christmas. William Morris Stained Glass Windows from St. Stephen's Church, Guernsey

(Des Two Degrees North. Litho Cartor)

2015 (6 Nov). Self-adhesive. Die-cut perf 14½.

1582	**1497**	37p. multicoloured	85	85
1583	**1498**	42p. multicoloured	95	95
1584	**1499**	56p. multicoloured	1·25	1·25
1585	**1500**	57p. multicoloured	1·40	1·40
1586	**1501**	62p. multicoloured	1·40	1·40
1587	**1502**	68p. multicoloured	1·50	1·50
1588	**1503**	77p. multicoloured	1·75	1·75
1582/8 *Set of 7*			8·25	8·25
First Day Cover				10·50
Presentation Pack			10·00	

  Plate Nos.: All values 1A (each ×4).
  Sheets: 10 (5×2).
  Imprint: Upper right-hand margin.

1504 Pte. Philip Carré (Sark postman) and Card from Postmaster

1505 Mailboat, SS *Vera*

1506 Card sent Home by Lt. Peter Le Page and Embroidered Sampler

1507 Privates J. G. Fowler, Albert Smith, Lawrence Burridge, H. F. Taylor and R. F. De Garis, Bailiwick Postmen who joined The Post Office Rifles

1508 Field Service Postcard sent by Pte. Yves Cataroche

1509 Robert and Ethel Bynam and Edward VII 1d. Stamp

Stories from the Great War (2nd issue)

(Des Charlotte Barnes. Litho BDT)

2015 (11 Nov). P 14×14½ (C).

1589	**1504**	42p. multicoloured		95	95
		a. Booklet pane. No. 1589×4 with margins all round		3·75	
1590	**1505**	56p. multicoloured		1·25	1·25
		a. Booklet pane. No. 1590×4 with margins all round		5·00	
1591	**1506**	57p. multicoloured		1·40	1·40
		a. Booklet pane. No. 1591×4 with margins all round		5·50	
1592	**1507**	62p. multicoloured		1·40	1·40
		a. Booklet pane. No. 1592×4 with margins all round		5·50	
1593	**1508**	68p. multicoloured		1·50	1·50
		a. Booklet pane. No. 1593×4 with margins all round		6·00	
1594	**1509**	77p. multicoloured		1·75	1·75
		a. Booklet pane. No. 1594×4 with margins all round		7·00	
1589/94 *Set of 6*				7·50	7·50
First Day Cover					10·00
Presentation Pack				9·50	

Plate Nos.: All values 1A (each×4).
Sheets: 10 (5×2).
Imprint: Bottom margin at right.

Yearbook 2015

2015 (1 Dec). Comprises Nos. **MS**1548/94 and A538/66 (price £75.41)

Yearbook £150

POST & GO STAMPS

Guernsey Post & Go stamps as type FTG**1** first appeared at Spring Stampex 2015 and were also made available via the philatelic bureau. On 2 September 2015 a machine was installed at Guernsey Post Headquarters, Envoy House, for the use of philatelic customers and machines have subsequently been sited at other philatelic events, showing various commemorative overprints. At the time of publication, no machine is in use in post offices in Guernsey.

FTG **1** Guernsey Flag

POSTAGE DUE STAMPS

D **1** Castle Cornet   D **2** Castle Cornet

(Des R. Barrett. Photo Delrieu)

1969 (1 Oct). Face value in black; background colour given. No wmk. P 12½×12 (C).

D1	D **1**	1d. plum		2·00	1·50
D2		2d. bright green		2·00	1·50
D3		3d. vermilion		3·00	4·00
D4		4d. ultramarine		4·00	5·00
D5		5d. yellow-ochre		6·00	5·00
D6		6d. turquoise-blue		6·00	5·00
D7		1s. lake-brown		10·00	9·00
D1/7 *Set of 7*				30·00	29·00

Sheets: 60 (10×6).
Quantities sold: 1d. 82,802; 2d. 75,340; 3d. 74,532; 4d. 74,659; 5d. 71,129; 6d. 72,912; 1s 71,659.
Withdrawn and Invalidated: 14.2.72.

Decimal Currency

(Des R. Granger Barrett. Photo Delrieu)

1971 (15 Feb)–**76**. No wmk. P 12½×12 (C).

D8	D **2**	½p. plum (a)		10	15
D9		1p. bright green (a)		10	15
D10		2p. vermilion (a)		10	15
D11		3p. ultramarine (a)		10	10
D12		4p. yellow-ochre (a)		10	15
D13		5p. turquoise-blue (a)		15	15
D14		6p. violet (c)		15	15
D15		8p. yellow-orange (b)		25	50
D16		10p. lake-brown (a)		25	25
D17		15p. grey (c)		35	60
D8/17 *Set of 10*				1·50	2·00
D1/13, 16 *Presentation Pack (a)*				75·00	
D8/17 *Presentation Pack (c)*				2·00	

Printings: (a) 15.2.71; (b) 7.10.75; (c) 10.2.76.
Sheets: 60 (10×6).
Withdrawn: 14.2.72 *Presentation Pack* (Nos. D1/13 and D16); 1.8.78 ½p. to 15p. (½ and 1p. sold out by 6.78).

D **3** St. Peter Port

(Photo Delrieu)

1977 (2 Aug)–**80**. Face value in black; background colour given. P 13 (C).

D18	D **3**	½p. lake-brown (a)		10	10
D19		1p. bright purple (a)		10	10
D20		2p. bright orange (a)		10	10
D21		3p. vermilion (a)		10	15
D22		4p. turquoise-blue (a)		15	15
D23		5p. yellow-green (a)		15	15
D24		6p. turquoise-green (a)		15	15
D25		8p. brown-ochre (a)		15	15
D26		10p. ultramarine (a)		15	15
D27		14p. green (b)		30	30
D28		15p. bright violet (a)		30	30
D29		16p. rose-red (b)		40	30
D18/29 *Set of 12*				2·00	2·00
D18/26, 28 *Presentation Pack*				2·50	

Printings: (a) 2.8.77; (b) 5.2.80.
Sheets: 50 (5×10).
Withdrawn: 12.7.83.
(Presentation Pack sold out earlier).

D **4** Milking Cow   D **5** Vale Mill

D **6** Sark Cottage   D **7** Quay-side, St. Peter Port

D **8** Well, Water Lane, Moulin Huet   D **9** Seaweed Gathering

D **10** Upper Walk, White Rock

D **11** Cobo Bay

D **12** Saint's Bay

D **13** La Coupée, Sark

D **14** Old Harbour, ST. Peter Port

D **15** Greenhouse, Doyle Road, ST. Peter Port

Guernsey Scenes, c. 1900

(Des C. Abbott. Litho Questa)

1982 (13 July). P 14½ (C).

D30	D **4**	1p. indigo, blue-black & brt grn	15	10
D31	D **5**	2p. yellow-brown, sepia & azure.........	15	10
D32	D **6**	3p. blackish green, black & lilac.........	15	10
D33	D **7**	4p. bottle green, blk & dull orge.........	15	15
D34	D **8**	5p. deep violet-blue, blue-black and turquoise-green..........	15	15
D35	D **9**	16p. dp grey-blue, dp bl & cobalt	35	40
D36	D **10**	18p. steel bl, indigo & apple grn	40	45
D37	D **11**	20p. brown-olive, agate & pale bl	45	50
D38	D **12**	25p. Prussian blue, blue-black and rose-pink....................	55	60
D39	D **13**	30p. deep bluish green, blackish olive and bistre-yellow	65	70
D40	D **14**	50p. olive-brown, sepia and dull violet-blue	1·25	1·20
D41	D **15**	£1 lt brown, brown & pale brn	2·25	2·40
D30/41		*Set of 12*	6·00	6·00
		Presentation Pack....................	7·00	

Sheets: 50 (5×10).
Imprint: Bottom corner, right-hand margin.
Withdrawn: 30.9.2001.

STAMP BOOKLETS

Prices given are for complete booklets. Booklets Nos. SB1/12 are stitched.

B **1** Military Uniforms

1969 (12 Dec). White covers as Type B **1**, 54×41 mm, printed in black.

SB1	2s. booklet containing 3×4d. (No. 18a), 2×5d. (No. 19a) and 2×1d. (No. 14c) (cover showing Trooper, Royal Guernsey Cavalry (Light Dragoons), 1814)		50
SB2	4s. booklet containing 6×4d. (No. 18a), 4×5d. (No. 19a) and 4×1d. (No. 14c) (cover showing Officer, St. Martin's Company (La Milice Bleue), Guernsey, 1720)...................		1·50

SB3	6s. booklet containing 9×4d. (No. 18a), 6×5d. (No. 19a) and 6×1d. (No. 14c) (cover showing Colour Sergeant of Grenadiers and Rifleman, East (Town) Regiment, Guernsey, 1833).............		1·50

Withdrawn: 14.2.72.

1970 (29 June). White covers as Type B **1**, 54×41 mm. Printed in black (SB4), green (SB5) or red (SB6). Same composition as Nos. SB1/3.

SB4	2s. booklet (cover showing Officer, Royal Guernsey Horse Artillery, 1793)...................		2·00
SB5	4s. booklet (cover showing Gunner, Royal Guernsey Artillery, 1743)..................		12·00
SB6	6s. booklet (cover showing Sergeant, Royal Guernsey Light Infantry, 1832)...................		12·00

Quantities sold: 2s (SB1, SB4), 81,928; 4s (SB2, SB5), 23,817; 6s (SB3, SB6), 25,123.
Withdrawn: 14.2.72.

Decimal Currency

1971 (15 Feb). White covers as Type B **1**, 54×41 mm. Printed in black (SB7), green (SB8) or red (SB9).

SB7	10p. booklet containing 2×½p. (No. 44a), 2×2p. (No. 47a) and 2×2½p. (No. 48b) (cover showing Officer, Royal Guernsey Horse Artillery, 1850)....	85
SB8	20p. booklet containing 4×½p. (No. 44a), 4×2p. (No. 47a) and 4×2½p. (No. 48b) (cover showing Sergeant, Guernsey Light Infantry (Grenadiers), 1826)	70
SB9	30p. booklet containing 6×½p. (No. 44a), 6×2p. (No. 47a) and 6×2½p. (No 48b) (cover showing Sergeant and Bandsman, Royal Guernsey Light Infantry (North Regiment), 1866).....................	1·10

Withdrawn: 27.6.73 (SB7); 12.3.75 (SB8); 15.1.75 (SB9).

1973 (2 Apr). White covers as Type B **1**, 54×41 mm. Printed in black (SB10), green (SB11) or red (SB12).

SB10	10p. booklet containing 2×½p. (No. 44ab), 2×2p. (No. 47ab) and 2×2½p. (No. 48ba) (cover showing Officer, Guernsey Horse Artillery, 1828)........................	40
SB11	20p. booklet containing 4×½p. (No. 44ab), 4×2p. (No. 47ab) and 4×2½p. (No. 48ba) (cover showing Grenadier, Guernsey Light Infantry, 1792)........................	50
SB12	30p. booklet containing 6×½p. (No. 44ab), 6×2p. (No. 47ab) and 6×2½p. (No. 48ba) (cover showing Insignia, Royal Guernsey Light Infantry)........................	1·00

Nos. SB10/12 are inscribed 'January 1973' on back cover.
Withdrawn: 1.4.75.

B **2** Arms of Guernsey

1974 (2 Apr). Silver (SB13) or gold cover (SB14 as Type B **2**), 53×32 mm.

SB13	10p. booklet containing five ½p. stamps and three 2½p. in *se-tenant* strip (No. 98a)................	35
SB14	35p. booklet containing four ½p. stamps, six 2½p. and six 3p. in *se-tenant* pane (No. 98b).............	85

The strips and panes have the left-hand selvedge stuck into booklet covers and then folded and supplied in plastic wallets.
Withdrawn: 6.2.79.

1977 (8 Feb). Green and white cover as Type B **2**, 53×32 mm.

SB15	20p. booklet containing No. 99a........................	55

The note beneath No. SB14 also applies here.
Withdrawn: 12.2.80.

BOOKLET PANES from Nos. SB16/18 are loose within card covers supplied in plastic sachets.

1978 (7 Feb). Blue and white cover as Type B **2**, 53×32 mm.

SB16	10p. booklet containing No. 99b........................	35

Withdrawn: 12.2.80.

1979 (13 Feb). Covers as Type B **2**.

SB17	10p. booklet containing No. 178a (black and green cover)	40

SB18   30p. booklet containing No. 179a (black and red
            cover)...   90
        Withdrawn: 23.2.82.

B **3** Castle Cornet (*Illustration reduced. Actual size
88×54 mm*)

1980 (6 May). Horiz covers as Type B **3**. Folded.
SB19   30p. booklet containing No. 177a (blue printed
            cover, Type C)...   60
SB20   50p. booklet containing No. 177b (brown printed
            cover showing view from the sea)...............   1·00
        Withdrawn: 4.5.83.
1981 (24 Feb). Covers similar to Type B **3**, but vert, 55×90 mm.
        Folded.
SB21   60p. booklet containing No. 180a (red printed cover
            showing Fort Grey)...................................   1·20
SB22   £1.20. booklet containing No. 180b (green printed
            cover showing Rokaine Castle)..................   2·50
        Withdrawn 23.2.84.

1982 (2 Feb). Covers similar to Type B **3** showing Fort George, 87×53
        mm. Folded.
SB23   70p. booklet containing No. 181b (orange printed
            cover showing main entrance) ....   1·50
SB24   £1.30. booklet containing No. 181c (magenta printed
            cover showing aerial view of Citadel)..........   2·50
        Withdrawn: 22.7.85.

1983 (14 Mar). Covers similar to Type B **3**, 87×53 mm. Folded.
SB25   £1 booklet containing No. 180c (new blue printed
            cover showing States Office, St. Peter Port).......   1·90
SB26   £1.30 booklet containing No. 180d (sepia printed
            cover showing Constable's Office, St. Peter Port)   2·50
        Withdrawn: 22.7.85.

BOOKLET PANES from Nos. SB27/38 are loose within card covers.

B **4** View of Post Office Headquarters, St. Peter
Port (*Illustration reduced. Actual size 87×53 mm*)

1984 (18 Sept). Multicoloured covers as Type B **4**.
SB27   £1 booklet containing No. 299a ....   2·00
SB28   £1.30 booklet containing No. 299b (cover showing
            Head Post Office, St. Peter Port).................   2·50
        Quantities sold: SB27 50,393; SB28 25,372.
        Withdrawn: 1.87.

1985 (19 Mar). Multicoloured covers as Type B **4**, 87×53 mm.
SB29   £1.20 booklet containing No. 304a (cover showing
            French Halles, St. Peter Port)...................   2·50
SB30   £1.30 booklet containing No. 304b (cover showing
            Market Halls, St. Peter Port)...................   2·50
        Quantities sold: SB29 49,248; SB30 45,463.
        Withdrawn: 8.87.

1985 (2 Dec). Multicoloured cover as Type B **4**, but vert, 52×86 mm.
SB31   50p. booklet containing No. 297a (cover showing
            Victoria Tower, St. Peter Port) ....   1·60
        Quantity sold: 55,768.
        Withdrawn: 8.87.

1986 (1 Apr). Multicoloured cover as Type B **4**, but vert, 52×86 mm.
SB32   £1.20 booklet containing No. 305a (cover showing
            St. James-the-Less, St. Peter Port)............   3·00

Quantity sold: 32,627.
        Withdrawn: 2.89.

1987 (30 Mar). Multicoloured covers as Type B **4**, but vert, 52×86 mm.
SB33   £1 booklet containing No. 298a (cover showing
            Lukis Observatory, St. Peter Port) ....   2·50
SB34   £1.30 booklet containing No. 306a (cover showing
            Weighbridge, St. Peter Port)...................   3·00
        Quantities sold: SB33 42,478; SB34 36,369.
        Withdrawn: 2.89.

1988 (28 Mar). Multicoloured covers as Type B **4**, but vert, 52×86 mm.
SB35   £1 booklet containing No. 299c (cover showing
            North Pier Light, St. Peter Port)..............   2·75
SB36   £1.40 booklet containing No. 306ba (cover showing
            Castle Light, St. Peter Port)...................   3·00
        Quantities sold: SB35 41,092; SB36 39,478.
        Withdrawn: 2.90.

1989 (28 Feb). Multicoloured covers as Type B **4**, but vert, 52×86 mm.
SB37   £1 booklet containing No. 299d (cover showing
            Town Church, St. Peter Port)...................   3·00
SB38   £1.20 booklet containing No. 306bb (cover showing
            St. Barnabas Church, St. Peter Port).........   3·50
        Quantities sold: SB37 47,175; SB38 41,235.
        Withdrawn: 12.90.

B **5** Opening Ceremony, 1939 (*Illustration reduced. Actual size
163×97 mm*)

50th Anniversary of Guernsey Airport

(Des A. Theobald)

1989 (5 May). Multicoloured cover, Type B **5**. Booklet contains text
        and Illustrations on panes and interleaving pages. Stitched.
SB39   £3.90 booklet containing Nos. 456a, 458a and 460a ..   9·00
        Quantity sold: 38,025.
        Sold out: By 11.89.

1989 (27 Dec). Multicoloured covers as Type B **4**, but vert, 54×87 mm.
SB40   £1.20 booklet containing No. 301a (cover showing
            Fish Market, St. Peter Port) ....   3·00
SB41   £1.70 booklet containing No. 308a (cover showing
            Lloyds Bank, St. Peter Port) ....   3·75
        Quantities sold: SB40 31,736; SB41 31,743.
        Withdrawn: 21.5.92.

B **6** Crown Hotel (*Illustration reduced. Actual size 163×97 mm*)

50th Anniversary of First Guernsey Stamps

(Des A. Theobald)

1991 (18 Feb). Multicoloured cover, Type B **6**. Booklet contains text on
        panes and text and illustrations on interleaving pages. Stitched.
SB42   £4.41 booklet containing No. 517a×3 ....   12·00
        Quantity sold: 31,955.
        Withdrawn: 17.2.92.

1991 (2 Apr). Multicoloured covers as Type B **4**, but vert, 55×87 mm.
SB43   £1.30 booklet containing No. 300a (cover showing
            Golden Lion Inn, St. Peter Port)..............   3·75

SB44   £1.80 booklet containing No. 309a (cover showing
            National Trust Building, St. Peter Port.....................   5·50
        Quantities sold: SB43 36,066; SB44 26,029.
        Withdrawn: 21.5.92.

B **7** Carnations (*Illustration reduced. Actual size
85×52 mm*)

1992 (22 May). Multicoloured covers as Type B **7**. Without barcode on
the reverse. Panes attached by selvedge.
SB45   £1.45 booklet containing pane No. 572ac (cover
            Type B **7**)...   4·00
SB46   £1.80 booklet containing pane No. 574ac (cover
            showing mixed freesias) ....   6·00
        Withdrawn: 31.8.99.

B **8** Bow of Ship and Relics (*Illusration reduced. Actual size
163×97 mm*)

'Operation Asterix'

1992 (18 Sept). Multicoloured cover, Type B **8**. Booklet contains text
and illustrations on interleaving pages. Stitched.
SB47   £5.60 booklet containing No. 583ax4...............................   15·00
        Quantity sold: 24,211.
        Withdrawn: 17.9.93.

1993 (2 Mar)–**95**. Multicoloured covers as Type B **7**, 85×52 mm, but
different Guernsey Post Office logo. Without barcode on the
reverse. Panes attached by selvedge.
SB48   £1.12 booklet containing pane No. 577ab (cover
            showing Lisianthus) ....   3·50
SB49   £1.28 booklet containing pane No. 572ad (cover
            Type B **7**)...   3·25
        a. With barcode sticker on reverse (6.95)....................   7·00
        b. Barcode printed on reverse (10.95)........................   4·00
SB50   £1.92 booklet containing pane No. 575ab (cover
            showing standard roses).................................   5·50
        a. With barcode sticker on reverse (3.95)....................   9·00
        b. Barcode printed on reverse (6.95) ....   5·25
        Withdrawn: 31.8.99.

B **9** Thomas de la Rue (*Illustration reduced. Actual size
163×97 mm*)

Birth Bicentenary of Thomas de la Rue (printer)

(Des M. Whyte)

1993 (27 July). Multicoloured cover as Type B **9**. Booklet contains text
and illustrations on interleaving pages. Stapled.
SB51   £5.60 booklet containing panes Nos. 617a/21a.............   13·00
        Withdrawn: 26.7.94.

1994 (18 Feb). Multicoloured cover as Type B **7**, 82×52 mm, but
different Guernsey Post Office logo. With barcode on reverse.
Pane attached by selvedge.
SB52   £1 booklet containing pane No. 576ab (cover
            showing Iris 'Ideal')..   3·00
        Withdrawn: 31.8.99.

B **10** Guernsey View and 1936 Bentley (*Illustration reduced.
Actual size 162×97 mm*)

Centenary of First Car in Guernsey

(Des R. Ollington)

1994 (19 July). Black and grey cover as Type B **10**. Booklet contains
text and Illustrations on labels attached to panes and on
interleaving pages. Stitched.
SB53   £7 booklet containing panes Nos. 639a/43a..............   19·00
        Withdrawn 18.7.95.

B **11** Coins, Postbox and Stamps 'Face'

Greetings Stamps. 'The Welcoming Face of Guernsey'

1995 (28 Feb). Multicoloured cover as Type B **11**, 83×61 mm.
Miniature sheet folded and attached by selvedge.
SB54   £1.92 booklet containing No. **MS**671.....................   4·50
        Withdrawn: 27.2.96.

B **12** Stamps and Magnifying Glass (*Illustration reduced. Actual size 97×163 mm*)

Centenary of Cinema. Screen Detectives

(Des R. Ollington)

1996 (6 Nov). Multicoloured cover as Type B **12**. Booklet contains text and illustrations on margins of panes and interleaving pages. Stitched.

SB55   £7.04 booklet containing panes Nos. 711a/15a............. 19·00

Quantity sold: 18,370.

Withdrawn: 5.11.97.

B **13** Freesia 'Pink Glow'

1997 (2 Jan). Multicoloured covers as Type B **13**, 83×52 mm. With barcode on reverse. Panes attached by selvedge.

SB56   £1.04 booklet containing pane No. 576bb (cover
       Type B **13**)... 4·50
SB57   £1.44 booklet containing pane No. 572bb (cover
       showing Standard Rose)................................... 4·75
SB58   £2 booklet containing No. 576ab×2 (cover
       showing Iris 'Ideal')... 14·00

Withdrawn: 31.8.99.

B **14** Castle Cornet, Guernsey

Guernsey Treasures (1st series)

1997 (24 Apr). Multicoloured covers as Type B **14**, 77×60 mm. Self- adhesive.

SB59   £1.04 booklet containing pane No. 739a (cover as
       Type B **14**)... 6·00
SB60   £1.44 booklet containing pane No. 737a (cover
       showing Shell Beach, Herm)........................... 7·50
SB61   £2 booklet containing pane No. 738a (cover
       showing La Seigneurie, Sark)......................... 8·50

Withdrawn: 31.3.98.

B **15** Queen Elizabeth and Prince Philip (*Illustration reduced. Actual size 162×95 mm*)

Golden Wedding

(Des M. Whyte)

1997 (20 Nov). Multicoloured cover as Type B **15**. Booklet contains text and illustrations on panes and interleaving pages. Stitched.

SB62   £8.48 booklet containing Nos. 754a/b, 756a and
       758a... 22·00

Withdrawn: 19.11.98.

B **16** Milennium Tapestry (*Illustration reduced. Actual size 162×97 mm*)

The Millennium Tapestries Project

(Des Morvan Diamond)

1998 (10 Feb). Multicoloured cover as Type B **16**. Booklet contains text and illustrations on pane margins and inter- leaving pages. Stitched.

SB63   £7.50 booklet containing Nos. 760b/c, 762a, 764a
       and 766a.. 18·00

Withdrawn: 9.2.99.

B **17** Fort Grey

Guernsey Treasures (2nd series)

1998 (25 Mar). Multicoloured covers as Type B **17**, 77×60 mm. Self-adhesive.

SB64	£1.60 booklet containing pane No. 770b (cover as Type B **17**)	7·00
SB65	£2 booklet containing pane No. 772b (cover showing Guernsey cow)	8·00

Sold out: 6.2001.

B **18** Queen Elizabeth the Queen Mother (*Illustration reduced. Actual size 160×100 mm*)

Life and Times of Queen Elizabeth the Queen Mother

(Des Morvan Diamond)

1999 (4 Feb). Multicoloured cover as Type B **18**. Booklet contains text and Illustrations on pane margins and interleaving pages. Stitched.

SB66	£7.50 booklet containing panes Nos. 817b/c, 819b, 821b and 923b	18·00

Withdrawn: 3.2.2000.

B **19** Supermarine Spitfire over St. Peter Port (*Illustration reduced. Actual size 163×97 mm*)

60th Anniversary of Battle of Britain

(Des Morvan Diamond)

2000 (28 Apr). Multicoloured cover as Type B **19**. Booklet contains text and Illustrations on interleaving pages. Stitched.

SB67	£6.99 booklet containing pages Nos. 857a/c, 858a and 862a	18·00

Withdrawn: 27.4.2001.

B **20** Telegraph Bay, Alderney (*Illustration reduced. Actual size 102×60 mm*)

Island Colours

2001 (26 Apr). Multicoloured covers as Type B **20**. Self-adhesive.

SB68	(£2.20) booklet containing pane No. 901b (cover as Type B **20**)	6·00
SB69	(£2.70) booklet containing pane No. 906b (cover showing Albecq Beach)	9·00

Sold out: By 7.2004.

B **21** Droplet of Water on Leaf (*Illustration reduced. Actual size 160×95 mm*)

Incorporation of Guernsey Post Ltd

(Des Small Limited)

2001 (1 Aug). Multicoloured cover as Type B **21**. Booklet contains text on panes and transparent interleaves. Stitched.

SB70	£8.05 booklet containing panes Nos. 921a/7a	18·00

Withdrawn: 31.7.02.

B **22** Queen Elizabeth carrying Bouquet (*Illustration reduced. Actual size 165×98 mm*)

Golden Jubilee

(Des Hamilton Brooke)

2002 (30 Apr). Multicoloured cover as Type B **22**. Booklet contains text and photographs on interleaving panes. Stitched.

SB71	£9.05 booklet containing panes Nos. 948a/c and 949a with Alderney No. **MS**A184	20·00

Withdrawn: 29.4.2003.

B **23** Prince William and His Coat of arms (*Illustration reduced. Actual size 162×98 mm*)

21st Birthday of Prince William of Wales

(Des Sally Diamond)

2003 (21 June). Multicoloured cover as Type B **23**. Booklet contains text and photographs on panes and interleaving pages. Stitched.

SB72   £8.10 booklet containing panes Nos. 998ba/bc and
999ba/bb.. 24·00
Withdrawn: 20.6.2004.

B **24** Clematis 'Pistachio' (*Illustration reduced. Actual size 100×60 mm*)

Raymond Evison's Guernsey Clematis

2004 (29 Jan). Multicoloured covers as Type B **24**. Self-adhesive (Nos. SB73/4) or stitched (Nos. SB75/6).

SB73   (£2.20) booklet containing pane No. 1017b (cover
Type B **24**)... 7·00
SB74   (£2.70) booklet containing pane No. 1022a) (cover
showing Clematis 'Anna Louise')............................ 8·75
SB75   (£22) booklet containing ten panes of No. 1017c
(cover as Type B **24**, but 181×59 mm)................. 55·00
SB76   (£27) booklet containing ten panes of No. 1022b)
(cover showing Clematis 'Anna Louise',
181×59 mm) .... 65·00
Sold out: By 10.2007.

B **25** Ruins of Ancient Greece (*Illustration reduced. Actual size 163×98 mm*)

Olympic Games, Athens, Greece

(Des A. Fothergill)

2004 (29 July). Multicoloured cover as Type B **25**. Booklet contains text and illustrations on panes and interleaving pages. Stitched.

SB77   £9.90 booklet containing panes Nos. 1045a/d, 1046a
and **MS**1049a .... 22·00
Withdrawn: 28.7.2005.

B **26** St. Peter Port Harbour and Castle Cornet at Dawn (*Illustration reduced. Actual size 164×98 mm*)

'Sea Guernsey 2005'

(Des Sally Diamond)

2005 (21 July). Multicoloured cover as Type B **26**. Booklet contains text and illustrations on panes and interleaving pages. Stitched.

SB78   £9.69 booklet containing panes Nos. 1080a/b,
1081a/b, 1082a and 1083a .... 22·00
Withdrawn: 20.7.2006.

B **27** Isambard Kingdom Brunel (*Illustration reduced. Actual size 163×98 mm*)

Birth Bicentenary of Isambard Kingdom Brunel (engineer)

(Des Small Limited)

2006 (20 May). Multicoloured cover as Type B **27**. Booklet contains text and illustrations on panes and interleaving pages. Stitched.

SB79   £10.60 booklet containing panes Nos. 1110a/d, 1111a
and 1112a.. 25·00
Withdrawn: 19.5.2007.

B **28** Seashore (*Illustration reduced. Actual size 101×59 mm*)

125th Anniversary of La Société Guernesiaise

2007 (8 Mar). Multicoloured covers as Type B **28**. Self-adhesive (Nos. SB80/1) or stitched (Nos. SB82/3).

SB80   (£3.20) booklet containing pane No. 1149b (cover
Type B **28**)... 8·00
SB81   (£3.70) booklet containing pane No. 1154a (cover
showing lighthouse).. 8·75
SB82   (£32) booklet containing ten panes of No. 1149c
(cover as Type B **28**, but 180×59 mm)................. 65·00
SB83   (£37) booklet containing ten panes of No. 1154b
(cover showing lighthouse, 180×59 mm)............. 75·00

B **29** Queen Elizabeth II and Duke of Edinburgh
(*Illustration reduced. Actual size 161×98 mm*)

Diamond Wedding of Queen Elizabeth II and Duke of Edinburgh

(Des M. Whyte)

2007 (2 Aug). Cover as Type B **29** showing black/white photograph. Booklet contains text and illustrations on panes and interleaving pages. Stitched.
SB84   £11.32 booklet containing panes Nos. 1174a/b and
         1175a/8a.. 27·00
Withdrawn: 1.8.2008.

B **30** Coastal Rocks (*Illustration reduced. Actual size 101×59 mm*)

'Abstract Guernsey' (1st series)

2008 (8 June). Multicoloured covers as Type B **30**. Self-adhesive (Nos. SB85/6) or stitched (Nos. SB87/8).
SB85   (£3.40) booklet containing pane No. 1232b (cover
          Type B **30**)... 9·00
SB86   (£4) booklet containing pane No. 1237a (cover
          showing coastal rocks at sunset)........................... 11·00
SB87   (£34) booklet containing ten panes of No. 1232c
          (cover as Type B **30**, but 182×58 mm)................. 80·00
SB88   (£40) booklet containing ten panes of No. 1237b (cover
          showing coastal rocks at sunset, 182×58 mm)....... £100

B **31** Ford Model T Production Line (*Illustration reduced. Actual size (161×97 mm)*)

Centenary of the Model T Ford

(Des M. Totty)

2008 (31 July). Multicoloured cover as Type B **31**. Booklet contains text and illustrations on panes and interleaving pages. Stitched.
SB89   £12 booklet containing panes Nos. 1242a/d, 1243a
         and 1244a.. 28·00
Withdrawn: 30.7.2009.

B **32** Henry VIII watching his Navy as *Mary Rose* sinks, 1545
(*Illustration reduced. Actual size 163×99 mm*)

500th Anniversary of the Coronation of King Henry VIII

(Des M. Totty)

2009 (30 July). Multicoloured cover as Type B **32**. Booklet contains text and illustrations on panes and interleaving pages. Stitched.
SB90   £12.68 booklet containing panes Nos. 1290a/5a........... 29·00
Withdrawn: 29.7.2010.

B **33** Beach and Headland (*Illustration reduced. Actual size 100×70 mm*)

'Abstract Guernsey' (2nd series)

2010 (18 Mar). Multicoloured covers as Type B **33**. Self-adhesive.
SB91   (£1.92) booklet containing pane No. 1327b (cover
          Type B **33**)... 4·50
SB92   (£2.32) booklet containing pane No. 1330a (cover
          showing rocky headlands at sunset).................... 5·50
SB93   (£24) booklet containing 5 panes No. 1327c (cover
          showing rocky bay, 180×59 mm)........................... 50·00
SB94   (£29) booklet conataining 5 panes No. 1330b (cover
          showing rocky headlands and off shore rocks
          at sunset, 180×59 mm)... 60·00
For operational reasons these booklets were charged at the new rates which did not change officially until 1 April 2010.

B **34** Cycling (*Illustration reduced. Actual size 163×98 mm*)

29th Commonwealth Games, Delhi, India.

(Des M. Totty)

2010 (23 Sept). Multicoloured cover as Type B **34**. Booklet contains text and illustrations on panes and interleaving pages. Stitched.
SB95   £12.68 booklet containing panes Nos. 1355a/60a.......... 29·00

B **35** Prince William *(Illustration reduced. Actual size 163×99 mm)*

30th Birthday of Prince William

(Des M. Totty)

2012 (8 May). Multicoloured cover as Type B **35**. Booklet contains text and illustrations on interleaving pages. Stitched.

SB96 £12.36 booklet containing panes Nos. 1421a/6a............ 29·00
Withdrawn: 7.5.2013.

B **36** Clematis Flower *(Illustration reduced. Actual size 163×98 mm)*

Raymond Evison 25 Years of Gold. Clematis

2013 (13 Nov). Booklet contains text and illustrations on panes and interleaving pages. Magenta cover, 163×98 mm, as Type B **36**. Stitched.

SB97 £14.44 booklet containing panes Nos. 1483a/8a............ 32·00

B **37** Guernsey Cow, The Little Chapel

'Love the Bailiwick'

2014 (30 July). Multicoloured covers as Type B **37**. Self-adhesive.

SB98 (£4.10) booklet containing pane No. 1525b
(cover Type B **37**, 102×59 mm)................ 9·50
SB99 (£5.50) booklet containing pane No. 1530b
(cover showing Vazon Bay, 102×59
mm) .... 12·50
SB100 (£41.00) booklet containing ten panes of
No. 1525c (181×60 mm) .... 85·00
SB101 (£55.00) booklet containing ten panes of
No. 1530c (181×60 mm) £110

B **38** Pte Yves Cataroche, Major George Le Page, Dorothy Nicolls, Lt. Frank Lainé, Ada Le Poidevin and Pte Latimer Le Poidevin

Stories from the Great War (1st issue)

(Des Charlotte Barnes)

2014 (11 Nov). Multicoloured cover, 162×98 mm, as Type B **38**. Booklet contains text and illustrations on interleaving pages. Stitched.

SB102 £14.92 booklet containing panes
Nos. 1542a/7a.. 34·00

B **39** Rejoicing Crowds outside The Royal Court, Guernsey

70th Anniversary of Liberation

(Des Mark Totty)

2015 (1 May). Multicoloured cover, 163×98 mm, as Type B **39**. Stitched.
SB103 £14.48 booklet containing panes Nos. 1563a/8a... 34·00

Stories from the Great War (2nd issue).

2015 (11 Nov). Multicoloured cover, 162×98 mm, as Type B **38**. Booklet contains text and illustrations on panes and interleaving pages. Stitched.

SB104 £14.48 booklet containing panes Nos. 1589a/94a.. 32·00

ALDERNEY

The following issues are provided by the Guernsey Post Office for use on Alderney. They are also valid for postal purposes throughout the rest of the Bailiwick of Guernsey.

A **1** Island Map

A **2** Hanging Rock

A **3** States' Building, St. Anne

A **4** St. Anne's Church

A **5** Yachts in Braye Bay

A **6** Victoria St, St. Anne

A **7** Map of Channel

A **8** Fort Clonque

A **9** Corblets Bay and Fort

A **10** Old Tower, St. Anne

A **11** Golf Course and Essex Castle

A **12** Old Harbour

A **12a** Quesnard Lighthouse

A **12b** Braye Harbour

A **12c** The Island Hall

A **12d** J. T. Daly (steam locomotive)

A **12e** Louis Marchesi of Round Table (lifeboat)

Island Scenes

(Des G. Drummond. Litho BDT (20p. to 28p.) or photo Courvoisier (others))

1983 (14 June)–**93**. Granite paper (1p to 18p.). P 15×14 (20p. to 28p.) or 11½ (others), both comb.

A1	A **1**	1p. multicoloured (a)	10	10
A2	A **2**	4p. multicoloured (a)	10	10
A3	A **3**	9p. multicoloured (a)	20	15
A4	A **4**	10p. multicoloured (a)	25	15
A5	A **5**	11p. multicoloured (a)	25	20
A6	A **6**	12p. multicoloured (a)	25	20
A7	A **7**	13p. multicoloured (a)	25	20
A8	A **8**	14p. multicoloured (a)	30	25
A9	A **9**	15p. multicoloured (a)	35	30
A10	A **10**	16p. multicoloured (a)	35	30
A11	A **11**	17p. multicoloured (a)	40	35
A12	A **12**	18p. multicoloured (a)	40	35
A12a	A **12a**	20p. multicoloured (b)	1·00	1·00
A12b	A **12b**	21p. multicoloured (c)	1·00	1·00
A12c	A **12c**	23p. multicoloured (d)	95	1·00
A12d	A **12d**	24p. multicoloured (e)	1·70	1·70
A12e	A **12e**	28p. multicoloured (e)	2·20	2·20
A1/12e *Set of 17*			9·00	9·00
First Day Covers (6)				22·00
Presentation Pack (2)			11·00	
Set of 17 Gutter Pairs			18·00	

Printings: (a) 14.6.83; (b) 27.12.89; (c) 2.4.91; (d) 6.2.92; (e) 2.3.93.
Plate and Cylinder Nos.: 1p., 12p., 13p., 17p., 20p. to 28p. 1A, 1B, 1C, 1D (each×4); others 1A, 1B, 1C, 1D (each×5).
Sheets: 40 (2 panes 5×4).
Imprint: Central, bottom margin.
Quantities sold: 1p. 1,337,865; 4p. 465,887; 9p. 680,896; 10p. 709,197; 11p. 778,483; 12p. 573,124; 13p. 671,772; 14p. 1,027,248; 15p. 740,519; 16p. 542,970; 17p. 404,323; 18p. 491,877; 20p. 248,694; 21p. 233,975; 23p. 237,345; 24p. 311,144; 28p. 134,765.
Withdrawn: 4.6.94.

A **13** Oystercatcher

A **14** Ruddy Turnstone

A **15** Ringed Plover

A **16** Dunlin

A **17** Curlew

Birds

(Des and photo Harrison)

1984 (12 June). P 14½ (C).

A13	A **13**	9p. multicoloured	1·10	90
A14	A **14**	13p. multicoloured	1·10	90
A15	A **15**	26p. multicoloured	2·50	2·75
A16	A **16**	28p. multicoloured	2·50	2·75
A17	A **17**	31p. multicoloured	2·50	2·25
A13/17 *Set of 5*			8·75	8·50
First Day Cover				9·00
Presentation Pack			10·00	
Set of 5 Gutter Pairs			17·00	

Cylinder Nos.: All values 1A, 1B (each×5).
Sheets: 50 (2 panes 5×5).
Imprint: Bottom margin, right-hand corner.
Quantities sold: 9p. 285,931; 13p. 360,619; 26p. 246,916; 28p. 261,370; 31p. 334,484.
Withdrawn: 11.6.85.

A **18** Westland Wessex HCC.4 Helicopter of the Queen's Flight

A **19** Britten Norman 'long-nose' Trislander

A **20** De Havilland D.H.114 Heron 1B

A **21** De Havilland D.H.89A Dragon Rapide *Sir Henry Lawrence*

A **22** Saro A.21 Windhover Amphibian *City of Portsmouth*

50th Anniversary of Alderney Airport

(Des A. Theobald. Photo Courvoisier)

1985 (19 Mar). Granite paper. P 11½ (C).

A18	A **18**	9p. multicoloured	1·40	1·00
A19	A **19**	13p. multicoloured	1·70	1·50
A20	A **20**	29p. multicoloured	3·00	2·75
A21	A **21**	31p. multicoloured	3·50	3·50
A22	A **22**	34p. multicoloured	3·50	3·50
A18/22 *Set of 5*			12·00	11·00
First Day Cover				14·00
Presentation Pack			14·00	

Cylinder Nos.: All values A1–1–1–1–1, B1–1–1–1–1.
Sheets: 25 (5×5).
Quantities sold: 9p. 294,437; 13p. 321,276; 29p. 231,422; 31p. 171,528; 34p. 162,429.
Withdrawn: 18.3.86.

A **23** Royal Engineers, 1890

A **24** Duke of Albany's Own Highlanders (72nd Highland Regt), 1856

A **25** Royal Artillery, 1855

A **26** South Hampshire Regiment, 1810

A **27** Royal IrishRegiment, 1782

Regiments of the Alderney Garrison

(Des E. Stemp. Litho Harrison)

1985 (24 Sept). P 14½ (C).

A23	A **23**	9p. multicoloured	40	30
A24	A **24**	14p. multicoloured	95	80
A25	A **25**	29p. multicoloured	95	80
A26	A **26**	31p. multicoloured	1·50	1·30
A27	A **27**	34p. multicoloured	1·75	1·60
A23/7 *Set of 5*			5·00	4·25
First Day Cover				6·00
Presentation Pack			6·00	
Set of 5 Gutter Pairs			10·00	

No. A24 shows the tartan and insignia of the 78th Highland Regiment in error.

Plate Nos.: All values 1A, 1B, 1C, 1D (each×5).
Sheets: 50 (2 panes 5×5).
Imprint: Central, left-hand margin of each pane.
Quantities sold: 9p. 286,572; 14p. 283,493; 29p. 224,196; 31p. 151,948; 34p. 145,422.
Withdrawn: 23.9.86.

A **28** Fort Grosnez

A **29** Fort Tourgis

A **30** Fort Clonque

A **31** Fort Albert

Alderney Forts

(Des R. Reed. Litho Cartor)

1986 (23 Sept). P 13×13½ (C).

A28	A **28**	10p. multicoloured	80	20
A29	A **29**	14p. multicoloured	90	80
A30	A **30**	31p. multicoloured	2·50	3·00
A31	A **31**	34p. multicoloured	2·50	3·00
A28/31 *Set of 4*			6·00	6·25
First Day Cover				8·00
Presentation Pack			7·00	
Set of 4 Gutter Pairs			12·00	

Plate Nos.: All values 1A, 1B, 1C, 1D (each×5).
Sheets: 50 (2 panes 5×5).
Imprint: Left-hand margin of left-hand pane.
Quantities sold: 10p. 325,706; 14p. 231,891; 31p. 143,423; 34p. 138,556.
Withdrawn: 22.9.87.

A **32** *Liverpool* (full-rigged ship), 1902

A **33** *Petit Raymond* (schooner), 1906

A **34** *Maina* (yacht), 1910

A **35** *Burton* (steamer), 1911

A **36** *Point Law* (oil tanker), 1975

Alderney Shipwrecks

(Des C. Jacques. Litho Questa)

1987 (5 May). P 14×14½ (C).

A32	A **32**	11p. multicoloured	1·40	1·20
A33	A **33**	15p. multicoloured	1·50	1·20
A34	A **34**	29p. multicoloured	2·75	3·00
A35	A **35**	31p. multicoloured	3·00	3·25
A36	A **36**	34p. multicoloured	3·50	3·75
A32/6 *Set of 5*			12·00	12·00
First Day Cover				13·00
Presentation Pack			15·00	
Set of 5 Gutter Pairs			24·00	

Plate Nos.: All values 1A, 1B, 1C, 1D (each×4).
Sheets: 50 (2 panes 5×5).
Imprint: Bottom, right-hand margin of each pane.
Quantities sold: 11p. 228,998; 15p. 233,861; 29p. 139,453; 31p. 148,572; 34p. 145,641.
Withdrawn: 4.5.88.

A **37** Moll's Map of 1724

A **38** Bastide's Survey of 1739

A **39** Goodwin's Map of 1831

A **40** General Staff Map of 1943

A **41** Ordnance Survey Map of 1988

250th Anniversary of Bastide's Survey of Alderney

(Des J. Cooter. Litho Enschedé)

1989 (7 July). P 13½×14 (C).

A37	A **37**	12p. multicoloured	30	25
A38	A **38**	18p. blk, greenish blue & orge-brn	45	30
A39	A **39**	27p. black, greenish blue and dull yellow-green	95	1·10
A40	A **40**	32p. black, greenish blue & brt rose-red	1·10	1·10
A41	A **41**	35p. multicoloured	1·50	1·40
A37/41 *Set of 5*			3·75	3·75
First Day Cover				4·75
Presentation Pack			5·00	
Set of 5 Gutter Pairs			7·50	

Plate Nos.: 12p. 1–1–1–1; 18p., 27p., 32p. 1–1–1; 35p. 1–1–1–1.
Sheets: 50 (2 panes 5×5).
Imprint: Central, both margins of each pane.
Quantities sold: 12p. 169,993; 18p. 194,667; 27p. 148,621; 32p. 158,600; 35p. 153,544.
Withdrawn: 6.7.90.

A **42** H.M.S. *Alderney* (bomb ketch), 1738

A **43** H.M.S. *Alderney* (frigate), 1742

A **44** H.M.S. *Alderney* (sloop), 1755

A **45** H.M.S. *Alderney* (submarine), 1945

A **46** H.M.S. *Alderney* (patrol vessel), 1979

Royal Navy Ships named after Alderney

(Des A. Theobald. Litho BDT)

1990 (3 May). P 13½ (C).

A42	A **42**	14p. black and olive-bistre	35	20
A43	A **43**	20p. black and orange-brown	50	35
A44	A **44**	29p. black and cinnamon	1·00	1·10
A45	A **45**	34p. black & pale turquoise-blue	1·20	1·50
A46	A **46**	37p. black and cobalt	1·40	1·50
A42/6 *Set of 5*			4·00	4·00

First Day Cover.. 5·50
Presentation Pack.. 5·00
Set of 5 Gutter Pairs... 8·00
    Plate Nos.: 14p., 20p., 29p, 34p. 1A–1A, 1B–1B, 37p. 1A–1A, 1B–1B,
    1C–1C, 1D–1D.
    Sheets: 50 (2 panes 5×5).
    Imprint: Central, side margins of each pane.
    Quantities sold: 14p. 290,801; 20p. 291,996; 29p. 142,011; 34p.
    146,711; 37p. 151,711.
    Withdrawn: 4.5.91.

A **47** Wreck of H.M.S. *Victory*, 1744

A **48** Lighthouse Keeper's Daughter rowing back to the Casquets

A **49** MBB-Bolkow Bo105D Helicopter leaving pad on St. Thomas Tower

A **50** Migrating Birds over Lighthouse

A **51** Trinity House Vessel *Patricia* and Arms

Automation of the Casquets Lighthouse

(Des A. Theobald. Litho Cartor)

1991 (30 Apr). P 14×13½ (C).

A47	A **47**	21p. multicoloured	80	50
A48	A **48**	26p. multicoloured	1·90	1·70
A49	A **49**	31p. multicoloured	2·00	2·20
A50	A **50**	37p. multicoloured	2·75	3·25
A51	A **51**	50p. multicoloured	3·75	3·50
A47/51	Set of 5		10·00	9·00
First Day Cover				9·00
Presentation Pack			10·50	
Set of 5 Gutter Pairs			20·00	

    Plate Nos.: All values 1A, 1B, 1C, 1D (each×4).
    Sheets: 50 (2 panes 5×5).
    Imprint: Central, side margins.
    Quantities sold: 21p. 280,555; 26p. 164,155; 31p. 158,465; 37p.
    158,375; 50p. 238,825.
    Withdrawn: 29.4.92.

A **52** Two French Warships on Fire   A **53** Crews leaving burning Ships   A **54** French Warship sinking

A **55** 'The Battle of La Hogue'

300th Anniversary of Battle of La Hogue

(Des C. Abbott. Litho BDT)

1992 (18 Sept). P 14×15 (50p) or 13½ (others), both comb.

A52	A **52**	23p. multicoloured	1·10	1·00
A53	A **53**	28p. multicoloured	2·40	2·50
A54	A **54**	33p. multicoloured	2·75	3·00
A55	A **55**	50p. multicoloured	3·00	3·50
A52/5	Set of 4		8·00	9·00
First Day Cover				8·50
Presentation Pack			9·00	
Set of 4 Gutter Pairs			16·00	

    Nos. A52/4 show details of the painting on the 50p value.
    Plate Nos.: All values 1A, 1B (each×5).
    Sheets: 50 (2 panes 5×5).
    Imprint: Central, right-hand margin (50p.) or central, side margins
    (others).
    Quantities sold: 23p. 238,820; 28p. 188,685; 33p. 172,565; 50p.
    186,096.
    Withdrawn: 17.9.93.

A **56** Spiny Lobster   A **57** Plumrose Anemone

A **58** Starfish   A **59** Sea Urchin

Endangered Species. Marine Life

(Des A. Peck. Litho Questa)

1993 (2 Nov). P 14½ (C).

A56	A **56**	24p. multicoloured	60	30
		a. Horiz strip of 4. Nos. A56/9	5·50	6·00
A57	A **57**	28p. multicoloured	60	35
A58	A **58**	33p. multicoloured	70	40
A59	A **59**	39p. multicoloured	90	60
A56/9	Set of 4		5·50	6·00
First Day Cover				6·00
Presentation Pack			6·50	

    Plate Nos.: All values 1A, 1B (each×5).
    Sheets: 16 (4×4). Nos. A56/9 were printed together, *se-tenant*, in
    horizontal strips of 4 throughout the sheet.
    Imprint: Central, right-hand margin.
    Quantity sold: 216,788 strips.
    Withdrawn: 1.11.94.

A **60** Blue-tailed Damselfly, Dark Hair Water Crowfoot and Branched Bur-reed

A **61** White-toothed Shrew and Flax–leaved St. John's Wort

A **62** Fulmar and Kaffir Fig

A **63** Clouded Yellow (butterfly) and Red Clover

A **64** Bumble Bee, Prostrate Broom and Giant Broomrape

A **65** Dartford Warbler and Lesser Dodder

A **66** Peacock (butterfly) and Stemless Thistle

A **67** Mole and Bluebell

A **68** Great Green Grasshopper and Common Gorse

A **69** Six-spot Burnet (moth) and Viper's Bugloss

A **70** Common Blue (butterfly) and Pyramidal Orchid

A **70a** Small Tortoiseshell (butterfly) and Buddleia

A **71** Common Rabbit and Creeping Buttercup

A **72** Greater Black-backed Gull and Sand Crocus

A **72a** Rock Pipit and Sea Stock

A **72b** Sand Digger Wasp and Sea Bindweed

A **73** Atlantic Puffin and English Stonecrop

A **74** Emperor (moth) and Bramble

A **75** Pale-spined Hedgehog and Pink Oxalis

A **76** Common Tern and Bermuda Grass

A **77** Northern Gannet and *Fucus vesiculosus* (seaweed)

Flora and Fauna

(Des Wendy Bramall. Litho BDT (No. A71a) or Questa (others))

1994 (5 May)–**98**. P 14½ (C).

A60	A **60**	1p. multicoloured (a)	10	10
A61	A **61**	2p. multicoloured (a)	10	10
A62	A **62**	3p. multicoloured (a)	10	10
A63	A **63**	4p. multicoloured (a)	10	10
A64	A **64**	5p. multicoloured (a)	10	10
A65	A **65**	6p. multicoloured (a)	15	20
A66	A **66**	7p. multicoloured (a)	15	20
A67	A **67**	8p. multicoloured (a)	15	20
A68	A **68**	9p. multicoloured (a)	20	25
A69	A **69**	10p. multicoloured (a)	20	25
A70	A **70**	16p. multicoloured (a)	55	40
		a. Perf 14×15	55	50
		ab. Booklet pane of 8	4·00	
A70b	A **70a**	18p. multicoloured (c)	35	40
		ba. Perf 14×15	35	40
		bb. Booklet pane of 8	3·00	
A71	A **71**	20p. multicoloured (a)	40	45
		a. Perf 14×15 (d)	40	45
		ab. Booklet pane of 8	3·75	
A72	A **72**	24p. multicoloured (a)	50	55
		a. Perf 14×15	50	55
		ab. Booklet pane of 8	4·25	
A72b	A **72a**	25p. multicoloured (c)	50	55
		ba. Perf 14×15	50	55
		bb. Booklet pane of 8	4·00	
A72c	A **72b**	26p. multicoloured (c)	50	55
A73	A **73**	30p. multicoloured (a)	60	65
A74	A **74**	40p. multicoloured (a)	80	85
A75	A **75**	50p. multicoloured (a)	1·50	1·20
A76	A **76**	£1 multicoloured (a)	2·50	2·20
A77	A **77**	£2 multicoloured (b)	5·00	4·50
A60/77 *Set of 21*			12·50	13·00
First Day Covers (5)				17·00
Presentation Packs (3)			16·00	
Stamp-cards (set of 21)			4·50	18·00
Set of 21 Gutter Pairs			25·00	

Nos. A70a, A70ba, A71a, A72a and A72ba were issued in booklets with the upper and lower edges of the panes imperforate. Unfolded booklet panes were also available from the Philatelic Bureau and Head Post Office.

Printings: (a) 5.5.94; (b) 28.2.95; (c) 2.1.97; (d) 25.3.98.
Plate Nos.: 1p., 3p., 5p., 7p., 9p., 16p., 18p., 20p., 25p., 26p., 40p.
1A, 1B (each×4); 2p., 4p., 6p., 8p., 10p., 24p., 30p., 50p. 1C, 1D
(each×4); £1, £2 1A, 1B, 1C, 1D (each×4).
Sheets: 50 (2 panes 5× 5).
Imprint: £1, £2 Central left margin of each pane; others central
left or right margin of each pane.
Sold out: 4.2001 (1p. to 16p., 20p., 24p., 30p to £1); by 10.2006
(18p., 25p., 26p. and £2).

A **78** Royal Aircraft Factory SE5A

A **79** Miles Master II and other Miles
Aircraft

A **80** Miles Aerovan and Miles Monitor

A **81** Miles Falcon Six winning King's
Cup Air Race, 1935

A **82** Miles Hawk Speed Six winning
Manx Air Derby, 1947

A **83** Miles Falcon Six breaking
U.K.–Cape Record, 1936

Birth Centenary of Tommy Rose (aviator)

(Des C. Abbott. Litho BDT)

1995 (1 Sept). P 14×15 (C).

A78	A **78**	35p. multicoloured	95	95
		a. Horiz strip of 3. Nos. A78/80	2·75	2·75
A79	A **79**	35p. multicoloured	95	95
A80	A **80**	35p. multicoloured	95	95
A81	A **81**	41p. multicoloured	1·10	1·10
		a. Horiz strip of 3. Nos. A81/3	3·25	3·25
A82	A **82**	41p. multicoloured	1·10	1·10
A83	A **83**	41p. multicoloured	1·10	1·10
A78/83 *Set of 6*			6·00	6·00
First Day Cover				6·75
Presentation Pack			7·50	
Gutter strips of 6 (2)			12·00	

Plate Nos.: Both values 1A, 1B, 1C (each×5).
Sheets: 12 (2 panes 3×2). Nos. A78/80 and A81/3 were printed
together, *se-tenant*, as horizontal strips of 3 throughout the sheet.
Imprint: Central, bottom margin.
Quantities sold: 35p. 361,895 strips; 41p. 362,801 strips.
Withdrawn: 31.8.96.

A **84** Returning Islanders (*Illustration reduced.
Actual size 93×70 mm*)

50th Anniversary of Return of Islanders to Alderney

(Des C. Abbott. Litho BDT)

1995 (16 Nov). Sheet 93×70 mm. P 13½ (C).

MSA84 A **84**	£1.65 multicoloured	5·00	5·00
First Day Cover			5·50
Presentation Pack		5·50	

Quantity sold: 139,665.
Withdrawn: 15.11.96.

A **85** Signallers training on
Alderney

A **86** Communications Station,
Falkland Islands

A **87** Dish Aerial and Land Rover,
Gulf War

A **88** Service with United
Nations

**25th Anniversary of Adoption of 30th Signal Regiment by
Alderney**

(Des A. Theobald. Litho Walsall)

1996 (24 Jan). P 14 (C).

A85	A **85**	24p. multicoloured	45	35
		a. Horiz strip of 4. Nos. A85/8	5·50	5·50
A86	A **86**	41p. multicoloured	75	55
A87	A **87**	60p. multicoloured	1·10	80
A88	A **88**	75p. multicoloured	1·10	1·10
A85/8 *Set of 4*			5·50	5·50
First Day Cover				6·00
Presentation Pack			6·75	
Gutter strip of 8 (4×2)			11·00	

A **153** Royal Engineers' Colour Party, 1859

A **154** Royal Artillery on Parade, Queen's 40th Birthday, 1859

A **155** Royal Artillery Guard of Honour

A **156** Arrival of Maj.–Gen. Marcus Slade, 1863

Garrison Island (4th series). Events

(Des R. Carter. Litho Cartor)

2000 (19 Oct). P 13 (C).

A154	A **149**	21p. multicoloured	45	25
		a. Horiz pair. Nos. A154/5	90	85
		b. Booklet pane. Nos. A154/7 with margins all round	2·40	
		c. Booklet pane. Nos. A154/5 and A160/1 with margins all round	3·00	
A155	A **150**	21p. multicoloured	45	25
A156	A **151**	26p. multicoloured	55	30
		a. Horiz pair. Nos. A156/7	1·10	1·10
		b. Booklet pane. Nos. A156/9 with margins all round	3·00	
A157	A **152**	26p. multicoloured	55	30
A158	A **153**	36p. multicoloured	75	40
		a. Horiz pair. Nos. 158/9	2·00	2·00
		b. Booklet pane. Nos. A158/61 with margins all round	4·50	
A159	A **154**	36p. multicoloured	75	40
A160	A **155**	40p. multicoloured	90	45
		a. Horiz pair. Nos. A160/1	2·50	2·50
A161	A **156**	40p. multicoloured	90	45
A154/61	*Set of 8*		6·00	6·00
First Day Cover				6·25
Presentation Pack			6·25	

Plate Nos.: All values 1A (×4).

Sheets: 20 (4×5), the two designs for each value were printed together, *se-tenant*, in horizontal pairs throughout the sheets, each pair forming a composite design.

Imprint: Central, right-hand margin.

Withdrawn: 18.10.2001.

A **157** Queen Elizabeth II (*Illustration reduced. Actual size 70×70 mm*)

75th Birthday of Queen Elizabeth II

(Des C. Abbott. Litho and die-stamped. BDT)

2001 (1 Feb). Sheet 70×70 mm. P 14 (C).

MSA162	A **157**	£1·75, multicoloured	4·50	4·50
First Day Cover				6·00
Presentation Pack			5·50	

Withdrawn: 31.1.2002.

A **158** Nurse with Clipboard and Patient in X-Ray

A **159** Nurse with Tray and Mignot Memorial Hospital

A **160** Doctor and Princess Anne visiting Hopital, 1972

A **161** Nurse from 1960s and Maternity Unit

A **162** Nurse from 1957 and Queen Elizabeth II laying Hospital Foundation Stone

A **163** Nurse of 1926 with Baby and opening of Original Hospital

Community Services (1st series). Healthcare

(Des Sally Diamond. Litho Walsall)

2001 (26 Apr)–**02**. P 14×14½ (C).

A163	A **158**	22p. multicoloured (a)	45	50
		a. Perf 13½×13 (b)	60	80
		ab. Booklet pane. Nos. A163a/6a with margins all round	3·75	
		ac. Booklet pane. Nos. A163a/4a and A167a/8a with margins all round	4·50	
A164	A **159**	27p. multicoloured (a)	55	60
		a. Perf 13½×13 (b)	55	60
A165	A **160**	36p. multicoloured (a)	70	75
		a. Perf 13½×13 (b)	70	75
		ab. Booklet pane. Nos. A165a/8a with margins all round	4·50	
A166	A **161**	40p. multicoloured (a)	80	85
		a. Perf 13½×13 (b)	1·00	1·20
A167	A **162**	45p. multicoloured (a)	90	95
		a. Perf 13½×13 (b)	1·30	1·50
A168	A **163**	65p. multicoloured (a)	1·20	1·40
		a. Perf 13½×13 (b)	1·50	2·00
A163/8	*Set of 6*		4·50	5·00
First Day Cover				6·00
Presentation Pack			7·50	

Nos. A163a/8a were only issued in £9.40 stamp booklets.

See also Nos. A197/202, A217/22 and A242/7.

Printings: (a) 26.4.01; (b) 17.10.02.

Plate Nos.: All values 1A (×4).

Sheets: 10 (2×5) with enlarged illustrated margin at left (22, 27, 36p.) or right (40, 45, 65p.).

Imprint: Central, right-hand margin (22, 27, 36p.) or central, left-hand margin (40, 45, 65p.).

Withdrawn: 25.4.2002 (sheets).

A **164** 'Feathery' Golf Ball, 1901

A **165** Golfing Fashions of the 1920s

A **166** Alderney Golf Course in 1970s

A **167** Modern
Putter

A **168** Modern Golf
Gloves and Shoes

A **169** Modern
'lofted wood'

30th Anniversary of Alderney Golf Club

(Des Colleen Corlett. Litho Questa)

2001 (1 Aug). P 14½ (C).

A169	A **164**	22p. multicoloured	45	50
A170	A **165**	27p. multicoloured	55	60
A171	A **166**	36p. multicoloured	80	75
A172	A **167**	40p. multicoloured	1·10	1·10
A173	A **168**	45p. multicoloured	1·50	1·50
A174	A **169**	65p. multicoloured	1·70	1·70
A169/74 *Set of 6*			6·00	6·00
First Day Cover				7·50
Presentation Pack			7·50	
Set of 6 Gutter Pairs			12·00	
MSA175 190×75 mm. Nos. A169/74			6·50	6·50
First Day Cover				9·00

No. **MS**A175 shows the 'Philanippon '01' logo on the margin.
Plate Nos.: All values 1A (×5).
Sheets: 50 (2 panes 5×5).
Imprint: Upper right-hand margin.
Withdrawn: 31.7.2002.

A **170** Construction of
New Breakwater, 1853

A **171** Official Party inspecting
Harbour, 1853

A **172** H.M.S. *Emerald* (steam
frigate) aground, 1860

A **173** Disembarking Troops
from H.M.S. *Emerald*, 1860

A **174** Moored Torpedo Boats,
1890

A **175** Quick-firing Gun on
Railway Wagon, 1890

A **176** H.M.S. *Majestic*
(battleship) at Anchor, 1901

A **177** Torpedo Boats outside
Harbour, 1901

Garrison Island (5th series). The Royal Navy

(Des R. Carter. Litho Cartor)

2001 (16 Oct). P 13 (C).

A176	A **170**	22p. multicoloured	45	25
		a. Horiz pair. Nos. A176/7	1·00	1·00
		b. Booklet pane. Nos. A176/9 with margins all round	2·50	
		c. Booklet pane. Nos. A176/7 and A182/3 with margins all round	3·00	
A177	A **171**	22p. multicoloured	45	25
A178	A **172**	27p. multicoloured	55	30
		a. Horiz pair. Nos. A178/9	1·20	1·20
		b. Booklet pane. Nos. A178/81 with margins all round	3·00	
		c. Booklet pane. Nos. A178/9 and A182/3 with margins all round	3·75	
A179	A **173**	27p. multicoloured	55	30
A180	A **174**	36p. multicoloured	70	40
		a. Horiz pair. Nos. A180/1	1·60	1·60
		b. Booklet pane. Nos. A180/3 with margins all round	3·50	
A181	A **175**	36p. multicoloured	70	40
A182	A **176**	40p. multicoloured	80	45
		a. Horiz pair. Nos. A182/3	2·00	2·00
A183	A **177**	40p. multicoloured	80	45
A176/83 *Set of 8*			6·00	6·00
First Day Cover				8·00
Presentation Pack			8·00	

Plate Nos: All values 1A (×4).
Sheets: 20 (4×5), the two designs for each value were printed together, *se-tenant*, in horizontal pairs throughout the sheets, each pair forming a composite design.
Imprint: Central, right-hand margin.
Withdrawn: 15.10.2002.

A **178** Queen Elizabeth and Prince Philip arriving at
London Airport, Feb 1952 (*Illustration reduced.
Actual size 159×98 mm*)

Golden Jubilee

(Des A. Fothergill. Litho BDT)

2002 (6 Feb). Sheet 159×98 mm. P 13½ (C).

MSA184 A **178** £2 blackish purple and gold		4·00	4·25
	a. Black omitted	£1200	
	b. Booklet pane. No. **MS**A184	4·00	
First Day Cover			7·50
Presentation Pack		5·50	

Withdrawn: 5.2.2003.
Booklet pane **MS**A18b comes from Guernsey booklet SB71.
Withdrawn: 29.4.2003.

A **179** Northern Hobby   A **180** Black Kite

A **181** Merlin   A **182** Honey Buzzard

A **183** Osprey   A **184** Marsh Harrier

Migrating Birds (1st series). Raptors

(Des G. Austin. Litho Questa)

2002 (30 Apr). P 14 (C).
A185	A **179**	22p. multicoloured	60	50
A186	A **180**	27p. multicoloured	70	60
A187	A **181**	36p. multicoloured	1·00	85
A188	A **182**	40p. multicoloured	1·20	1·00
A189	A **183**	45p. multicoloured	1·50	1·20
A190	A **184**	65p. multicoloured	1·70	1·70
A185/90 *Set of 6*			6·50	6·00
First Day Cover				6·50
Presentation Pack			7·50	
MSA191 170×80 mm. Nos. A185/90			7·00	6·50
First Day Cover				7·50

See also Nos. A210/15, A235/40 and A259/64.
Plate Nos.: All values 1A (×4).
Sheets: 10 (2×5).
Imprint: Central, left-hand margin.
Withdrawn: 29.4.2003.

A **185** Coal Fire   A **186** Oil Lantern,   A **187** Argand
Beacon, 1725   1779   Lamp, 1790

A **188** Revolving   A **189** Electric Light,
Light, 1818   1952

50th Anniversary of Electrification of Les Casquets Lighthouse

(Des N. Watton. Litho Enschedé)

2002 (30 July). P 13×13½ (C).
A192	A **185**	22p. multicoloured	50	50
A193	A **186**	27p. multicoloured	60	60
A194	A **187**	36p. multicoloured	75	75
A195	A **188**	45p. multicoloured	1·10	1·10
A196	A **189**	65p. multicoloured	1·50	1·50
A192/6 *Set of 5*			4·50	4·50
First Day Cover				7·50
Presentation Pack			7·50	
Set of 5 Gutter Pairs			8·00	

No. A196 is inscribed 'Elictrification' in error.
Plate Nos.: All values 1A (×4).
Sheets: 50 (2 panes 5×5).
Imprint: Lower left-hand margin.
Withdrawn: 29.7.2003.

A **190** Ambulance   A **191** Ambulance Technician
Technician, and Ambulance   using Radio, and Ambulance
Station

A **192** Doctor, and loading   A **193** Pilot, and Trislander
Patient onto Aircraft   over Alderney

A **194** Emergency Operator,   A **195** Lifebaotman, and
and Patient on Stretcher   *Roy Barker One* (lifeboat)

Community Services (2nd series). Emergency Medical Aid

(Des Sally Diamond. Litho Walsall)

2002 (17 Oct). P 14×14½ (C).
A197	A **190**	22p. multicoloured	45	50
		a. Perf 13½×13	90	90
		ab. Booklet pane. Nos. A197a/200a, with margins all round	5·75	
		ac. Booklet pane. Nos. A197a/200a and A201a/2a, with margins all round	11·00	
A198	A **191**	27p. multicoloured	55	60
		a. Perf 13½×13	1·00	1·00
A199	A **192**	36p. multicoloured	95	95
		a. Perf 13½×13	1·70	1·70
		ab. Booklet pane. Nos. A199a/202a, with margins all round	11·00	
A200	A **193**	40p. multicoloured	1·10	1·10
		a. Perf 13½×13	2·00	2·00
A201	A **194**	45p. multicoloured	1·70	1·70
		a. Perf 13½×13	3·00	3·00
A202	A **195**	65p. multicoloured	2·00	2·00
		a. Perf 13½×13	4·00	4·00
A197/202 *Set of 6*			6·00	6·00
First Day Cover				7·50
Presentation Pack			7·50	

Nos. A197a/202a were only issued in £9.40 stamp booklets.
Plate Nos.: All values 1A (×4).
Sheets: 10 (2×5) with enlarged illustrated margin at left.
Imprint: Central, right-hand margin.
Withdrawn: 16.10.2003.

A **196** St. Edward's Crown *(Illustration reduced.
Actual size 128×90 mm)*

50th Anniversary of Coronation

(Des A. Fothergill. Litho and embossed Enschedé)

2003 (30 Jan). Sheet 128×90 mm. P 13½ (C).
MSA203 A **196** £2 multicoloured	4·50	4·50
First Day Cover		7·50
Presentation Pack	6·00	

Withdrawn: 29.1.2004.

A **197** Wright Brothers' *Flyer I*, 1903

A **198** Alcock and Brown's Vickers FB-27 Vimy, 1919

A **199** Douglas DC-3, 1936

A **200** De Havilland DH106 Comet 4, 1946

A **201** British Aerospace/Aerospatiale Concorde, 1969

A **202** Projected Airbus Industrie A380

Centenary of Powered Flight

(Des M. Wilkinson. Litho BDT)

2003 (10 Apr). P 13½ (C).

A204	A **197**	22p. multicoloured	60	50
A205	A **198**	27p. multicoloured	75	75
A206	A **199**	36p. multicoloured	1·00	85
A207	A **200**	40p. multicoloured	1·20	1·00
A208	A **201**	45p. multicoloured	1·50	1·20
A209	A **202**	65p. multicoloured	1·50	1·50
A204/9	*Set of 6*		6·50	6·00
First Day Cover				7·50
Presentation Pack			7·50	
Set of 6 Gutter Pairs			13·00	

Plate Nos.: All values 1A (×4).
Sheets: 50 (2 panes 5×5).
Imprint: Central, left-hand margin.
Withdrawn: 9.4.2004.

A **203** Arctic Tern

A **204** Great Skua

A **205** Sandwich Tern

A **206** Sooty Shearwater

A **207** Arctic Skua

A **208** Manx Shearwater

Migrating Birds (2nd series). Seabirds

(Des G. Austin. Litho Questa)

2003 (3 July). P 14 (C).

A210	A **203**	22p. multicoloured	65	50
A211	A **204**	27p. multicoloured	75	60
A212	A **205**	36p. multicoloured	1·00	75
A213	A **206**	40p. multicoloured	1·20	1·00
A214	A **207**	45p. multicoloured	1·50	1·50
A215	A **208**	65p. multicoloured	2·00	2·00
A210/15	*Set of 6*		6·50	6·00
First Day Cover				7·50
Presentation Pack			7·50	
MSA216	80×170 mm. Nos. A210/15		6·50	6·00
First Day Cover				7·50

Plate Nos.: All values 1A (×4).
Sheets: 10 (2×5) with enlarged illustrated margin at right.
Imprint: Central, left-hand margin.
Withdrawn: 2.7.2004.

A **209** Policeman with Clipboard and Constable on Beat

A **210** Policeman and Land Rover

A **211** Forensic Team

A **212** Police Constable and Policeman with Child Cyclist

A **213** Policeman directing Traffic and Police at Scene of Accident

A **214** Policewoman and Policeman with Customs Officer

Community Services (3rd series). Alderney Police

(Des Sally Diamond. Litho Walsall)

2003 (16 Oct). P 13½×13 (C).

A217	A **209**	22p. multicoloured	50	50
		a. Booklet pane. Nos. A217/20	4·00	
		b. Booklet pane. Nos. A217/18 and A221/2	4·75	

c. Booklet pane. Nos. A217/19 and
A221 .... 4·00
d. Booklet pane. Nos. A217/18,
A220 and A222 .... 4·50

A218	A **210**	27p. multicoloured	60	60
A219	A **211**	36p. multicoloured	80	80
		a. Booklet pane. Nos. A219/22	5·50	
A220	A **212**	40p. multicoloured	1·00	1·00
A221	A **213**	45p. multicoloured	1·50	1·50
A222	A **214**	65p. multicoloured	2·00	2·00
A217/22	*Set of 6*	....	6·00	6·00
First Day Cover		....		7·50
Presentation Pack		....	6·50	

Plate Nos.: All values 1A (×4).
Sheets: 10 (2×5) with enlarged illustrated margin at left.
Imprint: Central, right-hand margin.
Withdrawn: 15.10.2004.

A **215** *Hypholoma fasciculare*   A **216** *Aleuria aurantia*   A **217** *Coprinus micaceus*

A **218** *Langermannia gigantea*   A **219** *Macrolepiota procera*   A **220** *Xylaria hypoxylon*

Fungi

(Des Petula Stone. Litho Enschedé)

2004 (29 Jan). P 13½ (C).

A223	A **215**	22p. multicoloured	70	70
A224	A **216**	27p. multicoloured	85	85
A225	A **217**	36p. multicoloured	1·20	1·20
A226	A **218**	40p. multicoloured	1·30	1·30
A227	A **219**	45p. multicoloured	1·40	1·40
A228	A **220**	65p. multicoloured	2·10	2·10
A223/8	*Set of 6*	....	7·50	7·50
First Day Cover		....		9·75
Presentation Pack		....	8·50	
Set of 6 Gutter Pairs		....	12·00	

Plate Nos.: All values 1A (×4).
Sheets: 50 (2 panes 5×5).
Imprint: Upper side margins.
Withdrawn: 28.1.2005.

A **221** Boys playing Football, Tourgis Close   A **222** Three Children playing Football, Braye Beach   A **223** Two Boys playing Football in Playground

A **224** Teenagers playing Football, Arch Bay   A **225** Football Match   A **226** Father and Two Children playing Football, Arch Bay

Centenary of FIFA (Fédération Internationale de Football Association)

(Des A. Robinson. Litho Cartor)

2004 (12 May). P 13½ (C).

A229	A **221**	26p. multicoloured	85	85
A230	A **222**	32p. multicoloured	1·10	1·10
A231	A **223**	36p. multicoloured	1·20	1·20
A232	A **224**	40p. multicoloured	1·30	1·30
A233	A **225**	45p. multicoloured	1·50	1·50
A234	A **226**	65p. multicoloured	2·10	2·10
A229/34	*Set of 6*	....	8·00	8·00
First Day Cover		....		10·00
Presentation Pack		....	10·00	

Nos. A229/34 were each perforated in a circle contained within an outer perforated square which continued the design.
Plate Nos.: All values 1A (×4).
Sheets: 50 (5×10).
Imprint: Upper and lower side margins.
Withdrawn: 11.5.2005.

A **227** Northern Wheatear   A **228** Common Redstart

A **229** Yellow Wagtail   A **230** Hoopoe

A **231** Ring Ousel ('Ouzel')   A **232** Sand Martin

Migrating Birds (3rd series). Passerines

(Des A. Robinson. Litho Enschedé)

2004 (29 July). P 13½ (C).

A235	A **227**	26p. multicoloured	85	85
A236	A **228**	32p. multicoloured	1·10	1·10
A237	A **229**	36p. multicoloured	1·20	1·20
A238	A **230**	40p. multicoloured	1·30	1·30
A239	A **231**	45p. multicoloured	1·50	1·50
A240	A **232**	65p. multicoloured	2·10	2·10
A235/40	*Set of 6*	....	8·00	8·00
First Day Cover		....		10·00
Presentation Pack		....	10·00	
MSA241	170×80 mm. Nos. A235/40	....	8·00	8·00
First Day Cover		....		10·00

Plate Nos.: All values 1A, 1B, 1C, 1D (each×4).
Sheets: 10 (2×5) with enlarged illustrated right-hand margin.
Imprint: Central, left-hand margin.
Withdrawn: 28.7.2005.

A **233** Fire Engine   A **234** Fireman up Ladder and Fire Engine at Fort Tourgis

A **235** Airport Service Fire Truck

A **236** Alderney Fire Station

A **237** Airport Training Ground

A **238** Road Accident Training Exercise

Community Services (4th series). Fire Service

(Des M. Legg. Litho Walsall)

2004 (28 Oct). P 13½×13 (C).

A242	A **233**	26p. multicoloured	85	85
		a. Booklet pane. Nos. A242/5 with margins all round	4·50	
		b. Booklet pane. Nos. A242/3 and A246/7 with margins all round	5·50	
		c. Booklet pane. Nos. A242/4 and A246 with margins all round	4·50	
		d. Booklet pane. Nos. A242/3, A245 and A247 with margins all round	5·50	
A243	A **234**	32p. multicoloured	1·10	1·10
A244	A **235**	36p. multicoloured	1·20	1·20
		a. Booklet pane. Nos. A244/7 with margins all round	6·00	
A245	A **236**	40p. multicoloured	1·30	1·30
A246	A **237**	45p. multicoloured	1·50	1·50
A247	A **238**	65p. multicoloured	2·10	2·10
A242/7	*Set of 6*		8·00	8·00
First Day Cover				10·00
Presentation Pack			10·00	

Plate Nos.: All values 1A×4.
Sheets: 10 (2×5) with enlarged illustrated left-hand margin.
Imprint: Central, right-hand margin.
Withdrawn: 27.10.2005.

A **239** Mermaid at her Undersea Home

A **240** Mermaid rescuing drowning Prince

A **241** Mermaid with Sea Witch bargaining her voice for a Human Life

A **242** Mermaids waving to Prince and his Lover on Seashore

A **243** Mermaid carried away by Angels

Birth Bicentenary of Hans Christian Andersen. Scenes from *The Little Mermaid*

(Des N. Watton. Litho Enschedé)

2005 (3 Feb). P 13½×14 (C).

A248	A **239**	26p. multicoloured	50	55
A249	A **240**	32p. multicoloured	65	70
A250	A **241**	36p. multicoloured	1·00	1·00
A251	A **242**	40p. multicoloured	2·00	2·00
A252	A **243**	65p. multicoloured	3·00	3·00
A248/52	*Set of 5*		7·00	7·00
First Day Cover				8·00
Presentation Pack			7·50	

Plate Nos.: All values 1A (×4).
Sheets: 50 (5×10).
Imprint: Upper left-hand margin.
Withdrawn: 2.2.2006.

A **244** Admiral Horatio Nelson

A **245** H.M.S. *Victory*

A **246** Marine firing musket

A **247** Wounded Nelson with Captain Hardy

A **248** H.M.S. *Victory* in battle with *Redoutable*

A **249** Admiral James Lord de Saumarez

Bicentenary of the Battle of Trafalgar

(Des S. Shackleton. Litho Enschedé)

2005 (9 May). P 14×13½ (C).

A253	A **244**	26p. multicoloured	50	55
		a. Booklet pane. Nos. A253/6 with margins all round	2·50	
		b. Booklet pane. Nos. A253/4 and A257/8 with margins all round	4·75	
		c. Booklet pane. Nos. A253 and A256/8 with margins all round	5·00	
A254	A **245**	32p. multicoloured	65	70
		a. Booklet pane. Nos. A254/5 and A257/8	5·00	

A255	A **246**	36p. multicoloured	70	75
		a. Booklet pane. Nos. A255/8 with		
		margins all round	5·00	
A256	A **247**	40p. multicoloured	80	85
A257	A **248**	45p. multicoloured	1·50	1·70
A258	A **249**	65p. multicoloured	2·00	2·50
A253/8	*Set of 6*		6·00	6·50
First Day Cover				7·50
Presentation Pack			7·50	

Plate Nos.: All values 1A (×4).
Sheets: 10 (2×5) with enlarged illustrated left margins.
Imprint: Central right-hand margins.
Withdrawn: 8.5.2006.

A **250** Little Stint

A **251** Common Greenshank

A **252** Golden Plover

A **253** Bar-tailed Godwit

A **254** Green Sandpiper

A **255** Sanderling

Migrating Birds (4th series). Waders

(Des A. Robinson. Litho Enschedé)

2005 (21 July). P 13½ (C).

A259	A **250**	26p. multicoloured	50	55
A260	A **251**	32p. multicoloured	65	70
A261	A **252**	36p. multicoloured	70	75
A262	A **253**	40p. multicoloured	1·00	85
A263	A **254**	45p. multicoloured	2·00	2·00
A264	A **255**	65p. multicoloured	3·00	3·00
A259/64	*Set of 6*		7·50	7·50
First Day Cover				8·50
Presentation Pack			8·50	
MSA265	170×80 mm. Nos. A259/64		8·00	8·00
First Day Cover				9·00

Plate Nos.: All values 1A (×4).
Sheets: 10 (2×5) with enlarged illustrated right margins.
Imprint: Lower left-hand margins.
Withdrawn: 20.7.2006.

A **256** Alderney Arms and Sunset (*Illustration reduced. Actual size 140×80 mm*)

60th Anniversary of Return of War Evacuees

(Des P. Furness. Litho BDT)

2005 (27 Oct). Sheet 140×80 mm. P 14 (C).

MSA266	A **256**	£2 multicoloured................................	6·00	7·50
First Day Cover				8·50
Presentation Pack			8·50	

Withdrawn: 26.10.2006.

A **257** Young King Arthur

A **258** Merlyn

A **259** Morgause

A **260** Queen Guenever

A **261** Lancelot

A **262** Mordred

'The Once and Future King'

(Des N. Watton. Litho Enschedé)

2006 (16 Feb). P 13½×14 (C).

A267	A **257**	29p. multicoloured	60	65
A268	A **258**	34p. multicoloured	70	75
A269	A **259**	38p. multicoloured	1·00	1·00
A270	A **260**	42p. multicoloured	1·50	1·50
A271	A **261**	47p. multicoloured	1·90	1·90
A272	A **262**	68p. multicoloured	2·20	2·20
A267/72	*Set of 6*		8·00	8·00
First Day Cover				9·00
Presentation Pack			9·00	
MSA273	120×90 mm. Nos. A267/72		8·50	8·50
First Day Cover				9·50

Nos. A267/**MS**A273 commemorate the birth centenary of Terence Hanbury White, author of *'The Once and Future King'*.
Plate Nos.: All values 1A (×4).
Sheets: 10 (2×5) with enlarged illustrated right margins.
Imprint: Lower left-hand margin.
Withdrawn: 15.2.2007.

A **263** Princess Elizabeth

A **264** Princess Elizabeth

A **265** Queen Elizabeth II, c. 1955

A **266** Wearing Brown Coat and Hat

A **267** Wearing Tiara

A **268** Wearing Red Jacket and Red and White Hat

A **269** Wearing Pale Pink Hat

A **270** Wearing Mauve Dress and Hat

80th Birthday of Queen Elizabeth II

(Des P. Furness. Litho Austrian State Ptg Wks, Vienna)

2006 (21 Apr). P 14 (C).

A274	A **263**	29p. multicoloured	30	30
		a. Horiz pair. Nos. A274/5	1·30	1·30
A275	A **264**	29p. multicoloured	30	30
A276	A **265**	34p. multicoloured	50	50
		a. Horiz pair. Nos. A276/7	1·50	1·50
A277	A **266**	34p. multicoloured	50	50
A278	A **267**	42p. multicoloured	85	90
		a. Horiz pair. Nos. A278/9	2·50	2·50
A279	A **268**	42p. multicoloured	85	90
A280	A **269**	45p. multicoloured	90	95
		a. Horiz pair. Nos. A280/1	3·00	3·00
A281	A **270**	45p. multicoloured	90	95
A274/81 Set of 8			8·00	8·00
First Day Cover				9·50
Presentation Pack			9·50	

Nos. A274/81 in sheets of ten were included in a souvenir folder, together with the £10 stamp issued by Guernsey to celebrate The Queen's birthday (see Guernsey No. 1122).

Plate Nos.: All values 1A (×4).

Sheets: 10 (2×5) with enlarged illustrated left margins. Nos. A274/5, A276/7, A278/9 and A280/1 were each printed together, *se-tenant*, in horizontal pairs throughout the sheets.

Imprint: Lower right-hand margin.

Withdrawn: 20.4.2007.

A **271** Fulmar

A **272** Gannet

A **273** Lesser Black-backed Gull

A **274** Storm Petrel

A **275** Kittiwake

A **276** Puffin

Resident Birds (1st series). Seabirds

(Des A. Robinson. Litho BDT)

2006 (27 July). P 14 (C).

A282	A **271**	29p. multicoloured	65	65
		a. Booklet pane. No. A282×4 with margins all round	2·50	
A283	A **272**	34p. multicoloured	75	75
		a. Booklet pane. No.A283×4 with margins all round	3·00	
A284	A **273**	42p. multicoloured	1·00	1·00
		a. Booklet pane. No. A284×4 with margins all round	4·00	
A285	A **274**	45p. multicoloured	1·50	1·50
		a. Booklet pane. No. 285×4 with margins all round	6·00	
A286	A **275**	47p. multicoloured	2·00	2·00
		a. Booklet pane. No.A286×4 with margins all round	8·00	
A287	A **276**	68p. multicoloured	3·00	3·00
		a. Booklet pane. No. A287×4 with margins all round	12·00	
A282/7 Set of 6			8·00	8·00
First Day Cover				9·50
Presentation Pack			9·50	

See also Nos. A316/21, A336/41 and A363/8.

Plate Nos.: All values 1A (×4).

Sheets: 10 (2×5) with enlarged illustrated margins at right and foot.

Imprint: Upper left-hand margin.

Withdrawn: 26.7.2007.

A **277** *Cerianthus lloydii* (burrowing anemone)

A **278** *Parazoanthus axinellae* (colonial anemone)

A **279** *Corynactis viridis* (jewel anemone colony)

A **280** *Sagartia elegans* (elegant anemone)

A **281** *Alcyonium glomeratum* (red fingers)

A **282** *Metridium senile* (plumose anemone)

A **283** *Eunicella verrucosa* (fan coral)

A **284** *Corynactis viridis* (jewel anemone)

A **285** *Actinothoe sphyrodeta* (sandalled anemone)

A **286** *Anemonia viridis* (snakelocks anemone)

A **287** *Caryophyllia smithii* (Devonshire cup coral)

A **290** *Actinothoe sphyrodeta* (fried egg anemone)

A **293** *Calliactis parasitica* (parasitic anemone)

A **295** *Actinia equina* (beadlet anemone)

A **296** *Leptopsammia pruvoti* (sunset cup coral)

A **297** *Actinia fragacea* (strawberry anemone)

Corals and Anemones

(Des Sue Daly. Litho (£4 also embossed) Austrian State Ptg Wks, Vienna (20p. to 50p., £4) or Enschedé (others))

2006 (2 Nov)–07. P 14 (20p. to 50p., £4) or 13×13½ (others), both comb.

A288	A **277**	1p. multicoloured (a)	10	10
A289	A **278**	2p. multicoloured (a)	10	10
A290	A **279**	3p. multicoloured (a)	10	10
A291	A **280**	4p. multicoloured (a)	10	15
A292	A **281**	5p. multicoloured (a)	10	15
A293	A **282**	6p. multicoloured (a)	10	15
A294	A **283**	7p. multicoloured (a)	15	20
A295	A **284**	8p. multicoloured (a)	15	20
A296	A **285**	9p. multicoloured (a)	20	25
A297	A **286**	10p. multicoloured (a)	20	25
A298	A **287**	20p. multicoloured (b)	45	45
A301	A **290**	40p. multicoloured (b)	95	95
A304	A **293**	50p. multicoloured (b)	1·20	1·20
A306	A **295**	£1 multicoloured (a)	2·00	2·10
A307	A **296**	£2 multicoloured (a)	4·00	4·25
A308	A **297**	£4 multicoloured (b)	9·50	9·50
A288/308 *Set of 16*			19·00	20·00
First Day Covers (4)				23·00
Presentation Packs (2)			22·00	
Set of 16 Gutter Pairs			38·00	

Nos. A299/300, A302/3 and A305 are left for additions to these definitive stamps.

Printings: (a) 2.11.2006; (b) 2.8.2007.
Plate Nos.: All values 1A (×4).
Sheets: 50 (2 panes 5×5).
Imprint: Central, side margins.

A **298** Cushion Starfish

A **299** Gannet Colony at Les Etacs

A **300** Spiny Squat Lobster

A **301** Grey Seal

A **302** Golden Samphire near Fort Clonque

A **303** Little Egret and Oystercatchers

Designation of Alderney West Coast and the Burhou Islands as Ramsar Site

(Des Wendy Bramall. Litho BDT)

2007 (8 Mar). P 13½ (C).

A309	A **298**	32p. multicoloured	75	75
A310	A **299**	37p. multicoloured	90	90
A311	A **300**	45p. multicoloured	1·10	1·10
A312	A **301**	48p. multicoloured	1·10	1·10
A313	A **302**	50p. multicoloured	1·20	1·20
A314	A **303**	71p. multicoloured	1·70	1·70
A309/14 *Set of 6*			6·75	6·75

First Day Cover			8·50
Presentation Pack		8·50	
MSA315 140×95 mm. Nos. A309/14		6·75	6·75
First Day Cover			8·50

Plate Nos.: All values 1A (×4).
Sheets: 10 (2×5) with enlarged illustrated margins at right and foot.
Imprint: Central, left-hand margin.
Withdrawn: 7.3.2007.

A **304** Balckbird

A **305** Dartford Warbler

A **306** Blue Tit

A **307** Wren

A **308** House Sparrow

A **309** Jackdaw

Resident Birds (2nd series). Passerines

(Des Andrew Robinson. Litho BDT)

2007 (24 May). P 14 (C).

A316	A **304**	32p. multicoloured	75	75
		a. Booklet pane. No. A316×4 with margins all round	3·00	
A317	A **305**	37p. multicoloured	90	90
		a. Booklet pane. No. A317×4 with margins all round	3·50	
A318	A **306**	45p. multicoloured	1·10	1·10
		a. Booklet pane. No. A318×4 with margins all round	4·50	
A319	A **307**	48p. multicoloured	1·25	1·25
		a. Booklet pane. No. A319×4 with margins all round	4·75	
A320	A **308**	50p. multicoloured	1·25	1·25
		a. Booklet pane. No. A320×4 with margins all round	5·25	
A321	A **309**	71p. multicoloured	1·75	1·75
		a. Booklet pane. No. A321×4 with margins all round	7·50	
A316/21 *Set of 6*			7·00	7·00
First Day Cover				8·50
Presentation Pack			8·50	

Plate Nos.: All values 1A (×4).
Sheets: 10 (2×5) with enlarged illustrated margins at right and foot.
Imprint: Central, left margin.
Withdrawn: 23.5.2008.

A **310** 'How the Camel got his Hump'

A **311** 'How the Whale got his Throat'

A **312** 'The Elephant's Child'

A **313** 'How the Leopard got his Spots' A **314** 'The Cat that walked by Himself' A **315** 'How the Rhinoceros got his Skin'

'Rudyard Kipling's *Just So Stories*

(Des Nick Watton. Litho BDT)

2007 (25 Oct). Rudyard Kipling's *Just So Stories*. P 13½ (C).

A322	A **310**	32p. multicoloured	75	75
A323	A **311**	37p. multicoloured	90	90
A324	A **312**	45p. multicoloured	1·10	1·10
A325	A **313**	48p. multicoloured	1·25	1·25
A326	A **314**	50p. multicoloured	1·25	1·25
A327	A **315**	71p. multicoloured	1·75	1·75
A322/7 *Set of 6*			7·00	7·00
First Day Cover				8·50
Presentation Pack			8·50	
MSA328 140×95 mm. Nos. A322/7			7·00	7·00
First Day Cover				8·50

Sheets: 10 (2×5) with enlarged illustrated margins at right and foot.
Imprint: Central, left-hand margin.
Withdrawn: 24.10.2008.

A **316** *Vanessa cardui* (painted lady) A **317** *Hipparchia semele* (grayling)

A **318** *Callophrys rubi* (green hairstreak) A **319** *Pararge aegeria* (speckled wood)

A **320** *Polymmatus icarus* (common blue) A **321** *Melitaea cinxia* (Glanvile fritillary)

Butterflies

(Des Petula Stone. Litho BDT)

2008 (28 Feb). P 14 (C).

A329	A **316**	34p. multicoloured	80	80
A330	A **317**	40p. multicoloured	95	95
A331	A **318**	48p. multicoloured	1·10	1·10
A332	A **319**	51p. multicoloured	1·20	1·20
A333	A **320**	53p. multicoloured	1·30	1·30
A334	A **321**	74p. multicoloured	1·70	1·70
A329/34 *Set of 6*			7·00	7·00
First Day Cover				8·75
Presentation Pack			8·75	
MSA335 140×100 mm. Nos. A329/34			7·00	7·00
First Day Cover				8·75

Plate Nos.: All values 1A (×4).
Sheets: 10 (2×5) with enlarged illustrated margins at right and foot.
Imprint: Central, left-hand margin.
Withdrawn: 27.2.2009.

A **322** Common Buzzard A **323** Peregrine Falcon

A **324** Kestrel A **325** Barn Owl

A **326** Long-eared Owl A **327** Sparrowhawk

Resident Birds (3rd series). Raptors

(Des Andrew Robinson. Litho BDT)

2008 (15 May). P 14 (C).

A336	A **322**	34p. multicoloured	80	80
		a. Booklet pane. No. A336×4 with margins all round	3·25	
A337	A **323**	40p. multicoloured	95	95
		a. Booklet pane. No. A337×4 with margins all round	3·75	
A338	A **324**	48p. multicoloured	1·10	1·10
		a. Booklet pane. No. A338×4 with margins all round	4·50	
A339	A **325**	51p. multicoloured	1·20	1·20
		a. Booklet pane. No. A339×4 with margins all round	4·75	
A340	A **326**	53p. multicoloured	1·30	1·30
		a. Booklet pane. No. A340×4 with margins all round	5·00	
A341	A **327**	74p. multicoloured	1·70	1·70
		a. Booklet pane. No. A341×4 with margins all round	7·00	
A336/41 *Set of 6*			7·00	7·00
First Day Cover				8·75
Presentation Pack			8·75	

Plate Nos.: All values 1A (×4).
Sheets: 10 (2×5) with enlarged illustrated margins at right and foot.
Imprint: Central, left-hand margin.
Withdrawn: 14.5.2009.

A **328** Old Harbour

A **329** The Breakwater

A **330** Fort Clonque Causeway

A **331** Golf Course

A **332** Hanging Rock

A **333** Fort Clonque

25th Anniversary of Alderney Stamps

(Des Andrew Fothergill. Litho Austrian State Ptg Wks, Vienna)

2008 (14 June)–**10**. P 14 (C).

A342	A **328**	34p. multicoloured (a)	80	80
A343	A **329**	40p. multicoloured (a)	95	95
A344	A **330**	48p. multicoloured (a)	1·10	1·10
A345	A **331**	51p. multicoloured (a)	1·20	1·20
A346	A **332**	53p. multicoloured (a)	1·30	1·30
A346a	A **332**	55p. multicoloured (b)	1·50	1·50
A347	A **333**	74p. multicoloured (a)	1·70	1·70
A342/7 Set of 7			7·75	7·75
First Day Covers (2)				11·00
Presentation Pack (A342/6, A347)			8·75	
Souvenir Folder (Nos. A342/6, A347/8)			55·00	

Nos. A342/6 and A347 have no imprint date.
No. A346a has an imprint date of "2010".
Printings: (a) 4.6.2008; (b) 18.6.2010.
Plate Nos.: All values 1A (×4).
Sheets: 34p. to 53p., 74p. 10 (2×5) with enlarged illustrated margins at left and foot; 55p. 50 (5×10).
Imprint: Lower right-hand margin (34p. to 53p., 74p.), upper side margins (55p.).
Withdrawn: 13.6.2009 (except 55p.).

A **334** Lion Rampant
from Alderney Flag

25 Years of Alderney Stamps (1983-2008)

(Des Andrew Fothergill. Litho and embossed Austrian State Ptg Wks, Vienna)

2008 (14 June). P 14½×13½ (C).

A348	A **334**	£5 multicoloured	12·00	12·00
First Day Cover				13·50
Presentation Pack			13·50	

No. A348 was retained as a definitive stamp.
Sheets: 5 (5×1) with enlarged illustrated margins.
Imprint: Top margin.

A **335** Britten-Norman Islander　　A **336** Britten-Norman Trislander

A **337** DHC-6 Twin Otter　　A **338** Short 360

A **339** Saab 340　　　　　　　　A **340** ATR 72

40th Anniv of Aurigny Air Services

(Des Mark Wilkinson. Litho BDT)

2008 (31 Oct). P 13½ (C).

A349	A **335**	34p. multicoloured	80	80
A350	A **336**	40p. multicoloured	95	95
A351	A **337**	48p. multicoloured	1·10	1·10
A352	A **338**	51p. multicoloured	1·20	1·20
A353	A **339**	53p. multicoloured	1·30	1·30
A354	A **340**	74p. multicoloured	1·70	1·70
A349/54 Set of 6			7·00	7·00
First Day Cover				8·75
Presentation Pack			8·75	
MSA355 140×95 mm. Nos. A349/54			7·00	7·00
First Day Cover				8·75

Plate Nos.: All values 1A (×4).
Sheets: 10 (2×5) with enlarged illustrated margins at right and foot.
Imprint: Central, left-hand margin.
Withdrawn: 29.10.2009.

A **341** Tawny Mining Bee
(Andrena fulva)

A **342** Early Bumble Bee
(Bombus pratorum)

A **343** Bug Mining Bee
(Colletes daviesanus)

A **344** Cuckoo Bee (Nomada
goodeniana)

A **345** Solitary Bee (Halictus
scabiosae)

A **346** Honey Bee (Apis
mellifera)

Alderney Bees

(Des Petula Stone. Litho BDT)

2009 (26 Feb). P 13½ (C).

A356	A **341**	36p. multicoloured	90	90
A357	A **342**	43p. multicoloured	1·00	1·00
A358	A **343**	51p. multicoloured	1·25	1·25
A359	A **344**	54p. multicoloured	1·25	1·25
A360	A **345**	56p. multicoloured	1·40	1·40
A361	A **346**	77p. multicoloured	1·75	1·75
A356/61 *Set of 6*			7·25	7·25
First Day Cover				9·25
Presentation Pack			9·25	
MSA362 140×100 mm. Nos. A356/61			8·00	8·00
First Day Cover				9·25

Plate Nos.: All values 1A (×4).
Sheets: 10 (2×5) with enlarged illustrated right margins.
Imprint: Central, left-hand margin.
Withdrawn: 27.2.2010.

A **347** Turnstone   A **348** Curlew

A **349** Oystercatcher   A **350** Snipe

A **351** Dunlin   A **352** Ringed Plover

Resident Birds (4th series). Waders

(Des Andrew Robinson. Litho BDT)

2009 (28 May). P 13½ (C).

A363	A **347**	36p. multicoloured	85	75
		a. Booklet pane. No. A363×4 with margins all round	3·25	
A364	A **348**	43p. multicoloured	1·10	1·10
		a. Booklet pane. No. A364×4 with margins all round	4·00	
A365	A **349**	51p. multicoloured	1·25	1·25
		a. Booklet pane. No. A365×4 with margins all round	4·75	
A366	A **350**	54p. multicoloured	1·25	1·25
		a. Booklet pane. No. A366×4 with margins all round	5·00	
A367	A **351**	56p. multicoloured	1·40	1·40
		a. Booklet pane. No. A367×4 with margins all round	5·00	
A368	A **352**	77p. multicoloured	1·60	1·60
		a. Booklet pane. No. A368×4 with margins all round	7·00	
A363/8 *Set of 6*			7·25	7·25
First Day Cover				9·00
Presentation Pack			9·00	

Plate Nos.: All values 1A (×4).
Sheets: 10 (2×5) with enlarged illustrated right margins.
Imprint: Central, left-hand margin.
Withdrawn: 27.5.2010.

A **353** Felixstowe F2A Flying Boat with 'Dazzle' Paint over Castle Cornet, 1918

A **354** Fairey Swordfish NE874 attacking U-boat

A **355** Blackburn Skuas dive bombing *Scharnhorst*

A **356** Hawker Sea Fury FB11 (VR930) over Alderney

A **357** Hawker Seahawk and Sea Fury

A **358** Agusta Westland HM101 Merlin Helicopter landing on HMS *Daring*

Centenary of Naval Aviation

(Des Robin Carter. Litho Enschedé)

2009 (30 July). P 14×13½ (C).

A369	A **353**	36p. multicoloured	85	85
A370	A **354**	43p. multicoloured	1·00	1·00
A371	A **355**	51p. multicoloured	1·25	1·25
A372	A **356**	54p. multicoloured	1·25	1·25
A373	A **357**	56p. multicoloured	1·40	1·40
A374	A **358**	77p. multicoloured	1·75	1·75
A369/74 *Set of 6*			7·25	7·25
First Day Cover				9·00
Presentation Pack			9·00	
Souvenir Album (complete sheets of A369/74, first day cover and prints of artwork)			80·00	

Plate Nos.: All values 1A, 1B (each×4).
Sheets: 10 (2×5) with enlarged illustrated right margins.
Imprint: Central, left-hand margin.
Withdrawn: 29.7.2010.

A **359** Alice West reporting Theft of Bull to Sherlock Holmes

A **360** Holmes studying Coded Message and Arrest of Herdsman

A **361** Holmes studying Message on Harbour Wall

A **362** Sherlock Holmes and Farmer West

A **363** Holmes and Watson observing Half-built Lighthouse

A **364** Arrest of Thief

150th Birth Anniversary of Sir Arthur Conan Doyle. Scenes from new story *Sherlock Holmes and the Curious Case of the Alderney Bull*

(Des Keith Robinson. Litho Cartor)

2009 (29 Oct). P 13½×13 (C).

A375	A **359**	36p. multicoloured	85	85
A376	A **360**	43p. multicoloured	1·00	1·00
A377	A **361**	51p. multicoloured	1·25	1·25
A378	A **362**	54p. multicoloured	1·25	1·25
A379	A **363**	56p. multicoloured	1·40	1·40
A380	A **364**	77p. multicoloured	1·75	1·75
A375/80 *Set of 6*			7·25	7·25
First Day Cover				9·00
Presentation Pack			9·00	

Plate Nos.: All values 1A (×4).
Sheets: 10 (2×5) with enlarged illustrated right margins.
Imprint: Central, left-hand margin.
Withdrawn: 28.10.2010.

A miniature sheet containing Nos. A375/80 was only available in a 'mystery pack' sold for 9·99.

A **365** Common Darter (*Sympetrum striolatum*)

A **366** Emperor Dragonfly (*Anax imperator*)

A **367** Blue-tailed Damselfly (*Ischnura elegans*)

A **368** Brown Hawker (*Aeshna grandis*)

A **369** Black-tailed Skimmer (*Orthetrum cancellatum*)

A **370** Red Veined Darter (*Sympetrum fonscolumbii*)

Dragonflies

(Des Petula Stone. Litho BDT)

2010 (25 Feb). P 13½ (C).

A381	A **365**	36p. multicoloured	85	85
A382	A **366**	45p. multicoloured	1·10	1·10
A383	A **367**	56p. multicoloured	1·40	1·40
A384	A **368**	66p. multicoloured	1·50	1·50
A385	A **369**	75p. multicoloured	1·75	1·75
A386	A **370**	83p. multicoloured	2·00	2·00
A381/6 *Set of 6*			8·50	8·50
First Day Cover				10·50
Presentation Pack			10·50	
MSA387 140×100 mm. Nos. A381/6			8·50	8·50
First Day Cover				10·50

Plate Nos.: All values 1A (each×4).
Sheets: 10 (2×5) with enlarged illustrated right margins.
Imprint: Central, left-hand margin.
Withdrawn: 24.2.2011.

A **371** Pilot Keith Gilman   A **372** Hurricanes

A **373** Pilots Scramble   A **374** Spitfire Sortie

A **375** Air Raid Warden   A **376** Evacuees

A **377** Sir Douglas Bader (birth centenary) (*Illustration reduced. Actual size 110×70 mm*)

70th Anniversary of the Battle of Britain

(Des The Westminster Collection. Litho BDT)

2010 (4 May). P 14 (C).

A388	A **371**	36p. black and brownish grey	80	80
A389	A **372**	45p. black and brownish grey	1·00	1·00
A390	A **373**	48p. black and brownish grey	1·10	1·10
A391	A **374**	50p. black and brownish grey	1·25	1·25
A392	A **375**	58p. black and brownish grey	1·40	1·40
A393	A **376**	80p. black and brownish grey	1·75	1·75
A388/93 *Set of 6*			7·25	7·25
First Day Cover				7·50
Presentation Pack			6·50	
MSA394 110×70 mm. A **377** £2 black and brownish grey			4·50	4·50
First Day Cover				10·00
Presentation Pack			9·00	

Plate Nos.: 1A (each×4).
Sheets: 6 (2×3) with enlarged illustrated margins.
Withdrawn: 3.5.2011.

A **378** Lamp and "Live your life while you have it. Life is a splendid gift"

A **379** Outstretched Hand and "How very little can be done under a spirit of fear"

A **380** Hands, Water Bowl and "The very first requirement in a hospital is that it should do the sick no harm"

A **381** Hands unrolling Bandage and "One's feelings waste themselves in words"

A **382** Hand writing and "I attribute my success to this – I never gave or took any excuse"

A **383** Clasped hands and "The greatest things grow by God's Law out of the smallest"

Death Centenary of Florence Nightingale

(Des The Potting Shed. Litho Southern Colour Print, New Zealand)

2010 (29 July). P 14½×14 (C).

A395	A **378**	36p. multicoloured	80	80
A396	A **379**	45p. multicoloured	1·00	1·00
A397	A **380**	48p. multicoloured	1·10	1·10
A398	A **381**	50p. multicoloured	1·25	1·25
A399	A **382**	58p. multicoloured	1·40	1·40
A400	A **383**	80p. multicoloured	1·75	1·75
A395/400 *Set of 6*			7·25	7·25
First Day Cover				10·00
Presentation Pack			9·00	

Plate Nos.: All values 1A (each×5).
Sheets: 10 (2×5) with enlarged illustrated right margins.
Imprint: Central, left-hand margins.
Withdrawn: 28.7.2011.

A **384** Children flying above London

A **385** Captain Hook falling into Crocodile's Jaws

A **386** Peter visits Captain Hook's Ship

A **387** Peter waving a Rainbow

A **388** Children at Top of Neverpeak

A **389** Bonfire

A **390** Peter Pan (*Illustration reduced. Actual size 110×70 mm*)

150th Birth Anniv of J. M. Barrie (author of *Peter Pan and Wendy*). Illustrations by David Wyatt from sequel *Peter Pan in Scarlet* by Geraldine McCaughrean

(Des Two Degrees North. Litho Cartor)

2010 (4 Nov). P 13½ (C).

A401	A **384**	36p. multicoloured	80	80
A402	A **385**	45p. multicoloured	1·00	1·00
A403	A **386**	48p. multicoloured	1·10	1·10
A404	A **387**	50p. multicoloured	1·25	1·25
A405	A **388**	58p. multicoloured	1·40	1·40
A406	A **389**	80p. multicoloured	1·75	1·75
A401/6 Set of 6			7·25	7·25
First Day Cover				10·00
Presentation Pack			9·00	
MSA407 110×70 mm. A **390** £3 multicoloured			7·00	7·00
First Day Cover				9·50
Presentation Pack			8·75	

Plate Nos.: All values 1A (each×4).
Sheets: 10 (2×5) with enlarged illustrated left and lower margins.
Imprint: Lower right-hand margins.
Withdrawn: 4.11.2011.

A **391** 'Oh Christmas Tree'

A **392** 'Away in a Manger'

A **393** 'While Shepherds Watched their Flocks by Night'

A **394** 'Hark the Herald Angels Sing'

A **395** 'O Holy Night'

A **396** 'O Little Town of Bethlehem'

A **397** 'Good King Wenceslas'

Christmas Carols

(Des Two Degrees North. Litho Enschedé)

2010 (4 Nov). P 13½×14 (C).

A408	A **391**	31p. multicoloured	90	90
A409	A **392**	36p. multicoloured	80	80
A410	A **393**	45p. multicoloured	1·00	1·00
A411	A **394**	48p. multicoloured	1·10	1·10
A412	A **395**	50p. multicoloured	1·25	1·25
A413	A **396**	58p. multicoloured	1·40	1·40
A414	A **397**	80p. multicoloured	1·75	1·75
A408/14 Set of 7			8·00	8·00
First Day Cover				10·50
Presentation Pack			9·75	

Plate Nos.: All values 1A (each×4).
Sheets: 50 (10×5).
Imprint: Central, bottom margin.
Withdrawn: 4.11.2011.

A **398** Elephant Hawk-moth (*Deilephila elpenor*)

A **399** Hummingbird Hawk-moth (*Macroglossum stellatarum*)

A **400** Convolvulus Hawk-moth (*Agrius convolvuli*)

A **401** Poplar Hawk-moth (*Laothoe populi*)

A **402** Striped Hawk-moth (*Hyles livornica*)

A **403** Privet Hawk-moth (*Sphinx ligustri*)

Alderney Hawk-moths

(Des Petula Stone. Litho BDT)

2011 (23 Feb). P 13½ (C).

A415	A **398**	36p. multicoloured	80	80
A416	A **399**	45p. multicoloured	1·00	1·00
A417	A **400**	52p. multicoloured	1·25	1·25
A418	A **401**	58p. multicoloured	1·40	1·40
A419	A **402**	65p. multicoloured	1·50	1·50
A420	A **403**	70p. multicoloured	1·70	1·60
A415/20 Set of 6			7·50	7·50
First Day Cover				10·00
Presentation Pack			9·50	
MSA421 140×100 mm. Nos. A415/20			7·50	7·50
First Day Cover				10·00

Plate Nos.: All values 1A (each×4).
Sheets: 10 (2×5) with enlarged illustrated margins at right and foot.
Imprint: Central, left-hand margins.
Withdrawn: 23.2.2012.

A **404** Mediterranean Gull (*Icthyaetus melanocephalus*)

A **405** Shelduck (*Tadorna tadorna*)

A **406** Firecrest (*Regulus ignicapilla*)

A **407** Balearic Shearwater (*Puffinus mauretanicus*)

A **408** Woodcock (*Scolopax rusticola*)

A **409** Little Grebe (*Tachybaptus ruficollis*)

Birds of the Bailiwick

(Des Wendy Bramall. Litho BDT)

2011 (4 May). P 13½ (C).

A422	A **404**	36p. multicoloured	85	85
A423	A **405**	45p. multicoloured	1·10	1·10
A424	A **406**	48p. multicoloured	1·10	1·10
A425	A **407**	52p. multicoloured	1·25	1·25
A426	A **408**	58p. multicoloured	1·40	1·40
A427	A **409**	65p. multicoloured	1·60	1·60
A422/7 *Set of 6*			7·25	7·25
First Day Cover				10·00
Presentation Pack			9·50	
MSA428 140×100 mm. Nos. A422/7			7·25	7·25
First Day Cover				10·00

Plate Nos.: All values 1A (each×4).
Sheets: 10 (2×5) with enlarged illustrated margins at right and foot.
Imprint: Central, left-hand margins.
Withdrawn: 3.5.2012.

A **410** Queen Elizabeth II and Lt. Philip Mountbatten, July 1949

A **411** Queen Elizabeth II and Prince Philip at Windsor Castle, 6 June 1959

A **412** Queen Elizabeth II and Prince Philip at Balmoral, 1 June 1972

A **413** Queen Elizabeth II and Prince Philip at Silver Jubilee Thanksgiving, St. Paul's Cathedral, 7 June 1977

A **414** Queen Elizabeth II and Prince Philip arriving at St. Paul's Cathedral, 15 June 2006

A **415** Queen Elizabeth II and Prince Philip at Sikh Temple, Hounslow, London, 15 October 2004

85th Birthday of Queen Eliizabeth II and 90th Birthday of Prince Philip

(Des The Potting Shed. Litho Enschedé)

2011 (2 June). P 13½ (C).

A429	A **410**	36p. sepia and silver	85	85
		a. Booklet pane. No. A429×4 with margins all round	3·50	
A430	A **411**	45p. sepia and silver	1·10	1·10
		a. Booklet pane. No. A430×4 with margins all round	4·25	
A431	A **412**	48p. sepia and silver	1·10	1·10
		a. Booklet pane. No. A431×4 with margins all round	4·50	
A432	A **413**	52p. sepia and silver	1·25	1·25
		a. Booklet pane. No. A432×4 with margins all round	5·00	
A433	A **414**	61p. sepia and silver	1·40	1·40
		a. Booklet pane. No. A433×4 with margins all round	5·50	
A434	A **415**	65p. sepia and silver	1·60	1·60
		a. Booklet pane. No. A434×4 with margins all round	6·25	
A429/34 *Set of 6*			7·25	7·25
First Day Cover				10·00
Presentation Pack			9·50	

Plate Nos.: All values 1A (each×2).
Sheets: 10 (5×2) with enlarged illustrated left and lower margins.
Imprint: Upper right-hand margins.
Withdrawn: 2.6.2012.

A **416** Female VAD (Voluntary Aid Detachment) Uniform, c. 1915

A **417** Male VAD Uniform, 1915

A **418** Nurse's Uniform, 1966-78

A **419** Uniform, 1981-2001

A **420** Uniform, 2001

A **421** British Red Cross Work Wear, 2011

Centenary of British Red Cross Uniforms

(Des Robin Carter. Litho Enschedé)

2011 (28 July). P 14×13½ (C).

A435	A **416**	36p. multicoloured	85	85
A436	A **417**	47p. multicoloured	1·10	1·10
A437	A **418**	48p. multicoloured	1·25	1·25
A438	A **419**	52p. multicoloured	1·25	1·25
A439	A **420**	61p. multicoloured	1·50	1·50
A440	A **421**	65p. multicoloured	1·60	1·60
A435/40 Set of 6			7·50	7·50
First Day Cover				10·50
Presentation Pack			9·50	

Plate Nos.: All values 1A (each×4).
Sheets: 10 (2×5) with enlarged illustrated right-hand margins.
Imprint: Central, left-hand margins.
Withdrawn: 27.7.2012.

A **422** Victoria Street

A **423** St. Anne's Church

A **424** Les Estacs Gannet Colonies

A **425** Mannez Lighthouse and Santa's Sleigh

A **426** The Alderney Train

A **427** Snowman and Children playing at The Breakwater

A **428** The Harbour

Christmas. 'Winter Wonderland'

(Des The Potting Shed. Litho Austrian State Ptg Wks, Vienna)

2011 (27 Oct). P 13½×14 (C).

A441	A **422**	31p. multicoloured	80	80
A442	A **423**	36p. multicoloured	90	90
A443	A **424**	47p. multicoloured	1·10	1·10
A444	A **425**	48p. multicoloured	1·10	1·10
A445	A **426**	52p. multicoloured	1·25	1·25
A446	A **427**	61p. multicoloured	1·50	1·50

A447	A **428**	65p. multicoloured	1·60	1·60
A441/7 Set of 7			8·00	8·00
First Day Cover				10·50
Presentation Pack			10·00	

Plate Nos.: All values 1A (each×5).
Sheets: 50 (5×10).
Imprint: Upper side margins.
Withdrawn: 26.10.2012.

A **429** *Titanic* leaving Southampton

A **430** *Titanic* sailing past Alderney

A **431** The Grand Staircase

A **432** Orchestra playing Final Tune

A **433** Captain Edward J. Smith

A **434** Lifeboats leaving *Titanic*

Centenary of the Sinking of the *Titanic*

(Des Nick Watton. Litho Enschedé)

2012 (22 Feb). P 13½ (C).

A448	A **429**	36p. multicoloured	1.10	1.10
		a. Booklet pane. No. A448×4 with margins all round	4.50	
A449	A **430**	47p. multicoloured	1.10	1.10
		a. Booklet pane. No. A449×4 with margins all round	4.50	
A450	A **431**	48p. multicoloured	1.10	1.10
		a. Booklet pane. No. A450×4 with margins all round	4.50	
A451	A **432**	52p. multicoloured	1.25	1.25
		a. Booklet pane. No. A451×4 with margins all round	5.00	
A452	A **433**	61p. multicoloured	1.50	1.50
		a. Booklet pane. No. A452×4 with margins all round	6.00	

A453 A **434** 65p. multicoloured 1.50 1.60
     a. Booklet pane. No. A453×4 with
        margins all round 6.00
A448/53 Set of 6 .... 7.00 7.00
First Day Cover 10.00
Presentation Pack .... 10·00
    Plate Nos.: All values 1A (each ×4).
    Sheets: 10 (2×5).
    Imprint: Central, left-hand margin.
    Withdrawn: 21.2.2013.

A **435** Magistrate spares the Terrified Oliver Twist from Apprenticeship as Chimneysweep

A **436** Noah Claypole

A **437** The Artful Dodger and Charley Bates make Oliver polish their Boots

A **438** Fagin and Monks appear before Oliver at Maylie's Residence

A **439** Nancy meeting Rose and Mr. Brownlow on London Bridge

A **440** Oliver and Rose Maylie see his Mother's Memorial in Village Church

Birth Bicentenary of Charles Dickens (writer). Original Illustrations from *Oliver Twist* by George Cruikshank

(Des Bridget Yabsley. Litho Austrian State Ptg Wks, Vienna)

2012 (8 May). P 14 (C).
A454 A **435** 36p. olive-sepia and black 90 90
A455 A **436** 47p. olive-sepia and black 1.10 1.10
A456 A **437** 48p. olive-sepia and black 1.10 1.10
A457 A **438** 52p. olive-sepia and black 1.25 1.25
A458 A **439** 61p. olive-sepia and black 1.50 1.50
A459 A **440** 65p. olive-sepia and black 1.60 1.60
A454/9 Set of 6 .... 7.00 7.00
First Day Cover 10.00
Presentation Pack .... 9·50
    Plate Nos.: All values 1A (each ×2).
    Sheets: 10 (2×5).
    Imprint: Lower right-hand margin.
    Withdrawn: 7.5.2013.

A **441** Garden Tiger Moth (*Arctia caja*)

A **442** Cream Spot Tiger Moth (*Arctia villica*)

A **443** Buff Ermine (*Spilosoma lutea*)

A **444** Ruby Tiger Moth (*Phragmatobia fuliginosa*)

A **445** Jersey Tiger Moth (*Euplagia quadripunctaria*)

A **446** Cinnabar Moth (*Tyria jacobaeae*)

Alderney Invertebrates: Tiger Moths and Ermines

(Des Petula Stone. Litho BDT)

2012 (25 July). P 13½ (C).
A460 A **441** 39p. multicoloured 95 95
A461 A **442** 52p. multicoloured 1.25 1.25
A462 A **443** 53p. multicoloured 1.25 1.25
A463 A **444** 59p. multicoloured 1.40 1.40
A464 A **445** 69p. multicoloured 1.75 1.75
A465 A **446** 74p. multicoloured 1.75 1.75
A460/5 Set of 6 .... 8.00 8.00
First Day Cover 10.50
Presentation Pack .... 10·00
MSA466 140×100 mm. Nos. A460/5 .... 8.00 8.00
First Day Cover 10.50
    Plate Nos.: All values 1A (each ×4).
    Sheets: 10 (2×5).
    Imprint: Central, left-hand margin.
    Withdrawn: 24.7.2013.

A **447** Douglas Quay, Braye Harbour, c. 1800

A **448** Breakwater, completed 1856

A **449** *SS Courier*, c. 1926

A **450** Little Crabby Harbour, c. 1985

A **451** RNLI Lifeboat *Roy Barker I*, c. 1995

A **452** Commercial Quay, built 2011

The History of Alderney Harbour

(Des Richard Thompson. Litho BDT)

2012 (31 Oct). P 13½ (C).
A467 A **447** 39p. multicoloured 95 95
A468 A **448** 52p. multicoloured 1.25 1.25
A469 A **449** 53p. multicoloured 1.25 1.25
A470 A **450** 59p. multicoloured 1.40 1.40
A471 A **451** 69p. multicoloured 1.75 1.75

A472	**A 452**	74p. multicoloured	1.75	1.75
A467/72 *Set of 6*			8.00	8.00
First Day Cover				10.50
Presentation Pack			10·50	
MSA473 140×100 mm. Nos. A467/72			8.00	8.00
First Day Cover				10.50

Plate Nos.: All values 1A (each ×4).
Sheets: 10 (2×5).
Imprint: Lower left-hand margin.
Withdrawn: 30.10.2013.

A **453** Angel visits Mary 'Annunciation'   A **454** No Room at the Inn

A **455** The Birth of Jesus   A **456** Whilst Shepherds watch their Flocks

A **457** The Three Kings   A **458** The Children of Bethlehem visit the Baby Jesus

A **459** The Flight to Egypt

Christmas. The Christmas Story

(Des Wendy Bramall. Litho Lowe-Martin Group)

2012 (31 Oct). P 13×12½ (C).

A474	A **453**	34p. multicoloured	85	85
A475	A **454**	39p. multicoloured	95	95
A476	A **455**	52p. multicoloured	1.25	1.25
A477	A **456**	53p. multicoloured	1.25	1.25
A478	A **457**	59p. multicoloured	1.40	1.40
A479	A **458**	69p. multicoloured	1.75	1.75
A480	A **459**	74p. multicoloured	1.75	1.75
A474/80 *Set of 7*			9.00	9.00
First Day Cover				11.00
Presentation Pack			10·50	

Plate Nos.: All values 1A (each ×5).
Sheets: 50 (10×5).
Imprint: Upper side margins.
Withdrawn: 30.10.2013.

A **460** Rose Chafer (*Cetonia aurata*)   A **461** Burying Beetle (*Nicrophorus genus*)

A **462** Green Tiger Beetle (*Cicindela campestris*)   A **463** May Bug or Cockchafer (*Melolontha melolontha*)

A **464** *Netocia morio*   A **465** Oil Beetle (*Meloegenus*)

Alderney Beetles

(Des Petula Stone. Litho BDT)

2013 (20 Feb). P 13½ (C).

A481	A **460**	39p. multicoloured	95	95
A482	A **461**	52p. multicoloured	1·25	1·25
A483	A **462**	53p. multicoloured	1·25	1·25
A484	A **463**	59p. multicoloured	1·40	1·40
A485	A **464**	69p. multicoloured	1·75	1·75
A486	A **465**	74p. multicoloured	1·75	1·75
A481/6 *Set of 6*			8·00	8·00
First Day Cover				11·00
Presentation Pack			10·50	
MSA487 140×100 mm. Nos. A481/6			8·00	
First Day Cover				11·00

Plate Nos.: All values 1A (each ×4).
Sheets: 10 (2×5).
Imprint: Lower left-hand margin.

A **466** Queen Elizabeth II wearing Imperial State Crown   A **467** Coronets and Tiaras from The Goldsmiths and Silversmiths Company, 1953

A **468** Queen Elizabeth II wearing George IV State Diadem arriving at Westminster Abbey   A **469** Queen Elizabeth II and Archbishops in Procession down Aisle

A **470** Queen Elizabeth II
(seated in Coronation
Chair) and Archbishops

A **471** Coronation
Portrait

60th Anniversary of the Coronation

(Des The Potting Shed. Litho BDT)

2013 (29 May). P 13½ (C).

A488	A **466**	40p. multicoloured	95	95
		a. Booklet pane. No. A488×4 with margins all round	3·75	
A489	A **467**	53p. multicoloured	1·25	1·25
		a. Booklet pane. No. A489×4 with margins all round	5·00	
A490	A **468**	55p. multicoloured	1·25	1·25
		a. Booklet pane. No. A490×4 with margins all round	5·00	
A491	A **469**	63p. multicoloured	1·40	1·40
		a. Booklet pane. No. A491×4 with margins all round	5·50	
A492	A **470**	71p. multicoloured	1·75	1·75
		a. Booklet pane. No. A492×4 with margins all round	6·75	
A493	A **471**	79p. multicoloured	1·75	1·75
		a. Booklet pane. No. A493×4 with margins all round	7·00	
A488/93	*Set of 6*		8·00	8·00
First Day Cover				11·50
Presentation Pack			10·50	

Plate Nos.: All values 1A (each ×4).
Sheets: 10 (5×2).
Imprint: Top margin at right.

A **472** Rabbit and
Beatrix Potter walking
Home to Near Sawrey

A **473** Beatrix Potter
feeding Duck

A **474** Mouse in Onion
Patch

A **475** Dog carrying
Branch

A **476** Beatrix Potter
sketching Cat

A **477** Beatrix Potter in
Farmyard

The Life of Beatrix Potter

(Des The Potting Shed. Litho Cartor)

2013 (31 July). P 13½×13 (C).

A494	A **472**	40p. multicoloured	95	95
A495	A **473**	53p. multicoloured	1·25	1·25
A496	A **474**	55p. multicoloured	1·25	1·25
A497	A **475**	63p. multicoloured	1·40	1·40
A498	A **476**	71p. multicoloured	1·75	1·75
A499	A **477**	79p. multicoloured	1·75	1·75
A494/9	*Set of 6*		8·00	8·00
First Day Cover				11·50
Presentation Pack			10·50	
MSA500	140×100 mm. Nos. A494/9		8·00	8·00
First Day Cover				11·50

Plate Nos.: All values 1A (each ×4).
Sheets: 10 (5×2).
Imprint: Central, top margin.

A **478** Santa and Rudolph

A **479** Elf comforting Rudolph

A **480** Rudolph with Snowmen

A **481** Rudolph mocked by
Other Reindeer

A **482** Santa looking into
the Fog

A **483** Rudolph's Glowing Nose

A **484** Rudolph leading Sleigh

Christmas. Rudolph the Red-nosed Reindeer

(Des Nick Watton. Litho Southern Colour Print, New Zealand)

2013 (13 Nov). P 13½ (C).

A501	A **478**	35p. multicoloured	85	85
A502	A **479**	40p. multicoloured	95	95
A503	A **480**	53p. multicoloured	1·25	1·25

A504	A **481**	55p. multicoloured	1·25	1·25
A505	A **482**	63p. multicoloured	1·40	1·40
A506	A **483**	71p. multicoloured	1·75	1·75
A507	A **484**	79p. multicoloured	1·75	1·75
A501/7		Set of 7	9·00	9·00
		First Day Cover		12·00
		Presentation Pack	11·50	

Plate Nos. All values 1A (each ×4).
Sheets: 50 (5×10).
Imprint: Upper side margins.

A **485** 7-spot Ladybird
(*Coccinella 7-punctata*)

A **486** 7-spot Ladybird
(*Coccinella 7-punctata*) Newly
Hatched

A **487** 2-spot Ladybird (*Adalia
2-punctata*)

A **488** Orange Ladybird
(*Halyzia 16-guttata*)

A **489** Harlequin Ladybirds
(*Harmonia axyridis*)

A **490** Harlequin Ladybirds
(*Harmonia axyridis*)

Alderney Ladybirds

(Des Petula Stone. Litho BDT)

2014 (12 Feb). P 13½ (C).

A508	A **485**	40p. multicoloured	95	95
A509	A **486**	53p. multicoloured	1·25	1·25
A510	A **487**	55p. multicoloured	1·25	1·25
A511	A **488**	63p. multicoloured	1·40	1·40
A512	A **489**	71p. multicoloured	1·75	1·75
A513	A **490**	79p. multicoloured	1·75	1·75
A508/13		Set of 6	7·50	7·50
		First Day Cover		9·75
		Presentation Pack	9·25	
MSA514		Nos. A508/13	8·00	8·00
		First Day Cover		9·75

Plate Nos.: All values 1A (each×4).
Sheets: 10 (2×5).
Imprint: Central, left-hand margin.

A **491** William the Conqueror
dining with Family after
Victory at the Battle of
Hastings

A **492** William the Conqueror
and Knights

A **493** The English Nobles and
Archbishops surrender

A **494** Sword of State and
Sceptre presented to William
the Conqueror

A **495** William the Conqueror
crowned by Archbishop
Ealdred of York with Geoffrey
of Coutances as Translator,
Westminster Abbey, 1066

A **496** William I acclaimed
as King of England and
Construction of the White
Tower, London

A **497** Complete Panel of Tapestry

Bayeux Tapestry Final Panel (Alderney community project)

(Des Bridget Yabsley. Litho Cartor)

2014 (28 May). Granite paper (**MS**521 only). P 13 (A515/20) or 14
(**MS**521) (both comb).

A515	A **491**	40p. multicoloured	95	95
		a. Booklet pane. No. A515×4 with		
		margins all round	3·75	
A516	A **492**	53p. multicoloured	1·25	1·25
		a. Booklet pane. No. A516×4 with		
		margins all round	5·00	
A517	A **493**	55p. multicoloured	1·25	1·25
		a. Booklet pane. No. A517×4 with		
		margins all round	5·00	
A518	A **494**	63p. multicoloured	1·40	1·40
		a. Booklet pane. No. A518×4 with		
		margins all round	5·50	
A519	A **495**	71p. multicoloured	1·75	1·75
		a. Booklet pane. No. A519×4 with		
		margins all round	7·00	
A520	A **496**	79p. multicoloured	1·75	1·75
		a. Booklet pane. No. A520×4 with		
		margins all round	7·00	
A515/20		Set of 6	7·50	7·50
		First Day Cover		9·75
		Presentation Pack	9·25	
MSA521		198×49 mm. A **497** £3 multicoloured	7·00	7·00
		First Day Cover		8·75
		Presentation Pack	8·00	

No. **MSA**521 was printed onto cotton and was accompanied by a
certificate of authenticity.
Plate Nos.: All values 1A (each×4).
Sheets: 10 (5×2).
Imprint: Central, top margin.

A **498** Queen Elizabeth II,
Prince Charles, Prince William
and Prince George

A **499** Duke and Duchess
of Cambridge and Prince
George

First Birthday of Prince George. Christening Photographs

(Des Bridget Yabsley. Litho Southern Colour Print, New Zealand)

2014 (22 July). P 14.

A522	A **498**	55p. multicoloured	1·25	1·25
		a. Horiz pair. Nos. A522/3	2·50	2·50
A523	A **499**	55p. multicoloured	1·25	1·25
First Day Cover				4·75
Presentation Pack			4·25	

Plate Nos.: 1A (each×4).
Sheets: 10 (2×5).
Nos. A522/3 were printed together, *se-tenant*, in horizontal pairs throughout the sheets.
Imprint: Lower right-hand margin.

A **500** Commander in Naval Intelligence during World War II

A **501** Ian Fleming and World Map

A **502** Ian Fleming in Jamaica

A **503** Holding son Caspar, 1952

A **504** At his desk in London

A **505** As a Journalist Abroad

A **506** Ian Fleming in Car

Life of Ian Fleming (1908–64, author of James Bond novels)

(Des Two Degrees North. Litho BDT)

2014 (30 July). P 14 (**MSA**530) or 13 (others) (both comb.).

A524	A **500**	41p. multicoloured	95	95
A525	A **501**	54p. multicoloured	1·25	1·25
A526	A **502**	55p. multicoloured	1·25	1·25
A527	A **503**	66p. multicoloured	1·50	1·50

A528	A **504**	74p. multicoloured	1·75	1·75
A529	A **505**	83p. multicoloured	1·90	1·90
A524/9 Set of 6			7·75	7·75
First Day Cover				10·00
Presentation Pack			9·50	

MSA530 118×94 mm. A **506** £3 black and gold

(43×43 mm)			
		7·00	7·00
First Day Cover			8·75
Presentation Pack		8·00	

Plate Nos.: All values 1A (each×2).
Sheets: 10 (2×5).
Imprint: Central, right-hand margin.

A **507** Father Christmas on Sleigh, Snowman and Star (Alexandra Campbell, Joe Blackham, Ian Adamson)

A **508** House, Stars in Sky, Lighthouse and Father Christmas (Louis Smart, Danielle Allen, Lydia Jenkins

A **509** Snowman and Igloo (Holly Neil, Libby Needham, Rosie Williams, Kamil Olbrycht)

A **510** Five Snowmen (Sian Craig, Amber Shaw, Grace Millan, Cameron Tugby-Maloy, Keira Scott, Harvey Olliver)

A **511** Elves making Presents (Jasmine Sayer, Frankie Jenkins, Matthew Burke, Cameron Burnham, Florence Carpenter, Scarlett Oldfield, Carl Evans, Andrew Page, Chloe Faulkner)

A **512** Lighthouse, Snowman and Children posting Letters (Katie Shaw, Kiri Winder)

A **513** Father Christmas and Snowman outside Grotto (Amelie Carpenter, Erin Atkinson, Bennett Blackham, Owen Carre)

Christmas. 'What Christmas Means'. Winning Designs in Children's Painting Competition

(Litho Lowe- Martin)

2014 (6 Nov). P 13×12½ (C).

A531	A **507**	36p. multicoloured	85	85
A532	A **508**	41p. multicoloured	95	95
A533	A **509**	54p. multicoloured	1·25	1·25
A534	A **510**	55p. multicoloured	1·25	1·25
A535	A **511**	66p. multicoloured	1·50	1·50
A536	A **512**	74p. multicoloured	1·75	1·75
A537	A **513**	83p. multicoloured	1·90	1·90
A531/7 Set of 7			8·50	8·50
First Day Cover				11·00
Presentation Pack			10·50	

Plate Nos.: All values 1A (each×4).
Sheets: 50 (5×10).
Imprint: Lower right-hand margin.

A **514** Alice

A **515** The White Rabbit

A **516** Hookah-smoking Caterpillar

A **517** Cheshire Cat

A **518** Mad Hatter

A **519** The Queen of Hearts

A **520** Alice at the Mad Hatter's Tea Party

150th Anniversary of the Publication of Alice's Adventures in Wonderland by Lewis Carroll

(Des Keith Robinson. Litho Cartor)

2015 (5 Feb). P 13 (A 538/43) or 13½ (**MS**A544) (both comb.).

A538	A **514**	41p. multicoloured	95	95
A539	A **515**	54p. multicoloured	1·25	1·25
A540	A **516**	55p. multicoloured	1·25	1·25
A541	A **517**	66p. multicoloured	1·50	1·50
A542	A **518**	74p. multicoloured	1·75	1·75
A543	A **519**	83p. multicoloured	1·90	1·90
A538/43 *Set of 6*			7·75	7·75
First Day Cover				10·00
Presentation Pack			9·50	
MSA543 110×70 mm. A **520** £3 multicoloured			7·00	7·00
First Day Cover				8·75
Presentation Pack			8·00	

Plate Nos.: All values 1A (each×4).
Sheets: 10 (5×2).
Imprint: Top margin.

A **521** Alderney Sea-Lavender

A **522** Dwarf Thistle

A **523** Blonde Hedgehog

A **524** Black Rabbit

A **525** Mole

A **526** Spotted Rock-rose

Alderney Flora and Fauna

(Des Petula Stone. Litho BDT)

2015 (1 May). P 13½ (C).

A545	A **521**	(42p.) multicoloured	95	95
A546	A **522**	(56p.) multicoloured	1·25	1·25
A547	A **523**	(57p.) multicoloured	1·25	1·25
A548	A **524**	(62p.) multicoloured	1·50	1·50
A549	A **525**	(68p.) multicoloured	1·75	1·75
A550	A **526**	(77p.) multicoloured	1·75	1·75
A545/50 *Set of 6*			7·50	7·50
First Day Cover				10·00
MSA551 140×100 mm. Nos. 545/50			8·50	8·50
Presentation Pack			9·50	
First Day Cover				10·00

Nos. A545/50 were inscr 'Local Letter', 'UK Letter', 'EUR Letter', 'Local Large Letter', 'UK Large Letter' and 'ROW Letter'.

Although the above rates were not introduced until a month after the stamps were issued, we understand that Nos. 1563/8 were only sold at the revised prices.

Plate Nos.: All values 1A (each×4).
Sheets: 10 (2×5).
Imprint: Central, left-hand margin.

A **527** Fort Tourgis

A **528** Fort Clonque

A **529** Fort Grosnez

A **530** Fort Houmet Herbé

A **531** Fort Château à l'Etoc

A **532** The Nunnery Roman Fort

2015 (22 July). P 14½×14 (C).

A552	A **527**	42p. multicoloured	95	95
A553	A **528**	56p. multicoloured	1·25	1·25
A554	A **529**	57p. multicoloured	1·40	1·40
A555	A **530**	62p. multicoloured	1·40	1·40
A556	A **531**	68p. multicoloured	1·50	1·50
A557	A **532**	77p. multicoloured	1·75	1·75
A552/7 Set of 6			7·50	7·50
First Day Cover				10·00
Presentation Pack			9·25	

Plate Nos.: All values 1A (each×4).
Sheets: 10 (2×5).
Imprint: Lower left-hand margin.

A **533** Queen Elizabeth II
at Royal York Hotel,
Toronto, Canada, 2010

Queen Elizabeth II Britain's Longest Reigning Monarch

(Des Bridget Yabsley. Litho Lowe-Martin)

2015 (9 Sept). P 12½ (C).

A558	A **533**	£10 multicoloured	23·00	23·00
First Day Cover				25·00
Presentation Pack			25·00	

Plate Nos.: 1A (×4).
Sheets: 5 (1×5).
Imprint: Top margin at right.

A **534** Alderney Boys   A **535** Jesus Christ
with Children

A **536** Alderney Girls   A **537** African Children
on Way to School

A **538** Scottish Girl,   A **539** Burmese Boy   A **540** Girls from
Canadian Boy and   and Girl on Steps   China, India and
American Boy   leading from Pagoda   New Guinea

Christmas. Stained Glass Windows dedicated to Anne French from St. Anne's Church, Alderney

(Des Two Degrees North. Litho Southern Colour Print, New Zealand)

2015 (6 Nov). P 14½ (C).

A559	A **534**	37p. multicoloured	85	85
A560	A **535**	42p. multicoloured	95	95
A561	A **536**	56p. multicoloured	1·25	1·25
A562	A **537**	57p. multicoloured	1·40	1·40
A563	A **538**	62p. multicoloured	1·40	1·40
A564	A **539**	68p. multicoloured	1·50	1·50
A565	A **540**	77p. multicoloured	1·75	1·75
A559/65 Set of 7			8·25	8·25
First Day Cover				10·50
Presentation Pack			10·00	

Plate Nos.: All values 1A (each×4).
Sheets: 50 (10×5).
Imprint: Central, right-hand margin.

A **541** Returning Islanders, 15 December 1945

70th Anniversary of Alderney Homecoming

(Des Robin Carter. Litho Lowe-Martin)

2015 (10 Nov). Sheet 130×85 mm. P 13 (C).

MSA566 A **541** £3 multicoloured	7·00	7·00
First Day Cover		8·75
Presentation Pack	8·00	

STAMP BOOKLETS

PRICES given are for complete booklets.

AB **1** Common Blue and Pyramidal Orchid
(*Illustration reduced. Actual size 99×60 mm*)

1994 (5 May)–**95**. Multicoloured covers as Type AB **1**. Without barcode on the reverse. Panes attached by selvedge.

ASB1	£1.28 booklet containing pane No. A70ab (cover Type AB **1**)		4·00
	a. With barcode sticker on reverse (1995)		8·50
ASB2	£1.92 booklet containing pane No. A72ab (cover showing Great Black-backed Gull and Sand Crocus)		4·50
	a. With barcode sticker on reverse (1995)		13·00

Withdrawn: By 10.2006.

1997 (2 Jan). Multicoloured covers as Type AB **1**, 100×61 mm. Without barcode on the reverse. Panes attached by selvedge.

| ASB3 | £1.44 booklet containing pane No. A70bb (cover showing Small Tortoiseshell (butterfly) and Buddleia) | | 3·00 |
| ASB4 | £2 booklet containing pane No. A72bb (cover showing Rock Pipit and Sea Stock) | | 4·00 |

Sold out: 9.99 (No. ASB3);
Withdrawn by 10.2006 (No. ASB4).

1998 (25 Mar). Multicoloured cover as Type AB **1**, 101×60 mm. With barcode on the reverse. Pane attached by selvedge.

ASB5 £1.60 booklet containing pane No. A71ab (cover showing Common Rabbit and Creeping Buttercup) .... 4·00
Sold out: By 11.2006.

AB **2** Map of Alderney (*Illustration reduced. Actual size 164×98 mm*)

Garrison Island (1st and 2nd series)

(Des Morvan Diamond)

1998 (10 Nov). Multicoloured cover as Type AB **2** containing text and Illustrations on panes and interleaving pages. Stitched.

ASB6 £8.48 booklet containing panes Nos. A102b/c, A104b, A106b, A116b/c, A118b and 120b .... 20·00
Withdrawn: 9.11.99.

Garrison Island (3rd series). Forts

(Des Morvan Diamond)

1999 (19 Oct). Multicoloured cover as Type AB **2**, 162×98 mm, containing text and Illustrations on panes and interleaving pages. Stitched.

ASB7 £6.78 booklet containing panes Nos. A132b/d, A134b/c. and A136b (cover showing view of fortified coastline).. 17·00
Withdrawn: 18.10.2000.

AB **3** Peregrine Falcon (*Illustration reduced. Actual size 105×60 mm*)

Endangered Species. Peregrine Falcon

2000 (4 Feb). Multicoloured covers as Type AB **3**. Panes attached by selvedge.

ASB8 £2.10 booklet containing pane No. A140a (cover Type AB **3**) .... 5·00
ASB9 £2.60 booklet containing pane No. A141a (cover showing falcon with prey)............................... 6·00
Withdrawn: 3.2.2001.

Garrison Island (4th series). Events

(Des Morvan Diamond)

2000 (19 Oct). Multicoloured cover as Type AB **2**, 163×98 mm, containing text and Illustrations on panes and interleaving pages. Stitched.

ASB10 £7.38 booklet containing panes Nos. A154b, A154c×2, A156b×2 and A158b (cover showing Braye Road with Fort Albert in the distance) .... 18·00
Withdrawn: 18.10.2001.

Garrison Island (5th series). The Royal Navy

(Des C. Morvan)

2001 (16 Oct). Multicoloured cover as Type AB **2**, 163×98 mm, containing text and Illustrations on panes and interleaving pages. Stitched.

ASB11 £7.50 booklet containing panes Nos. A176b, A176c×2, A178b/c, and A180b (cover showing Alderney Harbour)................................. 19·00
Withdrawn: 15.10.2002.

AB **4** Medical and Rescue Services (*Illustration reduced. Actual size 162×98 mm*)

Community Services (1st and 2nd series)

(Des Sally Diamond)

2002 (17 Oct). Multicoloured cover as Type AB **4** containing text and Illustrations on panes and interleaving pages. Stitched.

ASB12 £9.40 booklet containing panes Nos. A163ab/ac, A165ab, A197ab/ac and A199ab.............................. 30·00
Withdrawn: 16.10.2003.

Community Services (3rd series)

(Des Mish Legg)

2003 (16 Oct). Multicoloured cover as Type AB **4**, 163×98 mm, containing text and Illustrations on panes and interleaving pages. Stitched.

ASB13 £9.40 booklet containing panes Nos. A217a/d and A219a... 25·00
Withdrawn: 15.10.2004.

Community Services (4th series)

(Des Mish Legg)

2004 (28 Oct). Multicoloured cover as Type AB **4** containing text and Illustrations on panes and interleaving pages. Stitched.

ASB14 £9.76 booklet containing panes Nos. A242a/d and A244a.. 30·00
Withdrawn: 27.10.2005.

AB **5** Gun Carriage (*Illustration reduced. Actual size 162×98 mm*)

Bicentenary of the Battle of Trafalgar

(Des T. Langford)

2005 (9 May). Multicoloured cover as Type AB **5**. Booklet contains text and Illustrations on panes and interleaving pages. Stitched.

ASB15 £9.76 booklet containing panes Nos. A253a×2, A253b/c, A254a and A255a....................................... 25·00
Withdrawn: 8.5.2006.

AB **6** Gannet (*Illustration reduced. Actual size 164×98 mm*)

Resident Birds (1st series). Seabirds

(Des M. Totty)

2006 (27 July). Multicoloured cover as Type AB **6**. Booklet contains text and Illustrations on panes and interleaving pages. Stitched.
ASB16 £10.60 booklet containing panes Nos. A282a/7a .... 30·00
Withdrawn: 26.7.2007.

Resident Birds (2nd series). Passerines

(Des M. Totty)

2007 (24 May). Multicoloured cover as Type AB **6**, 164×98 mm. Booklet contains text and Illustrations on panes and interleaving pages. Stitched.
ASB17 £11.32 booklet containing panes Nos. A316a/21a .... 30·00
Withdrawn: 23.5.2008.

Resident Birds (3rd series). Raptors

(Des M. Totty)

2008 (15 May). Multicoloured cover as Type AB **6**, 163×97 mm. Booklet contains text and Illustrations on panes and interleaving pages. Stitched.
ASB18   £12 booklet containing panes Nos. A337a/41a .... 30·00
Withdrawn: 14.5.2009.

Resident Birds (4th series). Waders

(Des M. Totty)

2009 (28 May). Multicoloured cover as Type AB **6**. Booklet contains text and illustrations on panes and interleaving pages. Stitched.
ASB19 £12.68 booklet containing panes Nos. A363a/8a .... 29·00
Withdrawn: 27.5.2010.

AB **7** Queen Elizabeth II and Prince Philip (*Illustration reduced. Actual size 162×98 mm*)

85th Birthday of Queen Elizabeth II and 90th Birthday of Prince Philip

(Des The Potting Shed)

2011 (2 June). Sepia and silver cover as Type AB **7**. Booklet contains text and illustrations on panes and interleaving pages. Stitched.
ASB20 £12.16 booklet containing panes Nos. A429a/34a .... 29·00
Withdrawn: 2.6.2013.

AB **8** Titanic (*Illustration reduced. Actual size 162×98 mm*)

Centenary of the Sinking of the *Titanic*

(Des M. Totty)

2012 (22 Feb). Multicoloured cover as Type AB **8**. Booklet contains text and illustrations on panes and interleaving pages. Stitched.
ASB21 £12.36 booklet containing panes Nos. A448a/53a .... 29·00
Withdrawn: 21.2.2013.

AB **9** Union Jack (*Illustration reduced. Actual size 163×98 mm*)

60th Anniversary of the Coronation

2013 (29 May). Multicoloured cover, 163×98 mm, as Type AB **9**. Booklet contains text and illustrations on panes and interleaving pages. Stitched.
ASB22 £14.44 booklet containing panes Nos. A488a/93a .... 32·00

AB **10** Lion, Wounded Knight and Eagle

Bayeux Tapestry Final Panel

(Des Mark Totty)

2014 (28 May). Multicoloured cover, 163×98 mm, as Type AB **10**. Booklet contains text and illustrations on interleaving pages. Stitched.
ASB23   £14.44 booklet containing panes Nos. A515a/20a .... 33·00

Stanley Gibbons

399 Strand

Unsure how to progress your collection?

Visit 399 Strand to get advice from our experienced and knowledgeable staff. They will help you choose the stamps and philatelic accessories that will enhance and develop your collection. They will also offer guidance on techniques for the care and storage of your stamps and covers.

We have a superb range of stamps albums and philatelic accessories.

We strive to cater for every need a collector might have, and if we don't have the exact item you need, we will recommend an equivalent or an alternative.

Come in, browse our range and choose what's best for you.

Before you commit to a particular album, take the time to talk to our staff who will help you weigh up the pros and cons before you make your decision. We are always happy to demonstrate anything we sell from tweezers to Frank Godden luxury albums.

Everything for the philatelic collector.

Just down the road from the Savoy Hotel, two minutes from Charing Cross Tube station

For more information, please contact Stephen Bowyer on:
Tel. +44 (0)207 557 4436 or sbowyer@stanleygibbons.com
399 Strand opening hours **Mon-Fri 9am-5.30pm Sat 9:30am-5.30pm Sun Closed**

Est 1856

SG STANLEY GIBBONS

Stanley Gibbons Limited
399 Strand, London, WC2R 0LX
+44 (0)20 7557 4444
www.stanleygibbons.com

Isle of Man

REGIONAL ISSUES

Although specifically issued for regional use, these issues were initially valid for use throughout the U.K. Regional issues ceased to be valid in the Isle of Man from 5 July 1973 when the island established its own independent postal administration and introduced its own stamps.

DATES OF ISSUE. Conflicting dates of issue have been announced for some of the regional issues, partly explained by the stamps being released on different dates by the Philatelic Bureau in Edinburgh or the Philatelic Counter in London and in the regions. We have adopted the practice of giving the earliest known dates, since once released the stamps could have been used anywhere in the U.K.

INVALIDATION. Nos. 1/7 were invalidated as from 1 March 1972 in common with other British '£sd' stamps. Nos. 8/11 were invalidated for use in the Isle of Man on 5 July 1973, but, together with other British stamps, were accepted for the prepayment of postage on letters from the island until 5 August 1973. The Manx Regionals remained valid for use in the rest of the United Kingdom and were withdrawn from sale at the British Post Office Philatelic Sales counters on 4 July 1974.

        1   **2**

(Des J. Nicholson. Portrait by Dorothy Wilding Ltd. Photo Harrison)

1958–68. Wmk as Type **1b** of Guernsey. P 15×14 (C).

1	**1**	2½d. carmine-red (8.6.64)	50	1·25
2	**2**	3d. deep lilac (18.8.58)	50	20
		a. Chalk-surfaced paper (17.5.63)	12·00	12·00
		p. One centre phosphor band (27.6.68)	20	50
3		4d. ultramarine (7.2.66)	1·50	1·50
		p. Two phosphor bands (5.7.67)	20	30

1/3p. Set of 3 80   1·60
First Day Cover 1 .... 45·00
First Day Cover 2 .... 32·00
First Day Cover 3 .... 15·00

Cylinder Nos.: 2½d 1; 3d. (ord and phos) 1; 4d. (ord and phos) 1.
Sheets: 240 (12×20).
Quantities sold (ordinary only): 2½d. 4,298,160; 3d. 35,959,420 (up to 31.3.68 and including 1,080,000 on chalky paper); 4d. 4.,353,840.
Withdrawn: 31.8.66 2½d.
Sold out: 11.67 4d. ordinary; 12.68 3d. ordinary, 4d. phosphor; 4.69 3d. phosphor.

1968–69. No wmk. Chalk-surfaced paper. One centre phosphor band (Nos. 5/6) or two phosphor bands (others). P 15×14 (C).

4	**2**	4d. blue (24.6.68)	25	30
5		4d. olive-sepia (4.9.68)	25	30
		Ey. Phosphor omitted	22·00	
6		4d. bright vermilion (26.2.69)	45	75
7		5d. royal blue (4.9.68)	45	75
		Ey. Phosphor omitted	£175	

4/7 Set of 4 .... 1·25   2·00
5, 7 First Day Cover .... 4·00

Cylinder Nos.: 4d. (blue) 1; 4d. (olive-sepia) 1; 4d. (bright vermilion) 1; 5d. 1.
Sheets: 240 (12×20).
Sold out: 16.7.69 4d. blue.
Withdrawn: 14.3.71 (locally), 25.11.71 (British Philatelic Counters) 4d.

3

Decimal Currency

(Des J. Matthews. Portrait after plaster cast by Arnold Machin. Photo Harrison)

1971 (7 July). Chalk-surfaced paper. One centre phosphor band (2½p.) or two phosphor bands (others). P 15×14 (C).

8	**3**	2½p. bright magenta	20	15
		Ey. Phosphor omitted	£1500	
9		3p. ultramarine	20	15
10		5p. reddish violet	80	80
		Ey. Phosphor omitted	£275	
11		7½p. chestnut	90	90

8/11 Set of 4 .... 1·80   1·80
First Day Cover .... 3·25
Presentation Pack..

All values were originally issued on ordinary cream paper, but the 2½p. and 3p. later appeared on white fluorescent paper.
Cylinder Nos.: (dot and no dot): 2½p. 3, phos 5; 3p. 1, phos 4; 5p. 4, phos 12; 7½p. 4, phos 10.
Sheets: 200 (10×20).
Withdrawn: 4.7.73 (locally), 4.7.74 (British Philatelic Counters).

INDEPENDENT POSTAL ADMINISTRATION

The Isle of Man established an independent postal administration on 5 July 1973 and introduced its own stamps.

NO WATERMARK. All the following issues are on unwatermarked paper *unless otherwise stated*.

5 Castletown   **6** Port Erin

7 Snaefell   **8** Laxey

9 Tynwald Hill   **10** Douglas Promenade

11 Port St. Mary   **12** Fairy Bridge

13 Peel   **14** Cregneish

15 Ramsey Bay

16 Douglas Bay

17 Manx Cat

18 Monk's Bridge, Ballasalla

19 Derbyhaven

20 Manx Loaghtyn Ram

21 Manx Shearwater

22 Viking Longship

(Des J. Nicholson. Photo Courvoisier)

1973 (5 July)–**75**. Granite paper. P 11½ (C).

12	**5**	½p. multicoloured (ab)	10	10
13	**6**	1p. multicoloured (ae)	10	10
14	**7**	1½p. multicoloured (ak)	10	10
15	**8**	2p. multicoloured (aj)	10	10
16	**9**	2½p. multicoloured (a)	10	10
17	**10**	3p. mult (sage-green border) (ac)	10	10
		a. Error. Olive-bistre border †	£160	85·00
18	**11**	3½p. mult (olive-brown border) (ad)	10	10
		a. Error. Grey-brown border †	£225	85·00
19	**12**	4p. multicoloured (a)	10	10
20	**9**	4½p. multicoloured (f)	20	15
21	**13**	5p. multicoloured (ah)	15	10
22	**10**	5½p. multicoloured (g)	20	15
23	**14**	6p. multicoloured (al)	20	15
24	**8**	7p. multicoloured (g)	20	15
25	**15**	7½p. multicoloured (a)	20	20
26		8p. multicoloured (f)	25	25
27	**16**	9p. multicoloured (an)	20	20
28	**17**	10p. multicoloured (an)	35	20
29	**18**	11p. multicoloured (i)	35	30
30	**19**	13p. multicoloured (i)	40	35
31	**20**	20p. multicoloured (an)	50	50
32	**21**	50p. multicoloured (an)	1·20	1·30
33	**22**	£1 multicoloured (am)	2·50	2·50
12/33 Set of 22			6·25	6·25
First Day Covers (7)				7·75
Presentation Packs (6)			9·00	

† These errors occur on printings (c) and (d). That on the 3p. resembles the border colour of the ½p. and that on the 3½p. the 2p. Intermediate shades also exist, but are not covered by the listing.
Printings: (a) 5.7.73; (b) 1.11.73; (c) 16.4.74; (d) 29.7.74; (e) 2.9.74; (f) 8.1.75; (g) 28.5.75; (h) 16.6.75; (i) 29.10.75; (j) 1.12.75; (k) 2.2.76; (l) 20.9.76; (m) 16.2.77; (n) 7.7.77.
Printings (a) and (i) have thick shiny gum, but all the other printings have matt, almost invisible gum. Printings (f), (g) and (i) are inscribed '1975'. The remainder are inscribed '1973'.
Sheets: 50 (5×10) ½p. to 9p., 11p., 13p.; (10×5) 10p., 20p. to £1.
Withdrawn: 31.12.78 (except ½p., 3p. and 3½p. values in booklets withdrawn 15.5.79. In addition 2p and 3½p. values were kept available for use on postal orders after 31.12.78 until finally withdrawn on 30.6.83 (2p.) or 31.12.85 (3½p.)).

23 Vikings Landing on Man, A.D. 938

Inauguration of Postal Independence

(Des J. Nicholson. Photo Harrison)

1973 (5 July). P 14 (C).

34	**23**	15p. multicoloured	35	35
First Day Cover				1·10
Presentation Pack			1·40	

For 15p. inscr 'POST OFFICE DECENNIUM' 1983 see No. 256.
Cylinder Nos.: 1A (×4).
Sheets: 50 (10×5).
Quantity sold: 350,000.
Sold out: Soon after issue.

24 No. 1 *Sutherland*, 1873

25 No. 4 *Caledonia*, 1885

26 No. 13 *Kissack*, 1910

27 No. 3 *Pender*, 1873

Centenary of Steam Railway

(Des J. Nicholson. Photo Harrison)

1973 (4 Aug). P 15×14 (C).

35	**24**	2½p. multicoloured	15	10
36	**25**	3p. multicoloured	15	15
37	**26**	7½p. multicoloured	25	25
38	**27**	9p. multicoloured	25	25
35/8 Set of 4			70	70
First Day Cover				2·00
Presentation Pack			1·50	

Cylinder Nos.: All values 1A (×5).
Sheets: 50 (5×10).
Quantities sold: 2½p. 617,122; 3p. 808,173; 7½p. 331,695; 9p. 324,414.
Withdrawn: 3.8.74.

28 Leonard Randles, First Winner, 1923 on Sunbeam motorcycle

29 Alan Holmes, Double Winner, 1957 on Norton motorcycle

Golden Jubilee of Manx Grand Prix

(Des J. Nicholson. Litho John Waddington)

1973 (4 Sept). P 14 (C).

39	**28**	3p. multicoloured	10	15
40	**29**	3½p. multicoloured	15	15
39/40 Set of 2			25	25
First Day Cover				90
Presentation Pack			70	
Set of 2 Gutter Pairs			60	

Plate Nos.: Both values 1A, 1B, 1C, 1D (each×4).
Sheets: 50 (2 panes 5×5).
Imprint: Central, bottom margin.
Quantities sold: 3p. 550,347; 3½p. 653,355.
Withdrawn: 3.9.74.

30 Princess Anne and Capt. Mark Philips

Royal Wedding

(Des A. Larkins and litho DLR)

1973 (14 Nov). P 13½ (C).

41	**30**	25p. multicoloured	70	70
	First Day Cover			85
	Presentation Pack		90	
	Gutter Pair		1·40	

Plate Nos.: 1A, 1B (each×4).
Sheets: 50 (5 panes 5×5).
Imprint: Right-hand corner, bottom margin.
Quantity sold: 400,813.
Withdrawn: 13.11.74.

31 Badge, Citation and Sir Wiliam Hillary (founder)

32 Wreck of *St. George*, 1830

33 *Manchester & Salford*, 1868–87

34 *Osman Gabriel*

150th Anniversary of Royal National Lifeboat Institution

(Des J. Nicholson. Photo Courvoisier)

1974 (4 Mar). Granite paper. P 11½ (C).

42	**31**	3p. multicoloured	10	10
43	**32**	3½p. multicoloured	15	15
44	**33**	8p. multicoloured	25	25
45	**34**	10p. multicoloured	30	30
42/5	*Set of 4*		70	70
	First Day Cover			1·00
	Presentation Pack		1·00	

Sheets: 100 (10×10).
Quantities sold: 3p. 674,984; 3½p. 849,990; 8p. 374,941; 10p. 375,043.
Withdrawn: 3.3.75.

35 Stanley Woods, 1935 on Motoguzzi motorcycle

36 Freddy Frith, 1937 on Norton motorcycle

37 Max Deubel and Emil Horner, 1961 on BMW 500 with Sidecar

38 Mike Hailwood, 1961 on Honda 125 motorcycle

Tourist Trophy Motorcycle Races (1st issue)

(Des J. Nicholson. Litho DLR)

1974 (29 May). P 13×13½ (C).

46	**35**	3p. multicoloured	15	15
47	**36**	3½p. multicoloured	15	15
48	**37**	8p. multicoloured	40	45
49	**38**	10p. multicoloured	40	45
46/9	*Set of 4*		90	1·00
	First Day Cover			1·50
	Presentation Pack		1·50	
	Set of 4 Gutter Pairs		1·80	

See also Nos. 63/6.
Plate Nos.: All values 1A, 1B, 1C, 1D (each×6); 3p. also 1A (×4)–2A–2A, 1B (×4)–2B–2B, 1C (×4)–2C–2C, 1D (×4)–2D–2D; 8p. also 1A–1A–2A–1A (×3), 1B–1B–2B–1B (×3), 1C–1C–2C–1C (×3), 1D–1D–2D–1D (×3).
Sheets: 50 (2 panes 5×5).
Imprint: Right-hand corner, bottom margin.
Quantities sold: 3p. 578,045; 3½p. 816,235; 8p. 334,760; 10p. 403,177.
Withdrawn: 28.5.75.

39 Rushen Abbey and Arms

40 Magnus Haraldson rows King Edgar on the Dee

41 King Magnus and Norse Fleet

42 Bridge at Avignon and Bishop's Mitre

Historical Anniversaries

(Des J. Nicholson, from ideas by G. Kneale. Litho Questa (3½p., 10p.) or John Waddington (others))

1974 (18 Sept). P 14 (C).

50	**39**	3½p. multicoloured	20	20
51	**40**	4½p. multicoloured	20	20
52	**41**	8p. multicoloured	40	40
53	**42**	10p. multicoloured	40	40

50/3 *Set of 4*.. 1·00 1·00
First Day Cover.. 1·25
Presentation Pack... 1·50
Set of 4 Gutter Pairs... 2·00
    Plate Nos.: All values 1A, 1B, 1C, 1D (each×4).
    Sheets: 50 (2 panes 5×5).
    Imprint: Right-hand corner, bottom margin and left-hand corner,
    top margin.
    Quantities sold: 3½p. 931,610; 4½p. 1,025,044; 8p. 450,418; 10p.
    425,305.
    Withdrawn: 17.9.75.

43 Churchill and Bugler Dunne at
Colenso, 1899

44 Churchill and Government
Buildings, Douglas

45 Churchill and Manx A.A. Gun Crew

46 Churchill as Freeman of Douglas

Birth Centenary of Sir Winston Churchill

(Des G. Kneale. Photo Courvoisier)

1974 (22 Nov). Granite paper. P 11½ (C).
54   **43**   3½p. multicoloured 20 20
55   **44**   4½p. multicoloured 20 20
56   **45**   8p. multicoloured 40 40
57   **46**   20p. multicoloured 40 40
54/7 *Set of 4*.. 1·00 1·00
First Day Cover.. 1·25
Presentation Pack... 1·40
MS58 121×91 mm. Nos. 54/7 .... 1·00 1·00
First Day Cover.. 1·60
    No. **MS**58 is inscribed '30th NOV. 1974.
    Sheets: 25 (5×5).
    Quantities sold: 3½p. 916,748; 4½p. 853,537; 8p. 424,691; 20p.
    429,586; miniature sheet 362,089.
    Withdrawn: 21.11.75.

47 Cabin School and Names of
Pioneers

48 Terminal Tower Building,
John Gill and Robert Carran

49 Clague House Museum and
Robert and Margaret Clague

50 *William T. Graves* and
Thomas Quayle

Manx Pioneers in Cleveland, Ohio

(Des J. Nicholson. Photo Courvoisier)

1975 (14 Mar). Granite paper. P 11½ (C).
59   **47**   4½p. multicoloured 10 10
60   **48**   5½p. multicoloured 10 15
61   **49**   8p. multicoloured 15 20
62   **50**   10p. multicoloured 25 40
59/62 *Set of 4* 55 75
First Day Cover 90
Presentation Pack 80
    Sheets: 50 (5×10).
    Quantities sold: 4½p. 473,352; 5½p. 999,802; 8p. 433,352; 10p.
    447,945.
    Withdrawn: 13.3.76 (5½p. sold out 12.75).

51 Tom Sheard, 1923 and
Douglas motorcycle

52 Walter Handley, 1925 and
Rex-Acme motorcycle

53 Geoff Duke, 1955 and Gilera
motorcycle

54 Peter Williams, 1973 and
Norton motorcycle

Tourist Trophy Motorcycle Races (2nd issue)

(Des J. Nicholson. Litho John Waddington)

1975 (28 May). P 13½ (C).
63   **51**   5½p. multicoloured 10 10
64   **52**   7p. multicoloured 15 15
65   **53**   10p. multicoloured 15 15
66   **54**   12p. multicoloured 25 20
63/6 *Set of 4* 60 55
First Day Cover .... 2·40
Presentation Pack .... 1·00
Set of 4 Gutter Pairs .... 1·20
    Plate Nos.: 1A, 1B, 1C, 1D (each×5).
    Sheets: 50 (2 panes 5×5).
    Imprint: Right-hand corner, bottom margin.
    Quantities sold: 5½p. 633,250; 7p. 520,285; 10p. 399,710; 12p.
    440,208.
    Withdrawn: 27.5.76.

55 Sir George Goldie and
Birthplace

56 Goldie and Map
of Africa

57 Goldie as President of Royal Geographical Society

58 River Scene on the Niger

50th Death Anniversary of Sir George Goldie

(Des G. Kneale. Photo Courvoisier)

1975 (9 Sept). Granite paper. P 11½ (C).

67	**55**	5½p. multicoloured	10	10
68	**56**	7p. multicoloured	15	15
69	**57**	10p. multicoloured	15	15
70	**58**	12p. multicoloured	25	25
67/70 *Set of 4*			65	65
First Day Cover				90
Presentation Pack			1·00	

Sheets: 50 (10×5) 7p., 10p.; (5×10) others.
Quantities sold: 5½p. 488,317; 7p. 426,849; 10p. 373,771; 12p. 439,843.
Withdrawn: 8.9.76.

59 Title Page of Manx Bible

60 Rev. Philip Moore and Ballaugh Old Church

61 Bishop Hildesley and Bishops Court

62 John Kelly saving Bible Manuscript

Christmas and Bicentenary of Manx Bible

(Des J. Nicholson. Litho Questa)

1975 (29 Oct). P 14 (C).

71	**59**	5½p. multicoloured	20	20
72	**60**	7p. multicoloured	20	20
73	**61**	11p. multicoloured	40	40
74	**62**	13p. multicoloured	40	40
71/4 *Set of 4*			1·00	1·00
First Day Cover				1·25
Presentation Pack			1·00	
Set of 4 Gutter Pairs			2·00	

Plate Nos. 1A, 1B, 1C, 1D (each×4).
Sheets: 50 (2 panes 5×5).
Quantities sold: 5½p. 738,774; 7p. 607,377; 11p. 405,126; 13p. 402,463.
Withdrawn: 28.10.76.

63 William Christian listening to Patrick Henry

64 Conveying the Fincastle Resolutions

65 Patrick Henry and William Christian

66 Christian as an Indian Fighter

Bicentenary of American Revolution and Col. William Christian Commemoration

(Des and litho John Waddington)

1976 (12 Mar). P 13½ (C).

75	**63**	5½p. multicoloured	10	10
76	**64**	7p. multicoloured	15	15
77	**65**	13p. multicoloured	30	30
		a. *Black* (face value and inscr) printed double	£525	
78	**66**	20p. multicoloured	35	35
75/8 *Set of 4*			75	80
Set of 4 Gutter Pairs			1·50	
MS79 150×90 mm. Nos. 75/8. P 14 (C)			90	1·00
First Day Cover				3·00
Presentation Pack			1·90	

Plate Nos.: 1A, 1B, 1C, 1D (each×4).
Sheets: 50 (2 panes 5×5).
Quantities sold: 5½p. 487,310; 7p. 524,144; 13p. 558,348; 20p. 424,728; miniature sheet 209,367.
Withdrawn: 11.3.77.

67 First Horse Tram, 1876

68 'Toast-rack' Tram, 1890

69 Horse-bus, 1895

70 Royal Tram, 1972

Douglas Horse Trams Centenary

(Des J. Nicholson. Photo Courvoisier)

1976 (26 May). Granite paper. P 11½ (C).

80	**67**	5½p. multicoloured	20	20
81	**68**	7p. multicoloured	20	20
82	**69**	11p. multicoloured	40	40
83	**70**	13p. multicoloured	40	40
80/3 *Set of 4*			1·00	1·00

First Day Cover .... 1·25
Presentation Pack .... 1·00
     Sheets: 25 (5×5).
     Quantities sold: 5½p. 627,083; 7p. 480,417; 11p. 391,871; 13p.
     389,604.
     Withdrawn: 25.5.77.

71 Barroose Beaker   **72** Souvenir Teapot   **73** Laxey Jug

74 Cronk Aust Food Vessel   **75** Sansbury Bowl

76 Knox Urn

Europa. Ceramic Art

(Des J. Nicholson. Photo Courvoisier)

1976 (28 July). Granite paper. P 11½ (C).

84	**71**	5p. multicoloured	20	10
		a. Strip of 3. Nos. 84/6	60	70
85	**72**	5p. multicoloured	20	10
86	**73**	5p. multicoloured	20	10
87	**74**	10p. multicoloured	25	10
		a. Strip of 3 Nos. 87/9	70	90
88	**75**	10p. multicoloured	25	10
89	**76**	10p. multicoloured	25	10
84/9 *Set of 6*			1·20	1·40
First Day Cover				2·10
Presentation Pack			1·60	

     Sheets: 9 (3×3) containing the three designs of each value
horizontally and vertically *se-tenant*.
     Quantities sold: 5p. 256,400 of each design; 10p. 262,900 of each
design.
     Sold out: 20.11.76 (5p.); 12.76 (10p.).

77 Diocesan Banner   **78** Onchan Banner

79 Castletown Banner   **80** Ramsey Banner

Christmas and Centenary of Mothers' Union

(Des G. Kneale. Litho Questa)

1976 (14 Oct). P 14½ (C).

90	**77**	6p. multicoloured	10	10
91	**78**	7p. multicoloured	15	15
92	**79**	11p. multicoloured	25	25
93	**80**	13p. multicoloured	30	30
90/3 *Set of 4*			70	70
First Day Cover				90
Presentation Pack			1·00	

     Plate Nos.: All values 1A, 1B, 1C, 1D (each×5).
     Sheets: 50 (10×5).
     Imprint: Right-hand corner, bottom margin and left-hand corner,
top margin.
     Quantities sold: 6p. 905,752; 7p. 890,762; 11p. 397,807; 13p.
390,057.
     Withdrawn: 13.10.77.

81 Queen Elizabeth II   **82** Queen Elizabeth
and Prince Philip

83 Queen Elizabeth II

Silver Jubilee

(Des A. Larkins. Litho and recess DLR)

1977 (1 Mar). P 14×13 (7p.) or 13×14 (others), both comb.

94	**81**	6p. multicoloured	15	10
95	**82**	7p. multicoloured	20	20
96	**83**	25p. multicoloured	60	60
94/6 *Set of 3*			80	80
First Day Cover				90
Presentation pack			1·00	
Set of 3 Gutter Pairs			1·60	

     Plate Nos.: 6p., 7p. 1A (×6), 1A (×5)–2A, 1B (×6), 1B (×5)–2B, 1C
(×6), 1C (×5)–2C, 1D (×6), 1D (×5)–2D 25p. 1A, 1B, 1C, 1D (each×6).
     Sheets: 50 (2 panes 5×5).
     Imprint: Right-hand corner, bottom margin.
     Quantities sold: 6p. 942,356; 7p. 911,191; 25p. 651,101.
     Withdrawn: 28.2.78.

84 Carrick Bay from 'Tom-the-Dipper'

85 View from Ramsey

Europa. Landscapes

(Des J. Nicholson. Litho Questa)

1977 (26 May). P 13½×14 (C).

97	**84**	6p. multicoloured	15	30
98	**85**	10p. multicoloured	25	35
97/8 *Set of 2*			40	60
First Day Cover				75
Presentation Pack			1·00	

Set of 2 Gutter Pairs.. 80
Plate Nos.: 6p. 1A, 1B, 1C, 1D, 2A, 2B, 2C, 2D (each×4); 10p.
1A, 1B, 1C, 1D (each×5), 2A–1A–1A–2A–1A, 2B–1B–1B–2B–1B,
2C–1C–1C–2C–1C, 2D–1D–1D–2D–1D.
Sheets: 40 (2 panes 4×5).
Imprint: Right-hand corner, bottom margin and left-hand corner,
top margin.
Quantities sold: 6p. 778,685; 10p. 843,525.
Withdrawn: 25.5.78.

86 F. A. Applebee, 1912 riding Scott motorcycle
87 St. John Ambulance Brigade at Governor's Bridge, c. 1938

88 Scouts working Scoreboard
89 John Williams, 1976 on Norton motorcycle

Linked Anniversaries

(Des J. Nicholson. Litho John Waddington)

1977 (26 May). P 13½ (C).

99	86	6p. multicoloured	15	15
100	87	7p. multicoloured	20	20
101	88	11p. multicoloured	35	35
102	89	13p. multicoloured	40	40

99/102 Set of 4.................................. 1·00 1·00
First Day Cover.. 1·25
Presentation Pack.. 1·50
Set of 4 Gutter Pairs...................................... 2·00
The events commemorated are: 70th anniversary of Manx TT; 70th
anniversary of Boy Scouts; centenary of St. John Ambulance Brigade.
Plate Nos.: 6p. 1A, 1B, 1C, 1D (each×4); 11p. 1A, 1C (each×4);
others 1B, 1D (each×4).
Sheets: 50 (2 panes 5×5).
Imprint: Right-hand corner, bottom margin.
Quantities sold: 6p. 525,703; 7p. 875,303; 11p. 431,053; 13p. 440,403.
Withdrawn: 25.5.78.

90 Old Summer House, Mount Morrison, Peel
91 Wesley preaching in Castletown Square

92 Wesley preaching outside Bradden Church
93 New Methodist Church, Douglas

Bicentenary of the First Visit of John Wesley

(Des and photo Courvoisier)

1977 (19 Oct). Granite paper. P 11½ (C).

103	90	6p. multicoloured	15	15
104	91	7p. multicoloured	20	20
105	92	11p. multicoloured	35	35
106	93	13p. multicoloured	40	40

103/6 Set of 4................................. 1·00 1·00
First Day Cover.. 1·25
Presentation Pack.. 1·50
Sheets: 50 (5×10).
Quantities sold: 6p. 661,755; 7p. 976,155; 11p. 373,805; 13p.
366,905.
Withdrawn: 18.10.78.

94 Short Type 184 Seaplane and H.M.S. *Ben-My-Chree*, 1915

95 Bristol Scout C and H.M.S. *Vindex*, 1915

96 Boulton Paul Defiant over Douglas Bay, 1941

97 Sepecat Jaguar over Ramsey, 1977

R.A.F. Diamond Jubilee

(Des A. Theobald. Litho John Waddington)

1978 (28 Feb). P 13½×14 (C).

107	94	6p. multicoloured	15	15
108	95	7p. multicoloured	20	20
109	96	11p. multicoloured	35	35
110	97	13p. multicoloured	40	40

107/10 Set of 4............................... 1·00 1·00
First Day Cover.. 1·50
Presentation Pack.. 1·50
Set of 4 Gutter Pairs...................................... 2·00
Plate Nos.: All values 1A, 1B, 1C, 1D (each×4).
Sheets: 50 (2 panes 5×5).
Quantities sold: 6p. 690,536; 7p. 875,811; 11p. 416,082; 13p.
422,797.
Withdrawn: 27.2.79.

98 Watch Tower, Langness
99 Jurby Church
100 Government Buildings

101 Tynwald Hill
102 Milner's Tower
103 Laxey Wheel

104 Castle Rushen

105 St. Ninian's Church

106 Tower of Refuge

107 St. German's Cathedral

108 Point of Ayre Lighthouse

109 Corrin's Tower

110 Douglas Head Lighthouse

111 Fuchsia

112 Manx Cat

113 Red-billed Chough

114 Viking Warrior

114a Queen Elizabeth II

Landmarks and Queens Portrait (£2)

(Des G. Kneale (£2), J. Nicholson (others). Litho Questa (½p. to 16p.), photo Courvoisier (20p. to £2))

1978 (28 Feb)–**81**.

(a) P 14 (C)

111	98	½p. multicoloured (a)	10	10
		a. Perf 14½	20	10
112	99	1p. multicoloured (a)	10	10
		a. Perf 14½	20	10
113	100	6p. multicoloured (a)	30	30
114	101	7p. multicoloured (a)	35	35
		a. Perf 14½	8·50	6·50
115	102	8p. multicoloured (a)	25	25
		a. Perf 14½	35	35
116	103	9p. multicoloured (a)	35	35
		a. Perf 14½	35	35
117	104	10p. multicoloured (a)	40	40
		a. Perf 14½	35	35
118	105	11p. multicoloured (a)	40	40
		a. Perf 14½	40	40
119	106	12p. multicoloured (a)	40	25
		a. Perf 14½	50	40
120	107	13p. multicoloured (a)	60	60
		a. Perf 14½	30	25
121	108	14p. multicoloured (a)	75	75
		a. Perf 14½	30	25
122	109	15p. multicoloured (a)	90	90
		a. Perf 14½	30	25
123	110	16p. multicoloured (a)	75	75
		a. Perf 14½	20·00	20·00

(b) Granite paper. P 11½ (C)

124	111	20p. multicoloured (b)	90	90
125	112	25p. multicoloured (b)	90	90
126	113	50p. multicoloured (b)	1·25	1·25
127	114	£1 multicoloured (b)	2·50	2·50
128	114a	£2 multicoloured (c)	4·50	4·50
111/28 Set of 18 (cheapest)			12·00	12·00
First Day Covers* (5)				15·00
Presentation Packs (4)			14·00	

*The most common versions of the three low and medium value first day covers prepared by the Philatelic Bureau were franked with Nos. 111a, 112/15, 116a, 117/18, 119a, 120, 121a, 122 and 123a. Some examples can be found with the ½p. as No. 111, the 11p. as No. 118a or the 13p. as No. 120a. First day covers prepared by dealers or collectors on the island were franked with Nos. 111/18, 119a/20a, 121, 122a and 123.

Printings: (a) 28.2.78; (b) 18.10.78; (c) 29.9.81.

Although both perforations of Nos. 111/23 were printed at the same time, some did not appear in use until some time after 28 February 1978. Earliest dates for these are as follows: 1p. (112a) 8.79, 7p. (114a) 8.78, 8p. (115a) 6.80, 10p. (117a) 8.79, 12p. (119) 9.80.

Plate Nos.: ½, 6, 8, 9, 10, 11, 12, 13, 14, 15, 16p. 1A, 1B, 1C, 1D (each×4); 1p. 1A, 1B, 1C, 1D (each×4) (No. 112), 1A–1A–2A–1A, 1B–1B–2B–1B, 1C–1C–2C–1C, 1D–1D–2D–1D; 6p. 1D–1D–2D–1D; 7p. 1A, 1B, 1C, 1D (each×4) (No. 114); 2A, 2B, 2C, 2D (each×4), 2B–2B–3B–2B, 2C–2C–3C–2C (No. 114a); £2 A1–1–1–1, B1–1–1–1, others none.

Sheets: 25 (5×5) (£2); 50 (1, 7, 10, 12, 13, 14, 15, 16p. 5×10; others 10×5).

Imprint: ½p. to 16p. left-hand corner, top margin and right-hand corner, bottom margin; 20p. to £1 none; £2 central bottom margin.

Withdrawn: 30.6.83 1p to 16p; 31.12.83 20p. to £1; 31.12.85 ½p.; 30.6.90 £2.

115 Queen Elizabeth in Coronation Regalia

25th Anniversary of Coronation

(Des G. Kneale. Litho Questa)

1978 (24 May). P 14½×14 (C).

132	115	25p. multicoloured	75	75
First Day Cover				90
Presentation Pack			1·00	
Gutter Pair			1·50	

Plate Nos.: 1A, 1B, 1C, 1D (each×6).

Sheets: 50 (2 panes 5×5).

Imprint: Left-hand corner, top margin and right-hand corner, bottom margin.

Quantity sold: 575,996.

Withdrawn: 23.5.79.

116 Wheel-headed Cross-slab

117 Celtic Wheel-Cross

118 Keeil Chiggyrt Stone

119 Olaf Liotulfson Cross

120 Odd's and Thorleif's Crosses

121 Thor Cross

Europa. Celtic and Norse Crosses

(Des J. Nicholson. Photo Courvoisier)

1978 (24 May). Granite paper. P 11½ (C).

133	**116**	6p. multicoloured	15	10
		a. Strip of 3. Nos. 133/5	40	45
134	**117**	6p. multicoloured	15	10
135	**118**	6p. multicoloured	15	10
136	**119**	11p. multicoloured	25	15
		a. Strip of 3. Nos. 136/8	70	80
137	**120**	11p. multicoloured	25	15
138	**121**	11p. multicoloured	25	15
133/8	*Set of 6*		1·10	1·20
First Day Cover				1·40
Presentation Pack			1·50	

Sheets: 9 (3×3) The three designs of each value were printed together, *se-tenant*, in horizontal and vertical strips throughout.
Quantities sold: 6p. 3,821,152; 11p. 3,788,667.
Withdrawn: 23.5.79.

122 J. K. Ward and Ward Library, Peel

123 Swimmer, Cyclist and Walker

124 American Bald Eagle, Manx Arms and Maple Leaf

125 Lumber Camp at Three Rivers, Quebec

Anniversaries and Events

(Des John Waddington (7p.), G. Kneale (11p.), J. Nicholson (others). Litho John Waddington)

1978 (10 June). Invisible gum. P 13½ (C).

139	**122**	6p. multicoloured	15	15
140	**123**	7p. multicoloured	20	20
141	**124**	11p. multicoloured	35	35
142	**125**	13p. multicoloured	40	40
139/42	*Set of 4*		1·00	1·00
First Day Covers (3)				1·25
Presentation Packs (2)			1·50	
Set of 4 Gutter Pairs			2·00	

Plate Nos.: 1A, 1B, 1C, 1D (each×4).
Sheets: 50 (2 panes 5×5).
Imprint: Central, bottom margin.
Quantities sold: 6p. 629,041; 7p. 873,067; 11p. 393,907; 13p. 383,048.
Withdrawn: 9.6.79.

126 Hunt the Wren

Christmas

(Des J. Nicholson. Litho John Waddington)

1978 (18 Oct). P 13 (C).

143	**126**	5p. multicoloured	20	20
First Day Cover				40
Presentation Pack			45	
Gutter Pair			40	

Plate Nos.: 1A, 1B, 1C, 1D (each×4).
Sheets: 50 (2 panes 5×5).
Imprint: Central, bottom margin.
Quantity sold: 1,000,000.
Sold out: 4.79 (stamp) or 8.79 (presentation pack).

127 P. M. C. Kermode (founder) and *Nassa kermodei*

128 Peregrine Falcon

129 Fulmar

130 *Epitriptus cowini* (fly)

Centenary of Natural History and Antiquarian Society

(Des J. Nicholson. Litho Questa)

1979 (27 Feb). P 14 (C).

144	**127**	6p. multicoloured	15	15
145	**128**	7p. multicoloured	20	20
146	**129**	11p. multicoloured	35	35
147	**130**	13p. multicoloured	40	40
144/7	*Set of 4*		1·00	1·00
First Day Cover				1·20
Presentation Pack			1·50	
Set of 4 Gutter Pairs			2·00	

Plate Nos.: 1A, 1B, 1C, 1D (each×4).
Sheets: 50 (2 panes 5×5).
Imprint: Left-hand corner, top margin and right-hand corner, bottom margin.
Quantities sold: 6p. 642,126; 7p. 790,515; 11p. 411,863; 13p. 390,454.
Withdrawn: 26.2.80.

131 Postman, 1859

132 Postman, 1979

Europa. Communications

(Des A. Theobald. Litho Questa)

1979 (16 May). P 14½ (C).

148	**131**	6p. multicoloured	15	15
149	**132**	11p. multicoloured	40	45

148/9 Set of 2 .... 50 50
First Day Cover 75
Presentation Pack 85
Plate Nos.: 1A, 1B, 1C, 1D (each×6); 11p. 1A, 1B, 1C, 1D (each×5).
Sheets: 20 (5×4).
Imprint: Right-hand corner, bottom margin.
Quantities sold: 6p. 1,301,039; 11p. 1,290,318.
Sold out: By 10.79 (stamps).
Withdrawn: 15.5.80 (presentation pack).

133 Viking
Longship Emblem

134 'Three Legs of
Man' Emblem

135 Viking Raid at Garwick

136 10th-century Meeting
of Tynwald

137 Tynwald Hill and
St. John's Church

138 Procession to Tynwald
Hill

Two types of 3p.:

Type I. Wrongly inscribed 'INSULAREM'. '1979'
imprint date.

Type II. Inscription corrected to 'INSULARUM'.
'1980' imprint date.

Millennium of Tynwald

(Des J. Nicholson. Litho Harrison (3, 4p.), John Waddington (others))
1979 (16 May)–**80.**

(a) P 14½×14 (C)
150	**133**	3p. multicoloured (Type I) (a)................	10	10
		a. Booklet pane. Nos. 150×4, 151×2		
		(4p. stamps at top)............................	60	
		ab. Do. (4p. stamps in centre)................	1·20	
		b. Type II (b)..	10	10
		ba. Booklet pane. Nos. 150b×4, 151×2		
		(4p stamps at bottom).......................	50	
151	**134**	4p. multicoloured (ab)...........................	10	10

(b) P 13 (C)
152	**135**	6p. multicoloured (a)	15	15
153	**136**	7p. multicoloured (a)	20	20
154	**137**	11p. multicoloured (a)	35	35
155	**138**	13p. multicoloured (a)	40	40
150/5 Set of 6			1·20	1·20
First Day Cover				1·40
Presentation Pack			1·50	
Set of 6 Gutter Pairs...			2·40	

See also Nos. 188/9.
Printings: (a) 16.5.79. Inscribed 1979; (b) 29.9.80. Inscribed 1980.
Plate Nos.: 3p., 4p. 1A (×6); others 1A, 1B, 1C, 1D, 1E, 1F, 1G, 1H
(each×4).

Sheets: In addition to booklets SB8, SB9 and SB10, the 3p. and
4p. also from special sheets of 80 (10 panes 2×3, 5 panes 2×2);
others 40 (2 panes 4×5). The 3p. and 4p. values were printed
together, se-tenant, each pane of six containing four 3p. and
two 4p, the 4p being in either positions 1 and 2 or 3 and 4. The
panes of four contain the 4p value only. For details of No. 150ba
see after No. 189.
Imprint: 3p., 4p. right-hand corner, bottom margin; others central,
bottom margin.
Quantities sold: 6p. 381,334; 7p. 465,473; 11p. 341,204; 13p.
241,162.
Withdrawn: 15.5.80 6p. to 13p.; 25.3.87 3p., 4p.

139 Queen and Court on
Tynwald Hill

140 Queen and Procession from
St. John's Church to Tynwald Hill

Royal Visit

(Des G. Kneale. Litho Questa)
1979 (5 July). P 14½ (C).
156	**139**	7p. multicoloured.................................	20	20
157	**140**	13p. multicoloured...............................	35	35
156/7 Set of 2			50	50
First Day Cover				75
Presentation pack			1·00	
Set of 2 Gutter Pairs			1·00	

Plate Nos.: 7p. 1A, 1B, 1C, 1D (each×4); 13p. 1A, 1B, 1C, 1D
(each×4).
Sheets: 50 (2 panes 5×5).
Imprint: Right-hand corner, bottom margin.
Quantities sold: 7p. 641,930; 13p. 436,516.
Withdrawn: 4.7.80.

141 Odin's Raven

Voyage of Odin's Raven

(Des J. Nicholson. Litho Questa)
1979 (19 Oct). P 14×14½ (C).
158	**141**	15p. multicoloured	50	50
First Day Cover				75
Presentation Pack			75	
Gutter Pair			1·00	

See also No. MS180.
Plate Nos.: 1A, 1B, 1C, 1D (each×4).
Sheets: 50 (2 panes 5×5).
Imprint: Right-hand corner, bottom margin.
Quantity sold: 412,631.
Withdrawn: 18.10.80.

142 John Quilliam seized by
Press Gang

143 Steering H.M.S. Victory,
Battle of Trafalgar

144 Captain John Quilliam and
H.M.S. Spencer

145 Captain John Quilliam
(member of the House of Keys)

150th Death Anniversary of Captain John Quilliam

(Des A. Theobald. Litho Questa)

1979 (19 Oct). P 14 (C).

159	**142**	6p. multicoloured	15	15
160	**143**	8p. multicoloured	20	15
161	**144**	13p. multicoloured	35	35
162	**145**	15p. multicoloured	40	40
159/62 *Set of 4*			1·00	1·00
First Day Cover				1·20
Presentation Pack			1·50	
Set of 4 Gutter Pairs			2·00	

Plate Nos.: 6p. 1A, 1B, 1C, 1D (each×4); others 1A, 1B (each×4).
Sheets: 50 (2 panes 5×5).
Imprint: Right-hand corner, bottom margin.
Quantities sold: 6p. 608,876; 8p. 858,665; 13p. 360,821; 15p. 360,400.
Withdrawn: 18.10.80.

146 Young Girl with Teddybear and Cat

147 Father Christmas with Young Children

Christmas and International Year of the Child

(Des Mrs. E. Moore. Litho John Waddington)

1979 (19 Oct). P 13 (C).

163	**146**	5p. multicoloured	25	25
164	**147**	7p. multicoloured	40	40
163/4 *Set of 2*			50	50
First Day Cover				75
Presentation Pack			90	
Set of 2 Gutter Pairs			1·00	

Plate Nos.: Both values 1A, 1B, 1C, 1D (each×4).
Sheets: 50 (2 panes 5×5).
Imprint: Central, left-hand margin.
Quantities sold: 5p. 1,036,495; 7p. 1,087,734.
Withdrawn: 18.10.80.

148 Conglomerate Arch, Langness

149 Braaid Circle

150 Cashtal-yn-Ard

151 Volcanic Rocks at Scarlett

152 Sugar-loaf Rock

150th Anniversary of Royal Geographical Society

(Des J. Nicholson. Litho Questa)

1980 (5 Feb). P 14½ (C).

165	**148**	7p. multicoloured	15	15
166	**149**	8p. multicoloured	20	20
167	**150**	12p. multicoloured	35	35
168	**151**	13p. multicoloured	40	40
169	**152**	15p. multicoloured	40	45
165/9 *Set of 5*			1·40	1·40
First Day Cover				1·50
Presentation Pack			1·75	
Set of 5 Gutter Pairs			2·80	

Plate Nos.: 1A, 1B, 1C, 1D (each×4).
Sheets: 50 (2 panes 5×5).
Imprint: Right-hand corner, bottom margin.
Quantities sold: 7p. 842,859; 8p. 837,710; 12p. 361,362; 13p. 360,261; 15p. 360,310.
Withdrawn: 4.2.81.

153 Mona's Isle I

154 Douglas I

155 H.M.S. Mona's Queen II sinking U-boat

156 H.M.S. King Orry III at Surrender of German Fleet

157 Ben-My-Chree IV

158 Lady of Mann II

150th Anniversary of Isle of Man Steam Packet Company

(Des J. Nicholson. Photo Courvoisier)

1980 (6 May). Granite paper. P 11½ (C).

170	**153**	7p. multicoloured	15	15
171	**154**	8p. multicoloured	20	20
172	**155**	11½p. multicoloured	35	35
173	**156**	12p. multicoloured	35	35
174	**157**	13p. multicoloured	40	40
175	**158**	15p. multicoloured	45	45
170/5 *Set of 6*			1·70	1·70
First Day Cover				2·00
Presentation Pack			2·40	
Set of 6 Gutter Pairs			3·40	
MS176 180×125 mm. Nos. 170/5			1·70	1·70
First Day Cover				4·50

No. **MS**176 was issued to commemorate the 'London 1980' International Stamp Exhibition.
Cylinder Nos.: All values A1–1–1–1, B1–1–1–1, C1–1–1–1, D1–1–1–1.
Sheets: 40 (2 panes 5×4).
Imprint: Central, bottom margin.
Quantities sold: 7p. 512,449; 8p. 624,090; 11½p. 381,466; 12p. 367,943; 13p. 368,138; 15p. 376,596; miniature sheet 300,678.
Withdrawn: 5.5.81.

159 Stained Glass Window, T. E. Brown Room, Manx Museum

160 Clifton College, Bristol

Europa. Personalities. Thomas Edward Brown (poet and scholar) Commemoration

(Des G. Kneale. Photo Courvoisier)

1980 (6 May). Granite paper. P 11½ (C).

177	**159**	7p. multicoloured	15	15
178	**160**	13½p. multicoloured	40	40
177/8 *Set of 2*			50	50
First Day Cover				60
Presentation Pack			75	
Set of 2 Gutter Pairs			1·00	

Cylinder Nos.: Both values A1–1–1–1–1, B1–1–1–1–1, C1–1–1–1–1, D1–1–1–1–1.
Sheets: 20 (2 panes 2×5).
Imprint: Bottom margin at right-hand corner of left-hand pane.
Quantities sold: 7p. 1,726,009; 13½p. 1,708,590.
Withdrawn: 5.5.81.

161 King Olav V and *Norge* (Norwegian royal yacht)

Visit of King Olav V of Norway, August 1979

(Des J. Nicholson. Litho Questa)

1980 (13 June). P 14×14½ (C).

179	**161**	12p. multicoloured	30	30
MS180	125×157 mm. Nos. 158 and 179		75	75
First Day Cover				1·75

No. **MS**180 also commemorates the 'NORWEX 80' stamp exhibition, Oslo.
Plate Nos.: 1A, 1B, 1C, 1D (each×4).
Sheets: 40 (2 panes 5×4).
Imprint: Right-hand corner, bottom margin.
Quantities sold: 12p. 449,267; miniature sheet 401,424.
Withdrawn: 12.6.81.

162 Winter Wren and View of Calf of Man

163 European Robin and View of Port Erin Marine Biological Station

Christmas and Wildlife Conservation Year

(Des J. Nicholson. Litho John Waddington)

1980 (29 Sept). P 13½×14 (C).

181	**162**	6p. multicoloured	15	10
182	**163**	8p. multicoloured	30	35
181/2 *Set of 2*			45	40
First Day Cover				1·20
Presentation Pack			80	
Set of 2 Gutter Pairs			90	

Plate Nos.: 6p. 1A, 1B, 1C, 1D (each×4); 8p. 1A, 1C, 1D (each×4).
Sheets: 40 (2 panes 4×5).
Imprint: Right-hand corner, bottom margin.
Quantities sold: 6p. 967,976; 8p. 942,323.
Withdrawn: 28.9.81.

164 William Kermode and Brig *Robert Quayle*, 1819

166 Ross Bridge, Tasmania

165 'Mona Vale', Van Diemen's Land, 1834

167 'Mona Vale', Tasmania (completed 1868)

168 Robert Q. Kermode and Parliament Buildings, Tasmania

Kermode Family in Tasmania Commemoration

(Des A. Theobald. Litho Questa)

1980 (29 Sept). P 14½ (C).

183	**164**	7p. multicoloured	15	15
184	**165**	9p. multicoloured	20	20
185	**166**	13½p. multicoloured	30	30
186	**167**	15p. multicoloured	40	40
187	**168**	17½p. multicoloured	45	45
183/7 *Set of 5*			1·30	1·30
First Day Cover				1·50
Presentation Pack			2·00	
Set of 5 Gutter Pairs			2·50	

Plate Nos.: All values 1A, 1C, 1D (each×4).
Sheets: 40 (2 panes 5×4).
Imprint: Right-hand corner, bottom margin.
Quantities sold: 7p. 416,487; 9p. 498,880; 13½p. 318,353; 15p. 314,837; 17½p. 315,107.
Withdrawn: 28.9.81.

169 Peregrine Falcon

170 Loaghtyn Ram

Booklet stamps

(Des J. Nicholson. Litho Harrison)

1980 (29 Sept). P 14½×14 (C).

188	**169**	1p. multicoloured	20	20
		a. Booklet pane. Nos. 151, 188 and		
		189, each×2	60	
189	**170**	5p. multicoloured	30	30
188/9	*Set of 2*		50	50

First Day Cover (Nos. 150bx2, 151×2, 188 and 189) .... 1·10
Presentation Pack (Nos. 150bx2, 151×2, 188 and 189).. 1·20

In addition to Booklets SB11/12 Nos. 188/9 also come from special booklet sheets of 60. These sheets contain No. 150ba×5 and No. 188a×5.
Plate Nos.: 1A, 1B (each×7).
Withdrawn: 25.3.87.

171 Luggers passing Red Pier, Douglas

172 Peel Lugger *Wanderer* rescuing survivors from the *Lusitania*

173 Nickeys leaving Port St. Mary Harbour

174 Nobby entering Ramsey Harbour

175 Nickeys *Sunbeam* and *Zebra* at Port Erin

Centenary of Royal National Mission to Deep Sea Fishermen

(Des J. Nicholson. Litho Questa)

1981 (24 Feb). P 14 (C).

190	**171**	8p. multicoloured	15	15
191	**172**	9p. multicoloured	20	20
192	**173**	18p. multicoloured	40	40
193	**174**	20p. multicoloured	45	45
194	**175**	22p. multicoloured	50	50
190/4	*Set of 5*		1·50	1·50
				1·70

First Day Cover .... 2·00
Presentation pack .... 3·00
Set of 5 Gutter Pairs ....
Plate Nos.: 8p. 1A, 1B, 1E, 1F (each×4); 9p. 1A, 1B, 1E, 1G, 1H (each×4); 18p., 20p. 1A, 1B, 1C, 1D, 1E (each×4); 22p. 1A, 1B, 1E (each×4).
Sheets: 40 (2 panes 5×4).
Imprint: Right-hand corner, bottom margin.
Quantities sold: 8p. 566,522; 9p. 583,358; 18p. 334,765; 20p. 315,511; 22p 324,607.
Withdrawn: 23.2.82.

176 'Crosh Cuirn' Superstition   **177** 'Bollan Cross' Superstition

Europa. Folklore

(Des J. Nicholson. Litho Questa)

1981 (22 May). P 14½ (C).

195	**176**	8p. multicoloured	20	20
196	**177**	18p. multicoloured	50	50
195/6	*Set of 2*		60	60

First Day Cover 75
Presentation Pack 80
Set of 2 Gutter Pairs .... 1·20
Plate Nos.: 1A, 1B (each×4).
Sheets: 24 (2 panes 3×4).
Imprint: Right-hand corner, bottom margin.
Quantities sold: 8p. 1,261,267; 18p. 1,243,459.
Withdrawn: 21.5.82.

178 Lt. Mark Wilks (Royal Manx Fencibles) and Peel Castle

179 Ensign Mark Wilks and Fort St. George, Madras

180 Governor Mark Wilks and Napoleon, St. Helena

181 Col. Mark Wilks (speaker of the House of Keys) and Estate, Kirby

150th Death Anniversary of Colonel Mark Wilks

(Des A. Theobald. Litho Questa)

1981 (22 May). P 14 (C).

197	**178**	8p. multicoloured	15	15
198	**179**	20p. multicoloured	45	45
199	**180**	22p. multicoloured	50	50
200	**181**	25p. multicoloured	60	60
197/200	*Set of 4*		1·50	1·50
				2·00

First Day Cover .... 1·60
Presentation Pack ....
Set of 4 Gutter Pairs .... 3·00
Plate Nos.: 8p. 1A, 1B (each×5); 20p. 1A, 1B, 1C (each×5); 22p. 1A, 1B, 1C (each×4); 25p. 1A, 1B (each×4).
Sheets: 40 (2 panes 5×4).
Imprint: 22p none; others right-hand corner, bottom margin.
Quantities sold: 8p. 371,280; 20p. 278,840; 22p. 294,480; 25p. 272,640.
Withdrawn: 21.5.82.

182 Miss Emmeline Goulden (Mrs. Pankhurst) and Mrs. Sophia Jane Goulden

Centenary of Manx Women's Suffrage

(Des A. Theobald. Litho Questa)

1981 (22 May). P 14 (C).

201	**182**	9p. black, olive-grey and stone	30	30
				75

First Day Cover 50
Presentation Pack 60
Gutter Pair ....
Plate Nos.: 1A, 1B, 1C, 1D (each×3).
Sheets: 40 (2 panes 5×4).
Imprint: Right-hand corner, bottom margin.
Quantity sold: 657,760.
Withdrawn: 21.5.82.

183 Prince Charles and Lady Diana Spencer

Royal Wedding

(Des G. Kneale. Litho Harrison)

1981 (29 July). P 14 (C).

202	**183**	9p. black, bright blue and pale blue ...		15	20
203		25p. black, bright blue and pink.............		75	80
202/3 *Set of 2*				90	1·00
First Day Cover					1·70
Presentation Pack...				1·70	
Set of 2 Gutter Pairs..				1·80	
MS204 130×183 mm. Nos. 202/3×2........................				2·00	2·00
First Day Cover					9·00

Plate Nos.: 9p. 1C, 1D (each×3); 25p. 1A, 1B, 1C, 1D (each×3).
Sheets: 50 (2 panes 5×5).
Imprint: Central, bottom margin.
Quantities sold: 9p. 668,864; 25p. 474,364; miniature sheet 327,094.
Withdrawn: 28.7.82.

184 Douglas War Memorial, Poppies and Inscription

185 Major Robert Cain (war hero)

186 Festival of Remembrance, Royal Albert Hall

187 T.S.S. *Tynwald* at Dunkirk, May, 1940

60th Anniversary of the Royal British Legion

(Des A. Theobald. Photo Courvoisier)

1981 (29 Sept). Granite paper. P 11½ (C).

205	**184**	8p. multicoloured		15	15
206	**185**	10p. multicoloured		20	20
207	**186**	18p. multicoloured		40	40
208	**187**	20p. multicoloured		45	45
205/8 *Set of 4*				1·00	1·00
First Day Cover					1·20
Presentation Pack...				1·40	
Set of 4 Gutter Pairs..				2·00	

Cylinder Nos.: 8p. A1–1–1–1, B1–1–1–1; others A1–1–1–1–1, B1–1–1–1–1.
Sheets: 40 (2 panes 4×5).
Imprint: Central, bottom margin.
Quantities sold: 8p. 314,794; 10p. 799,326; 18p. 284,059; 20p. 261,194.
Withdrawn: 28.9.82.

188 Nativity Scene (stained glass window, St. Georges Church)

189 Children from Special School Performing Nativity Play

Christmas

(Des John Waddington (7p.), G. Kneale (9p.). Litho John Waddington)

1981 (29 Sept). P 14 (C).

209	**188**	7p. multicoloured......................................		15	15
210	**189**	9p. multicoloured......................................		40	40
209/10 *Set of 2*..				50	50
First Day Cover..					75
Presentation pack..				75	
Set of 2 Gutter Pairs...				1·00	

The 7p. value also commemorates the bicentenary of St. George's Church, Douglas and the 9p. the International Year for Disabled Persons.
Plate Nos.: 9p. 1A, 1B, 1C, 1D (each×6).
Sheets: 40 (2 panes 2×10).
Imprint: Right-hand corner, bottom margin.
Quantities sold: 7p. 855,407; 9p. 862,892.
Withdrawn: 28.9.82.

190 Joseph and William Cunningham (founders of Manx Boy Scout Movement) and Cunningham House Headquarters

191 Baden-Powell visiting Isle of Man, 1911

192 Baden-Powell and Scout Emblem

193 Scouts and Baden-Powell's Last Message

194 Scout Salute, Handshake, Emblem and Globe

75th Anniversary of Boy Scout Movement and 125th Birth Anniversary of Lord Baden-Powell

(Des G. Kneale. Litho Questa)

1982 (23 Feb). P 14×14½ (19½p.) or 13½×14 (others), all comb.

211	**190**	9p. multicoloured	15	15
212	**191**	10p. multicoloured	20	20
213	**192**	19½p. multicoloured	45	45
214	**193**	24p. multicoloured	60	60
215	**194**	29p. multicoloured	80	80
211/15	Set of 5		2·00	2·00
	First Day Cover			2·20
	Presentation Pack		2·40	
	Set of 5 Gutter Pairs		4·00	

Plate Nos.: 9p. 1A, 1B, 1C (each×4); 10p., 19½p., 24p. 1A, 1B, 1C, 1D (each×4); 29p. 1A, 1B, 1C (each×5).
Sheets: 40 (2 panes 5×4).
Imprint: Right-hand corner, bottom margin.
Quantities sold: 9p. 748,353; 10p. 868,401; 19½p. 364,487; 24p. 368,346; 29p. 370,466.
Withdrawn: 22.2.83.

195 The Principals and Duties of Christianity (first book printed in Manx, 1707), and Bishop T. Wilson

196 Landing at Derbyhaven (visit of Thomas, 2nd Earl of Derby, 1507)

Europa. Historic Events

(Des A. Theobald. Photo Courvoisier)

1982 (1 June). Granite paper. P 12×12½ (C).

216	**195**	9p. multicoloured	25	25
217	**196**	19½p. multicoloured	50	50
216/17	Set of 2		70	70
	First Day Cover			1·00
	Presentation Pack		1·00	
	Set of 2 Gutter Pairs		1·50	

Cylinder Nos.: Both values A1–1–1–1–1, B1–1–1–1–1.
Sheets: 24 (2 panes 3×4).
Imprint: Right-hand corner, bottom margin.
Quantities sold: 9p. 1,120,457; 19½p. 1,129,315.
Withdrawn: 31.5.83.

197 Charlie Collier (first TT race (single cylinder) winner) and Tourist Trophy Race, 1907

198 Freddie Dixon (Sidecar and Junior TT winner) and Junior TT race, 1927

199 Jimmie Simpson (TT winner and first to lap at 60, 70 and 80 mph) and Senior TT, 1932

200 Mike Hailwood (winner of fourteen TTs) and Senior TT, 1961

201 Jock Taylor (Sidecar TT winner, 1978, 1980 and 1981) and Sidecar TT (with Benga Johansson), 1980

75th Anniversary of Tourist Trophy Motorcycle Races

(Des J. Nicholson. Litho Questa)

1982 (1 June). P 14 (C).

218	**197**	9p. multicoloured	15	15
219	**198**	10p. multicoloured	20	20
220	**199**	24p. multicoloured	60	60
221	**200**	26p. multicoloured	60	60
222	**201**	29p. multicoloured	80	80
218/22	Set of 5		2·10	2·10
	First Day Cover			2·30
	Presentation Pack		3·00	
	Stamp Cards (set of 5)		1·20	4·00
	Set of 5 Gutter Pairs		4·00	

Plate Nos.: All values 1B, 1C, 1D (each×4).
Sheets: 40 (2 panes 5×4).
Imprint: Right-hand corner, bottom margin.
Quantities sold: 9p. 837,930; 10p. 866,223; 24p. 351,406; 26p. 361,063; 29p. 355,690.
Withdrawn: 11.6.83.

202 Mona I

203 Manx Maid II

150th Anniversary of Isle of Man Steam Packet Company Mail Contract

(Des J. Nicholson. Litho Questa)

1982 (5 Oct). P 13½ (C).

223	**202**	12p. multicoloured	30	25
224	**203**	19½p. multicoloured	45	45
223/4	Set of 2		75	70

First Day Cover.. 90
Presentation Pack... 1·20
Set of 2 Gutter Pairs.. 1·50
    Plate Nos.: Both values 1A, 1B (each×4).
    Sheets: 40 (2 panes 5×4).
    Imprint: Right-hand bottom margin.
    Quantities sold: 12p. 701,044; 19½p. 291,100.
    Withdrawn: 4.10.83.

204 The Three Wise Men   **205** Snow Scene and
                                    European Robin

Christmas

(Des and litho John Waddington)

1982 (5 Oct). P 13 (C).
225	**204**	8p. multicoloured...........................	20	20
226	**205**	11p. multicoloured.........................	40	40
225/6		Set of 2..	55	55
First Day Cover...				75
Presentation Pack..			85	
Set of 2 Gutter Pairs.....................................			1·00	

    Plate Nos.: 8p.: 1A, 1B, 1C, 1D (each×4), 11p. 1B, 1D (each×4).
    Sheets: 40 (8p. 2 panes 5×4), (11p. 2 panes 4×5).
    Imprint: Right-hand corner, bottom margin (8p.); Top right-hand margin (11p.).
    Quantities sold; 8p. 740,651; 11p. 787,552.
    Withdrawn: 4.10.83.

206 Princess Diana with
Prince William

21st Birthday of the Princess of Wales and Birth of Prince William

(Des G. Kneale. Litho Questa)

1982 (12 Oct). Sheet 100×83 mm. P 14½×14 (C).
MS227	**206**	50p multicoloured........................	1·50	1·50
First Day Cover...				4·50
Presentation Pack..			1·70	

    Quantity sold: 218,759.
    Withdrawn: 11.10.83.

207 Opening of Salvation Army
Citadel, and T. H. Cannell, J.P.

208 Early Meeting Place and
Gen. William Booth

209 Salvation Army Band

210 Treating Lepers, and Lt.-Col.
Thomas Bridson

Centenary of Salvation Army in Isle of Man

(Des A. Theobald. Photo Courvoisier)

1983 (15 Feb). Granite paper. P 11½ (C).
228	**207**	10p. multicoloured.......................	15	15
229	**208**	12p. multicoloured.......................	25	25
230	**209**	19½p. multicoloured....................	45	45
231	**210**	26p. multicoloured.......................	65	60
228/31		Set of 4.......................................	1·40	1·20
First Day Cover...				1·60
Presentation Pack..			2·10	
Set of 4 Gutter Pairs.....................................			2·75	

    Cylinder Nos.: All values A1–1–1–1–1, B1–1–1–1–1.
    Sheets: 40 (2 panes 4×5).
    Imprint: Central, bottom margin.
    Quantities sold: 10p. 467,665; 12p. 567,863; 19½p. 267,929; 26p. 288,069.
    Withdrawn: 14.2.84.

211 Atlantic Puffins   **212** Northern Gannets

213 Lesser Black-backed Gulls   **214** Great Cormorants

215 Black-legged Kittiwakes   **216** Shags

217 Grey Herons   **218** Herring Gulls

219 Razorbills   **220** Greater Black-backed
                                   Gulls

221 Common Shelducks

222 Oystercatchers

223 Arctic Terns   **224** Common Guillemots

225 Common Redshanks

226 Mute Swans

227 'Queen Elizabeth II'
(Ricardo Macarron)

Sea Birds and Queen's Portrait (£5)

(Des Colleen Corlett (£5), J. Nicholson (others). Litho Questa)

1983 (15 Feb)–**85**. P 14 (20p. to £1), 14×13½ (£5) or 14½ (others), all comb.

232	**211**	1p. multicoloured (a)	30	30
233	**212**	2p. multicoloured (a)	30	30
234	**213**	5p. multicoloured (a)	60	40
235	**214**	8p. multicoloured (a)	60	40
236	**215**	10p. multicoloured (a)	60	35
237	**216**	11p. multicoloured (a)	60	35
238	**217**	12p. multicoloured (a)	70	40
239	**218**	13p. multicoloured (a)	70	40
240	**219**	14p. multicoloured (a)	70	40
241	**220**	15p. multicoloured (a)	80	50
242	**221**	16p. multicoloured (a)	80	50
243	**222**	18p. multicoloured (a)	80	50
244	**223**	20p. multicoloured (b)	1·00	70
245	**224**	25p. multicoloured (b)	1·20	75
246	**225**	50p. multicoloured (b)	1·70	1·50
247	**226**	£1 multicoloured (b)	2·50	2·75
248	**227**	£5 multicoloured (c)	9·00	8·50

232/48 *Set of 17* .... 18·00   19·00
First Day Covers (4) ....   25·00
Presentation Packs (4) .... 20·00

Printings: (a) 15.2.83; (b) 14.9.83; (c) 31.1.85.
Plate Nos.: 1p. to £1 1A, 1B, 1C, 1D (each×4); £5 1A, 1B (each×4).
Sheets: 10 (5×2) £5; 50 (5×10) others.
Imprint: £5 Right-hand margin; others right-hand corner, bottom margin.
Withdrawn: 30.6.88 1p. to 18p.; 31.12.88 20p. to £1; 4.7.94 £5.

228 Design Drawings by Robert Casement for the Great Laxey Wheel

229 Robert Casement and the Great Laxey Wheel

Europa. The Great Laxey Wheel

(Des J. Nicholson. Litho Questa)

1983 (18 May). P 14 (C).

249	**228**	10p. black, azure and buff	25	20
250	**229**	20½p. multicoloured	50	55

249/50 *Set of 2* 75   75
First Day Cover ....   1·00
Presentation Pack .... 1·10
Set of 2 Gutter Pairs .... 1·50

Plate Nos. 10p. 1A, 1B (each×3); 20½p. 1A, 1B (each×4).
Sheets: 12 (2 panes 2×3).
Imprint: Right-hand corner, bottom margin.
Quantities sold: 10p. 653,743; 20½p. 686,084.
Withdrawn 17.5.84.

230 Nick Keig (international yachtsman) and Trimaran *Three Legs of Man III*

231 King William's College, Castletown

232 Sir William Bragg (winner of Nobel Prize for Physics) and Spectrometer

233 General Sir George White V.C. and Action at Charasiah

150th Anniversary of King William's College

(Des J. Nicholson (10p., 31p.), Colleen Corlett (12p., 28p.). Photo Courvoisier)

1983 (18 May). Granite paper. P 11½ (C).

251	**230**	10p. multicoloured	20	20
252	**231**	12p. multicoloured	25	25
253	**232**	28p. multicoloured	60	60
254	**233**	31p. multicoloured	70	70

251/4 *Set of 4* .... 1·75   1·75
First Day Cover ....   2·00
Presentation Pack .... 2·00
Set of 4 Gutter Pairs .... 3·50

Cylinder Nos.: 10p. B1-1-1-1-1, C1-1-1-1-1, D1-1-1-1-1; 31p. A1-1-1-1-1, B1-1-1-1-1, D1-1-1-1-1, others A1-1-1-1-1, B1-1-1-1-1, C1-1-1-1-1, D1-1-1-1-1.
Sheets: 40 (2 panes 5×4).
Imprint: Central, bottom margin.
Quantities sold: 10p. 552,573; 12p. 693,004; 28p. 263,814; 31p. 242,393.
Withdrawn: 17.5.84.

234 New Post Office Headquarters, Douglas

235 Vikings Landing on Man, AD 938

World Communications Year and tenth Anniversary of Isle of Man Post Office Authority

(Des Colleen Corlett (10p.), J. Nicholson (15p.). Litho Questa)

1983 (5 July). P 14½ (C).

255	**234**	10p. multicoloured	20	20
256	**235**	15p. multicoloured	40	40
255/6 Set of 2			55	55
First Day Cover				1·25
Presentation Pack			90	
Stamp Cards (set of 2)			90	1·40
Set of 2 Gutter Pairs			1·10	

Plate Nos.: Both values 1A, 1B, 1C, 1D (each×5).
Sheets: 40 (2 panes 4×5).
Imprint: Central, right-hand margin.
Quantities sold: 10p. 269,843; 15p. 222,013.
Withdrawn: 4.7.84.

236 Shepherds   **237** Three Kings

Christmas

(Des Colleen Corlett. Litho John Waddington)

1983 (14 Sept). P 13 (C).

257	**236**	9p. multicoloured	20	20
258	**237**	12p. multicoloured	30	30
257/8 Set of 2			50	50
First Day Cover				85
Presentation Pack			85	
Set of 2 Gutter Pairs			1·00	

Plate Nos.: Both values 1A, 1B, 1C, 1D (each×5).
Sheets: 40 (2 panes 5×4).
Imprint: Right-hand corner, bottom margin.
Quantities sold: 9p. 642,763; 12p. 656,060.
Withdrawn: 13.9.84.

238 *Manx King* (full-rigged ship)   **239** *Hope* (barque)

240 *Rio Grande* (brig)   **241** *Lady Elizabeth* (barque)

242 *Sumatra* (barque)   **243** Wreck of *Lady Elizabeth* as shown on Falkland Islands Stamp

The Karran Fleet

(Des J. Nicholson (10p. to 31p.); Colleen Corlett, J. Nicholson and J. Smith (miniature sheet). Litho Questa)

1984 (14 Feb). P 14 (C).

259	**238**	10p. multicoloured	20	20
260	**239**	13p. multicoloured	30	30
261	**240**	20½p. multicoloured	45	45
262	**241**	28p. multicoloured	65	65
263	**242**	31p. multicoloured	70	70
259/63 Set of 5			2·20	2·20
First Day Cover				2·50
Presentation Pack			2·75	
Set of 5 Gutter pairs			4·25	

MS264 103×94 mm. 28p. Type **241**; 31p. Type **243**

(sold at 60p.)	2·20	2·20
First Day Cover		3·00
Presentation Pack	2·75	

No. **MS**264 was issued to commemorate links between the Isle of Man and the Falkland Islands.
Plate Nos.: All values 1A, 1B, 1C, 1D (each×4).
Sheets: 40 (2 panes 5×4).
Imprint: Right-hand corner, bottom margin.
Quantities sold: 10p. 389,728; 13p. 417,637; 20½p. 253,949; 28p. 238,292; 31p. 236,196; miniature sheet 137,031.
Withdrawn: 13.2.85.

244 C.E.P.T. 25th Anniversary Logo

Europa

(Des J. Larrivière, adapted Colleen Corlett. Photo Courvoisier)

1984 (27 Apr). Granite paper. P 12×11½ (C).

265	**244**	10p. dull orange, deep reddish brown and pale orange	30	25
266		20½p. lt blue, dp blue and pale blue	50	50
265/6 Set of 2			75	70
First Day Cover				2·00
Presentation Pack			2·50	

Cylinder Nos.: Both values A1–1–1, B1–1–1.
Sheets: 20 (4×5).
Imprint: Central, right-hand margin.
Quantities sold: 10p. 705,410; 20½p. 715,479.
Withdrawn: 26.4.85.

245 Railway Air Services de Havilland D.H.84 Dragon Mk 2   **246** West Coast Air Services de Havilland DH.86A Dragon Express *Ronaldsway*

247 B.E.A. Douglas DC-3   **248** B.E.A. Vickers Viscount 800

249 Telair Britten Norman Islander

50th Anniversary of First Official Airmail to the Isle of Man and 40th Anniversary of International Civil Aviation Organization

(Des A. Theobald. Litho Questa)

1984 (27 Apr). P 14 (C).

267	**245**	11p. multicoloured	25	25
268	**246**	13p. multicoloured	40	40
269	**247**	26p. multicoloured	70	70
270	**248**	28p. multicoloured	70	70
271	**249**	31p. multicoloured	80	80
267/71 Set of 5			2·50	2·50
First Day Cover				2·75
Presentation Pack			2·75	
Set of 5 Gutter Pairs			5·00	

Plate Nos.: All values 1A, 1B, 1C, 1D (each×4).
Sheets: 40 (2 panes 5×4).
Imprint: Right-hand corner, bottom margin.
Quantities sold: 11p. 399,155; 13p. 440,623; 26p. 234,165; 28p. 173,841; 31p. 171,890.
Withdrawn: 26.4.85.

Year Pack 1983

1984. Comprises Nos. 228/47, 249/58.
Year Pack .... 15·00
    Withdrawn: 31.3.85.

250 Window from Glencrutchery House, Douglas

251 Window from Lonan Old Church

Christmas. Stained-glass Windows

(Des D. Swinton. Litho John Waddington)

1984 (21 Sept). P 14 (C).

272	**250**	10p. multicoloured	30	30
273	**251**	13p. multicoloured	60	60
272/3	*Set of 2*		80	80
First Day Cover				1·25
Presentation Pack			1·50	
Set of 2 Gutter Pairs			1·50	

    Plate Nos.: Both values 1A, 1B, 1C, 1D (each×6).
    Sheets: 40 (2 panes 4×5).
    Imprint: Top right-hand margin.
    Quantities sold: 10p. 652,870; 13p. 668,084.
    Withdrawn: 20.9.85.

252 William Cain's Birthplace, Ballasalla

253 The *Anna* Leaving Liverpool, 1852

254 Early Australian Railway

255 William Cain as Mayor of Melbourne, and Town Hall

256 Royal Exhibition Buildings, Melbourne

William Cain (civic leader, Victoria) Commemoration

(Des J. Nicholson. Litho Questa)

1984 (21 Sept). P 14½×14 (C).

274	**252**	11p. multicoloured	25	20
275	**253**	22p. multicoloured	50	50
276	**254**	28p. multicoloured	60	60
277	**255**	30p. multicoloured	70	70
278	**256**	33p. multicoloured	75	75
274/8	*Set of 5*		2·50	2·50
First Day Cover				2·75
Presentation Pack			3·00	
Set of 5 Gutter Pairs			5·00	

    Plate Nos.: 11p., 33p. 1A, 1B, 1C, 1D (each×4); others, 1B, 1C, 1D (each×4).
    Sheets: 40 (2 panes 5×4).
    Imprint: Right-hand corner, bottom margin.
    Quantities sold: 11p. 393,219; 22p. 280,598; 28p. 223,515; 30p. 220,913; 33p. 213,933.
    Withdrawn: 20.9.85.

257 Queen Elizabeth II and Commonwealth Parliamentary Association Badge

258 Queen Elizabeth II and Manx Emblem

Links with the Commonwealth. 30th Commonwealth Parliamentary Association Conference

(Des and litho John Waddington)

1984 (21 Sept). P 14 (C).

279	**257**	14p. multicoloured	35	35
280	**258**	33p. multicoloured	65	65
279/80	*Set of 2*		1·00	1·00
First Day Cover				1·50
Presentation Pack			2·75	
Set of 2 Gutter Pairs			2·00	

    Plate Nos.: Both values 1A, 1B, 1C (each×7).
    Sheets: 40 (2 panes 5×4).
    Imprint: Right-hand corner, bottom margin.
    Quantities sold: 14p. 373,204; 33p. 231,073.
    Withdrawn: 20.9.85.

Year Pack 1984

1985 (1 Jan). Comprises Nos. 259/80 (price £6).
Year Pack .... 17·00
    Withdrawn: 31.12.85.

259 Cunningham House Headquarters, and Mrs. Willie Cunningham and Mrs. Joseph Cunningham (former Commissioners)

260 Princess Margaret, Isle of Man Standard and Guides

261 Lady Olave Baden-Powell opening Guide Headquarters, 1955

262 Guide Uniforms from 1910 to 1985

263 Guide Handclasp, Salute and Early Badge

75th Anniversary of Girl Guide Movement

(Des Colleen Corlett. Photo Courvoisier)

1985 (31 Jan). Granite paper. P 11½ (C).

281	**259**	11p. multicoloured	30	25
282	**260**	14p. multicoloured	35	35
283	**261**	29p. multicoloured	70	70
284	**262**	31p. multicoloured	75	75
285	**263**	34p. multicoloured	85	85
281/5		Set of 5	2·75	2·50
		First Day Cover		3·00
		Presentation Pack	3·00	
		Set of 5 Gutter Pairs	5·50	

Cylinder Nos.: 11p., 34p. A1–1–1–1–1, B1–1–1–1–1; others A1–1–1–1, B1–1–1–1.
Sheets: 40 (2 panes 4×5).
Imprint: Central, bottom margin of each pane.
Withdrawn: 30.1.86.

264 Score of Manx National Anthem

265 William H. Gill (lyricist)

266 Score of Hymn 'Crofton'

267 Dr. John Clague (composer)

Europa. European Music Year

(Des D. Swinton. Photo Courvoisier)

1985 (24 Apr). Granite paper. P 11½ (C).

286	**264**	12p. black, orange-brn and chestnut	30	15
		a. Horiz pair. Nos. 286/7	75	90
287	**265**	12p. black, orange-brn and chestnut	30	15
288	**266**	22p. black, brt blue and new bl	80	25
		a. Horiz pair. Nos. 288/9	1·60	1·60
289	**267**	22p. black, brt new blue and new bl	80	25
286/9		Set of 4	2·10	2·30
		First Day Cover		2·75
		Presentation Pack	2·50	

Cylinder Nos.: Both values A1–1–1, B1–1–1.
Sheets: 20 (4×5). The two designs for each value printed together, se-tenant, in horizontal pairs throughout the sheets.
Imprint: Central, bottom margin.
Withdrawn: 23.4.86.

268 Charles Rolls in 20 h.p. Rolls Royce Light Twenty tourer (1906 Tourist Trophy Race)

269 W. Bentley in 3 litre Bentley (1922 Tourist Trophy Race)

270 F. Gerard in E.R.A. (1950 British Empire Trophy Race)

271 Brian Lewis in Alfa Romeo (1934 Mannin Moar Race)

272 Jaguar XJ-SC ('Roads Open' Car, 1984 Motorcycle T.T. Races)

273 Tony Pond and Mike Nicholson in Vauxhall Chevette (1981 Rothmans International Rally)

Century of Motoring

(Des A. Theobald. Litho Questa)

1985 (25 May). P 14 (C).

290	**268**	12p. multicoloured	25	15
		a. Horiz pair. Nos. 290/1	60	70
291	**269**	12p. multicoloured	25	15
292	**270**	14p. multicoloured	25	15
		a. Horiz pair. Nos. 292/3	60	70
293	**271**	14p. multicoloured	25	15
294	**272**	31p. multicoloured	60	40
		a. Horiz pair. Nos. 294/5	2·00	2·25
295	**273**	31p. multicoloured	60	40
290/5		Set of 6	2·50	3·25
		First Day Cover		3·50
		Presentation Pack	3·50	
		Stamp Cards (set of 6)	3·00	7·25
		Set of 3 Gutter Blocks of 4	5·00	

Plate Nos.: All values 1A, 1B (each×6).
Sheets: 40 (2 panes 4×5). The two designs for each value printed together, se-tenant, in horizontal pairs throughout the sheets.
Imprint: Right-hand corner, bottom margin of each pane.
Withdrawn: 24.5.86.

274 Queen Alexandra and Victorian Sergeant with Wife

275 Queen Mary and Royal Air Force Family

276 Earl Mountbatten and Royal Navy Family

277 Prince Michael of Kent and Royal Marine with Parents, 1982

Centenary of the Soldiers', Sailors' and Airmen's Families Association

(Des Colleen Corlett. Litho Questa)

1985 (4 Sept). P 14 (C).

296	**274**	12p. multicoloured	20	20
297	**275**	15p. multicoloured	40	40
298	**276**	29p. multicoloured	75	75
299	**277**	34p. multicoloured	1·00	1·00
296/9		Set of 4	2·25	2·25
		First Day Cover		3·00
		Presentation Pack	2·50	
		Set of 4 Gutter Pairs	4·50	

Plate Nos. 12p., 34p. 1A, 1B, 1C, 1D, 1E, 1F, 1G, 1H (each×6); others 1A, 1B, 1C, 1D, 1E, 1F, 1G, 1H (each×5).
Sheets: 40 (2 panes 5×4).
Imprint: Right-hand corner, bottom margin of each pane.
Withdrawn: 3.9.86.

278 Kirk Maughold (Birthplace)

279 Lieut. Gen.
Sir Mark Cubbon

280 Memorial Statue,
Bangalore, India

Birth Bicentenary of Lieut.-Gen. Sir Mark Cubbon (Indian administrator)

(Des A. Theobald. Litho Questa)

1985 (2 Oct). P 14 (C).

300	**278**	12p. multicoloured	35	35
301	**279**	22p. multicoloured	65	65
302	**280**	45p. multicoloured	1·25	1·25
300/2		Set of 3	2·00	2·00
		First Day Cover		2·50
		Presentation Pack	2·50	
		Set of 3 Gutter pairs	4·50	

Plate Nos.: All values 1A, 1B, 1C, 1D (each×4).
Sheets: 40 (2 panes 5×4) 12p. or (2 panes 4×5) others.
Imprint: Right-hand corner, bottom margin of each pane.
Withdrawn: 1.10.86.

281 St. Peter's Church, Onchan

282 Royal Chapel of St. John,
Tynwald

283 Bride Parish Church

Christmas. Manx Churches

(Des A. Theobald. Litho John Waddington)

1985 (2 Oct). P 13×13½ (C).

303	**281**	11p. multicoloured	30	25
304	**282**	14p. multicoloured	40	35
305	**283**	31p. multicoloured	1·00	90
303/5		Set of 3	1·50	1·40
		First Day Cover		1·70
		Presentation Pack	2·00	
		Set of 3 Gutter Pairs	3·00	

Plate Nos.: All values 1A, 1B, 1C, 1D (each×4).
Sheets: 40 (2 panes 5×4).
Imprint: Right-hand corner, bottom margin of each pane.
Withdrawn: 1.10.86.

Post Office Yearbook

1985 (9 Dec). Comprises Nos. 248 and 281/305 in slipcase (price £12).
Yearbook .... 25·00
The 1985 Yearbook was originally advertised at £11 and that price was honoured until 31 December, when it was raised to £12.
Withdrawn: 9.92.

Year Pack 1985

1986 (1 Jan). Comprises Nos. 281/305 with or without No. 248 (price £10.50 with No. 248, £6 without 248).
Year Pack with No. 248 .... 29·00
Year Pack without No. 248 .... 21·00
Withdrawn: 30.12.86.

284 Swimming

285 Race Walking

286 Rifle-shooting

287 Cycling

Commonwealth Games, Edinburgh

(Des C. Abbott. Litho Questa)

1986 (5 Feb). P 14½ (C).

306	**284**	12p. multicoloured	20	15
307	**285**	15p. multicoloured	25	30
308	**286**	31p. multicoloured	90	95
309	**287**	34p. multicoloured	1·00	95
306/9		Set of 4	2·10	2·10
		First Day Cover		2·50
		Presentation Pack	3·00	
		Set of 4 Gutter Pairs	4·25	

No. 309 also commemorates the 50th anniversary of Manx International Cycling Week.
Plate Nos.: All values 1A, 1B, 1C, 1D (each×5).
Sheets: 40 (2 panes 5×4).
Imprint: Right-hand corner, bottom margin of each pane.
Withdrawn: 4.2.87.

288 Viking Necklace and Peel
Castle

289 Meayll Circle, Rushen

290 Skeleton of
Great Deer and
Manx Museum

291 Viking Longship
Model

292 Open Air Museum, Cregneash

Centenary of Manx Museum

(Des J. Nicholson. Litho Questa)

1986 (5 Feb). P 14 (C).
310	288	12p. multicoloured	20	15
311	289	15p. multicoloured	25	20
312	290	22p. multicoloured	65	50
313	291	26p. multicoloured	80	60
314	292	29p. multicoloured	90	60
310/14		Set of 5	2·50	1·90
		First Day Cover		2·50
		Presentation Pack	2·75	
		Set of 5 Gutter Pairs	5·00	

Plate Nos.: All values 1A, 1B, 1C, 1D (each×6).
Sheets: 40 (2 panes 5×4) 12p., 15p., 29p.; (2 panes 4×5) others.
Imprint: Right-hand corner, bottom margin (12p., 15p., 29p.) or bottom left-hand margin (others).
Withdrawn: 4.2.87.

293 Viking Longship

294 Celtic Cross Logo

Manx Heritage Year. Booklet stamps

(Des Colleen Corlett. Litho Harrison)

1986 (10 Apr). P 14½×14 (C).
315	293	2p. multicoloured	40	40
		a. Booklet pane. Nos. 315×2 and 316×4	2·00	
316	294	10p. black, apple green and brownish grey	35	35
		a. Booklet pane. No. 316×3 and 3 stamp size labels	1·20	
315/16		Set of 2	70	70
		First Day Cover (Nos. 315×1 and 316×2)		2·00
		Presentation Pack (Nos. 315×1 and 316×2)	2·25	

In addition to Booklets SB14/15 Nos. 315/16 also come from special booklet sheets of 60 containing five each of Nos. 315a and 316a.
Plate Nos.: 1A, 1B (each×7).
Withdrawn: 25.3.87.

295 Usnea articulata (lichen) and Neotinea intacta (orchid), The Ayres

296 Hen Harrier, Calf of Man

297 Manx Stoat, Eary Chuslin

298 Stenobothus stigmaticus (grasshopper), St. Michael's Isle

Europa. Nature and Environment Protection

(Des J. Nicholson and Nancy Corkish. Photo Courvoisier)

1986 (10 Apr). Granite paper. P 11½ (C).
317	295	12p. multicoloured	35	35
		a. Horiz pair. Nos. 317/18	75	75
318	296	12p. multicoloured	35	35
319	297	22p. multicoloured	90	90
		a. Horiz pair. Nos. 319/20	1·80	1·80
320	298	22p. multicoloured	90	90
317/20		Set of 4	2·25	2·25
		First Day Cover		2·75
		Presentation Pack	3·00	

Cylinder Nos.: Both values A1–1–1–1–1.
Sheets: 20 (4×5). The two designs for each value printed together, se-tenant, in horizontal pairs throughout the sheets.
Imprint: Central, right-hand margin.
Withdrawn: 9.4.87.

299 Ellanbane (home of Myles Standish)

300 Mayflower crossing the Atlantic, 1620

301 Pilgrim Fathers landing at Plymouth, 1620

302 Captain Myles Standish

'Ameripex '86' International Stamp Exhibition, Chicago. Captain Myles Standish of the Mayflower

(Des C. Abbott. Litho Cartor)

1986 (22 May). P 13½ (C).
321	299	12p. multicoloured	20	20
322	300	15p. multicoloured	25	25
323	301	31p. multicoloured	90	90
324	302	34p. multicoloured	95	95
321/4		Set of 4	2·10	2·10
		First Day Cover		2·50
		Presentation Pack	2·75	
MS325		100×75 mm. Nos. 323/4. P 12½	2·10	2·10
		First Day Cover		3·75
		Presentation Pack	2·50	

No. MS325 also commemorates the 75th anniversary of the World Manx Association.
Plate Nos.: All values 1A, 1B, 1C, 1D (each×5).
Sheets: 20 (5×4).
Imprint: Right-hand corner, bottom margin.
Withdrawn: 21.5.87.

303 Prince Andrew in Naval Uniform and Miss Sarah Ferguson

304 Engagement Photograph

Royal Wedding

(Des Colleen Corlett. Litho BDT)

1986 (23 July). P 15×14 (C).
326	303	15p. multicoloured	30	30
327	304	40p. multicoloured	1·50	1·50
326/7		Set of 2	1·60	1·60
		First Day Cover		2·00
		Presentation Pack	2·25	

Plate Nos.: Both values 1A, 1B (each×5).
Sheets: 20 (4×5).
Imprint: Right-hand corner, bottom margin.
Withdrawn: 22.7.87.

305 Prince Philip

306 Queen Elizabeth II

307 Queen Elizabeth II and Prince Philip

Royal Birthdays

(Des Colleen Corlett from photos by Karsh. Photo Courvoisier)

1986 (28 Aug). Granite paper. P 11½ (C).

328	**305**	15p. multicoloured	30	30
		a. Horiz pair. Nos. 328/9...................	60	75
329	**306**	15p. multicoloured	30	30
330	**307**	34p. multicoloured	1·10	1·10
328/30 Set of 3			1·60	1·70
First Day Cover..				2·00
Presentation Pack..			2·40	
Souvenir Folder (complete sheets)...................			15·00	

Nos. 328/30 also commemorate 'Stockholmia '86' and 350th anniversary of Swedish Post Office.

Cylinder Nos.: 15p. A1–1–1–1–1–1, B1–1–1–1–1–1, C1–1–1–1–1–1, D1–1–1–1–1–1; 34p. A1–1–1–1–1, B1–1–1–1–1, C1–1–1–1–1, D1–1–1–1–1.

Sheets: 15p. 12 (4×3). The two designs printed together, se-tenant, in horizontal pairs throughout the sheets; 34p. six (2×3).

Imprint: Central, bottom margin.

Withdrawn: 27.8.87.

308 European Robins on Globe and 'Peace and Goodwill' in Braille

309 Hands releasing Peace Dove

310 Clasped Hands and 'Peace' in Sign Language

Christmas and International Peace Year

(Des Colleen Corlett. Litho Questa)

1986 (25 Sept). P 14 (C).

331	**308**	11p. multicoloured	30	30
332	**309**	14p. multicoloured	30	30
333	**310**	31p. multicoloured	80	80
331/3 Set of 3			1·20	1·20
First Day Cover..				1·50
Presentation Pack...			1·70	
Set of 3 Gutter Pairs...			2·40	

No. 331 also commemorates the 50th anniversary of Manx Blind Welfare Society.

Plate Nos.: All values 1A, 1B, 1C, 1D (each×5).

Sheets: 40 (2 panes 4×5).

Imprint: Right-hand corner, bottom margin of each pane.

Withdrawn: 24.9.87.

Year Pack 1986

1986 (25 Sept). Comprises Nos. 306/33 (price £6.50).

Year Pack.. 28·00

Withdrawn: 31.12.87.

Post Office Yearbook

1986 (Dec). Comprises Nos. 306/14, 315a, 316a, 317/27, 328/30 in complete sheets, and 331/3 in slipcase (price £12).

Yearbook .... 50·00

Sold out: 9.90.

311 North Quay

312 Old Fishmarket

313 The Breakwater

314 Jubilee Clock

315 Loch Promenade

316 Beach

Victorian Douglas

(Des A. Theobald. Litho Questa)

1987 (21 Jan–26 Mar). P 14×14½ (C).

334	**311**	2p. multicoloured (a)	10	10
		a. Booklet pane. Nos. 334×2, 335×2 and 336×4 (2p. stamps at top) (b)	1·70	
		ab. Ditto, but 2p. stamps at bottom (b)	1·70	
		b. Booklet pane. Nos. 334/7, each×2 (2p. stamps at top) (b)...........	2·00	
		ba. Ditto, but 2p stamps at bottom (b)	2·00	
335	**312**	3p. multicoloured (a)	10	10
336	**313**	10p. multicoloured (a)	25	25
337	**314**	15p. multicoloured (a)	30	30
338	**315**	31p. multicoloured (a)	90	90
339	**316**	34p. multicoloured (a)	1·00	1·00
334/9 Set of 6			2·40	2·40
First Day Cover (Nos. 334/9)				2·60
First Day Covers (2) (se-tenant strips)				5·00
Presentation Pack (Nos. 334/9)			3·00	
Set of 6 Gutter Pairs.................................			5·00	

Printings: (a) 21.1.87; (b) 26.3.87.

Plate Nos.: All values 1A, 1B, 1C, 1D (each×4).

Sheets: 40 (2 panes 5×4). In addition to booklets SB16/17 Nos. 334/7 also come from special booklet sheets of 48 (6×8), containing either three each of Nos. 334a/ab or three each of Nos. 334b/ba.

Imprint: Right-hand corner, bottom margin of each pane.

Withdrawn: 20.1.88 sheets; 15.3.88 booklets.

317 'The Old Fishmarket and Harbour, Douglas'

318 'Red Sails at Douglas'

319 'The Double Corner, Peel'

320 'Peel Harbour'

Paintings by John Miller Nicholson

(Des A. Theobald. Litho Cartor)

1987 (18 Feb). P 13½ (C).

340	**317**	12p. multicoloured	30	30
341	**318**	26p. multicoloured	70	60
342	**319**	29p. multicoloured	90	80
343	**320**	34p. multicoloured	1·00	1·00
340/3	*Set of 4*		2·60	2·60
	First Day Cover			2·75
	Presentation Pack		3·00	
	Set of 4 Gutter Pairs		5·00	

Plate Nos.: All values 1A, 1B, 1C, 1D (each×5).
Sheets: 40 (2 panes 5×4).
Imprint: Right-hand corner, bottom margin of each pane.
Withdrawn: 17.2.88.

321 Sea Terminal, Douglas

322 Tower of Refuge, Douglas

323 Gaiety Theatre, Douglas

324 Villa Marina, Douglas

Europa. Architecture

(Des R. Maddox. Litho BDT)

1987 (29 Apr). P 13½ (C).

344	**321**	12p. multicoloured	45	85
		a. Horiz pair. Nos. 344/5	90	1·70
345	**322**	12p. multicoloured	45	85
346	**323**	22p. multicoloured	65	1·25
		a. Horiz pair. Nos. 346/7	1·50	2·50
347	**324**	22p. multicoloured	65	1·25
344/7	*Set of 4*		2·20	3·50
	First Day Cover			3·75
	Presentation Pack		2·50	

Plate Nos.: Both values 1A, 1B (each×5).
Sheets: 10 (2×5). The two designs for each value printed together, *se-tenant*, in horizontal pairs throughout the sheets.
Imprint: Central, right-hand margin.
Withdrawn: 28.4.88.

325 Supercharged BMW 500cc, 1939

326 Manx Kneeler Norton 350cc, 1953

327 MV Agusta 500cc 4, 1956

328 Moto Guzzi 500cc V8, 1957

329 Honda 250cc 6, 1967

80th Anniversary of Tourist Trophy Motor-cycle Races

(Des B. Dix. Litho Cartor)

1987 (27 May). P 13½×13 (C).

348	**325**	12p. multicoloured	45	30
349	**326**	15p. multicoloured	50	40
350	**327**	29p. multicoloured	90	80
351	**328**	31p. multicoloured	90	80
352	**329**	34p. multicoloured	1·00	1·00
348/52	*Set of 5*		2·75	3·00
	First Day Cover			4·00
	Presentation Pack		4·00	
	Stamp Cards (Set of 5)		3·25	4·00
	Set of 5 Gutter Pairs		7·00	
MS353	150×140 mm. Nos. 348/52. P 14×13½ (C)		3·00	3·50
	Souvenir Folder		5·50	

Nos. 348/53 also commemorate the centenary of the St. John Ambulance Brigade and the miniature sheet also carries the logo of 'Capex '87' International Stamp Exhibition, Toronto on its margin.
Plate Nos.: 12p., 15p., 29p., 31p., 34p. 1A, 1B, 1C, 1D (each×4); miniature sheet 1A (×4).
Sheets: 40 (2 panes 5×4).
Imprint: Right-hand corner, bottom margin of each pane (sheets) or bottom, right-hand margin (miniature sheet).
Withdrawn: 11.6.88.

330 Fuchsia and Wild Roses

332 Wood Anemone and Celandine

331 Field Scabious and Ragwort

333 Violets and Primroses

Wild Flowers

(Des Nancy Corkish. Litho Enschedé)

1987 (9 Sept). P 14½×13 (C).

354	**330**	16p. multicoloured	50	40
355	**331**	29p. multicoloured	90	80
356	**332**	31p. multicoloured	90	1·00
357	**333**	34p. multicoloured	1·00	1·20
354/7	*Set of 4*		3·00	3·00
	First Day Cover			3·25
	Presentation Pack		4·00	

Plate Nos.: All values 1A, 1B (each×4).
Sheets: 20 (5×4).
Imprint: Right-hand corner, bottom margin.
Withdrawn: 8.9.88.

334 Stirring the Christmas Pudding

335 Bringing Home the Christmas Tree

336 Decorating the Christmas Tree

Christmas. Victorian Scenes

(Des Colleen Corlett. Litho Questa)

1987 (16 Oct). P 14 (C).

358	**334**	12p. multicoloured	50	50
359	**335**	15p. multicoloured	70	70
		a. *Black* printed triple	£525	
360	**336**	31p. multicoloured	90	90
358/60	*Set of 3*		1·75	1·75
First Day Cover				2·25
Presentation Pack			2·50	
Set of 3 Gutter Pairs			3·50	

Plate Nos.: All values 1A, 1B, 1C, 1D (each×4).
Sheets: 40 (2 panes 4×5).
Imprint: Right-hand corner, bottom margin of each pane.
Withdrawn: 15.10.88.

Year Pack 1987

1987 (16 Oct). Comprises Nos. 334/52 and 354/60 (price £6).

Year Pack		31·00

Withdrawn: 31.12.88.

Post Office Yearbook

1987 (Dec). Comprises Nos. 334/43, 344/7 in complete sheets, and **MS**353/60 in slipcase (price £12).

Yearbook		40·00

Sold out: 5.91.

337 Russell Brookes in Vauxhall Opel (Manx Rally winner, 1985)

338 Ari Vatanen in Ford Escort RS2000 Mk 1 (Manx Rally winner, 1976)

339 Terry Smith in Repco March 761 (Hill Climb winner, 1980)

340 Nigel Mansell in Williams/Honda FW1B F1 (British Grand Prix winner, 1986 and 1987)

Motor Sport

(Des C. Abbott. Litho Enschedé)

1988 (10 Feb). P 13½×14½ (C).

361	**337**	13p. multicoloured	75	40
362	**338**	26p. multicoloured	1·20	1·20
		a. *Black* printed double	£525	
363	**339**	31p. multicoloured	1·40	1·50
364	**340**	34p. multicoloured	1·60	1·70
361/4	*Set of 4*		4·50	4·50
First Day Cover				5·00
Presentation Pack			4·75	

Plate Nos.: All values 1A, 1B (each×4).
Sheets: 10 (2×5).
Imprint: Central, right-hand margin.
Withdrawn: 9.2.89.

341 Horse Tram Terminus, Douglas Bay Tramway

342 Snaefell Mountain Railway

343 Marine Drive Tramway

343a Douglas Cable Tramway

344 Douglas Head Incline Railway

345 Douglas and Laxey Coast Electric Tramway Car at Maughold Head

346 Douglas Cable Tramway

347 Manx Northern Railway No. 4, *Caledonia*, at Gob-y-Deigan

348 Laxey Mine Railway Lewin Locomotive *Ant*

349 Port Erin Breakwater Tramway Locomotive *Henry B. Loch*

350 Ramsey Harbour Tramway

351 Locomotive No. 7, *Tynwald*, on Foxdale Line

351a T.P.O. Special leaving Douglas, 3 July 1991

352 Baldwin Reservoir Tramway Steam Locomotive No. 1, *Injebreck*

353 I.M.R. No. 13, *Kissack*, near St. Johns

353a Manx Northern Railway No. 4, *Caledonia*, at Gob-y-Deigan

353b Double-deck Horse Tram, Douglas

354 I.M.R. No. 12, *Hutchinson*, leaving Douglas

355 Groudle Glen Railway Locomotive *Polar Bear*

356 I.M.R. No. 11, *Maitland*, pulling Royal Train, 1963

356a Queen Elizabeth II taking Salute at Trooping the Colour

Manx Railways and Tramways, and Queen's Portrait (£2)

(Des Colleen Corlett (£2), A. Theobald (others). Litho BDT (1p. to 19p., 21p., 23p.), Questa (20p., 25p. to £2))

1988 (10 Feb)–**92**. P 13 (1p. to 19p., 21p., 23p.), 14½×15 (20p., 25p. to £1) or 14½ (£2), all comb.

365	341	1p. multicoloured (a)	10	10
366	342	2p. multicoloured (a)	10	10
367	343	3p. multicoloured (a)	10	10
		a. Booklet pane. Nos. 367×2, 370 and 373×2 (b)	3·00	
		b. Booklet pane. Nos. 367×2, 371×2 and 374 (d)	2·50	
367c	343a	4p. multicoloured (g)	20	10
		ca. Booklet pane. Nos. 367c×3, 374 and 377a	4·00	
		cb. Booklet pane. Nos. 367c×3, 374×4 and 377a	4·75	
368	344	5p. multicoloured (a)	20	20
369	345	10p. multicoloured (a)	30	30
370	346	13p. multicoloured (a)	50	50
		a. Booklet pane. Nos. 370×4 and 373×6 (b)	4·00	
371	347	14p. multicoloured (a)	50	50
		a. Booklet pane. Nos. 371×4 and 374×6 (d)	4·00	
372	348	15p. multicoloured (af)	50	50
		a. Booklet pane. Nos. 372 and 376×2 (e)	2·75	

		b. Booklet pane. Nos. 372×4 and 376×6 (e)	6·25	
373	349	16p. multicoloured (a)	50	50
374	350	17p. multicoloured (ag)	50	50
375	351	18p. multicoloured (a)	55	55
375a	351a	18p. multicoloured (h)	70	70
		ab. Booklet pane. Nos. 375a×3 and 377b×2	4·00	
		ac. Booklet pane. Nos. 375a×6 and 377b×4	7·00	
376	352	19p. multicoloured (af)	60	60
377	353	20p. multicoloured (c)	60	60
377a	353a	21p. multicoloured (g)	60	60
377b	353b	23p. multicoloured (h)	80	80
378	354	25p. multicoloured (c)	60	60
379	355	50p. multicoloured (ci)	1·30	1·20
380	356	£1 multicoloured (ci)	2·50	2·50
380a	356a	£2 multicoloured (e)	5·00	5·00
365/80a	*Set of 21*		15·00	14·00
First Day Covers (6)				18·00
First Day Covers (se-tenant strips) (5)				18·00

Presentation Packs (4) (ex 4p., 18p. (No. 375a), 21p., 23p.) ...... 18·00

Stamp Cards (1p. to £1 ex 4p., 18p. (No. 375a), 21p., 23p.) ...... 8·00 22·00

Souvenir Folder (1p. to £1 ex 4p., 18p. (No. 375a), 21p. 23p.) ...... 11·00

Printings: (a) 10.2.88. Inscribed '1988'; (b) 16.3.88. Inscribed '1988'; (c) 21.9.88. Inscribed '1988'; (d) 16.10.89. Inscribed '1989'; (e) 14.2.90. Inscribed '1990'; (f) 1.3.90. Inscribed '1990'; (g) 9.1.91. Inscribed '1991'; (h) 8.1.92. Inscribed '1992'; (i) 16.11.92. Inscribed '1992'.

Plate Nos.: 20p., 25p., 50p., £1 1A, 1B (each×4); £2 1A, 1B (each×5); others 1A, 1B, 1C, 1D (each×4).

Sheets: 25 (5×5) (£2) or 50 (5×10) (others). In addition to Booklets Nos. SB18/19 and SB21/4 Nos. 367 and 370/4 also come from special booklet sheets of 50 containing either ten examples of the strips of five or five examples of the strips of ten. No. 372a, a strip of three, was taken from the top or bottom of the strip of ten, No. 372b. The 4p. value was issued in Booklets Nos. SB26/7 and special booklet sheets of 50 containing five vertical strips of No. 367cb, from which No. 367ca could also be obtained, and five extra examples of both Nos. 367c and 377a. In addition to Booklets Nos. SB29/30 No. 375aac was also issued in special booklet sheets of 50 from which No. 375aab could also be obtained. Nos. 367c and 377a were also issued in a miniature sheet, No. **MS**484.

Imprints: Left-hand margin (£2) or right-hand corner, bottom margin (others).

Withdrawn: 31.12.93 1p. to £1; 11.1.94 £2.

357 Laying Isle of Man–U.K. Submarine Cable

358 *Flex Service 3* (cable ship)

359 Earth Station, Braddan

360 'INTELSAT 5' Satellite

Europa. Transport and Communications

(Des C. Abbott. Litho Cartor)

1988 (14 Apr). P 14×13½ (C).

381	**357**	13p. multicoloured	50	45
		a. Horiz pair. Nos. 381/2	1·00	1·10
382	**358**	13p. multicoloured	50	45
383	**359**	22p. multicoloured	75	75
		a. Horiz pair. Nos. 383/4	1·50	1·60
384	**360**	22p. multicoloured	75	75
381/4		*Set of 4*	2·20	2·50
		First Day Cover		4·00
		Presentation Pack	3·00	

Plate Nos.: Both values 1A, 1B, 1C, 1D (each×4).
Sheets: 16 (4×4). The two designs of each value printed together, *se-tenant*, in horizontal pairs throughout the sheets.
Imprint: Central, right-hand margin.
Withdrawn: 13.4.89.

361 *Euterpe* (full-rigged ship) off Ramsey, 1863

362 *Vixen* (topsail schooner) leaving Peel for Australia, 1853

363 *Ramsey* (full-rigged ship) off Brisbane, 1870

364 *Star of India* (formerly *Euterpe*) (barque) off San Diego, 1976

Manx Sailing Ships

(Des J. Nicholson. Litho Questa)

1988 (11 May). P 14 (C).

385	**361**	16p. multicoloured	45	40
386	**362**	29p. multicoloured	90	90
387	**363**	31p. multicoloured	90	90
388	**364**	34p. multicoloured	1·10	1·10
385/8		*Set of 4*	3·00	3·00
		First Day Cover		3·25
		Presentation Pack	3·75	
MS389		110×85 mm. Nos. 385 and 388	1·90	2·00
		First Day Cover		3·00
		Presentation Pack	2·50	

Nos. 386/7 also commemorate the Bicentenary of Australian Settlement.
Plate Nos.: All values 1A, 1B (each×5).
Sheets: 15 (3×5).
Imprint: Bottom, left-hand margin.
Withdrawn: 10.5.89.

365 'Magellanica'

366 'Pink Cloud'

367 'Leonora'

368 'Satellite'

369 'Preston Guild'

370 'Thalia'

50th Anniversary of British Fuchsia Society

(Des Colleen Corlett. Litho Enschedé)

1988 (21 Sept). P 13½×14 (C).

390	**365**	13p. multicoloured	40	25
391	**366**	16p. multicoloured	45	35
392	**367**	22p. multicoloured	65	60
393	**368**	29p. multicoloured	90	90
394	**369**	31p. multicoloured	1·00	1·00
395	**370**	34p. multicoloured	1·10	1·20
390/5		*Set of 6*	4·00	3·60
		First Day Cover		3·75
		Presentation Pack	5·00	

Plate Nos.: All values 1A, 1B (each×5).
Sheets: 20 (4×5).
Imprint: Right-hand margin.
Withdrawn: 20.9.89.

371 Long-eared Owl

372 European Robin

373 Grey Partridge

Christmas. Manx Birds

(Des Audrey North. Litho Questa)

1988 (12 Oct). P 14 (C).

396	**371**	12p. multicoloured	40	30
397	**372**	15p. multicoloured	60	65
398	**373**	31p. multicoloured	1·20	1·20
396/8		*Set of 3*	2·00	2·00
		First Day Cover		2·50
		Presentation Pack	2·50	
		Set of 3 Gutter Pairs	4·00	

Plate Nos.: All values 1A, 1B, 1C, 1D (each×5).
Sheets: 40 (2 panes 5×4).
Imprint: Right-hand corner, bottom margin of each pane.
Withdrawn: 11.10.89.

Year Pack 1988

1988 (1 Nov). Comprises Nos. 361/7, 368/75, 376/7, 378/80 and 381/98 (price £10).

Year Pack	40·00	

Withdrawn: 31.12.89.

Post Office Yearbook

1988 (1 Dec). Comprises Nos. 361/7, 368/75, 376/7, 378/80 and 381/98 in slipcase (price £12).

Yearbook	45·00	

Sold out: By 9.93.

374 Ginger Cat

375 Black and White Cat

376 Tortoiseshell and White Cat

377 Tortoiseshell Cat

Manx Cats

(Des P. Layton. Litho Questa)

1989 (8 Feb). P 14 (C).

399	**374**	16p. multicoloured	50	30
400	**375**	27p. multicoloured	90	85
401	**376**	30p. multicoloured	1·20	1·00
402	**377**	40p. multicoloured	1·50	1·30
399/402 Set of 4			3·75	3·00
First Day Cover				3·50
Presentation Pack			4·50	
Stamp Cards (set of 4)			3·00	8·00
Set of 4 Gutter Pairs			7·50	

Plate Nos.: 16p., 27p. 1C, 1D, 1G, 1H (each×4); 30p., 40p. 1A, 1B, 1E, 1F (each×4).
Sheets: 40 (2 panes 5×4).
Imprint: Right-hand corner, bottom margin of each pane.
Withdrawn: 7.2.90.

378 Tudric Pewter Clock, c. 1903   **379** 'Celtic Cross' Watercolour   **380** Silver Cup and Cover, 1902–03

381 Gold and Silver Brooches from Liberty's Cymric Range   **382** Silver Jewel Box, 1900

125th Birth Anniversary of Archibald Knox (artist and designer)

(Des Colleen Corlett. Litho Cartor)

1989 (8 Feb). P 13 (C).

403	**378**	13p. multicoloured	20	20
404	**379**	16p. multicoloured	30	25
405	**380**	23p. multicoloured	50	50
406	**381**	32p. multicoloured	1·20	1·00
407	**382**	35p. multicoloured	1·40	1·00
403/7 Set of 5			3·00	2·75
First Day Cover				3·00
Presentation Pack			4·00	
Set of 5 Gutter Pairs			6·00	

Plate Nos.: All values 1A, 1B, 1C, 1D (each×5).
Sheets: 40 (2 panes 4×5) 13p., 16p., 23p.; (2 panes 5×4) others.
Imprint: Bottom, left-hand margin of each pane (13p., 16p., 23p.) or right-hand corner, bottom margin of each pane.
Withdrawn: 7.2.90.

383 William Bligh and Old Church, Onchan   **384** Bligh and Loyal Crew cast Adrift

385 Pitcairn Islands 1989 Bicentenary 90c. Stamp   **386** Norfolk Island 1989 39c. *Bounty* Stamp

387 Midshipman Peter Heywood and Tahiti   **388** H.M.S. *Bounty* anchored off Pitcairn

389 Fletcher Christian and Pitcairn Island

Bicentenary of the Mutiny on the *Bounty*

(Des C. Abbott. Litho BDT)

1989 (28 Apr). P 14 (C).

408	**383**	13p. multicoloured	30	20
		a. Booklet pane. Nos. 408/10 and 412/14	4·25	
		b. Booklet pane. Nos. 408/9 and 411/14	4·00	
409	**384**	16p. multicoloured	35	30
410	**385**	23p. multicoloured	1·00	1·00
		a. Booklet pane. Nos. 410/11, each×3	5·50	
411	**386**	27p. multicoloured	1·00	1·00
412	**387**	30p. multicoloured	60	60
413	**388**	32p. multicoloured	70	70
414	**389**	35p. multicoloured	80	80
408/14 Set of 7			4·25	4·25
First Day Cover (ex Nos. 410/11)				4·75
Presentation Pack (ex Nos. 410/11)			5·50	
MS415 110×85 mm. Nos. 410/11 and 414			3·75	3·75
		a. Booklet pane. As No. **MS**415, but 147×101 mm with line of roulettes at left	4·00	
First Day Cover				5·00
Presentation Pack			5·00	

Plate Nos.: 13p., 16p., 30p., 32p., 35p. 1A, 1B (each×4).
Sheets: 20 (4×5) 13p., 16p., 30p., 32p., 35p. The 23p. and 27p. values were only issued in £5.30 booklets and in the miniature sheet. Booklet panes Nos. 408a/b and 410a each contain two vertical rows of three stamps, separated by a central gutter.
Imprint: 13p., 16p., 30p., 32p., 35p. Central, left-hand margin.
Withdrawn: 27.4.90 13, 16, 30, 32, 35p.

390 Skipping and Hopscotch   **391** Wheelbarrow, Leapfrog and Piggyback

 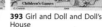

392 Building Model House and Blowing Bubbles   **393** Girl and Doll and Doll's House

Europa. Childrens Games

(Des Colleen Corlett. Litho Enschedé)

1989 (17 May). P 13½ (C).

416	**390**	13p. multicoloured	45	40
		a. Horiz pair. Nos. 416/17	90	1·00
417	**391**	13p. multicoloured	45	40
418	**392**	23p. multicoloured	70	75
		a. Horiz pair. Nos. 418/19	1·40	1·60
419	**393**	23p. multicoloured	70	75
416/19 Set of 4			2·10	2·20

451 Oliver Godfrey with Indian 500cc at Start, 1911

452 Freddie Dixon on Douglas 'Banking' Sidecar, 1923

453 Bill Ivy on Yamaha 125cc, 1968

454 Giacomo Agostini on MV Agusta 500cc, 1972

455 Joey Dunlop on RVF Honda 750cc, 1985

80th Anniversary of Tourist Trophy Mountain Course

(Des A. Theobald. Litho Enschedé)

1991 (30 May). P 14½×13 (C).

478	**451**	17p. multicoloured	50	40
479	**452**	21p. multicoloured	65	60
480	**453**	26p. multicoloured	80	80
481	**454**	31p. multicoloured	1·20	1·10
482	**455**	37p. multicoloured	1·50	1·50
478/82 Set of 5			4·25	4·00
First Day Cover				4·50
Presentation Pack			4·75	
Stamp Cards (set of 5)			3·00	6·00
Set of 5 Gutter Pairs			8·50	
MS483 149×144 mm. Nos. 478/82			4·00	4·00
First Day Cover				9·00
Souvenir Folder			5·50	

No. **MS**483 was reissued on 16 November 1991 overprinted for the Phila Nippon exhibition, Japan.
　　Plate Nos.: All values 1A, 1B, 1C, 1D (each×4).
　　Sheets: 40 (2 panes 5×4).
　　Imprint: Right-hand corner, bottom margin of each pane.
　　Withdrawn: 29.5.92.

Ninth Conference of Commonwealth Postal Administrations, Douglas

(Des Colleen Corlett. Litho BDT)

1991 (1 July). P 13 (C).

MS484 119×77 mm. Nos. 367c and 377a, each×2		1·90	2·00
First Day Cover			2·50
Presentation Pack		2·75	
Withdrawn: 30.6.92.			

456 Laxey Hand-cart, 1920

457 Horse-drawn Steamer, Douglas, 1909

458 Merryweather Hatfield Pump, 1936

459 Dennis F8 Pumping Appliance, Peel, 1953

460 Volvo Turntable Ladder, Douglas, 1989

Fire Engines

(Des C. Abbott. Litho Questa)

1991 (18 Sept). P 14½ (C).

485	**456**	17p. multicoloured	45	40
486	**457**	21p. multicoloured	65	65
487	**458**	30p. multicoloured	85	90
488	**459**	33p. multicoloured	1·20	1·20
489	**460**	37p. multicoloured	1·40	1·50
485/9 Set of 5			4·25	4·25
First Day Cover				4·75
Presentation Pack			4·75	
Set of 5 Gutter Pairs			8·50	

　　Plate Nos.: All values 1A, 1B, 1C, 1D (each×5).
　　Sheets: 40 (2 panes 4×5).
　　Imprint: Central, gutter margin.
　　Withdrawn: 17.9.92.

461 Mute Swans, Douglas Harbour

462 Black Swans, Curraghs Wildlife Park

463 Whooper Swans, Bishop's Dub, Ballaugh

464 Tundra ('Bewick's') Swans, Eairy Dam, Foxdale

465 Coscoroba Swans, Curraghs Wildlife Park

466 Whopper ('Trumpeter') Swans, Curraghs Wildlife Park

Swans

(Des Colleen Corlett. Litho Cartor)

1991 (18 Sept). P 13 (C).

490	**461**	17p. multicoloured	40	20
		a. Horiz pair. Nos. 490/1	80	1·00
491	**462**	17p. multicoloured	40	20
492	**463**	26p. multicoloured	1·10	30
		a. Horiz pair. Nos. 492/3	2·10	2·20
493	**464**	26p. multicoloured	1·10	30
494	**465**	37p. multicoloured	1·20	40
		a. Horiz pair. Nos. 494/5	2·40	2·75
		ab. Black ptg double		
495	**466**	37p. multicoloured	1·20	40
490/5 *Set of 6*			4·50	5·00
First Day Cover				6·00
Presentation Pack			5·25	

Plate Nos: All values 1A, 1B (each×4).
Sheets: 20 (4×5). The two designs of each value were printed together, *se-tenant*, in horizontal pairs throughout the sheets, with the backgrounds forming composite designs.
Imprint: Central, bottom margin.
Withdrawn: 17.9.92.

467 The Three Kings

468 Mary with Manger

469 Shepherds with Sheep

470 Choir of Angels

Christmas. Paper Sculptures

(Des D. Swinton. Litho Walsall)

1991 (14 Oct).

(a) Sheet stamps. P 14×14½ (C)

496	**467**	16p. multicoloured	45	35
497	**468**	20p. multicoloured	65	70
498	**469**	26p. multicoloured	85	85
499	**470**	37p. multicoloured	1·10	1·10
496/9 *Set of 4*			2·75	2·50
First Day Cover				3·25
Presentation Pack			3·50	

Plate Nos: All values 1A, 1B, 1C, 1D (each×4).
Sheets: 40 (2 panes 4×5).
Imprint: Central, gutter margin.
Withdrawn: 13.10.92.

(b) Booklet stamps. Self-adhesive. Stamps die-cut

500	**467**	16p. multicoloured	60	60
		a. Booklet pane. Nos. 500×8 and 501×4	7·50	
501	**468**	20p. multicoloured	1·20	1·20

Year Pack 1991

1991 (14 Oct). Comprises Nos. 367c, 377a, 464/82 and **MS**484/99 (price £12).
Year Pack .... 40·00
Withdrawn: 31.12.92.

Post Office Yearbook

1991 (14 Oct). Comprises Nos. 367c, 377a, 464/82 and **MS**484/99 (price £15.50).
Yearbook .... 45·00
Withdrawn: 30.11.94.

471 North African and Italian Campaigns, 1942–43

472 D-Day, 1944

473 Arnhem, 1944

474 Rhine Crossing, 1945

475 Operations in Near, Middle and Far East, 1945–68

476 Liberation of Falkland Islands, 1982

50th Anniversary of Parachute Regiment

(Des A. Theobald. Litho Questa)

1992 (6 Feb). P 14 (C).

502	**471**	23p. multicoloured	70	25
		a. Horiz pair. Nos. 502/3	1·50	1·50
503	**472**	23p. multicoloured	70	25
504	**473**	28p. multicoloured	80	30
		a. Horiz pair. Nos. 504/5	1·60	1·70
505	**474**	28p. multicoloured	80	30
506	**475**	39p. multicoloured	1·20	40
		a. Horiz pair. Nos. 506/7	2·50	2·75
507	**476**	39p. multicoloured	1·20	40
502/7 *Set of 6*			5·00	5·00
First Day Cover				6·00
Presentation Pack			6·00	
Souvenir Folder (complete sheets)			24·00	

Plate Nos: All values 1A, 1B (each×5).
Sheets: 8 (2×4). The two designs of each value were printed together, *se-tenant*, in horizontal pairs throughout the sheets.
Imprint: Top, left-hand margin.
Withdrawn: 5.2.93.

477 Queen Elizabeth II at Coronation, 1953

478 Queen visiting Isle of Man, 1979

479 Queen in Evening Dress

480 Queen visiting Isle of Man, 1989

481 Queen arriving for Film Premiere, 1990

40th Anniversary of Accession

(Des D. Miller. Litho BDT)

1992 (6 Feb). P 14 (C).

508	**477**	18p. multicoloured	45	40
509	**478**	23p. multicoloured	60	60
510	**479**	28p. multicoloured	70	70
511	**480**	33p. multicoloured	1·20	1·40
512	**481**	39p. multicoloured	1·40	1·40
508/12 *Set of 5*			4·00	4·00
First Day Cover				5·00
Presentation Pack			5·00	

Plate Nos: All values 1A, 1B (each×5).
Sheets: 20 (5×4).
Imprint: Central, bottom margin.
Withdrawn: 5.2.93.

482 Brittle-stars

483 Phytoplankton

484 Atlantic Herring

485 Great Scallop

486 Dahlia Anemone and Delesseria

Centenary of Port Erin Marine Laboratory

(Des Jennifer Toombs. Litho Questa)

1992 (16 Apr.) P 14×14½ (C).

513	**482**	18p. multicoloured	40	35
514	**483**	23p. multicoloured	60	55
515	**484**	28p. multicoloured	60	60
516	**485**	33p. multicoloured	1·20	1·20
517	**486**	39p. multicoloured	1·50	1·50
513/17 Set of 5			4·00	4·00
First Day Cover				4·50
Presentation Pack			4·75	
Set of 5 Gutter Pairs			8·00	

Plate Nos.: All values 1A, 1B, 1C, 1D (each×4).
Sheets: 40 (2 panes 5×4).
Imprint: Top right-hand side, gutter margin.
Withdrawn: 15.4.93.

487 The Pilgrim Fathers embarking at Delfshaven

488 *Speedwell* leaving Delfshaven

489 *'Mayflower and Speedwell* at Dartmouth' **490**

(L. Wilcox)

Europa. 500th Anniversary of Discovery of America by Columbus

(Des C. Abbott. Litho Enschedé)

1992 (16 Apr.) P 14×13½ (C).

518	**487**	18p. multicoloured	40	20
		a. Horiz pair. Nos. 518/19	1·60	1·60
519	**488**	18p. multicoloured	40	30
520	**489**	28p. multicoloured	75	30
		a. Horiz pair. Nos. 520/1	3·50	3·50
521	**490**	28p. multicoloured	75	30
518/21 Set of 4			4·50	4·50
First Day Cover				5·00
Presentation Pack			5·25	

Plate Nos.: Both values 1A, 1B (each×5).
Sheets: 20 (4×5). The two designs of each value were printed together, *se-tenant*, in horizontal pairs throughout the sheets, each pair forming a composite design.
Imprint: Central, bottom margin.
Withdrawn: 15.4.93.

491 Central Pacific Locomotive *Jupiter,* 1869

492 Union Pacific Locomotive No. 119, 1869

493 Union Pacific Locomotive No. 844, 1992

494 Union Pacific Locomotive No. 3985, 1992

495 Golden Spike Ceremony, 10 May 1869 (*Illustration reduced. Actual size 105×73 mm*)

Construction of Union Pacific Railroad, 1866–69

(Des A. Peck. Litho Enschedé)

1992 (22 May). P 13½×14 (C).

522	**491**	33p. multicoloured	90	35
		a. Horiz. pair. Nos. 522/3 plus label	2·50	2·50
		b. Booklet pane. Nos. 522/5×2 and **MS**526	12·00	
523	**492**	33p. multicoloured	90	35
524	**493**	39p. multicoloured	1·20	40
		a. Horiz. pair. Nos. 524/5 plus label	3·00	3·00
525	**494**	39p. multicoloured	1·20	40
522/5 Set of 4			4·00	4·50
First Day Cover				5·00
Presentation Pack			5·50	
Souvenir Folder (sheets of 10)			22·00	
Stamp Cards (set of 4)			3·25	
MS526 105×73 mm. **495** £1·50 multicoloured			4·25	4·50
First Day Cover				6·00
Presentation Pack			5·50	
Stamp Card			70	

Nos. 522b and **MS**526 also commemorated the 'World Columbian Stamp Expo'.

Booklet pane No. 522b contains two blocks of four of Nos. 522/5 with No. **MS**526 between them. Miniature sheets from the booklet show a white margin and line of roulettes at left and right. In the blocks of four each horizontal pair is separated by a half stamp-size label.

Plate Nos.: Both values 1A, 1B (each×4).
Sheets: 10 (2×5). The two designs for each value were printed together in horizontal pairs separated by a half stamp-size label showing Union Pacific emblem or portraits of Dan and Jack Casement (railroad contractors).
Imprint: Central, right-hand margin.
Withdrawn: 21.5.93.

496 *King Orry V* in Douglas Harbour

497 Castletown

498 Port St. Mary

499 Ramsey

Manx Harbours

(Des Colleen Corlett. Litho Walsall)

1992 (18 Sept). P 14½×14 (C).

527	**496**	18p. multicoloured	45	45
528	**497**	23p. multicoloured	55	55
529	**498**	37p. multicoloured	1·20	1·20
530	**499**	40p. multicoloured	1·40	1·40
527/30 *Set of 4*			3·25	3·25
First Day Cover				3·75
Presentation Pack			4·00	

Plate Nos.: All values 1A, 1B (each×4).
Sheets: 10 (2×5).
Imprint: Right-hand corner, bottom margin.
Withdrawn: 17.9.93.

500 *King Orry V* (ex *Saint Eloi*) in 1972 and 1992
(*Illustration reduced. Actual size 111×68 mm*)

'Genova '92' International Thematic Stamp Exhibition

(Des Colleen Corlett. Litho Walsall)

1992 (18 Sept). Sheet 111×68 mm. P 14½×14 (C).

MS531 **500** 18p, £1 multicoloured		3·25	3·50
First Day Cover			3·75
Presentation Pack		3·75	

Withdrawn: 17.9.93.

501 Window,
St. German's
Cathedral, Peel

502 Reredos,
St. Matthew the
Apostle, Douglas

503 Window,
St. George's,
Douglas

504 Reredos,
St. Mary of the
Isle Catholic
Church, Douglas

505 Window,
Trinity Methodist
Church, Douglas

Christmas. Manx Churches

(Des Colleen Corlett, Litho Questa)

1992 (13 Oct). P 14½ (C).

532	**501**	17p. multicoloured	50	50
533	**502**	22p. multicoloured	75	75
534	**503**	28p. multicoloured	1·00	1·00
535	**504**	37p. multicoloured	1·00	1·00
536	**505**	40p. multicoloured	1·50	1·50
		a. Gold ptg double		
532/6 *Set of 5*			4·50	4·50
First Day Cover				4·75
Presentation Pack			5·00	
Set of 5 Gutter Pairs			9·00	

Plate Nos.: 17p., 22p. 1A, 1B, 1C, 1D (each×5); others 1A, 1B
(each×5).
Sheets: 40 (2 panes 4×5).
Imprint: Right-hand corner, bottom margin of each pane.
Withdrawn: 12.10.93.

Year Pack 1992

1992 (13 Oct). Comprises Nos. 502/36 (price £12.50).

Year Pack	40·00	

Withdrawn: 31.12.93.

Post Office Yearbook

1992 (13 Oct). Comprises Nos. 375a, 377b, 502/36 and D25 (price £17).

Yearbook	45·00	

Withdrawn: 30.11.94.

506 Mansell on Lap of Honour,
British Grand Prix, 1992

507 Mansell in French Grand
Prix, 1992

**Nigel Mansell's Victory in Formula 1 World Motor Racing
Championship**

(Des A. Theobald. Litho Walsall)

1992 (8 Nov). P 13½ (C).

537	**506**	20p. multicoloured	80	80
538	**507**	24p. multicoloured	1·00	1·00
537/8 *Set of 2*			1·80	1·80
First Day Cover				2·75
Presentation Pack			2·75	

Plate Nos.: Both values 1A, 1B (each×4).
Sheets: 50 (5×10).
Imprint: Bottom margin.
Withdrawn: 7.11.93.

508 H.M.S. *Amazon* (frigate)

509 *Fingal* (lighthouse tender)

510 *Sir Winston Churchill*
(cadet schooner)

511 *Dar Mlodziezy* (full-rigged
cadet ship)

512 *Tynwald I* (paddle-steamer)

513 *Ben Veg* (freighter)

514 *Waverley* (paddle-steamer)

515 Royal Yacht *Britannia*

516 *Francis Drake* (ketch)

517 *Royal Viking Sky* (liner)

518 *Lord Nelson* (cadet barque)

519 *Europa* (liner)

520 *Snaefell V* (ferry) leaving Androssan

520a *Seacat* (catamaran ferry)

521 *Lady of Man I* (ferry) off Ramsey

522 *Mona's Queen II* (paddle ferry) leaving Fleetwood

523 *Queen Elizabeth 2* (liner) and *Mona's Queen V* (ferry) off Liverpool

523a Manx Red Ensign

523b Queen Elizabeth II (hologram)

Ships

(Des A. Theobald (1p. to 27p.), J. Nicholson (30p., 40p., 50p., £1),
   IOMPO from a photograph by M.C. Thompson (35p.), Colleen
Corlett (£2, £5). Litho Questa (£2), Walsall (£5) (hologram by Applied
         Holographics), Enschedé (others))

1993 (4 Jan)–'97. P 14½ (£2), 14½×14 (£5) or 13½×13 (others), all comb.

539	**508**	1p. multicoloured (a)	10	10
540	**509**	2p. multicoloured (a)	10	10
541	**510**	4p. multicoloured (a)	10	10
		a. Booklet pane. Nos. 541, 544 and 548 each×2 (g)	5·00	
542	**511**	5p. multicoloured (a)	10	10
543	**512**	20p. multicoloured (ae)	40	25
		a. Booklet pane. Nos. 543×2 and 547×3	3·00	
		b. Booklet pane. Nos. 543×4 and 547×6	6·50	
544	**513**	21p. multicoloured (ag)	50	50
545	**514**	22p. multicoloured (a)	50	50
546	**515**	23p. multicoloured (a)	55	55
547	**516**	24p. multicoloured (ae)	50	35
548	**517**	25p. multicoloured (ag)	60	60
549	**518**	26p. multicoloured (a)	65	65
550	**519**	27p. multicoloured (a)	65	65
551	**520**	30p. multicoloured (b)	75	75
552	**520a**	35p. multicoloured (f)	85	85
553	**521**	40p. multicoloured (b)	1·00	90
554	**522**	50p. multicoloured (b)	1·20	1·10
555	**523**	£1 multicoloured (bg)	2·50	2·40
556	**523a**	£2 multicoloured (c)	3·75	4·00
557	**523b**	£5 multicoloured (d)	10·00	12·00
539/57 Set of 19			22·00	23·00
First Day Covers (6)				30·00
Presentation Packs (6)			30·00	
Stamp Cards (Nos. 539/51, 553/5)			8·00	22·00
Souvenir Folder (Nos. 539/51, 553/5)			12·00	

For 4p., 20p. and 24p. in similar designs, but smaller, see Nos. 687/93.

Printings: (a) 4.1.93. Inscribed '1993'; (b) 15.9.93. Inscribed '1993'; (c) 12.1.94. Inscribed '1994'; (d) 5.7.94. Inscribed 1994; (e) 8.2.95. Inscribed '1995'; (f) 11.1. '1996'. Inscribed '1996'; (g) 14.5.97. Inscribed '1997'. The 23p value also exists with an imprint date of 1997, from miniature sheet **MS**760.
Plate Nos.: £2, £5 1A, 1B (each×4); others 1A, 1B, 1C, 1D (each×4). Sheets: 25 (5×5) (£2), 10 (5×2) (£5) or 50 (5×10) (others). In addition to stamp booklets Nos. 543a/b also come from a special booklet sheet of 50 (5×10) which provides either ten examples of No. 543a or five of 543b. No. 541a comes from a special booklet sheet of 30 (5×6), which provides five examples of the pane.
Imprint: Central, bottom margin (£2, £5) or right-hand corner, bottom margin (others).
Withdrawn: 30.11.98 1p. to £1; 12.1.99 £2; 5.7.99 £5.

524 No. 1 Motor Car and No. 13 Trailer at Groudle Glen Hotel

525 No. 9 Tunnel Car and No. 19 Trailer at Douglas Bay Hotel

526 No. 19 Motor Car and No. 59 Royal Trailer Special at Douglas Bay

527 No. 33 Motor Car, No. 45 Trailer and
No. 13 Van at Derby Castle

Centenary of Manx Electric Railway

(Des A. Theobald. Litho BDT)

1993 (3 Feb). P 14 (C).

559	**524**	20p. multicoloured	60	60
		a. Booklet pane. Nos. 559/62	3·50	
560	**525**	24p. multicoloured	90	90
561	**526**	28p. multicoloured	1·00	1·00
562	**527**	39p. multicoloured	1·40	1·40
559/62	Set of 4		3·50	3·50
	First Day Cover			3·75
	Presentation Pack		3·75	

Booklet pane No. 559a exists in four versions, which differ in the order of the stamps within the block of four and in the information printed on the pane margin.
Plate Nos.: All values 1A, 1B (each×4).
Sheets: 10 (2×5).
Imprint: Central, left-hand margin.
Withdrawn: 2.2.94.

528 'Sir Hall Caine'
(statue)

529 'The Brass Bedstead'
(painting)

530 Abstract Bronze
Sculpture

531 'Polar Bear Skeleton'
(drawing)

Europa. Contemporary Art by Bryan Kneale

(Des Colleen Corlett. Litho BDT)

1993 (14 Apr). P 14 (C).

563	**528**	20p. multicoloured	40	20
		a. Horiz pair. Nos. 563/4	1·20	1·20
564	**529**	20p. multicoloured	40	20
565	**530**	28p. multicoloured	75	30
		a. Horiz pair. Nos. 565/6	2·00	2·00
566	**531**	28p. multicoloured	75	30
563/6	Set of 4		3·00	3·00
	First Day Cover			3·50
	Presentation Pack		3·75	

Plate Nos.: Both values 1A, 1B, 1C (each×4).
Sheets: 20 (4×5). The two designs for each value printed together, se-tenant, in horizontal pairs throughout the sheets.
Imprint: Central, right-hand margin.
Withdrawn: 13.4.94.

532 Graham Oates and Bill Marshall
(1933 International Six Day Trial) on
Ariel Square Four

533 Sergeant Geoff Duke (1947 Royal
Signals Display Team) on Triumph 3T Twin

534 Dennis Parkinson (1953 Senior
Manx Grand Prix) on Manx Norton

535 Richard Swallow (1991 Junior
Classic MGP) on Aermacchi

536 Steve Colley (1992 Scottish Six
Day Trial) on Beta Zero

Manx Motor Cycling Events

(Des C. Abbott. Litho Walsall)

1993 (3 June). P 13½×14 (C).

567	**532**	20p. multicoloured	35	35
568	**533**	24p. multicoloured	45	45
569	**534**	28p. multicoloured	70	60
570	**535**	33p. multicoloured	90	90
571	**536**	39p. multicoloured	1·00	95
567/71	Set of 5		3·00	3·00
	First Day Cover			4·00
	Presentation Pack		4·00	
	Stamp Cards (set of 5)		3·00	6·00
MS572	165×120 mm. Nos. 567/71		4·50	4·50
	Souvenir Folder		4·75	

Plate Nos.: All values 1A, 1B, 1C, 1D (each×4).
Sheets: 20 (4×5).
Imprint: Right-hand corner, bottom margin.
Withdrawn: 2.6.94.

537 Inachis io (Peacock)

538 Argynnis aglaja
(Dark Green Fritillary)

539 *Cynthia cardui* (Painted Lady)

540 *Celastrina argiolus* (Holly Blue)

541 *Vanessa atalanta* (Red Admiral)

Butterflies

(Des Colleen Corlett. Litho Questa)

1993 (15 Sept). P 14½ (C).

573	**537**	24p. multicoloured	75	65
		a. Horiz strip of 5. Nos. 573/7	3·50	
574	**538**	24p. multicoloured	75	65
575	**539**	24p. multicoloured	75	65
576	**540**	24p. multicoloured	75	65
577	**541**	24p. multicoloured	75	65
573/7 Set of 5			3·50	3·00
First Day Cover				4·25
Presentation Pack			4·00	

Examples of Nos. 573/7 sold at 'Philakorea '94' and 'Singpex '94' come with commemorative cachets on the bottom margin.
Plate Nos.: 1A, 1B (each×4).
Sheets: 20 (5×4). The five designs for each value printed together, *se-tenant*, in horizontal strips throughout the sheets.
Imprint: Right-hand corner, bottom margin.
Withdrawn: 14.9.94.

542 Children decorating Christmas Tree

543 Girl with Snowman

544 Boy opening Presents

545 Girl with Teddy Bear

546 Children with Toboggan

Christmas

(Des Christine Haworth. Litho Questa)

1993 (12 Oct). P 14 (C).

578	**542**	19p. multicoloured	50	50
579	**543**	23p. multicoloured	60	60
580	**544**	28p. multicoloured	70	70
581	**545**	39p. multicoloured	1·10	1·10
582	**546**	40p. multicoloured	1·10	1·10
578/82 Set of 5			3·50	3·50

First Day Cover			4·00
Presentation Pack		4·25	
Set of 5 Gutter Pairs		7·00	

Nos. 578 and 579 were also issued in booklets, SB35 and SB36.
Plate Nos.: All values 1A, 1B, 1C, 1D (each×4).
Sheets: 40 (2 panes 4×5).
Imprint: Bottom, right-hand margin of each pane.
Withdrawn: 11.10.94.

Year Pack 1993

1993 (12 Oct). Comprises Nos. 539/51, 553/5, 559/71 and 573/82 (price £12·50).
Year Pack		32·00

Withdrawn: 31.12.94.

Post Office Yearbook

1993 (12 Oct). Comprises Nos. 539/51, 553/5, 559/71 and 573/82 (price £17).
Yearbook		40·00

Sold out: 8.95.

547 White-throated Robin

548 Black-eared Wheatear

549 Goldcrest

550 Northern Oriole

551 River Kingfisher

552 Hoopoe

553 Black-billed Magpie (*Illustration reduced. Actual size 100×71 mm*)

Calf of Man Bird Observatory

(Des Colleen Corlett. Litho BDT)

1994 (18 Feb). P 13½×13 (No. **MS**589) or 14 (others), both comb.

583	**547**	20p. multicoloured	50	20
		a. Pair. Nos. 583/4	1·00	1·20
584	**548**	20p. multicoloured	50	20
585	**549**	24p. multicoloured	80	25
		a. Pair. Nos. 585/6	1·60	1·70
586	**550**	24p. multicoloured	80	25
587	**551**	30p. multicoloured	1·00	30
		a. Pair. Nos. 587/8	2·00	2·00
588	**552**	30p. multicoloured	1·00	30
583/8 Set of 6			4·25	4·75
First Day Cover				5·50
Presentation Pack			5·00	
Souvenir Folder (complete sheets)			20·00	

MS589 100×71 mm. **553** £1 multicoloured...................... 3·00   3·50
First Day Cover.. 4·50
Presentation Pack.. 4·50

No. **MS**589 also commemorates the 'Hong Kong '94' philatelic exhibition.

Plate Nos.: All values 1A, 1B (each×4).
Sheets: 10 (2×5). The two designs for each value printed together, *se-tenant*, in horizontal and vertical pairs throughout the sheets.
Imprint: Central, right-hand margin.
Withdrawn: 17.2.95.

554 Gaiety Theatre, Douglas

555 Sports

556 Artist at work and Yachts racing

557 T.T. Races and British Aerospace Hawk T.1s of Red Arrows

558 Musical Instruments

559 Laxey Wheel and Manx Cat

560 Tower of Refuge, Douglas, with Bucket and Spade

561 Cyclist

562 Tynwald Day and Bentley 3 Litre Racing Car (1922)

563 Santa Mince Pie Train, Groudle Glen

Manx Tourism Centenary. Booklet Stamps

(Des Colleen Corlett. Litho Cartor)

1994 (18 Feb). P 13½ (C).

590	**554**	24p. multicoloured............................	60	60
		a. Booklet pane. Nos. 590/9 with margins all round	5·00	
591	**555**	24p. multicoloured............................	60	60
592	**556**	24p. multicoloured............................	60	60
593	**557**	24p. multicoloured............................	60	60
594	**558**	24p. multicoloured............................	60	60
595	**559**	24p. multicoloured............................	60	60
596	**560**	24p. multicoloured............................	60	60
597	**561**	24p. multicoloured............................	60	60
598	**562**	24p. multicoloured............................	60	60
599	**563**	24p. multicoloured............................	60	60
590/9	*Set of 10*..		5·00	5·00

First Day Cover.. 6·50
Presentation Pack.. 6·50
Stamp Cards (set of 3)... 1·50

Nos. 590/9 were issued in £2.40 stamp booklets, but were also available from the Philatelic Bureau as a loose pane, which was also inserted into the *Presentation Pack*.
Withdrawn: 17.2.95.

564 *Eubranchus tricolor* (sea slug)

565 *Loligo forbesii* (common squid)

566 Edward Forbes and Signature

567 *Solaster moretonis* (fossil starfish)

568 *Adamsia carciniopados* (anemone) on Hermit Crab

569 *Solaster endeca* (starfish)

Europa. Discoveries of Edward Forbes (marine biologist)

(Des Jennifer Toombs. Litho Enschedé)

1994 (5 May). P 13×14½ (C).

600	**564**	20p. multicoloured............................	40	20
		a. Horiz strip of 3. Nos. 600/2..............	1·50	1·50
601	**565**	20p. multicoloured............................	40	20
602	**566**	20p. multicoloured............................	40	20
603	**567**	30p. multicoloured............................	75	30
		a. Horiz strip of 3. Nos. 603/5..............	2·75	2·75
604	**568**	30p. multicoloured............................	75	30
605	**569**	30p. multicoloured............................	75	30
600/5	*Set of 6*..		3·75	3·75

First Day Cover.. 4·25
Presentation Pack.. 4·50

Plate Nos.: Both values 1A, 1B (each×4).
Sheets: 15 (3×5). The three designs for each value printed together, *se-tenant*, in horizontal strips of three throughout the sheets.
Imprint: Central, bottom margin.
Withdrawn: 4.5.95.

570 Maj.-Gen. Bedell Smith and Naval Landing Force including *Ben-My-Chree IV* (ferry)

571 Admiral Ramsay and Naval Ships including *Victoria* and *Lady of Man* (ferries)

572 Gen. Motogomery and British Landings

573 Lt.-Gen. Dempsey and 2nd Army Landings

574 Air Chief Marshal Leigh-Mallory, U.S. Paratroops and Aircraft

575 Air Chief Marshal Tedder, British Paratroops and Aircraft

576 Lt.-Gen. Bradley and U.S. 1st Army Landings

577 Gen. Eisenhower and American Landings

50th Anniversary of D-Day

(Des A. Theobald. Litho Questa)

1994 (6 June). P 14 (C).

606	**570**	4p. multicoloured	10	10
		a. Horiz pair. Nos. 606/7	30	30
607	**571**	4p. multicoloured	10	10
608	**572**	20p. multicoloured	50	20
		a. Horiz pair. Nos. 608/9	1·40	1·40
609	**573**	20p. multicoloured	50	20
610	**574**	30p. multicoloured	75	30
		a. Horiz pair. Nos. 610/11	2·00	2·00
611	**575**	30p. multicoloured	75	30
612	**576**	41p. multicoloured	85	45
		a. Horiz pair. Nos. 612/13	2·50	2·50
613	**577**	41p. multicoloured	85	45
606/13		Set of 8	5·50	5·50
		First Day Cover		6·00
		Presentation Pack	6·25	
		Souvenir Folder (complete sheets)	26·00	

Plate Nos.: All values 1A, 1B (each×5).
Sheets: 8 (2×4). The two designs for each value printed together, *se-tenant*, in horizontal pairs throughout the sheets.
Imprint: Central, left-hand margin.
Withdrawn: 5.6.95.

578 Postman Pat, Jess and Ffinlo at Sea Terminal, Douglas

579 Laxey Wheel

580 Cregneash

581 Manx Electric Railway Trains

582 Peel Harbour

583 Douglas Promenade

584 Postman Pat, Jess, Policeman and Children at Zebra Crossing (*Illustration reduced. Actual size 110×85 mm*)

Postman Pat visits the Isle of Man

(Des Colleen Corlett. Litho BDT)

1994 (14 Sept). P 13 (No. **MS**620) or 15×14 (others), both comb.

614	**578**	1p. multicoloured	15	15
		a. Booklet pane of 2 with margins all round	50	
615	**579**	20p. multicoloured	60	60
		a. Booklet pane of 2 with margins all round	1·70	
616	**580**	24p. multicoloured	80	80
		a. Booklet pane of 2 with margins all round	2·20	
617	**581**	30p. multicoloured	90	90
		a. Booklet pane of 2 with margins all round	2·50	
618	**582**	36p. multicoloured	1·10	1·10
		a. Booklet pane of 2 with margins all round	2·75	
619	**583**	41p. multicoloured	1·20	1·20
		a. Booklet pane of 2 with margins all round	3·25	
614/19		Set of 6	4·25	4·25
		First Day Cover		4·50
		Presentation Pack	4·50	
		Stamp Cards (set of 6)	3·00	7·50
MS620		110×85 mm. **584** £1 multicoloured	2·20	2·20
		a. Booklet pane. As No. **MS**620 but with line of roulettes at left	2·20	
		First Day Cover		3·50
		Presentation Pack	3·00	

Examples of No. **MS**620 from stamp booklets show a line of roulettes at left.

Plate Nos.: All values 1A, 1B (each×4).
Sheets: 10 (2×5).
Imprint: Right-hand corner, bottom margin.
Withdrawn: 13.9.95.

585 Cycling

586 Downhill Skiing

587 Swimming

588 Hurdling

589 Centenary Logo

Centenary of International Olympic Committee

(Des D. Miller. Litho Walsall)

1994 (11 Oct). P 14×14½ (C).

621	**585**	10p. multicoloured	35	25
622	**586**	20p. multicoloured	55	50
623	**587**	24p. multicoloured	70	65
624	**588**	35p. multicoloured	95	1·00
625	**589**	48p. multicoloured	1·60	1·80
621/5 *Set of 5*			3·75	3·75
First Day Cover				4·00
Presentation Pack			4·00	

Plate Nos.: 10p. 1A (×4); 20p. 1B (×4); 24p. 1C (×4); 35p. 1D (×4); 48p. 1E (×4).
Sheets: 20 (5×4).
Imprint: Central, left-hand margin.
Withdrawn: 10.10.95.

590 Santa Train to Santon

591 Father Christmas and Postman Pat on Mini Tractor, Douglas

592 Father Christmas and Majorettes in Sleigh, Port St. Mary

Christmas. Father Christmas in the Isle of Man

(Des Colleen Corlett. Litho Cartor)

1994 (11 Oct). P 13½×14 (23p.) or 14×13½ (others), all comb.

626	**590**	19p. multicoloured	60	60
627	**591**	23p. multicoloured	80	80
628	**592**	60p. multicoloured	2·00	2·00
626/8 *Set of 3*			3·00	3·00
First Day Cover				3·50
Presentation Pack			3·75	
Set of 3 Gutter Pairs			6·00	

Plate Nos.: All values 1A, 1B, 1C, 1D (each×4).
Sheets: 40 (2 panes 5×4).
Imprint: Central, side margins of each pane.
Withdrawn: 10.10.95.

Year Pack 1994

1994 (11 Oct). Comprises Nos. 556 and 583/628, with (price £20) or without No. 557 (price £15).

Year Pack with No. 557		50·00
Year Pack without No. 557		40·00

Withdrawn: 31.12.95.

Post Office Yearbook

1994 (Nov). Comprises Nos. 556/7 and 583/628 (price £21).

Yearbook		55·00

Sold out: 3.96.

593 Foden Steam Wagon, Highway Board Depot, Douglas

594 Clayton & Shuttleworth and Fowler engines pulling Dead Whale

595 Wallis & Steevens at Ramsey Harbour

596 Marshall Engine with Threshing Machine, Ballarhenny

597 Marshall Convertible Steam Roller

Steam Traction Engines

(Des A. Peck. Litho Enschedé)

1995 (8 Feb). P 13½×13 (C).

629	**593**	20p. multicoloured	60	60
630	**594**	24p. multicoloured	70	70
631	**595**	30p. multicoloured	85	85
632	**596**	35p. multicoloured	1·10	1·10
633	**597**	41p. multicoloured	1·20	1·20
629/33 *Set of 5*			4·00	4·00
First Day Cover				4·50
Presentation Pack			4·50	

Plate Nos.: 35p. 1A, 1B, 1C, 1D (each×4); others 1A, 1B (each×4).
Sheets: 20 (4×5).
Withdrawn: 7.2.96.

598 Car No. 2 and First Train, 1895

599 Car No. 4 in Green Livery and Car No. 3 in Laxey Valley

600 Car No. 6 and Car No. 5 in 1971

601 Goods Car No. 7 and *Caledonia* Steam
Locomotive pulling Construction Train

602 Passenger Car and Argus Char-a-banc at Bungalow Hotel
(*Illustration reduced. Actual size* 110×87 *mm*)

Centenary of Snaefell Mountain Railway

(Des A. Theobald. Litho BDT)

1995 (8 Feb). P 14 (C).

634	**598**	20p. multicoloured	70	70
		a. Booklet pane. Nos. 634/7 with margins all round	3·50	
635	**599**	24p. multicoloured	80	80
636	**600**	35p. multicoloured	1·10	1·10
637	**601**	42p. multicoloured	1·20	1·20
634/7 Set of 4			3·50	3·50
First Day Cover				4·25
Presentation Pack			4·50	
MS638 110×87 mm. **602** £1 multicoloured			3·50	3·50
		a. Booklet pane. As No. **MS**638 with additional margins all round showing further inscriptions at right and left	3·75	
First Day Cover				4·25
Presentation Pack			4·00	

Booklet pane No. 634a exists in three versions which differ in the
order of the stamps within the block of four.
Examples of No. **MS**638 from booklet No. SB39 show a white
margin, description of the design and line of roulettes at left and
an additional inscription, '1895. CENTENARY SNAEFELL MOUNTAIN
RAILWAY. 1995', vertically in the margin at right.
Plate Nos.: All values 1A, 1B (each×4).
Sheets: 10 (2×5).
Imprint: Central, left-hand margin.
Withdrawn: 7.2.96.

603 Peace Doves forming
Wave and Tower of
Refuge, Douglas Bay

604 Peace Dove
breaking Barbed Wire

Europa. Peace and Freedom

(Des Colleen Corlett and M. Magleby (20p.), Colleen Corlett (30p.).
Litho Enschedé)

1995 (28 Apr). P 14×13½ (C).

639	**603**	20p. multicoloured	60	75
640	**604**	30p. multicoloured	1·00	1·00
639/40 Set of 2			1·60	1·70
First Day Cover				2·20
Presentation Pack			2·40	

Plate Nos.: Both values 1A, 1B (each×5).
Sheets: 10 (5×2).
Imprint: Central, bottom margin.
Withdrawn: 27.4.96.

605 Spitfire, Tank and Medals

606 Typhoon, Anti-aircraft Gun
and Medals

607 Lancaster, H.M.S. *Biter*
(escort carrier) and Medals

608 Grumman Avenger, Jungle
Patrol and Medals

609 Celebrations in Parliament
Square

610 V.E. Day Bonfire

611 Street Party

612 King George VI and Queen
Elizabeth on Isle of Man in
July, 1945

50th Anniversary of End of Second World War

(Des A. Theobald. Litho BDT)

1995 (8 May). P 14 (C).

641	**605**	10p. multicoloured	30	15
		a. Horiz. pair. Nos. 641/2	60	60
642	**606**	10p. multicoloured	30	15
643	**607**	20p. multicoloured	55	25
		a. Horiz. pair. Nos. 643/4	1·10	1·10
644	**608**	20p. multicoloured	55	25
645	**609**	24p. multicoloured	70	25
		a. Horiz. pair. Nos. 645/6	1·40	1·40
646	**610**	24p. multicoloured	70	25
647	**611**	40p. multicoloured	1·10	50
		a. Horiz. pair. Nos. 647/8	2·20	2·20
648	**612**	40p. multicoloured	1·10	50
641/8 Set of 8			4·75	4·75
First Day Cover				5·50
Presentation Pack			6·00	
Souvenir Folder (complete sheets)			19·00	

Plate Nos.: All values 1A, 1B, 1C (each×4).
Sheets: 8 (2×4). The two designs for each value printed together,
se-tenant, in horizontal pairs throughout the sheets.
Imprint: Central, left-hand margin.
Withdrawn: 7.5.96.

613 Reg Parnell in Maserati 4
CLT, 1951

614 Stirling Moss in Frazer Nash
Le Mans Replica car, 1951

615 Richard Seaman in Delage, 1936

616 Prince Bira in ERA R2B Romulus, 1937

617 Kenelm Guinness in Sunbeam 1, 1914

618 Freddie Dixon in Riley 6 Cylinder Special Racing Car, 1934

619 John Napier in Arrol Johnston 18 h.p. Racing Car, 1905 (*Illustration reduced. Actual size 103×73 mm*)

90th Anniversary of Motor Racing on Isle of Man

(Des N. Sykes. Litho Questa)

1995 (8 May). P 14 (C).

649	**613**	20p. multicoloured	65	60
650	**614**	24p. multicoloured	80	75
651	**615**	30p. multicoloured	90	85
652	**616**	36p. multicoloured	1·10	1·00
653	**617**	41p. multicoloured	1·20	1·20
654	**618**	42p. multicoloured	1·20	1·50
649/54	*Set of 6*		5·50	5·50
First Day Cover				5·75
Presentation Pack			6·00	
MS655	103×73 mm. **619** £1 multicoloured		3·75	3·75
First Day Cover				3·25
Presentation Pack			3·25	

Plate Nos.: All values 1A, 1B (each×5).
Sheets: 20 (5×4).
Imprint: Right-hand corner, bottom margin.
Withdrawn: 7.5.96.

620 Thomas the Tank Engine and Bertie Bus being Unloaded

621 Mail Train

622 Bertie and Engines at Ballasalla

623 Viking the Diesel Engine, Port Erin

624 Thomas and Railcar at Snaefell Summit

625 Engines racing past Laxey Wheel

50th Anniversary of Thomas the Tank Engine Stories by Revd. Awdry. '*Thomas the Tank Engines Dream*'

(Des O. Bell. Litho BDT)

1995 (15 Aug). P 14 (C).

656	**620**	20p. multicoloured	65	60
		a. Booklet pane. Nos. 656/7 with margins all round	1·70	
		b. Booklet pane. Nos. 656 and 661 with margins all round	2·20	
657	**621**	24p. multicoloured	80	75
		a. Booklet pane. Nos. 657/8 with margins all round	1·70	
658	**622**	30p. multicoloured	90	85
		a. Booklet pane. Nos. 658/9 with margins all round	2·00	
659	**623**	36p. multicoloured	1·10	1·10
		a. Booklet pane. Nos. 659/60 with margins all round	2·20	
660	**624**	41p. multicoloured	1·20	1·10
		a. Booklet pane. Nos. 660/1 with margins all round	2·50	
661	**625**	45p. multicoloured	1·50	1·20
656/61	*Set of 6*		5·50	5·00
First Day Cover				5·50
Presentation Pack			6·00	
Stamp Cards (*set of 6*)			3·00	9·00

Plate Nos.: All values 1A, 1B (each×4).
Sheets: 10 (2×5).
Imprint: Central, bottom margin.
Withdrawn: 14.8.96.

626 *Amanita muscaria*

627 *Boletus edulis*

628 *Coprinus disseminatus*

629 *Pleurotus ostreatus*

630 *Geastrum triplex*

631 Shaggy Ink Cap and Bee Orchid
(*Illustration reduced. Actual size 100×71 mm*)

Fungi

(Des Colleen Corlett. Litho Enschedé)

1995 (1 Sept). P 13½ (C).

662	**626**	20p. multicoloured	60	60
663	**627**	24p. multicoloured	70	70
664	**628**	30p. multicoloured	70	70
665	**629**	35p. multicoloured	90	90
666	**630**	45p. multicoloured	1·50	1·50
662/6	*Set of 5*		4·25	4·25
	First Day Cover			4·75
	Presentation Pack		4·75	
MS667	100×71 mm. **631** £1 multicoloured		3·00	3·00
	First Day Cover			3·50
	Presentation Pack		3·50	

No. **MS**667 is inscribed 'Singapore World Stamp Exhibition 1st–10th September 1995' on the sheet margin.
Plate Nos.: All values 1A, 1B, 1C (each×4).
Sheets: 20 (4×5).
Imprint: Right-hand corner, bottom margin.
Withdrawn: 31.8.96.

632 St. Catherine's Church, Port Erin

633 European Robin on Holly Branch

634 St. Peter's Church and Wild Flowers

635 Hedgehog hibernating under Farm Machinery

Christmas

(Des Colleen Corlett. Litho BDT)

1995 (10 Oct). P 14 (C).

668	**632**	19p. multicoloured	55	55
669	**633**	23p. multicoloured	70	70
670	**634**	42p. multicoloured	1·50	1·50
671	**635**	50p. multicoloured	1·70	1·70
668/71	*Set of 4*		4·00	4·00
	First Day Cover			4·50
	Presentation Pack		4·50	
	Set of 4 Gutter Pairs		8·00	

Plate Nos.: All values 1A, 1B, 1C (each×4).
Sheets: 40 (2 panes 5×4) Imprint: Right-hand corner, bottom margin.
Withdrawn: 9.10.96.

Year Pack 1995

1995 (10 Oct). Comprises Nos. 629/71 (price £19).
Year Pack .... 42·00
　Withdrawn: 31.12.96.

Post Office Yearbook

1995 (Oct). Comprises Nos. 629/38, 639/40 in sheets of 10 and 641/71 (price £21).
Yearbook .... 45·00
　Sold out: By 5.97.

636 Langness Lighthouse

637 Point of Ayre Lighthouse

638 Chicken Rock Lighthouse

639 Calf of Man Lighthouse

640 Douglas Head Lighthouse

641 Maughold Head Lighthouse

Lighthouses

(Des D. Swinton. Litho Questa)

1996 (24 Jan). P 14 (C).

672	**636**	20p. multicoloured	50	50
		a. Booklet pane. No. 672×4 with margins all round	2·20	
673	**637**	24p. multicoloured	60	60
		a. Booklet pane. No. 673×4 with margins all round	3·00	
674	**638**	30p. multicoloured	90	90
		a. Booklet pane. Nos. 674 and 676, each×2, with margins all round	3·75	
675	**639**	36p. multicoloured	1·00	1·00
		a. Booklet pane. Nos. 675 and 677, each×2, with margins all round	4·00	
676	**640**	41p. multicoloured	1·10	1·10
677	**641**	42p. multicoloured	1·20	1·20
672/7	*Set of 6*		5·00	5·00
	First Day Cover			5·50
	Presentation Pack		5·50	
	Set of 6 Gutter Pairs		10·00	

Plate Nos.: All values 1A, 1B (each×5).
Sheets: 40 (2 panes 4×5) 20p., 30p., 41p.; (2 panes 5×4) others.
Imprint: Central, left-hand margin (20p., 30p., 41p.) or central, bottom margin (others).
Withdrawn: 22.1.97.

642 White Manx Cat and Celtic Interlaced Ribbons

643 Cat and Union Jack Ribbons

644 Cat on Rug in German Colours, Mouse and Brandenburg Gate

645 Cat, U.S.A. Flag and Statue of Liberty

646 Cat, Map of Australia and Kangaroo

647 Cat and Kittens (*Illustration reduced. Actual size 100×71 mm*)

Manx Cats

(Des Nancy Corkish. Litho BDT)

1996 (14 Mar). P 13×13 (No. **MS**683) or 14 (others), both comb.

678	642	20p. multicoloured	50	50
679	643	24p. multicoloured	60	60
680	644	36p. multicoloured	90	90
681	645	42p. multicoloured	1·10	1·10
682	646	48p. multicoloured	1·20	1·20
678/82 Set of 5			4·00	4·00
First Day Cover				5·00
Presentation Pack			5·00	
Stamp Cards (set of 5)			2·50	6·50
MS683 100×71 mm. **647** £1·50, multicoloured			4·00	4·00
First Day Cover				4·50
Presentation Pack			4·50	

For No. **MS**683 with 'CAPEX '96' logo see No. **MS**712.
Plate Nos.: All values 1A, 1B (each×4).
Sheets: 10 (2×5).
Imprint: Central, left-hand margin.
Withdrawn: 13.3.97.

648 Douglas Borough Arms

Centenary of Douglas Borough

(Des Colleen Corlett. Litho BDT)

1996 (14 Mar). Self-adhesive. Die-cut P 9×10.

684	648	(20p.) multicoloured	70	1·00
First Day Cover				1·50
Presentation Pack			1·50	

No. 684 was printed in sheets of 40, each stamp surrounded by white backing paper divided by roulettes. The actual stamps are separated from the backing paper by die-cut perforations. It was initially sold for 20p. and was only valid for postage within the Isle of Man.
Plate Nos.: 1A, 1B (each×4).
Sheets: 40 (8×5).
Imprint: Right-hand corner, bottom margin.
Withdrawn: 30.11.98.

651 Sir Winston Churchill (cadet schooner)

653 Tynwald I (paddle-steamer), 1846

657 Francis Drake (ketch)

Ships

(Des A. Theobald. Litho Walsall)

1996 (21 Apr). As Nos. 541, 543 and 547, but smaller as T **651**/7. P 14 (C).

687	651	4p. multicoloured	20	15
		a. Booklet pane. Nos. 687, 689 and 693, each×2	10·00	
689	653	20p. multicoloured	60	70
693	657	24p. multicoloured	90	90
687/93 Set of 3			1·50	1·60
First Day Cover				2·50
Presentation Pack			2·50	

The 20p. and 24p. show the positions of the face value and Queens head reversed.
Plate Nos.: All values 1A, 1B (each×4).
Sheets: 100 (10×10).
Imprint: Right-hand corner, bottom margin.
Withdrawn: 30.11.98.

665 Princess Anne (President, Save the Children Fund) and Children

666 Queen Elizabeth II and People of the Commonwealth

Europa. Famous Women

(Des D. Miller. Litho BDT)

1996 (21 Apr). P 14 (C).

701	665	24p. multicoloured	70	75
702	666	30p. multicoloured	90	1·00
701/2 Set of 2			1·60	1·70
First Day Cover				2·20
Presentation Pack			3·50	

The background designs of Nos. 701/2 continue onto the vertical sheet margins.
Plate Nos.: Both values 1A, 1B (each×4).
Sheets: 10 (2×5).
Withdrawn: 20.4.97.

667 Alec Bennett

668 Stanley Woods

669 Artie Bell

670 Joey and Robert Dunlop

671 R.A.F. Red Arrows Display Team (*Illustration reduced. Actual size 100×70 mm*)

Tourist Trophy Motorcycle Races. Irish Winners

(Des J. Dunne. Litho Questa)

1996 (30 May). P 14 (C).

703	**667**	20p. multicoloured	60	60
704	**668**	24p. multicoloured	75	75
705	**669**	45p. multicoloured	1·00	1·00
706	**670**	60p. multicoloured	1·75	1·75
703/6 Set of 4			3·75	3·75
First Day Cover				4·25
Presentation Pack			4·00	
Souvenir Folder			12·00	
Set of 4 Gutter Pairs			7·50	
MS707 100×70 mm. **671** £1 multicoloured			3·00	3·00
First Day Cover				4·00
Presentation Pack			4·00	

The souvenir folder contains Nos. 703/7, together with the stamps and miniature sheet in similar designs issued by Ireland.
Plate Nos.: 20p. 1A, 1B (each×4); 24p. 1A (×4); 45p. 1C (×4); 60p. 1D (×4).
Sheets: 40 (2 panes 2×10).
Imprint: Right-hand corner, bottom margin.
Withdrawn: 29.5.97.

672 National Poppy Appeal Trophy

673 Manx War Memorial, Braddan

674 Poppy Appeal Collection Box

675 Royal British Legion Badge

75th Anniversary of Royal British Legion

(Des C. Abbott. Litho BDT)

1996 (8 June). P 14 (C).

708	**672**	20p. multicoloured	65	55
709	**673**	24p. multicoloured	70	60
710	**674**	42p. multicoloured	1·10	1·20
711	**675**	75p. multicoloured	2·00	2·00
708/11 Set of 4			4·00	4·00
First Day Cover				4·25
Presentation Pack			4·50	

Plate Nos.: 75p. 1A, 1B, 1C (each×4): others 1A (×4).
Sheets: 40 (8×5).
Imprint: Right-hand corner, bottom margin.
Withdrawn: 7.6.97.

'CAPEX '96' International Stamp Exhibition, Toronto

1996 (8 June). No. **MS**683 additionally inscribed with 'CAPEX '96' exhibition logo on sheet margin.

MS712 100×71 mm. **647** £1.50, multicoloured		6·00	6·50
First Day Cover			8·00

Withdrawn: 31.7.97.

676 U.N.I.C.E.F. Projects in Mexico

677 Projects in Sri Lanka

678 Projects in Colombia

679 Projects in Zambia

680 Projects in Afghanistan

681 Projects in Vietnam

50th Anniv of U.N.I.C.E.F.

(Des C. Abbott. Litho Enschedé)

1996 (18 Sept). P 13½×14 (C).

713	**676**	24p. multicoloured	50	30
		a. Horiz pair. Nos. 713/14	1·30	1·20
714	**677**	24p. multicoloured	50	30
715	**678**	30p. multicoloured	60	60
		a. Horiz pair. Nos. 715/16	1·60	1·60
716	**679**	30p. multicoloured	60	60
717	**680**	42p. multicoloured	80	80
		a. Horiz pair. Nos. 717/18	2·50	2·50
718	**681**	42p. multicoloured	80	08
713/18 Set of 6			4·75	4·75
First Day Cover				5·50
Presentation Pack			5·25	

Plate Nos.: All values 1A, 1B (each×4).
Sheets: 40 (10×4). The two designs for each value printed together, se-tenant, in horizontal pairs throughout the sheets.
Imprint: Right-hand corner, bottom margin.
Withdrawn: 17.9.97.

682 Labrador

683 Border Collie

684 Dalmatian

685 Mongrel

686 English Setter   **687** Alsatian

688 Dogs at Work (Illustration reduced. Actual size 100×71 mm)

Dogs

(Des Colleen Corlett. Litho Questa)

1996 (18 Sept). P 13½×14 (No. **MS**725) or 14½ (others), both comb.

719	**682**	20p. multicoloured	60	55
		a. Booklet pane. No. 719×4 with margins all round	2·00	
720	**683**	24p. multicoloured	70	65
		a. Booklet pane. No. 720×4 with margins all round	2·20	
721	**684**	31p. multicoloured	1·00	90
		a. Booklet pane. Nos. 721/4 with margins all round	3·75	
722	**685**	38p. multicoloured	1·10	1·10
723	**686**	43p. multicoloured	1·50	1·50
724	**687**	63p. multicoloured	2·00	2·00
719/24 Set of 6			6·25	6·25
First Day Cover				6·50
Presentation Pack			6·75	
MS725 100×71 mm. **688** £1.20, multicoloured			3·75	3·75
		a. Booklet pane. As No. **MS**725, but with additional white margins all round separated by roulette	4·00	
First Day Cover				4·25
Presentation Pack			4·50	

Plate Nos.: All values 1A (×4).
Sheets: 10 (2×5).
Imprint: Left-hand corner, bottom margin.
Withdrawn: 17.9.97.
MS725a is known with "AT WORK" omitted from the upper right corner of the pane.

689 'Snowman and Pine Trees' (David Bennett)

690 'Three-legged Father Christmas' (Louis White)

691 'Family around Christmas Tree' (Robyn Whelan)

692 'Father Christmas in Sleigh' (Claire Bradley)

Christmas. Children's Paintings

(Adapted Colleen Corlett. Litho Walsall)

1996 (2 Nov). P 14×14½ (C).

726	**689**	19p. multicoloured	55	50
727	**690**	23p. multicoloured	70	65
728	**691**	50p. multicoloured	1·60	1·60
729	**692**	75p. multicoloured	2·10	2·20
726/9 Set of 4			4·50	4·50
First Day Cover				5·00
Presentation Pack			5·00	

Plate Nos.: All values 1A, 1B (each×4).
Sheets: 40 (5×8).
Imprint: Right-hand corner, bottom margin.
Withdrawn: 1.11.97.

Year Pack 1996

1996 (Nov). Comprises Nos. 552 and 672/729 (price £19·50).
Year Pack ... 45·00
Withdrawn: 30.11.98.

Post Office Yearbook

1996 (Nov). Comprises Nos. 552 and 672/729 (price £21).
Yearbook ... 48·00
Withdrawn: 30.11.98.

693 Primroses and Cashtyl ny Ard

694 Lochtan Sheep and Lambs

695 Daffodils, Mallard and Ducklings

696 Little Grebe with Young and Frog on Lily Pad

Spring in Man

(Des Colleen Corlett. Litho BDT)

1997 (12 Feb). P 14 (C).

730	**693**	20p. multicoloured	50	50
731	**694**	24p. multicoloured	70	70
732	**695**	43p. multicoloured	1·10	1·10
733	**696**	63p. multicoloured	1·60	1·60
730/3 Set of 4			3·50	3·50
First Day Cover				4·25
Presentation Pack			4·25	
Set of 4 Gutter Pairs			7·00	

Plate Nos.: All values 1A, 1B (each×4).
Sheets: 40 (2 panes 5×4).
Imprint: Right-hand corner, bottom margin.
Withdrawn: 11.2.98.

697 Barn Owl   **698** Short-eared Owl   **699** Long-eared Owl

700 Little Owl   **701** Snowy Owl   **702** Eurasian Tawny Owl

703 Long-eared Owl (*Illustration reduced. Actual size 100×71 mm*)

Owls

(Des J. Paul. Litho BDT)

1997 (12 Feb). P 13 (No. **MS**740) or 14 (others), both comb.

734	**697**	20p. multicoloured	65	60
		a. Booklet pane. No. 734×4 with margins all round	1·60	
735	**698**	24p. multicoloured	80	75
		a. Booklet pane. No. 735×4 with margins all round	2·00	
736	**699**	31p. multicoloured	1·00	90
		a. Booklet pane. Nos. 736/9 with margins all round	3·75	
737	**700**	36p. multicoloured	1·20	1·10
738	**701**	43p. multicoloured	1·40	1·50
739	**702**	56p. multicoloured	1·60	1·70
734/9 Set of 6			6·00	6·00
First Day Cover				6·50
Presentation Pack			6·75	
Stamp Cards (set of 6)			2·75	7·00
MS740 100×71 mm. **703** £1·20 multicoloured			4·00	4·25
		a. Booklet pane. As No. **MS**740 but with additional white margins all round and with line of roulettes at left	4·75	
First Day Cover				5·50
Presentation Pack			5·00	

No. **MS**740 includes the 'HONG KONG '97' International Stamp Exhibition logo on the sheet margin.
Plate Nos.: All values 1A, 1B (each×4).
Sheets: 10 (5×2).
Imprint: Bottom, right-hand margin.
Withdrawn: 11.2.98.

704 Moddey Dhoo, Peel Castle   **705** Fairies in Tree and Cottage

706 Fairies at Fairy Bridge   **707** Giant Finn Maccoil and Calf of Man

708 The Buggane of St. Trinian's   **709** Fyonderee and Farm

Europa. Tales and Legends

(Des Colleen Corlett. Litho Enschedé)

1997 (24 Apr). P 13½×14 (C).

741	**704**	21p. multicoloured	55	55
742	**705**	25p. multicoloured	65	65
743	**706**	31p. multicoloured	85	85
744	**707**	36p. multicoloured	1·10	1·10
745	**708**	37p. multicoloured	1·10	1·10
746	**709**	43p. multicoloured	1·40	1·40
741/6 Set of 6			5·00	5·00
First Day Cover				5·50
Presentation Pack			5·75	

Nos. 742/3 include the 'EUROPA' emblem.
Plate Nos.: All values 1A, 1B, 1C, 1D (each×4).
Sheets: 10 (2×5).
Withdrawn: 23.4.98.

710 Sopwith Tabloid   **711** Grumman Tiger (1996 Schneider Trophy)

712 BAe ATP (15th anniv of Manx Airlines)   **713** BAe 146-200 (15th anniv of Manx Airlines)

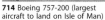

714 Boeing 757-200 (largest aircraft to land on Isle of Man)   **715** Farman Biplane (1st Manx flight, 1911)

716 Supermarine Spitfire   **717** Hawker Hurricane

Manx Aircraft

(Des R. Carter. Litho Questa)

1997 (24 Apr). P 14 (C).

747	**710**	21p. multicoloured	30	25
		a. Horiz pair. Nos. 747/8	90	90
748	**711**	21p. multicoloured	30	25
749	**712**	21p. multicoloured	35	25
		a. Horiz pair. Nos. 749/50	1·10	1·10
750	**713**	31p. multicoloured	35	25
751	**714**	31p. multicoloured	70	35
		a. Horiz pair. Nos. 751/2	1·50	1·50

752	**715**	31p. multicoloured	70	35
753	**716**	36p. multicoloured	75	40
		a. Horiz pair. Nos. 753/4	1·70	1·70
754	**717**	36p. multicoloured	75	40
747/54 *Set of 8*			5·00	5·00
First Day Cover				5·50
Presentation Pack			6·00	
Souvenir Folder (complete sheets)			20·00	

No. 752 is inscribed 'EARMAN' in error.
Plate Nos.: All values 1A (×4).
Sheets: 8 (2×4) the two designs for each value printed together, *se-tenant*, in horizontal pairs throughout the sheets, the backgrounds forming composite designs.
Withdrawn: 23.4.98.

718 14th Hole, Ramsey Golf Club

719 15th Hole, King Edward Bay Golf and Country Club

720 17th Hole, Rowany Golf Club

721 8th Hole, Castletown Golf Links

722 Golf Ball (*Illustration reduced. Actual size 100×71 mm*)

Golf

(Des D. Swinton. Litho Questa)

1997 (29 May). P 14 (C).

755	**718**	21p. multicoloured	50	50
		a. Booklet pane. No. 755×3 with margins all round	1·70	
756	**719**	25p. multicoloured	60	60
		a. Booklet pane. No. 756×3 with margins all round	2·00	
757	**720**	43p. multicoloured	1·10	1·10
		a. Booklet pane. Nos. 757/8 each×2 with margins all round	4·25	
758	**721**	50p. multicoloured	1·50	1·50
755/8 *Set of 4*			3·25	3·25
First Day Cover				4·00
Presentation Pack			3·75	
Set of 4 Gutter Pairs			6·50	
MS759 100×71 mm. **722** £1.30, multicoloured			3·50	3·50
		a. Booklet pane. As No. **MS**759, but with additional white margins all round	4·00	
First Day Cover				3·75
Presentation Pack			3·75	

No. **MS**759 includes the 'PACIFIC '97' International Stamp Exhibition logo on the sheet margin.
Plate Nos.: All values 1A, 1B (each×4).
Sheets: 40 (2 panes 5×4).
Imprint: Right-hand corner, bottom margin of each pane.
Withdrawn: 28.5.98.

723 Royal Yacht *Britannia* (*Illustration reduced. Actual size 130×90 mm*)

Return of Hong Kong to China

(Litho Walsall)

1997 (1 July). Sheet 130×90 mm containing stamp as No. 546 with changed imprint date. Wmk Mult Crown CA Diagonal. P 13×13½ (C).

MS760	**723**	23p. multicoloured	1·75	1·95
		Withdrawn: 30.6.98.		

No. **MS**760 was provided free to bureau customers with a standing order account. Additional copies could be purchased at face value. No presentation packs or first day covers were produced.

724 Steve Colley

725 Steve Saunders

726 Sammy Miller

727 Don Smith

F.I.M. 'Trial des Nations' Motorcycle Team Trials

(Des R. Organ. Litho Cartor)

1997 (17 Sept). P 13½ (C).

761	**724**	21p. multicoloured	55	50
762	**725**	25p. multicoloured	65	60
763	**726**	37p. multicoloured	1·20	1·00
764	**727**	44p. multicoloured	1·50	1·20
761/4 *Set of 4*			3·50	3·00
First Day Cover				4·00
Presentation Pack			4·50	
Set of 4 Gutter Pairs			7·00	

Plate Nos.: All values 1A, 1B (each×4).
Sheets: 40 (2 panes 5×4) 21p., 44p.; (2 panes 4×5) 25p., 37p.
Imprint: Central, gutter margin.
Withdrawn: 16.9.98.

728 Angel and Shepherd

729 Angel and King

730 The Nativity

Christmas

(Des Jennifer Toombs. Litho BDT)

1997 (3 Nov). P 14 (C).
765	**728**	20p. multicoloured	65	55
766	**729**	24p. multicoloured	75	70
767	**730**	63p. multicoloured	1·80	1·80
765/7	*Set of 3*		3·00	3·00
	First Day Cover			3·25
	Presentation Pack		3·50	

Plate Nos.: 20p., 24p. 1A (×5); 63p. 1A, 1B (each×5).
Sheets: 40 (8×5) 20p., 24p.; 20 (4×5) 63p.
Imprint: Central, left-hand margin.
Withdrawn: 2.11.98.

731 Engagement of Princess Elizabeth and Lieut. Philip Mountbatten, 1947

732 Wedding Photograph, 1947

733 At Ascot, 1952

734 Golden Wedding Photograph, 1997

735 Queen Elizabeth and Prince Philip at Peel, 1989
(*Illustration reduced. Actual size 100×72 mm*)

Golden Wedding of Queen Elizabeth and Prince Philip

(Des Colleen Corlett. Litho and die-stamped Questa)

1997 (3 Nov). P 14 (No. **MS**772) or 14×14½, both comb.
768	**731**	50p. sepia and gold	1·00	1·00
		a. Strip of 4. Nos. 768/71	5·00	5·00
769	**732**	50p. multicoloured	1·00	1·00
770	**733**	50p. multicoloured	1·00	1·00
771	**734**	50p. multicoloured	1·00	1·00
768/71	*Set of 4*		5·00	5·00
	First Day Cover			5·50
	Presentation Pack		5·50	
	Souvenir Folder (complete sheet and MS772)		21·00	
MS772	100×72 mm. **735** £1 multicoloured		3·00	3·00
	First Day Cover			3·50

Plate Nos.: 1A (x5).
Sheets: 16 (4×4). Nos. 768/71 were printed together, *se-tenant*, as horizontal or vertical strips of four throughout the sheets.
Imprint: Right-hand corner, bottom margin.
Withdrawn: 2.11.98.

Year Pack 1997

1997 (3 Nov). Comprises Nos. 730/72 (price £18.50).
Year Pack		37·00

Withdrawn: 30.11.98.

Post Office Yearbook

1997 (3 Nov). Comprises Nos. 730/72 (price £21).
Yearbook		40·00

Sold out: By 8.2001.

736 Bearded Iris

737 Daisy

738 Shamrock

739 Silver Jubilee Rose

740 Oriental Poppy

741 Heath Spotted Orchid

742 Cushag

743 Gorse

744 Princess of Wales Rose

745 Dog Rose

746 Fuchsia 'Lady Thumb'

747 Daffodil

748 Spear Thistle

753 Queen Elizabeth II and Queen Elizabeth the Queen Mother

Two Types of 4p.:—

    I. 'WSP' imprint aligns with 'N of 'MAN' (sheet stamps and 1998 booklet)
    II. WSP ends to right of 'N' of 'MAN' (1999 booklet)

Flowers

(Des Colleen Corlett (1p. to £1). Litho Cartor (£2.50), Walsall (others))

1998 (12 Feb)–**99**. P 13 (1p., 2p, 10p., 20p., 30p.) or 13×13½ (others), both comb.

773	**736**	1p. multicoloured (b)	10	10
774	**737**	2p. multicoloured (b)	10	10
775	**738**	4p. multicoloured (l) (a)	10	10
		a. Booklet pane. Nos. 775, 779 and 781, each×2 (a)	4·00	
		b. Type II (c)	50	60
		ba. Booklet pane. Nos. 775b×2, 780×3 and 782 (c)	3·00	
776	**739**	5p. multicoloured (c)	10	15
777	**740**	10p. multicoloured (b)	20	25
778	**741**	20p. multicoloured (b)	40	30
779	**742**	21p. multicoloured (a)	40	45
780	**743**	22p. multicoloured (c)	45	50
781	**744**	25p. multicoloured (a)	50	40
782	**745**	26p. multicoloured (c)	50	40
783	**746**	30p. multicoloured (b)	60	60
784	**747**	50p. multicoloured (a)	1·00	1·00
785	**748**	£1 multicoloured (a)	2·00	2·00
790	**753**	£2.50 multicoloured (b)	5·00	4·75
773/85, 790 Set of 14			10·50	10·00
First Day Covers (4)				13·50
Presentation Packs (4)			13·50	
Souvenir Folder (Nos. 773/5, 777/9, 781 and 783/5)			8·00	
Souvenir Folder (Nos. 773/85)			8·00	
Souvenir Folder (Nos. 773/85, 790 and 982)			16·00	
Gutter Pair (No. 790)			10·00	

Printings: (a) 12.2.98. Inscribed '1998'; (b) 2.7.98. Inscribed '1998'; (c) 26.4.99. Inscribed '1999'.
Plate Nos.: 4p., 21p., 25p., 50p., £1, £2.50 1A, 1B (each×4); others 1A (×4).
Sheets: 40 (2 panes 5×4) £2.50, 50 (10×5) (others). In addition to stamp booklets Nos. 775a and 775ba also come from separate special booklet sheets of 36 (6×5), each containing five strips.
Imprint: Central, bottom margin.

756 Viking Figurehead

757 Viking Longship at Sea

758 Viking Longship on Beach

759 Stern of Ship

760 Viking Ship at Peel Castle (*Illustration reduced. Actual size* 100×71 *mm*)

Viking Longships

(Des A. Bell. Litho BDT)

1998 (14 Feb). P 14 (C).

793	**756**	21p. multicoloured	55	50
794	**757**	25p. multicoloured	75	75
795	**758**	31p. multicoloured	90	90
796	**759**	75p. multicoloured	2·20	2·50
793/6 Set of 4			4·00	4·25
First Day Cover				4·75
Presentation Pack			5·00	
Set of 4 Gutter Pairs			8·00	
MS797 100×71 mm. **760** £1 multicoloured			3·00	3·00
First Day Cover				4·50
Presentation Pack			4·75	

Plate Nos.: All values 1A, 1B (each×4).
Sheets: 40 (2 panes 4×5).
Imprint: Central, right-hand margin.
Withdrawn: 13.2.99.

761 Bottle-nosed Dolphins

762 Basking Shark

763 Front View of Basking Shark

764 Minke Whale

765 Killer Whale and Calf

U.N.E.S.C.O. International Year of the Ocean

(Des J. Paul. Litho Questa)

1998 (14 Mar). P 14 (C).

798	**761**	10p. multicoloured	30	30
		a. Booklet pane. Nos. 798/9, each×3 and 3 labels with margins all round	2·75	
		b. Booklet pane. Nos. 798/9 and 800/2, each×2, and 1 central label with margins all round	7·00	
799	**762**	21p. multicoloured	50	50
800	**763**	25p. multicoloured	65	65
801	**764**	31p. multicoloured	75	75
802	**765**	63p. multicoloured	1·60	1·60
798/802 Set of 5			3·50	3·50
First Day Cover				4·25
Presentation Pack			5·00	
Souvenir Folder			25·00	
Stamp Cards (set of 5)			3·00	6·00

Plate Nos.: All values 1A, 1B (each×4).
Sheets: 10 (2×5).
Withdrawn: 13.3.99.

766 Locomotive No. 12 *Hutchinson*

767 Locomotive No. 10 *G. H. Wood*

768 Locomotive No. 11 *Maitland*

769 Locomotive No. 4 *Loch*

770 Pillar Box and Train at Douglas Station (25p.); Locomotive No. 1 *Sutherland* (£1) (*Illustration reduced. Actual size 143×105 mm*)

125th Anniversary of Isle of Man Steam Railway

(Des A. Peck. Litho Questa)

1998 (2 May). P 14½×14 (C).

803	**766**	21p. multicoloured	60	50
		a. Booklet pane. Nos. 803/6 with margins all round	3·50	
804	**767**	25p. multicoloured	70	60
805	**768**	31p. multicoloured	90	80
806	**769**	63p. multicoloured	1·60	1·60
803/6		Set of 4	3·50	3·25
		First Day Cover		3·50
		Presentation Pack	4·00	
		Souvenir Folder	25·00	
MS807		120×54 mm. **770** 25p. mult; £1 mult	3·00	3·00
		a. Booklet pane. As No. **MS**807, but 143×105 mm with additional margins showing diagram all round	3·00	
		First Day Cover		4·00
		Presentation Pack	4·00	

Booklet pane No. 803a exists in two versions, which differ in the order of the stamps within the block of four.
    Plate Nos.: All values 1A (×4).
    Sheets: 40 (5×8).
    Imprints: Right-hand corner, bottom margin.
    Withdrawn: 31.5.99.

771 Purple Helmets Display Team

772 Joey Dunlop

773 Dave Molyneux

774 Naomi Taniguchi

775 Mike Hailwood

Isle of Man T.T. Races and 50th Anniversary of Honda (motorcycle manufacturer)

(Des The Agency. Litho BDT)

1998 (1 June). P 14 (C).

808	**771**	21p. multicoloured	45	45
809	**772**	25p. multicoloured	55	55
810	**773**	31p. multicoloured	70	65
811	**774**	43p. multicoloured	1·10	1·00
812	**775**	63p. multicoloured	1·50	1·50
808/12		Set of 5	3·75	3·75
		First Day Cover		4·50
		Presentation Pack	4·50	
		Souvenir Folder	20·00	
		Set of 5 Gutter Pairs	7·00	

    Plate Nos.: All values 1A (×4).
    Sheets: 40 (2 panes 5×4 with double gutter).
    Withdrawn: 31.5.99.

776 Princess Diana wearing Protective Clothing, Angola

777 Receiving Award from United Cerebral Palsy Charity, New York, 1995

778 With Children, South Korea, 1992

779 Wearing Blue Jacket, July 1993

Diana, Princess of Wales Commemoration

(Litho Cartor)

1998 (19 June). P 13½×13 (C).

813	**776**	25p. multicoloured	50	30
		a. Strip of 4. Nos. 813/16	2·50	2·50
814	**777**	25p. multicoloured	50	30
815	**778**	25p. multicoloured	50	30
816	**779**	25p. multicoloured	50	30
813/16		Set of 4	2·50	2·50
		First Day Cover		3·00
		Presentation Pack	3·00	
		Souvenir Folder	20·00	

    Plate Nos.: 1A (×4).
    Sheets: 16 (4×4). Nos. 813/16 were printed together, *se-tenant*, as horizontal or vertical strips of four throughout the sheet.
    Withdrawn: 18.6.99.

780 Tynwald Day Ceremony

781 Traditional Dancers, Tynwald Fair

Europa. Festivals

(Des M. Thompson. Litho Cartor)

1998 (2 July). P 13×13½ (C).

817	**780**	25p. multicoloured	50	45
818	**781**	30p. multicoloured	1·10	1·20
817/18 *Set of 2*			1·50	1·50
First Day Cover				2·00
Presentation Pack			2·20	

Plate Nos.: Both values 1A (×4).
Sheets: 10 (2×5).
Withdrawn: 30.10.99.

782 Father Christmas at North Pole

783 Father Christmas checking List

784 Flying over Spring Valley Sorting Office

785 Passing through Baldrine Village

786 Father Christmas delivering Presents

Christmas. 'A Very Special Delivery'

(Des A. Bell. Litho Enschedé)

1998 (25 Sept). P 14½×14 (C).

819	**782**	20p. multicoloured	40	30
820	**783**	24p. multicoloured	50	45
821	**784**	30p. multicoloured	75	75
822	**785**	43p. multicoloured	95	95
823	**786**	63p. multicoloured	1·40	1·40
819/23 *Set of 5*			3·75	3·75
First Day Cover				4·50
Presentation Pack			4·50	
Set of 5 Gutter Pairs			7·50	

Plate Nos.: All values 1A (×4).
Sheets: 40 (2 panes 5×4).
Imprint: Right-hand corner, bottom margin.
Withdrawn: 30.10.99.

Year Pack 1998

1998 (25 Sept). Comprises Nos. 773/823 (price £18).

Year Pack		36·00

Sold out: 9.99.

Post Office Yearbook

1998 (25 Sept). Comprises Nos. 773/823 (price £21).

Yearbook		38·00

Sold out: 8.2000.

787 Large Oval Pillar Box, Kirk Onchan

788 Wall Box, Ballaterson

789 King Edward VII Pillar Box, Laxey Station

790 Wall Box, Spaldrick

791 Small Oval Pillar Box, Derby Road, Douglas

792 Wall Box, Baldrine Station

Local Post Boxes

(Des The Agency. Litho Walsall)

1999 (4 Mar). P 14 (C).

824	**787**	10p. multicoloured	25	25
825	**788**	20p. multicoloured	45	45
826	**789**	21p. multicoloured	50	50
827	**790**	25p. multicoloured	85	85
828	**791**	44p. multicoloured	1·50	1·50
829	**792**	63p. multicoloured	1·75	1·75
824/9 *Set of 6*			4·50	4·50
First Day Cover				5·00
Presentation Pack			5·50	
Set of 6 Gutter Pairs			9·00	

Plate Nos.: All values 1A, 1B (each×4).
Sheets: 50 (2 panes 5×5).
Imprint: Right-hand corner, bottom margin.
Withdrawn: 3.3.2000.

793 Cottage, Ballaglass Glen

794 Glen Maye Waterfall

Europa. Parks and Gardens

(Des Julia Ashby-Smyth. Litho BDT)

1999 (4 Mar). P 14 (C).

830	**793**	25p. multicoloured	70	70
831	**794**	30p. multicoloured	1·00	1·00
830/1 *Set of 2*			1·50	1·50
First Day Cover				2·00
Presentation Pack			2·00	

Plate Nos.: Both values 1A, 1B (each×4).
Sheets: 10 (5×2).
Withdrawn: 3.3.2000.

795 *Ann and James Ritchie*, Ramsey

796 *Sir William Hillary*, Douglas

797 *Ruby Clery*, Peel

798 *Herbert and Edith* (inshore lifeboat), Port Erin

799 1974 150th Anniversary 8p. Stamp

800 *Gough Ritchie II*, Port St. Mary

801 1991 Manx Lifeboats 21p. Stamp

802 Sir William Hillary (founder) (*Illustration reduced. Actual size 100×70 mm*)

175th Anniversary of Royal National Lifeboat Institution

(Des Mainstream Media (No. **MS**839), R. Tomlinson (others). Litho Questa)

1999 (4 Mar). P 13½×14 (No. **MS**839) or 14, both comb.

832	795	21p. multicoloured	50	50
		a. Booklet pane. Nos. 832/5 and 837, plus 4 printed labels, with margins all round	4·00	
		b. Booklet pane. Nos. 832/4, 836 and 838, plus 4 printed labels, with margins all round	5·00	
833	796	25p. multicoloured	55	55
834	797	37p. multicoloured	80	80
835	798	43p. multicoloured	90	90
836	799	43p. multicoloured	1·00	1·00
837	800	56p. multicoloured	1·20	1·20
838	801	56p. multicoloured	1·50	1·50
832/8		Set of 7	4·00	4·00
		First Day Cover (Nos. 832/5, 837)		4·50
		Presentation Pack (Nos. 832/5, 837)	5·00	
		Set of 5 Gutter Pairs (Nos. 832/5, 837)	8·00	
MS839		100×70 mm. **802** £1 multicoloured	4·00	4·00
		a. Booklet pane. As No. **MS**839, but with additional margins showing lifeboats all round	3·50	
		First Day Cover		4·50
		Presentation Pack	5·00	

Nos. 836 and 838 were available in £4.64 stamp booklets or as a single pane (with no stitch holes), obtainable from the Philatelic Bureau.

No. 832b includes an 'iBRA' Stamp Exhibition label and No. **MS**839 the 'Australia '99' World Stamp Exhibition emblem on the sheet margin.

Plate Nos.: All values 1A (×4).
Sheets: 40 (2 panes 5×4).
Withdrawn: 3.3.2000.

803 Winter

804 Spring

805 Summer

806 Autumn

Centenary of Yn Cheshaght Ghailckagh (Manx Gaelic Society). The Seasons

(Des C. Alexander. Litho Walsall)

1999 (11 May). P 14½×14 (C).

840	**803**	22p. multicoloured	60	60
841	**804**	26p. multicoloured	65	65
842	**805**	50p. multicoloured	1·10	1·10
843	**806**	63p. multicoloured	1·60	1·60
840/3		Set of 4	3·50	3·50
		First Day Cover		4·25
		Presentation Pack	4·50	
		Set of 4 Gutter Pairs	7·00	

Nos. 840/3 are inscribed 'Ellan Vannin', the Manx name for the Isle of Man.

Plate Nos.: All values 1A, 1B (each×4).
Sheets: 50 (2 panes 5×5).
Imprint: Right-hand corner, bottom margin.
Withdrawn: 10.5.2000.

807 Queen Victoria; King Edward VII; King George V; King Edward VIII; King George VI; Queen Elizabeth II (*Illustration reduced. Actual size 170×75 mm*)

British Monarchs of the 20th Century

(Des Colleen Corlett. Litho Walsall)

1999 (2 June). Sheet 170×75 mm. P 14 (C).

MS844	**807**	26p.×6, multicoloured	4·00	4·00
		First Day Cover		6·00
		Presentation Pack	5·00	
		Souvenir Folder (Nos. 824/9, **MS**844)	25·00	

Withdrawn: 1.6.2000.

808 Tilling-Stevens Double Deck Bus, 1922

809 Thornycroft BC Single Deck, 1928

810 Cumberland ADC 416 Single Deck, 1927

811 Straker-Squire Single Deck, 1914

812 Thornycroft A2 Single Deck, 1927

813 Leyland Lion LT9 Single Deck, 1938

Manx Buses

(Des P. Hearsey. Litho BDT)

1999 (18 June). P 14 (C).

845	**808**	22p. multicoloured		50	50
		a. Booklet pane. Nos. 845/6 and 847×2, with margins all round		2·50	
		b. Booklet pane. Nos. 845/6 and 848×2, with margins all round		3·50	
		c. Booklet pane. Nos. 845/6 and 849×2, with margins all round		4·00	
		d. Booklet pane. Nos. 845/6 and 850×2, with margins all round		4·50	
846	**809**	26p. multicoloured		55	55
847	**810**	28p. multicoloured		65	65
848	**811**	37p. multicoloured		1·25	1·25
849	**812**	38p. multicoloured		1·50	1·50
850	**813**	40p. multicoloured		1·75	1·75
845/50 Set of 6				4·75	4·75
First Day Cover					5·00
Presentation Pack				5·00	
Stamp Cards (set of 6)				3·00	7·50

Plate Nos.: All values 1A (×4).
Sheets: 25 (5×5).
Imprint: Central, bottom margin.
Withdrawn: 17.6.2000.

814 Miss Sophie Rhys-Jones

815 Leaving St. George's Chapel, Windsor

816 Prince Edward

817 Miss Sophie Rhys-Jones and Prince Edward

818 In Landau

Royal Wedding

(Des Catherine James. Litho BDT)

1999 (19 June–1 Sept). P 14 (C).

851	**814**	22p. multicoloured (a)		60	60
852	**815**	26p. multicoloured (b)		60	60
853	**816**	39p. multicoloured (a)		1·10	1·10
854	**817**	44p. multicoloured (a)		1·50	1·50
855	**818**	53p. multicoloured (b)		1·75	1·75
851/5 Set of 5				5·00	5·00
First Day Covers (2)					5·75
Presentation Pack				5·50	

Printings: (a) 19.6.99; (b) 1.9.99.
Plate Nos.: All values 1A, 1B (each×4).
Sheets: 25 (5×5).
Imprint: Central, bottom margin.
Withdrawn: 31.8.2000.

'PhilexFrance 99' International Stamp Exhibition, Paris

1999 (2 July). No. **MS**807 additionally inscribed with 'PhilexFrance' exhibition logo on sheet margin.

MS856 119×54 mm. **770** 25p. mult; £1 mult .... 8·00   8·00
Withdrawn: 1.7.2000.

819 St. Luke's Church, Baldwin

820 St. Mark's Chapel, Malew

821 St. German's Parish Church and Cathedral, Peel

822 Kirk Christ Church, Rushen

Christmas. Churches

(Des N. Sayle. Litho Cartor)

1999 (22 Sept). P 13½ (C).

857	**819**	21p. multicoloured		45	45
858	**820**	25p. multicoloured		60	60
859	**821**	30p. multicoloured		70	70
860	**822**	64p. multicoloured		1·50	1·50
857/60 Set of 4				3·00	3·00
First Day Cover					4·00
Presentation Pack				4·50	
Set of 4 Gutter Pairs				6·00	

Plate Nos.: All values 1A (×4).
Sheets: 40 (2 panes 4×5).
Imprint: Central, bottom margin.
Withdrawn: 21.9.2000.

823 'Massachusetts', 1967

824 'Words', 1968

825 I've Gotta Get a Message to You', 1968

826 'Ellan Vannin', 1998

827 'You Win Again', 1987

828 'Night Fever', 1978

829 'Immortality', 1998 (*Illustration reduced. Actual size* 119×108 *mm*)

830 'Stayin' Alive', 1978 (*Illustration reduced. Actual size* 119×108 *mm*)

Legends of Music. The Bee Gees (pop group)

(Des The Agency. Litho Cartor (Nos. 861/6), Walsall (No. **MS**867))

1999 (12 Oct). P 15 (No. **MS**867) or 13½, both comb.

861	**823**	22p. multicoloured	60	50
862	**824**	26p. multicoloured	70	65
863	**825**	29p. multicoloured	75	75
864	**826**	37p. multicoloured	90	90
865	**827**	38p. multicoloured	90	90
866	**828**	66p. multicoloured	1·50	1·70
861/6 *Set of 6*			4·75	5·00
First Day Cover				5·50
Presentation Pack			6·00	
Set of 6 Gutter Pairs			9·50	
Souvenir Folder (*complete sheets + CD*)			45·00	

MS867 Two sheets, each 119×108 mm. (a) **829** 60p. multicoloured (circular, 40 mm diam). (b) **830** 90p. multicoloured, (circular 40 mm diam) .... 8·00　10·00

Set of 2 sheets	8·00	10·00
First Day Cover		25·00

Sheets: 9 stamps and three labels, arranged 3×4, with the labels in the third horizontal row.
Withdrawn: 11.10.2000.

Year Pack 1999

1999 (12 Oct). Comprises Nos. 776, 780, 782, 824/35, 837 and 840/67 (price £25).

Year Pack .... 50·00
　　　Withdrawn: 2.8.2001.

Post Office Yearbook

1999 (12 Oct). Comprises Nos. 776, 780, 782, 824/35, 837 and **MS**839/67 (price £28·95).

Yearbook .... 58·00
　　　Sold out: 8.2000.

831 Sky at Sunset over Calf of Man (50p.); Sky at Dawn over Maughold Head (50p.); Constellations over Man at Start of New Millennium (£2) (*Illustration reduced. Actual size* 169×74 *mm*)

New Millennium

(Des The Agency. Litho Questa)

1999 (31 Dec). Sheet 169×74 mm. P 14½ (C).

MS868 **831** 50p.×2, £2 multicoloured	8·00	8·00
First Day Cover		10·00
Presentation Pack	9·00	

The first day cover has three cancellations, one on each stamp, running in a two minute sequence from 23.59 on 31 Dec 99 to 00.01 on 01 Jan 00.
　　　Withdrawn: 30.12.2000.
　　　A postcard showing **MS**868 was provided free to bureau customers with a standing order account.

832 Harrison's Chronometer, 1735, and Map

833 Daniel's Chronometer, 2000, and Clock Face

834 Harrison's Chronometer, 1767, Map and Clock

835 Mudge's Chronometer, 1769, and Steam Locomotives

836 Arnold's Chronometer, 1779, and Map of Africa

837 Earnshaw's Chronometer, 1780, and Map of Caribbean

'The Story of Time'

(Des E. Cassidy. Litho Cartor)

2000 (24 Jan). P 13×13½ (C).

869	**832**	22p. multicoloured	50	55
870	**833**	26p. multicoloured	55	60
871	**834**	29p. multicoloured	65	70
872	**835**	34p. multicoloured	90	90
873	**836**	38p. multicoloured	1·20	1·20
874	**837**	44p. multicoloured	1·50	1·50
869/74 *Set of 6*			5·00	5·00
First Day Cover				5·50
Presentation Pack			5·50	

Plate Nos.: 29p., 38p. 1A, 1B (each×4); others 1A (×4).
Sheets: 25 (5×5).
Imprint: Top left-hand margin and bottom right-hand margin.
Withdrawn: 23.1.2001.

838 Duke and Duchess of York on Wedding Day, 1923

839 Queen Elizabeth with Princess Elizabeth, 1940

840 King George VI and Queen Elizabeth visiting Troops, 1944

841 Queen Mother and Queen Elizabeth, 1954

842 Queen Mother with Prince Charles, 1985

843 Queen Mother, 1988

844 Queen Mother visiting Isle of Man (*Illustration reduced. Actual size 100×70 mm*)

'Queen Elizabeth the Queen Mothers Century'

(Des E.D.L. Litho BDT)

2000 (29 Feb). P 14 (C).

875	**838**	22p. multicoloured	50	55
		a. Horiz strip of 3. Nos. 875/7	2·00	2·00
876	**839**	26p. sepia and black	55	60
877	**840**	30p. sepia and black	65	70
878	**841**	44p. multicoloured	95	80
		a. Horiz strip of 3. Nos. 878/80	3·50	3·50
879	**842**	52p. multicoloured	1·00	1·00
880	**843**	64p. multicoloured	1·10	1·10
875/80 *Set of 6*			5·00	5·00
First Day Cover				5·75
Presentation Pack			5·50	
Souvenir Folder (complete sheets and **MS**881*)*			21·00	
MS881 100×70 mm. **844** £1 multicoloured			10·00	10·00
First Day Cover				3·00
Presentation Pack			3·00	

Plate Nos.: All values 1A (×4).
Sheets: 12 (3×4). Nos. 875/7 and 878/80 were each printed together, *se-tenant*, as horizontal strips of three throughout the sheets.
Withdrawn: 28.2.2001.
See also **MS**886.

845 Barn Swallow

846 Spotted Flycatcher

847 Eurasian Skylark

848 Yellowhammer

Endangered Species. Song Birds

(Des Catherine James. Litho Walsall)

2000 (5 May). P 14½ (C).

882	**845**	22p. multicoloured	50	55
		a. Strip of 4. Nos. 882/5	4·50	4·50
883	**846**	26p. multicoloured	55	60
884	**847**	64p. multicoloured	80	80
885	**848**	77p. multicoloured	1·00	1·00
882/5 *Set of 4*			4·50	4·50
First Day Cover				5·50
Presentation Pack			6·00	

Plate Nos.: All values 1A (×4).
Sheets: 20 (4×5). Nos. 882/5 were printed together, *se-tenant*, both horizontally and vertically, within the sheets.
Withdrawn: 4.5.2001.

'The Stamp Show 2000' International Stamp Exhibition, London

2000 (22 May). As No. **MS**881, but with 'The Stamp Show 2000' multicoloured logo added to the bottom sheet margin. P 14 (C).

MS886 100×70 mm. **844** £1 multicoloured		5·00	5·00

Withdrawn: 21.5.2001.

849 Lieut. John Quilliam and Admiral Lord Nelson, Battle of Trafalgar

850 Ensign Caesar Bacon and Duke of Wellington, Battle of Waterloo

851 Col. Thomas Leigh Goldie and Earl of Cardigan, Crimea

852 Bugler John Dunne and Sir Robert Baden-Powell, Boer War

853 George Kneale and Viscount Kitchener of Khartoum, First World War

854 First Officer Alan Watterson and Sir Winston Churchill, Second World War

855 Two Supermarine Spitfires (60p.); Spitfire on Ground, (60p.) (*Illustration reduced. Actual size 170×75 mm*)

Isle of Man at War

(Des P. Hannon (Nos. 887/92), P. Hearsey (No. **MS**893). Litho BDT)

2000 (22 May). P 15×14 (No. **MS**893) or 13, both comb.

887	**849**	22p. multicoloured	50	55
		a. Booklet pane. Nos. 887/91	4·75	
		b. Booklet pane. Nos. 887 and 890/2	5·00	
888	**850**	26p. multicoloured	55	60
889	**851**	36p. multicoloured	75	80
890	**852**	48p. multicoloured	1·00	1·10
891	**853**	50p. multicoloured	1·10	1·20
892	**854**	77p. multicoloured	1·50	1·60
887/92 *Set of 6*			4·75	5·25
First Day Cover				6·00
Presentation Pack			6·00	
MS893 170×75 mm. **855** 60p.×2 multicoloured			2·75	2·75
		a. Booklet pane. As No. **MS**893, but with line of roulettes at left	2·75	
First Day Cover				3·50
Presentation Pack			3·50	

MS893 commemorated the 60th anniversary of the Battle of Britain.
Plate Nos.: All values A1 (×4).
Sheets: 8 (2×4). Nos. 887/8, 889/90 and 891/2 were each printed in sheets containing vertical strips of the two designs separated by a gutter margin.
Imprint: Lower left-hand margin.
Withdrawn: 21.5.2001.

856 Prince William as a Child (22p.); With Queen Mother (26p.); As a teenager (45p.); With Prince Charles and Prince Harry (52p.); Wearings ski-suit (56p.) (*Illustration reduced. Actual size 170×75 mm*)

18th Birthday of Prince William

(Des The Agency. Litho BDT)

2000 (21 June). Sheet 170×75 mm. P 14 (C).

MS894 **856** 22p., 26p., 45p., 52p., 56p. multicoloured		5·00	4·50
First Day Cover			5·25
Presentation Pack		5·25	

Withdrawn: 20.6.2001.

857 Ballet Shoes and Painted Ceiling

858 Comedy Mask and Box Decoration

859 Drama Mask and Statue

860 Pantomime Dame with Wig and Mosaic

861 Opera Glasses and Decoration

862 Top Hat with Cane and Painted Ceiling

Centenary of Gaiety Theatre, Douglas

(Des The Agency. Litho BDT)

2000 (16 July). P 14 (C).

895	**857**	22p. multicoloured	50	55
896	**858**	26p. multicoloured	55	60
897	**859**	36p. multicoloured	75	80
898	**860**	45p. multicoloured	95	1·00
899	**861**	52p. multicoloured	1·10	1·20
900	**862**	65p. multicoloured	1·40	1·50
895/900 *Set of 6*			4·75	5·25
First Day Cover				6·25
Presentation Pack			6·25	
Stamp Cards (set of 6)			3·50	9·50

Plate Nos.: All values 1A (×4).
Sheets: 20 (4×5) with enlarged illustrated margin at left.
Imprint: Central, right-hand margin.
Withdrawn: 14.7.2001.

863 Map of Great Britain, Union Jack and Liner

864 Sydney Opera House, Australian Flag and Map

865 New Zealand Map and Flag

866 Map of Buenos Aires and Waterfront

867 U.S. Flag, Map of Boston and Harbour

868 South African Flag, Map and Table Mountain

'BT Global Challenge' Round the World Yacht Race

(Des The Agency. Litho Cartor)

2000 (10 Sept). P 13½ (C).

901	**863**	22p. multicoloured	50	55
902	**864**	26p. multicoloured	55	60
903	**865**	36p. multicoloured	75	80
904	**866**	40p. multicoloured	85	90
905	**867**	44p. multicoloured	95	1·00
906	**868**	65p. multicoloured	1·40	1·50
901/6 *Set of 6*			4·50	4·75
First Day Cover				5·75
Presentation Pack			5·75	
Set of 6 Gutter Pairs			9·00	

Plate Nos.: All values 1A (×4).
Sheets: 40 (2 panes 2×10).
Imprint: Centre, side margins.
Withdrawn: 8.9.2001.

869 Sailing and Holiday Tours Poster, 1925

870 Isle of Man for Happy Holidays

871 Woman in Swimsuit standing on Isle of Man, 1929

872 Stewardess and Ferry

873 'Isle of Man for Holidays 1931' and Ferry

170th Anniversary of Steam Packet Company. Tourism Posters

(Des The Agency. Litho Cartor)

2000 (6 Oct). P 13½ (C).

907	869	22p. multicoloured	50	55
908	870	26p. multicoloured	55	60
909	871	36p. multicoloured	75	80
910	872	45p. multicoloured	1·50	1·50
911	873	65p. multicoloured	1·90	2·00
907/11 *Set of 5*			4·75	5·00
First Day Cover				5·50
Presentation Pack			5·50	

Plate Nos.: All values 1A (×4).
Sheets: 20 (5×4).
Imprint: Centre, side margins.
Withdrawn: 5.10.2001.

874 Girl with Christingle Candle

875 Children dancing around Christmas Tree

876 'Building Europe'

877 Girl hugging Teddy Bear

878 Children with Stars

Christmas and Europa

(Des R. Wetherall (36p. after J.-P. Cousin). Litho Questa)

2000 (7 Nov). P 14 (C).

912	874	21p. multicoloured	45	50
913	875	25p. multicoloured	55	60
914	876	36p. multicoloured	75	80
		a. Sheetlet of 10	7·50	
915	877	45p. multicoloured	1·50	1·50
916	878	65p. multicoloured	1·90	2·00
912/16 *Set of 5*			4·75	5·00
First Day Cover				5·50
Presentation Pack			5·50	
Set of 5 Gutter Pairs			7·50	

Plate Nos.: All values 1A (×4).
Sheets: 40 (2 panes 4×5); 36p. also 10 (5×2).
Imprint: Right-hand corner, bottom margin.
Withdrawn: 6.11.2001.

Year Pack 2000

2000 (7 Nov). Comprises Nos. **MS**868/85 and 887/916 (price £27).

Year Pack ...... 55·00

Sold out: By 10.2002.

Post Office Yearbook

2000 (7 Nov). Comprises Nos. **MS**868/85 and 887/916 (price £28.95).

Yearbook ...... 58·00

Sold out: By 10.2003.

879 Wyon Medal, Penny Black and Queen Victoria

880 Great Exhibition Medal and Albert Tower, Ramsey

881 Silver Coin and *Great Britain* (early steamship)

882 Manx Coin of 1839, *Oliver Twist* and St. Thomas' Church, Douglas

883 Silver Coin of 1887, Arrival of First Train at Vancouver and Jubilee Lamp Standard

884 Silver Coin of 1893, Joe Mylchreest at Kimberley Diamond Mine and Foxdale Clock Tower

Death Centenary of Queen Victoria

(Des Mannin Design. Litho Walsall)

2001 (22 Jan). P 13½ (C).

917	879	22p. multicoloured	50	55
918	880	26p. multicoloured	55	60
919	881	34p. multicoloured	75	80
920	882	39p. multicoloured	1·10	1·20
921	883	40p. multicoloured	1·10	1·20
922	884	52p. multicoloured	1·60	1·70
917/22 *Set of 6*			5·25	5·50
First Day Cover				6·00
Presentation Pack			6·00	

Plate Nos.: All values 1A (×4).
Sheets: 20 (4×5).
Imprint: Right-hand corner, bottom margin.
Withdrawn: 21.1.2002.

885 St. Patrick and Snakes (*Illustration reduced. Actual size 110×85 mm*)

Chinese New Year (Year of the Snake)

(Des The Agency. Litho and die-stamped Questa)

2001 (22 Jan). Sheet 110×85 mm. P 13½×14 (C).

MS923	885	£1 multicoloured	3·00	3·50
First Day Cover				4·00
Presentation Pack			4·00	

No. **MS**923 includes the 'Hong Kong 2001' logo on the sheet margin.
    Withdrawn: 21.1.2002.

886 White-tailed Bumble Bee

887 Seven-spot Ladybird

888 Lesser Mottled Grasshopper

889 Manx Robber Fly

890 Elephant Hawkmoth

Insects

(Des R. Lewington. Litho Questa)

2001 (1 Feb). P 14 (C).

924	886	22p. multicoloured	50	55
925	887	26p. multicoloured	55	60
926	888	29p. multicoloured	80	90
927	889	59p. multicoloured	1·50	1·60
928	890	66p. multicoloured	1·90	2·00
924/8 Set of 5			5·00	5·25
First Day Cover				5·00
Presentation Pack			5·50	

Plate Nos.: All values 1A, 1B (each×4).
Sheets: 10 (5×2).
Imprint: Right-hand corner, bottom margin.
Withdrawn: 31.1.2002.

891 Letter-carrier, 1805

892 Postman, 1859

893 Postman, 1910

894 Postman, 1933

895 Postman, 1983

896 Postman, 2001

Postal Uniforms

(Des Colleen Corlett. Litho BDT)

2001 (18 Apr). P 14 (C).

929	891	22p. multicoloured	50	55
930	892	26p. multicoloured	55	60
931	893	36p. multicoloured	75	80
932	894	39p. multicoloured	1·10	1·20
933	895	40p. multicoloured	1·10	1·20
934	896	66p. multicoloured	1·90	2·00
929/34 Set of 6			5·50	5·75
First Day Cover				6·00
Presentation Pack			6·00	

Plate Nos.: All values 1A (×4).
Sheets: 20 (5×4).
Imprint: Central, bottom margin.
Withdrawn: 17.4.2002.

897 1967–70 Great Britain ½d. Machin (29p.); 1952–1954 Great Britain 6d. Wilding (34p.); 1971 Isle of Man 2½p. Regional (37p.); 1958–68 Isle of Man 4d. Regional (50p.). (*Illustration reduced. Actual size 170×75 mm*)

75th Birthday of Queen Elizabeth II

(Des The Agency. Litho BDT)

2001 (18 Apr). Sheet 170×75 mm. P 14 (C).

MS935	897	29p., 34p., 37p., 50p. multicoloured	3·75	4·00
First Day Cover				4·50
Presentation Pack			4·50	

Withdrawn: 17.4.2002.

898 Joey Dunlop on Rea Yamaha, Parliament Square, 1977 TT Races

899 At Governor's, 1983 TT Races

900 Leaving Ramsey, 1988
TT Races

901 On Honda motorbike, 1991

902 On 250cc Honda at
Ballaspur, 1999

903 On the Mountain

Joey Dunlop (motorcycle champion) Commemoration

(Des Ruth Sutherland. Litho BDT)

2001 (17 May). P 14 (C).

936	**898**	22p. multicoloured	50	55
937	**899**	26p. multicoloured	55	60
938	**900**	36p. multicoloured	75	80
939	**901**	45p. multicoloured	95	1·00
940	**902**	65p. multicoloured	1·40	1·50
941	**903**	77p. multicoloured	1·60	1·70
936/41 *Set of 6*			5·25	5·75
First Day Cover				6·50
Presentation Pack			7·00	
Souvenir Folder (containing 5 sets of Nos. 936/41, 6				
Postcards (PC20/5) and special commemorative cover)..			40·00	
Set of 6 Gutter Pairs			10·50	

Plate Nos.: All values 1A (each×5).
Sheets: 20 (2 panes 2×5).
Withdrawn: 16.5.2002.
On 3 June 2013 Nos. 940/1, each×6, were issued as an illustrated sheetlet of 12 stamps (price £9.97).

904 'The Manx Derby, 1627'
(Johnny Jonas)

905 'Post Haste' (Johnny Jonas)

906 'Red Rum' (Hamilton-Rennick)

907 'Hyperion' (Sir Alfred Munnings)

908 'Isle of Man' (Johnny Jonas)

Horse Racing Paintings

(Des The Agency. Litho Cartor)

2001 (18 May). P 13½ (C).

942	**904**	22p. multicoloured	50	55
943	**905**	26p. multicoloured	55	60
944	**906**	36p. multicoloured	85	80
945	**907**	52p. multicoloured	1·50	1·60
946	**908**	63p. multicoloured	1·70	1·70
942/6 *Set of 5*			4·50	4·75
First Day Cover				5·00
Presentation Pack			5·00	

Plate Nos: All values 1A (×4).
Sheets: 20 (4×5).
Withdrawn: 17.5.2002.

909 Beef

910 Queenies with
Salmon Caviar

911 Seafood

912 Lamb

913 Kipper Tart

914 Lemon Tart with
Raspberries

Europa. Water, a Natural Treasure, Local Dishes prepared by Kevin Woodford

(Des The Agency. Litho BDT)

2001 (10 Aug). P 14 (C).

947	**909**	22p. multicoloured	50	55
948	**910**	26p. multicoloured	55	60
		a. Panel at foot of stamp in pale lilac (R. 2/1)	20·00	
		b. Sheetlet of 10	5·50	
949	**911**	36p. multicoloured	75	80
		b. Sheetlet of 10	7·75	
950	**912**	45p. multicoloured	1·20	1·20
951	**913**	50p. multicoloured	1·30	1·50
952	**914**	66p. multicoloured	1·90	2·00
947/52 *Set of 6*			5·75	6·25
First Day Cover				6·50
Presentation Pack			7·00	
Recipe Cards (set of 6)			20·00	

The 26p. and 36p. show the inscription 'EUROPA 2001' at bottom right.
On Nos. 947/52 the panel at the foot of each stamp, on which the designer and printer imprints occur, is normally white. On R. 2/1 of the 26p. in sheets of 25 this panel is in pale lilac.
The set of recipe cards show a strip of four stamps plus label and first day of issue postmark.
Plate Nos.: All values 1A (×4).
Sheets: 30 (6×5) containing 25 stamps and five stamp-size labels, different for each value, in the first vertical row; 26p., 36p. also 10 (2×10).
Withdrawn: 9.8.2002.

915 Castletown Police Station

916 Leafield (semi-detached house)

917 'The Red House'
(Baillie Scott's home)

918 'Ivydene' (detached house)

919 Onchan Village Hall

The Architecture of Mackay Hugh Baillie Scott

(Des Tracey Harding. Litho Cartor)

2001 (3 Sept). P 13½ (C).

953	**915**	22p. multicoloured	50	55
954	**916**	26p. multicoloured	55	60
955	**917**	37p. multicoloured	80	85
956	**918**	40p. multicoloured	1·00	1·10
957	**919**	80p. multicoloured	2·00	2·10
953/7 *Set of 5*			4·50	4·75
First Day Cover				5·50
Presentation Pack			6·00	

Nos. 953/7 are inscribed 'HUGH MACKAY' in error.
Plate Nos.: All values 1A (×4).
Sheets: 20 (4×5) with a further view of the building depicted on the sheet margins.
Withdrawn: 2.9.2002.

'Hafnia '01' International Stamp Exhibition, Denmark

2001 (16 Oct). No. **MS935** additionally inscribed with 'Hafnia '01' logo in red on sheet margin.

MS958 170×75 mm. **897a** 29p., 34p., 37p., 50p.			
multicoloured		6·50	7·00
First Day Cover			7·50

Sold out: By 8.2003.

920 Royal Refreshments at Glasgow

921 Queen on Visit to Lancaster

922 Queen with Labradors, Sandringham

923 Queen meeting Scottish Korean War Veterans

924 Queen at Desk, Sandringham

925 Queen with Bouquet, Oxford

Golden Jubilee (1st issue). 'The Daily Life of the Queen—An Artists Diary' (paintings by Michael Noakes)

(Adapted The Agency. Litho Questa)

2001 (29 Oct)–**02**. P 14 (C).

959	**920**	22p. multicoloured (a)	50	55
		a. Booklet pane. Nos. 959/61 with margins all round (b)	2·20	
960	**921**	26p. multicoloured (a)	55	60
961	**922**	39p. multicoloured (a)	85	90
962	**923**	40p. multicoloured (a)	85	90
		a. Booklet pane. Nos. 962/4 with margins all round (b)	4·00	
963	**924**	45p. multicoloured (a)	95	1·00
964	**925**	65p. multicoloured (a)	1·90	2·00
959/64 *Set of 6*			5·00	5·50
First Day Cover				6·00
Presentation Pack			6·25	
Souvenir Folder (complete sheets)			42·00	

See also Nos. 970/**MS**975.
Printings: (a) 29.10.2001; (b) 6.2.2002.
Plate Nos.: All values 1A (×4).
Sheets: 8 (4×2) with enlarged illustrated margin at left.
Withdrawn: 28.10.2002 (sheets).

926 Christmas Tree Wall Decoration

927 Traditional Wreath

928 Table Decoration

929 Topiary Tree

930 Contemporary Wreath

Christmas. Decorations by Isle of Man Floreat Workshop

(Des The Agency. Litho Questa)

2001 (5 Nov). P 14×14½ (C).

965	**926**	21p. multicoloured	45	50
966	**927**	25p. multicoloured	55	60
967	**928**	37p. multicoloured	1·00	1·10
968	**929**	45p. multicoloured	1·20	1·30
969	**930**	65p. multicoloured	1·90	2·00
965/9 *Set of 5*			4·75	5·00
First Day Cover				5·25
Presentation Pack			5·50	
Set of 5 Gutter Pairs			9·50	

Plate Nos.: All values 1A, 1B (each×4).
Sheets: 25 (5×5) with horizontal rows of stamps interspersed by rows of inscribed greetings labels. The 21p. and 25p. values were also available with personal photographs shown on these labels.
Withdrawn: 4.11.2002.

Year Folder 2001

2001 (5 Nov). Comprises Nos. 917/57 and 959/69 (price £23).

Year Folder	45·00

Sold out: By 11.2003.

Year Pack 2001

2001 (5 Nov). Comprises Nos. 917/57 and 959/69 (price £28).

Year Pack	55·00

Sold out: By 11.2003.

Post Office Yearbook

2001 (5 Nov). Comprises Nos. 917/57 and 959/69 (price £29·95).
Yearbook .... 60·00
    Sold out: By 4.2002.

931 'The Coronation, 1953' (Terence Cuneo)
932 'Queen Elizabeth II as Colonel-in-Chief of Grenadier Guards on Imperial, 1962' (Terence Cuneo)
933 'Queen Elizabeth II in Evening Dress, 1981' (June Mendoza)

934 'Queen Elizabeth II in Garter Robes, 2000' (Chen Yan Ning)
935 'The Royal Family' (John Wonnacott)

936 Sculpture of Queen Elizabeth II by David Cregeen (*Illustration reduced. Actual size 110×85 mm*)

Golden Jubilee (2nd issue). Royal Paintings

(Des The Agency. Litho and die-stamped Questa)

2002 (6 Feb). P 14½×14 (No. **MS**975) or 14 (others), both comb.

970	**931**	50p. multicoloured	80	60
		a. Vert strip of 5. Nos. 970/4	5·00	5·50
		b. Booklet pane. Nos. 970/2 with margins all round	3·50	
971	**932**	50p. multicoloured	80	60
972	**933**	50p. multicoloured	80	60
973	**934**	50p. multicoloured	80	60
		b. Booklet pane. Nos. 973/4 with margins all round	2·40	
974	**935**	50p. multicoloured	80	60
970/4		*Set of 5*	5·00	5·50
		First Day Cover		6·00
		Presentation Pack	6·00	
		Souvenir Folder (*complete sheet*)	20·00	
		Gutter Strip	10·50	

MS975 110×85 mm. **936** £1 multicoloured .... 2·00 2·10
   b. Booklet pane. As No. **MS**975,
   but 152×97 mm with a line of
   roulettes at left .... 2·40 2·50
First Day Cover .... 5·50
Presentation Pack .... 3·00
    Plate Nos.: 1A (×4).
    Sheets: 20 (2 panes 2×5). Nos. 970/4 were printed together, *se-tenant*, as vertical strips of five. The panes are separated by an enlarged vertical gutter illustrated with further royal portraits. Withdrawn: 5.2.2003.

937 Cycling
938 Running

939 Javelin and High Jump
940 Swimming

941 Decathlon
942 Wheelchair Racing

17th Commonwealth Games, Manchester. Photographic Montages

(Des The Agency. Litho BDT)

2002 (11 Mar). P 14 (C).

976	**937**	22p. multicoloured	45	50
977	**938**	26p. multicoloured	50	55
978	**939**	29p. multicoloured	60	65
979	**940**	34p. multicoloured	70	75
980	**941**	40p. multicoloured	1·00	1·10
981	**942**	45p. multicoloured	1·10	1·20
976/81		*Set of 6*	4·25	4·75
		First Day Cover		5·25
		Presentation Pack	5·50	
		Set of 6 Gutter Pairs	8·50	

    Plate Nos.: All values 1A (×4).
    Sheets: 9 (3×3) with an illustrated gutter between the second and third horizontal rows, and an enlarged right margin. Withdrawn: 10.3.2003.

943 'Queen Elizabeth the Queen Mother' (Johnny Jonas)

Queen Elizabeth the Queen Mother Commemoration

(Des The Agency. Litho Cartor)

2002 (23 Apr). P 13×13½ (C).

982	**943**	£3 multicoloured	6·00	6·25
		First Day Cover		7·00
		Presentation Pack	7·00	

    No. 982 was retained in use as a definitive stamp.
    Plate Nos.: 1A (×4).
    Sheets: 10 (5×2).

944 Ireland v Czech Republic

945 England v Greece

946 Italy v Belgium

947 France v Portugal

948 England v Brazil

949 France v Japan

World Cup Football Championship, Japan and South Korea

(Des E. Cassidy. Litho Cartor)

2002 (1 May). P 13½ (C).

983	**944**	22p. multicoloured	45	50
984	**945**	26p. multicoloured	50	55
985	**946**	39p. multicoloured	80	85
986	**947**	40p. multicoloured	80	85
987	**948**	66p. multicoloured	1·20	1·40
988	**949**	68p. multicoloured	1·40	1·50
983/8 Set of 6			5·00	5·50
First Day Cover				6·00
Presentation Pack			6·25	

Plate Nos.: All values 1A (×4).
Sheets: 25 (5×5).
Withdrawn: 30.4.2003.

950 'Monk's Bridge, Ballasalla'

951 'Laxey'

952 'Langness Lighthouse'

953 'King William's College'

954 'The Mull Circle and Bradda Head'

Watercolours by Toni Onley

(Des The Agency. Litho Cartor)

2002 (1 May). P 13½ (C).

989	**950**	22p. multicoloured	45	50
990	**951**	26p. multicoloured	50	55
991	**952**	37p. multicoloured	75	80
992	**953**	45p. multicoloured	1·10	1·20
993	**954**	65p. multicoloured	1·50	1·60
989/93 Set of 5			4·25	4·50
First Day Cover				5·25
Presentation Pack			5·50	

Plate Nos.: All values 1A (×4).
Sheets: 25 (5×5).
Withdrawn: 30.4.2003.

Golden Jubilee Celebrations

2002 (4 June). No. **MS**975 additionally inscribed 'THE ISLE OF MAN CELEBRATES THE JUBILEE 4th June 2002' in purple on the sheet margin.

MS994 110×85 mm. **935a** £1 multicoloured			6·50	6·50

Withdrawn: 3.6.2003.

955 Magenta Flower on Yellow Background

956 Green Flower on Pink Background

957 Purple Flower on Green Background

958 Maroon Flower on Brown Background

959 Red Flower on Blue Background

960 Orange Flower on Yellow Background

Memories of the Isle of Man

(Des Sir Paul McCartney. Litho Walsall)

2002 (1 July). P 13½×13 (C).

995	**955**	22p. multicoloured	45	50
996	**956**	26p. multicoloured	50	55
997	**957**	29p. multicoloured	60	65
998	**958**	52p. multicoloured	1·00	1·10
999	**959**	63p. multicoloured	1·20	1·40
1000	**960**	77p. multicoloured	1·50	1·60
995/1000 Set of 6			5·25	5·75
First Day Cover				6·25
Presentation Pack			6·50	
Souvenir Folder (complete sheets and first day cover)			50·00	

Plate Nos.: All values 1A (×4).
Sheets: 8 (4×2) with inscribed margins and a photograph of Sir Paul McCartney at left.
Withdrawn: 30.6.2003.

961 Manx Milestone (Mrs. B. Trimble)

962 Plough Horses (Miss D. Flint)

963 Manx Emblem (Ruth Nicholls)

964 Loaghtan Sheep (Diana Burford)

965 Fishing Fleet, Port St. Mary (Phil Thomas)

966 Peel (Michael Thompson)

967 Daffodils (Michael Thompson)

968 Millennium Sword (Mr. F. K. Smith)

969 Peel Castle (Kathy Brown)

970 Snaefell Railway (Joan Burgess)

971 Laxey Wheel (Kathy Brown)

972 Sheep at Druidale (John Hall)

973 Carousel at Silverdale (Colin Edwards)

974 Grandma (Stephanie Corkhill)

975 Manx Rock (Ruth Nicholls)

976 T.T. Riders at Signpost (Neil Brew)

977 Groudle Railway (Albert Lowe)

978 Royal Cascade (Brian Speedie)

979 St. Johns (John Hall)

980 Niarbyl Cottages with Poppies (Cathy Galbraith)

Photography – The People's Choice. Competition Winners

(Des The Agency. Litho Walsall)

2002 (30 Aug–1 Oct).

		(a) PVA gum. P 14 (C)		
1001	**961**	23p. multicoloured (b)	30	25
		a. Block of 10. Nos. 1001/10	5·00	5·00
1002	**962**	23p. multicoloured (b)	30	25
1003	**963**	23p. multicoloured (b)	30	25
1004	**964**	23p. multicoloured (b)	30	25
1005	**965**	23p. multicoloured (b)	30	25
1006	**966**	23p. multicoloured (b)	30	25
1007	**967**	23p. multicoloured (b)	30	25
1008	**968**	23p. multicoloured (b)	30	25
1009	**969**	23p. multicoloured (b)	30	25
1010	**970**	23p. multicoloured (b)	30	25
1011	**971**	27p. multicoloured (a)	35	30
		a. Block of 10. Nos. 1011/20	6·00	6·00
1012	**972**	27p. multicoloured (a)	35	30
1013	**973**	27p. multicoloured (a)	35	30
1014	**974**	27p. multicoloured (a)	35	30
1015	**975**	27p. multicoloured (a)	35	30
1016	**976**	27p. multicoloured (a)	35	30
1017	**977**	27p. multicoloured (a)	35	30
1018	**978**	27p. multicoloured (a)	35	30
1019	**979**	27p. multicoloured (a)	35	30
1020	**980**	27p. multicoloured (a)	35	30
1001/20 Set of 20			11·00	11·00
First Day Covers (2)				12·00
Presentation Packs (2)			12·00	
		(b) Booklet stamps. Self-adhesive. P 6½ (die-cut)		
1021	**961**	23p. multicoloured (b)	45	50
		a. Booklet pane. Nos. 1021/30	6·50	
1022	**962**	23p. multicoloured (b)	45	50
1023	**963**	23p. multicoloured (b)	45	50
1024	**964**	23p. multicoloured (b)	45	50
1025	**965**	23p. multicoloured (b)	45	50
1026	**966**	23p. multicoloured (b)	45	50
1027	**967**	23p. multicoloured (b)	45	50
1028	**968**	23p. multicoloured (b)		
1029	**969**	23p. multicoloured (b)	45	50
1030	**970**	23p. multicoloured (b)	45	50
1031	**971**	27p. multicoloured (b)	55	60
		a. Booklet pane. Nos. 1031/40	8·00	
1032	**972**	27p. multicoloured (b)	55	60
1033	**973**	27p. multicoloured (b)	55	60
1034	**974**	27p. multicoloured (b)	55	60
1035	**975**	27p. multicoloured (b)	55	60
1036	**976**	27p. multicoloured (b)	55	60
1037	**977**	27p. multicoloured (b)	55	60
1038	**978**	27p. multicoloured (b)	55	60
1039	**979**	27p. multicoloured (b)	55	60
1040	**980**	27p. multicoloured (b)	55	60

1021/40 *Set of 20* .... 10·00   11·00
    Nos. 1021/30 and 1031/40 were only available in £2.30 and £2.70 stamp booklets with the surplus self-adhesive paper around each stamp retained.
    Printings: (a) 30.8.02; (b) 1.10.02.
    Plate Nos.: Both values 1A (×5).
    Sheets: 40 (5×8) Nos. 1001/10 and 1011/20 were each printed together, *se-tenant*, as blocks of ten, in sheets of 40.
    Withdrawn: 29.8.2003 27p. sheets; 30.9.2003 23p. sheets.

981 Father Christmas   **982** Virgin Mary and   **983** Clown
                              Jesus

984 Bandsman playing   **985** Fairy
     Cymbals

986 'CHRISTMAS' and Festive Characters (*Illustration reduced. Actual size 123×55 mm*)

Christmas. Entertainment

(Des Anthea Radcliffe. Litho Questa)

2002 (5 Nov). P 15×14½ (No. **MS**1046) or 14×14½ (others), both comb.

1041	**981**	22p. multicoloured	45	50
1042	**982**	26p. multicoloured	50	55
1043	**983**	37p. multicoloured	75	80
1044	**984**	47p. multicoloured	95	1·00
1045	**985**	68p. multicoloured	1·40	1·50

1041/5 *Set of 5* .... 4·00   4·25
First Day Cover .... 5·00
Presentation Pack .... 5·00
MS1046 123×55 mm. **986** £1.30 multicoloured .... 3·00   3·25
First Day Cover .... 4·00
Presentation Pack .... 4·25
    The 37p. value includes the 'EUROPA' emblem.
    Plate Nos.: All values 1A (each×4).
    Sheets: 40 (5×8). The 37p. Europa stamp also exists in a sheetlet of ten (5×2).
    Withdrawn: 4.11.2003.

Year Folder 2002

2002 (5 Nov). Comprises Nos. 970/93, 995/1020 and 1041/5 (price £23).
Year Folder .... 45·00
    Sold out: By 31.7.2004.

Year Pack 2002

2002 (5 Nov). Comprises Nos. 970/93, 995/1020 and 1041/5 (price £27).
Year Pack .... 55·00
    Sold out: By 31.7.2004.

Post Office Yearbook

2002 (5 Nov). Comprises Nos. 970/93, 995/1020 and 1041/5 (price £29.95).
Yearbook .... 60·00
    Sold out: By 5.2005.

987 Dish Aerial and Peel Castle   **988** Dish Aerial, Tromode Teleport

989 Camp on Moon and lunar vehicle   **990** Astronaut exploring lunar service

991 *Sea Launch Odyssey* (marine launch platform)   **992** *Sea Launch Commander* (assembly and command ship)

993 *Loral Telstar* 1 satellite   **994** *Loral Telstar* 8 satellite

995 Phobos and American Spaceship (75p.); Mars, Astronauts and Transfer Vehicle (75p.) (*Illustration reduced. Actual size 110×85 mm*)

Isle of Man Involvement in Space Exploration

(Des R. McCall (27p., 75p.), E. Gignac (others). Litho Cartor)

2003 (14 Feb). P 13½×13 (**MS**1055) or 13½ (others), both comb.

1047	**987**	23p. multicoloured	45	50
		a. Horiz pair. Nos. 1047/8	90	1·00
1048	**988**	23p. multicoloured	45	50
1049	**989**	27p. multicoloured	55	60
		a. Horiz pair. Nos. 1049/50	1·10	1·10
1050	**990**	27p. multicoloured	55	60
1051	**991**	37p. multicoloured	75	80
		a. Horiz pair. Nos. 1051/2	1·50	1·60
1052	**992**	37p. multicoloured	75	80
1053	**993**	42p. multicoloured	85	90
		a. Horiz pair. Nos. 1053/4	2·10	2·20
1054	**994**	42p. multicoloured	85	90

1047/54 *Set of 8* .... 6·00   6·00
First Day Cover .... 6·50
Presentation Pack .... 6·75
MS1055 110×85 mm. **995** 75p.×2 multicoloured .... 4·00   4·00
First Day Cover .... 4·50
Presentation Pack .... 4·50

Plate Nos.: All values 1A (×4).
Sheets: 8 (2×4). Nos. 1047/8, 1049/50, 1051/2 and 1053/4 were each printed together, as horizontal *se-tenant* pairs forming composite designs, in sheets with enlarged illustrated right margins.
Withdrawn: 13.2.2004.

996 Delivery Handcart (1900-45)

997 Morris Z Van (1942)

998 Morris L Diesel Van (1960s)

999 D1 BSA Bantam Telephone Delivery Motorbikes

1000 Ford Escort 55 Van

Post Office Vehicles

(Des P. Hearsey. Litho Questa)

2003 (14 Feb). P 14½ (C).

1056	**996**	23p. multicoloured	45	50
1057	**997**	27p. multicoloured	55	60
1058	**998**	37p. multicoloured	1·00	1·10
1059	**999**	42p. multicoloured	1·10	1·20
1060	**1000**	89p. multicoloured	2·20	2·40
1056/60 Set of 5			5·25	5·50
First Day Cover				6·00
Presentation Pack			6·00	

Plate Nos.: All values 1A (×4).
Sheets: 25 (5×5).
Imprint: Right-hand side, bottom margin.
Withdrawn: 13.2.2004.

1001 Queen Elizabeth II wearing St. Edward's Crown

1002 The Ring

1003 The Orb

1004 Royal Sceptre and Rod of Equity and Mercy

1005 Queen Elizabeth II wearing Imperial State Crown

1006 State Coach

50th Anniversary of Coronation

(Des Diane Fawcett. Litho Walsall)

2003 (12 Apr). P 13½ (C).

1061	**1001**	50p. multicoloured	70	75
		a. Block of 6. Nos. 1061/6	6·00	6·50
1062	**1002**	50p. multicoloured	70	75
1063	**1003**	50p. multicoloured	70	75
1064	**1004**	50p. multicoloured	70	75
1065	**1005**	50p. multicoloured	70	75
1066	**1006**	50p. multicoloured	70	75
1061/6 Set of 6			6·00	6·50
First Day Cover				7·00
Presentation Pack			7·00	
Souvenir Folder			25·00	

Plate Nos.: 1A (×5).
Sheets: 24. Nos. 1061/6 were printed together, *se-tenant*, as four blocks of six with Nos. 1061 and 1065 at either end, 1062/4 in the top row and 1066 at the bottom.
Withdrawn: 10.4.2004.

1007 de Havilland D.H.83 Fox Moth and Saro Cloud (amphibian)

1008 de Havilland D.H.61 Giant Moth and D.H.80 Puss Moth

1009 Avro Anson Type 652 and Boeing B-17 Flying Fortress

1010 Eurofighter Typhoon and Avro Vulcan

1011 Handley Page Herald and Bristol Wayfarer

1012 Aerospatiale Concorde and projected Airbus Industrie A380

Centenary of Powered Flight

(Des K. Woodcock. Litho BDT)

2003 (9 May). P 13½ (C).

1067	**1007**	23p. multicoloured	45	50
		a. Horiz strip of 3. Nos. 1067/9	1·80	2·00
1068	**1008**	27p. multicoloured	60	60
1069	**1009**	37p. multicoloured	70	80
1070	**1010**	40p. multicoloured	70	85
		a. Horiz strip of 3. Nos. 1070/2	4·00	4·50
1071	**1011**	67p. multicoloured	80	1·50
1072	**1012**	89p. multicoloured	1·20	1·90
1067/72 Set of 6			5·50	6·00
First Day Cover				6·50
Presentation Pack			6·75	
Souvenir Folder (complete sheets and **MS**1073)			28·00	

Plate Nos.: All values 1A (×4).
Sheets: 12 (2 panes 3×2). Nos. 1067/9 and 1070/2 were each printed together, *se-tenant*, as horizontal strips of three, within sheets containing two blocks of six separated by large illustrated gutters.
Withdrawn: 8.5.2004.

1012a Avro Lancaster attacking Mohne Dam
(*Illustration reduced. Actual size 170×75 mm*)

60th Anniversary of Attack on German Dams by No. 617 ('Dambusters') Squadron

(Des R. Taylor. Litho BDT)

2003 (9 May). Sheet 170×75 mm. P 13 (C).

MS1073	**1012a** £2 multicoloured	4·50	4·25
First Day Cover			6·00
Presentation Pack		5·00	

Withdrawn: 8.5.2004.

1013 Prince William   **1014** Prince William

1015 Prince William   **1016** Prince William

21st Birthday of Prince William of Wales

(Des The Agency Ltd. Litho Cartor)

2003 (9 June). P 13½ (C).

1074	**1013**	42p. black and grey	1·00	90
1075	**1014**	47p. black and grey	1·25	1·00
1076	**1015**	52p. black and grey	2·00	1·60
1077	**1016**	68p. black and grey	2·50	2·00
1074/7 Set of 4			6·00	5·50
First Day Cover				6·00
Presentation Pack			6·25	

Plate Nos.: All values 1A (×4).
Sheets: 25 (5×5).
Imprint: Central, side margins.
Withdrawn: 8.6.2004.

Trilaterale Ticino Exhibition, Locarno, Switzerland

2003 (18 June). No. **MS**1073 additionally inscribed with 'Ticino 2003' logo in blue on sheet Margin.

MS1078 £2 multicoloured	4·75	4·75

Withdrawn: 17.6.2004.

1017 Manx Gold (Agatha Christie)   **1018** Quatermass and the Pit (Nigel Kneale)   **1019** Flashman at the Charge (George MacDonald Fraser)

1020 The Eternal City (Hall Caine)   **1021** Islanders (Mona Douglas)   **1022** Emmas Secret (Barbara Taylor Bradford)

'The Manx Bookshelf'. Book Covers

(Des D. Macdonald. Litho Walsall)

2003 (5 July). P 13½ (C).

1079	**1017**	23p. multicoloured	45	50
1080	**1018**	27p. multicoloured	55	60
1081	**1019**	30p. multicoloured	60	65
1082	**1020**	38p. multicoloured	75	80
1083	**1021**	40p. multicoloured	1·00	1·10
1084	**1022**	53p. multicoloured	1·20	1·30
1079/84 Set of 6			4·50	5·00
First Day Cover				5·75
Presentation Pack			5·75	

The 38p. value includes the 'EUROPA 2003' emblem.
Plate Nos: All values 1A (×4).
Sheets: 20 (5×4) with small *se-tenant* label giving the author's name at the foot of each stamp; 38p. also 10 (5×2).
Withdrawn: 3.7.2004.

1023 King Henry VII and Henry Tudor crowned by Sir Thomas Stanley on Bosworth Battlefield   **1024** King Henry VIII and Manx Church (Dissolution of the Monasteries)

1025 Queen Elizabeth I and Globe showing Route of Drake's Circumnavigation

1026 King Henry VIII, Cardinal Wolsey and Hampton Court Palace

1027 Queen Mary I and Tudor Rose

1028 Queen Elizabeth I and Ships of Spanish Armada

400th Anniversary of End of the Tudor Reign

(Des D. Kearney. Litho BDT)

2003 (15 Sept). P 14 (C).

1085	**1023**	23p. multicoloured	45	50
1086	**1024**	27p. multicoloured	55	60
1087	**1025**	38p. multicoloured	75	80
1088	**1026**	40p. multicoloured	80	85
1089	**1027**	47p. multicoloured	95	1·00
1090	**1028**	67p. multicoloured	1·40	1·50
1085/90 *Set of 6*			4·75	5·25
First Day Cover				5·75
Presentation Pack			5·50	
Stamp Cards (set of 6)			4·25	10·00

Plate Nos.: All values 1A (×4).
Sheets: 25 (5×5).
Withdrawn: 14.9.2004.

1029 Henry Bloom Noble and Orphanage Boys

1030 Nurse and Ramsey Cottage Hospital

1031 Children and Children's Home

1032 Bathers at Noble's Baths

1033 Scout and Headquarters

1034 Noble's Hospital c.1912

1035 Villa Marina

1036 Noble's Park

1037 St. Ninian's Church

1038 Noble's Library

Centenary of Henry Bloom Noble Trust

(Des Tracey Harding. Litho Walsall)

2003 (1 Oct).

(a) PVA gum. P 14 (C)

1091	**1029**	23p. multicoloured	40	25
		a. Horiz strip of 5. Nos. 1091/5	2·50	2·75
1092	**1030**	23p. multicoloured	40	25
1093	**1031**	23p. multicoloured	40	25
1094	**1032**	23p. multicoloured	40	25
1095	**1033**	23p. multicoloured	40	25
1096	**1034**	27p. multicoloured	45	30
		a. Horiz strip of 5. Nos. 1096/1100	3·00	3·25
1097	**1035**	27p. multicoloured	45	30
1098	**1036**	27p. multicoloured	45	30
1099	**1037**	27p. multicoloured	45	30
1100	**1038**	27p. multicoloured	45	30
1091/1100 *Set of 10*			5·00	5·50
First Day Cover				6·00
Presentation Pack			6·00	

(b) Self-adhesive booklet stamps. Roul 6½

1101	**1029**	23p. multicoloured		
		a. Booklet pane. Nos. 1101/5, each×2		
1102	**1030**	23p. multicoloured	45	50
1103	**1031**	23p. multicoloured	45	50
1104	**1032**	23p. multicoloured	45	50
1105	**1033**	23p. multicoloured	45	50
1106	**1034**	27p. multicoloured	55	60
		a. Booklet pane. Nos. 1106/1110, each×2		
1107	**1035**	27p. multicoloured		
1108	**1036**	27p. multicoloured	55	60
1109	**1037**	27p. multicoloured	55	60
1110	**1038**	27p. multicoloured	55	60
1101/10 *Set of 10*			5·00	5·50

Plate Nos.: Both values 1A (×4).
Sheets: 50 (5×10). Nos. 1091/5 and 1096/1100 were each printed together, *se-tenant*, in horizontal strips of five throughout the sheets. Nos. 1101/5 and 1106/1110 were only issued in £2.30 and £2.70 booklets, Nos. SB57/8.
Withdrawn: 30.9.2004 (sheets).

1039 Boy tying Scarf on Snowman

1040 Snowman (wearing black hat and scarf)

1041 Boy and Snowman holding Hands

1042 Snowman (wearing brown hat and scarf)

1043 Boy flying with Snowman

Christmas. *The Snowman* by Raymond Briggs.

(Litho DLR)

2003 (5 Nov). P 14½ (C).

1111	**1039**	22p. multicoloured	45	50
1112	**1040**	26p. multicoloured	50	55
1113	**1041**	38p. multicoloured	75	80
1114	**1042**	47p. multicoloured	95	1·00
1115	**1043**	68p. multicoloured	1·40	1·50
1111/15 *Set of 5*			4·00	4·25
First Day Cover				5·00
Presentation Pack			5·25	

Plate Nos.: All values 1A (×4).
Sheets: 40 (5×8).
Withdrawn: 4.11.2004.

Year Folder 2003

2003 (12 Nov). Comprises Nos. 1047/77, 1079/1100 and 1111/15 (price £25).

Year Folder	50·00	

Sold out: By 12.2004.

Year Pack 2003

2003 (12 Nov). Comprises Nos. 1047/77, 1079/1100 and 1111/15 (price £30).

Year Pack	60·00	

Sold out: By 5.2005.

Post Office Yearbook

2003 (12 Nov). Comprises Nos. 1047/77, 1079/1100 and 1111/15 (price £29.95).

Yearbook	60·00	

Sold out: By 12.2006.

1044 Aragorn

1045 Gimli

1046 Gandalf

1047 Legolas on Horseback

1048 Gollum

1049 Frodo and Sam

1050 Legolas drawing Bow

1051 Aragon on Horseback

1052 The Ring (*Illustration reduced. Actual size* 120×78 mm)

Making of *The Lord of the Rings* Film Trilogy: *The Return of the King*

(Des The Agency Ltd. Litho BDT)

2003 (17 Dec). P 13½ (C).

1116	**1044**	23p. multicoloured	45	50
1117	**1045**	27p. multicoloured	55	60
1118	**1046**	30p. multicoloured	60	65
1119	**1047**	38p. multicoloured	1·00	90
1120	**1048**	42p. multicoloured	1·50	1·00
1121	**1049**	47p. multicoloured	2·00	2·00
1122	**1050**	68p. multicoloured	3·00	3·50
1123	**1051**	85p. multicoloured	3·50	3·00
1116/23 *Set of 8*			9·75	9·75
First Day Cover				11·00
Presentation Pack			11·00	
Souvenir Folder (complete sheets and **MS**1124)			60·00	
Stamp Cards (pre-paid) (set of 8)			9·50	9·50
MS1124 120×78 mm. **1052** £2 multicoloured (44×40 mm)			5·00	5·50
First Day Cover				6·00
Presentation Pack			6·00	

Plate Nos.: All values 1A (×4).
Sheets: 6 (3×2) with enlarged illustrated margins.
Withdrawn: 16.12.2004.

1053 *Maitland* (Simon Hall)

1054 *Evening Star* (Terence Cuneo)

1055 *Pen-y-Darren* Tramroad Locomotive (Terence Cuneo)

1056 *Duchess of Hamilton* (Craig Tiley)

1057 *City of Truro* (B. J. Freeman)

1058 *Mallard* (Terence Cuneo)

The Power of Steam Bicentenary of Running of First Steam Locomotive. Paintings of Steam Locomotives.

(Des Fusion Graphics from paintings. Litho Cartor)

2004 (21 Feb). P 13×13½ (C).

1125	**1053**	23p. multicoloured	75	75
1126	**1054**	27p. multicoloured	90	90
1127	**1055**	40p. multicoloured	1·30	1·30
1128	**1056**	57p. multicoloured	1·80	1·80
1129	**1057**	61p. multicoloured	2·00	2·00
1130	**1058**	90p. multicoloured	3·00	3·00
1125/30	*Set of 6*		9·75	9·75
First Day Cover				11·00
Presentation Pack			11·50	
Collectors Folder (Nos. 1125/30 in panes of 5)			45·00	45·00

Plate Nos.: All values 1A (×4).
Sheets: 25 (5×5).
Withdrawn: 20.2.2005.

1059 Troops on Landing Craft and Tanks going Ashore
1060 Troops leaving Landing Craft and Tanks going Ashore

1061 Troops leaving Landing Craft
1062 Landing Craft and Troops wading Ashore

1063 *Lady of Mann* (ferry used as landing craft carrier)
1064 *Ben-my-Chree* (ferry used as landing craft carrier)

1065 Consolidated B-24 Liberators (bombers) and North American P-51 Mustang (fighter)
1066 Airspeed A.S.51 Horsa Gliders (troop carriers)

1067 Winston Churchill; Troops and Aircraft; Military Vehicles on Street; Soldiers with *France* Guidebook (*Illustration reduced. Actual size 170×75 mm*)

60th Anniversary of D-Day

(Des B. Sanders (Nos. 1131/8 only) and The Agency Ltd. Litho DLR (Nos. 1131/8) or Enschedé (**MS**1139))

2004 (6 Apr). P 14 (C).

1131	**1059**	23p. multicoloured	50	25
		a. Horiz pair. Nos. 1131/2	1·50	1·50
1132	**1060**	23p. multicoloured	50	25
1133	**1061**	27p. multicoloured	60	30
		a. Horiz pair. Nos. 1133/4	1·80	1·80
1134	**1062**	27p. multicoloured	60	30
1135	**1063**	47p. multicoloured	1·00	50
		a. Horiz pair. Nos. 1135/6	3·00	3·00

1136	**1064**	47p. multicoloured	1·00	50
1137	**1065**	68p. multicoloured	1·20	70
		a. Horiz pair. Nos. 1137/8	5·00	5·00
1138	**1066**	68p. multicoloured	1·20	70
1131/8	*Set of 8*		10·50	10·50
First Day Cover				12·50
Presentation Pack			12·50	
Collectors Folder (complete sheets and **MS**1139)			40·00	

MS1139 170×75 mm. **1067** 50p.×4 multicoloured. P 13½×14 (C).

		6·50	6·50
First Day Cover			8·00
Presentation Pack		8·25	

Plate Nos.: All values 1A (×4).
Sheets: 10 (2×5) Nos. 1131/2, 1133/4, 1135/6 and 1137/8 were each printed together, *se-tenant*, in horizontal pairs throughout the sheets, each pair forming a composite design.
Withdrawn: 5.4.2005.

1068 Lesser Celandine
1069 Red Campion

1070 Devil's-bit Scabious
1071 Northern Harebell

1072 Wood Anemone
1073 Common Spotted Orchid

Bicentenary of Royal Horticultural Society. Wild Flowers

(Des The Agency Ltd. Litho Cartor)

2004 (3 May). P 13½ (C).

1140	**1068**	25p. multicoloured	85	85
1141	**1069**	28p. multicoloured	95	95
1142	**1070**	37p. multicoloured	1·20	1·20
1143	**1071**	40p. multicoloured	1·30	1·30
1144	**1072**	68p. multicoloured	2·20	2·20
1145	**1073**	85p. multicoloured	2·75	2·75
1140/5	*Set of 6*		9·25	9·25
First Day Cover				11·00
Presentation Pack			11·00	

Plate Nos.: All values 1A (×4).
Sheets: 40 (5×8).
Withdrawn: 2.5.2005.

1074 In *No Limit*, 1936
1075 Pushing Motorcycle

1076 Riding in TT Race
1077 With Florence Desmond

1078 On Motorcycle

1079 Close-up of George Formby

Birth Centenary of George Formby (entertainer). Scenes from *No Limit* (film)

(Des Ruth Sutherland. Litho BDT)

2004 (26 May). P 13½ (C).

1146	**1074**	25p. multicoloured	80	80
1147	**1075**	28p. multicoloured	90	90
1148	**1076**	40p. multicoloured	1·30	1·30
1149	**1077**	43p. multicoloured	1·40	1·40
1150	**1078**	50p. multicoloured	1·70	1·70
1151	**1079**	74p. multicoloured	2·40	2·40
1146/51 *Set of 6*			8·50	8·50
First Day Cover				10·00
Presentation Pack			10·00	

Sheets: 25 (5×5).
Withdrawn: 25.5.2005.

1080 Johnny Weissmuller (gold, 100m & 400m freestyle), Paris, 1924

1081 Jesse Owens (gold, 100m, 200m, long jump), Berlin, 1936

1082 John Mark carrying Olympic Flame, London, 1948

1083 Fanny Blankers-Koen (gold, 100m, 200m, 80m hurdles), London, 1948

1084 James Cracknell, Steven Redgrave, Tim Foster and Matthew Pinsent (gold, men's coxless fours), Sydney, 2000

Olympic Games, Athens. Olympic Legends

(Des Fusion Graphics. Litho BDT)

2004 (1 July). P 14 (C).

1152	**1080**	25p. multicoloured	85	85
1153	**1081**	28p. multicoloured	95	95
1154	**1082**	43p. multicoloured	1·40	1·40
1155	**1083**	55p. multicoloured	1·80	1·80
1156	**1084**	91p. multicoloured	3·00	3·00
1152/6 *Set of 5*			8·00	8·00
First Day Cover				9·75
Presentation Pack			10·00	

Plate Nos.: All values 1A (×4).
Sheets: 25 (5×5).
Imprint: Central, bottom margin.
Withdrawn: 30.6.2005.

1085 Celtic Islanders and Viking Invaders

1086 Fisherman ('Ships and the Sea')

1087 Miner and Laxey Wheel ('Laxey Miners')

1088 Soldier with Longbow and Castle ('Kings and Lords of Mann')

1089 Woman with Spinning Wheel ('Farmers and Crofters')

1090 Calf of Man

1091 Peel Castle

1092 Laxey Wheel

1093 Castle Rushen

1094 Cregneash

Manx National Heritage 'The Story of Mann'

(Des The Agency Ltd. Litho BDT)

2004 (3 Aug).

(a) PVA gum. P 14 (C)

1157	**1085**	(25p.) multicoloured	1·00	25
		a. Horiz strip of 5. Nos. 1157/61	5·00	4·00
1158	**1086**	(25p.) multicoloured	1·00	25
1159	**1087**	(25p.) multicoloured	1·00	25
1160	**1088**	(25p.) multicoloured	1·00	25
1161	**1089**	(25p.) multicoloured	1·00	25
1162	**1090**	(28p.) multicoloured	1·20	30
		a. Horiz strip of 5. Nos. 1162/6	6·00	5·00
1163	**1091**	(28p.) multicoloured	1·20	30
1164	**1092**	(28p.) multicoloured	1·20	30
1165	**1093**	(28p.) multicoloured	1·20	30
1166	**1094**	(28p.) multicoloured	1·20	30
1157/66 *Set of 10*			11·00	8·50
First Day Cover				10·50
Presentation Pack			12·00	

(b) Self-adhesive booklet stamps. P 12½ (die-cut)

1167	**1085**	(25p.) multicoloured	1·00	60
		a. Booklet pane. Nos. 1167/71, each×2	10·00	
1168	**1086**	(25p.) multicoloured	1·00	60
1169	**1087**	(25p.) multicoloured	1·00	60
1170	**1088**	(25p.) multicoloured	1·00	60

1171	**1089**	(25p.) multicoloured...........................	1·00	60
1172	**1090**	(28p.) multicoloured...........................	1·20	75
		a. Booklet pane. Nos. 1172/6,		
		each×2...............................	12·00	
1173	**1091**	(28p.) multicoloured...........................	1·20	75
1174	**1092**	(28p.) multicoloured...........................	1·20	75
1175	**1093**	(28p.) multicoloured...........................	1·20	75
1176	**1094**	(28p.) multicoloured...........................	1·20	75
1167/76 *Set of 10*..			11·00	8·50

Nos. 1157/61 and 1167/71 are inscribed 'IOM' and were initially sold at 25p. Nos. 1162/6 and 1172/6 are inscribed 'UK' and were initially sold at 28p.

Plate Nos. Both values 1A (×4).

Sheets: 50 (5×10). Nos. 1157/61 and 1162/6 were each printed together, *se-tenant*, in horizontal strips of five throughout the sheets. Nos. 1167/71 and 1172/6 were only issued in £2.50 and £2.80 booklets, Nos. SB59/60.

Withdrawn: 2.8.2005.

1095 Laxey Wheel (*Illustration reduced. Actual size 120×78 mm*)

150th Anniversary of the Great Laxey Wheel

(Des The Agency Ltd. Litho BDT)

2004 (3 Aug). Sheet 120×78 mm. P 14 (C).

MS1177 **1095** £2 multicoloured	6·50	6·50
First Day Cover		8·50
Presentation Pack	8·50	

Withdrawn: 2.8.2005.

1096 'Maughold Church'

1097 'Port St. Mary'

1098 'Ballaugh Old Church'

1099 'Douglas Bay (A Midsummer's Night)'

1100 'Point of Ayre'

1101 'Peel Harbour and Castle'

The Isle of Man Watercolours by Alfred Heaton Cooper

(Des The Agency Ltd. Litho Enschedé)

2004 (21 Oct). P 13½×13 (C).

1178	**1096**	25p. multicoloured..........................	80	80
1179	**1097**	28p. multicoloured..........................	90	90
1180	**1098**	40p. multicoloured..........................	1·30	1·30
1181	**1099**	41p. multicoloured..........................	1·30	1·30
1182	**1100**	43p. multicoloured..........................	1·40	1·40
1183	**1101**	74p. multicoloured..........................	2·40	2·40
1178/83 *Set of 6*..			8·00	8·00
First Day Cover				10·00
Presentation Pack			8·75	

The 28p. and 40p. values include the 'EUROPA 2004' emblem.

Plate Nos.: All values 1A (×4).

Sheets: 25 (5×5); 28p. and 40p. also 10 (2×5).

Withdrawn: 20.10.2005.

Sindelfingen International Stamp Exhibition, Sindelfingen, Germany

2004 (29 Oct). No. **MS**1177 additionally inscribed with SINDELFINGEN logo on the sheet margin.

MS1184 **1095** £2 multicoloured	6·50	6·50

Withdrawn: 28.10.2005.

1102 Robin on Flower Pot

1103 Robin at Foot of Tree

1104 Robin perched on Branch among Bracken

1105 Robin on Window Ledge

1106 Robin on Snowy Logs

Robins—'Winters Friends'

(Des Dr. J. Paul. Litho Lowe-Martin, Canada)

2004 (9 Nov). P 12½×13 (C).

1185	**1102**	25p. multicoloured..........................	80	80
1186	**1103**	28p. multicoloured..........................	90	90
1187	**1104**	40p. multicoloured..........................	1·30	1·30
1188	**1105**	47p. multicoloured..........................	1·50	1·50
1189	**1106**	68p. multicoloured..........................	2·30	2·30
1185/9 *Set of 5*..			6·75	6·75
First Day Cover				8·75
Presentation Pack			8·75	
Collectors Folder (**MS**1190 and signed first day cover)			30·00	
MS1190 148×200 mm. Nos. 1185/9×2..................			13·50	13·50

Plate Nos.: All values 1A (×7).

Sheets: 40 (5×8).

Withdrawn: 8.11.2005.

Year Folder 2004

2004 (9 Nov). Comprises Nos. 1116/66, **MS**1177/83 and 1185/9 (price £31).

Year Folder...	60·00

Sold out: By 7.2005.

Year Pack 2004

2004 (9 Nov). Comprises Nos. 1116/66, **MS**1177/83 and 1185/9 (price £39).

Year Pack..	75·00

Sold out: By 8.2006.

Post Office Yearbook

2004 (9 Nov). Comprises Nos. 1116/66, **MS**1177/83 and 1185/9 (price £29.95).
Yearbook .... 60·00
Sold out: By 12.2006.

1107 Harry Potter, Ron Weasley and Hermione Granger

1108 Snowy Owl delivering Owl Post

1109 Harry Potter and White Stag

1110 *Hogwarts Express*

1111 Rubeus Hagrid

1112 Purple Triple-decker Bus

1113 Dementor and Harry Potter flying

1114 Harry Potter on the Hippogriff Buckbeak

Harry Potter and the Prisoner of Azkaban (film)

(Des The Agency Ltd. Litho Enschedé)

2004 (7 Dec). P 13½ (C).
1191	**1107**	25p. multicoloured	80	80
1192	**1108**	28p. multicoloured	90	90
1193	**1109**	39p. multicoloured	1·30	1·30
1194	**1110**	40p. multicoloured	1·30	1·30
1195	**1111**	49p. multicoloured	1·60	1·60
1196	**1112**	55p. multicoloured	1·80	1·80
1197	**1113**	57p. multicoloured	1·90	1·90
1198	**1114**	68p. multicoloured	2·20	2·20

1191/8 Set of 8.. 11·50   11·50
First Day Cover ....   13·50
Presentation Pack.. 13·50
*Collectors Folder (contains complete sheets and Owl
Post Office first day cover)* .... 60·00
Stamp Cards (pre-paid) (set of 8) .... 11·50   11·50
Plate Nos.: All values 1A (×5).
Sheets: 5 (1×5). with enlarged illustrated right margins.
Withdrawn: 6.12.2005.

1115 'The Nile Campaign'

1116 'The Battle of Copenhagen'

1117 Emma, Horatia and Nelson

1118 Band of Brothers

1119 'Prepare for Battle'

1120 'Victory in Sight'

1121 'The Fall of Nelson'

1122 'The Death of Nelson'

1123 2000 Isle of Man at War 22p. Stamp (£1); 1979 150th Death Anniversary of Captain John Quilliam 8p. Stamp (£1) (*Illustration reduced. Actual size 170×75 mm*)

Bicentenary of the Battle of Trafalgar

(Des E. Cassidy. Litho Enschedé Nos. 1199/1206) or Lowe-Martin (**MS**1207))

2005 (9 Jan–1 Feb). P 12½×13 (C).
1199	**1115**	25p. multicoloured	50	55
		a. Horiz pair. Nos. 1199/1200...........	1·00	1·10
1200	**1116**	25p. multicoloured	50	55
1201	**1117**	28p. multicoloured	55	60
		a. Horiz pair. Nos. 1201/2..................	1·10	1·20
1202	**1118**	28p. multicoloured	55	60
1203	**1119**	50p. multicoloured	1·00	1·10
		a. Horiz pair. Nos. 1203/4..................	2·00	2·20
1204	**1120**	50p. multicoloured	1·00	1·10
1205	**1121**	65p. multicoloured	1·30	1·40
		a. Horiz pair. Nos. 1205/6..................	2·50	2·75
1206	**1122**	65p. multicoloured	1·30	1·40

1199/206 Set of 8... 6·50   7·00
First Day Cover ....   8·00
Presentation Pack.. 8·00
Collectors Folder (complete sheets and MS1207).... 32·00
MS1207 170×75 mm. **1123** £1×2 multicoloured (1 Feb) 4·00   4·25
First Day Cover ....   5·00
Presentation Pack.. 5·00
Plate Nos.: All values 1A (×5).
Sheets: 8 (2×4). Nos. 1199/1200, 1201/2, 1203/4 and 1205/6 were each printed together, *se-tenant*, in horizontal pairs throughout the sheets.
Withdrawn: 8.1.2006.

1124 Two Couples by Waterside **1125** Group celebrating in the Street

1126 Man trying on Hat **1127** Civil Service Personnel

1128 King George VI and Winston Churchill on Balcony of Buckingham Palace **1129** King George VI and Queen Elizabeth in Carriage

1130 Servicemen **1131** War Graves

1132 The Manx Regiment (£1); Royal Visit, 1945 (£1) (*Illustration reduced. Actual size 170×75 mm*)

60th Anniversary of the End of World War II

(Des The Agency Ltd. Litho Enschedé)

2005 (15 Apr.). P 13½×14 (C).

1208	**1124**	26p. multicoloured	45	30
		a. Horiz pair. Nos. 1208/9	1·00	1·10
1209	**1125**	26p. multicoloured	45	30
1210	**1126**	29p. multicoloured	50	30
		a. Horiz pair. Nos. 1210/11	1·20	1·30
1211	**1127**	29p. multicoloured	50	30
1212	**1128**	60p. multicoloured	1·25	70
		a. Horiz pair. Nos. 1212/13	2·50	2·50
1213	**1129**	60p. multicoloured	1·25	70
1214	**1130**	65p. multicoloured	1·25	70
		a. Horiz pair. Nos. 1214/15	2·75	2·75
1215	**1131**	65p. multicoloured	1·25	70
1208/15	*Set of 8*		7·00	7·75
First Day Cover				8·25
Presentation Pack			8·25	
Collectors Folder (complete sheets)			40·00	
MS1216 170×75 mm. **1132** £1×2 multicoloured			4·50	4·50
First Day Cover				6·00
Presentation Pack			5·50	

Plate Nos.: All values 1A (×4).
Sheets: 10 (2×5). Nos. 1208/9, 1210/11, 1212/13 and 1214/15 were each printed together, *se-tenant*, in horizontal pairs throughout the sheets.
Withdrawn: 14.4.2006.

1133 '*Mona's Isle*' (Samuel Walters) **1134** '*Viking*' (Norman Wilkinson)

1135 '*King Orry*' (Robert Lloyd) **1136** '*Mona's Queen*' (Arthur Burgess)

1137 '*Ben-my-Chree*' (John Nicholson) **1138** '*King Orry*' (Robert Lloyd)

1139 '*Ben-my-Chree*' (Robert Lloyd) **1140** '*Lady of Mann*' (Robert Lloyd)

175th Anniversary of Steam Packet Company

(Des Tracey Harding. Litho BDT)

2005 (6 May). P 14 (C).

1217	**1133**	26p. multicoloured	45	30
		a. Horiz pair. Nos. 1217/18	1·00	1·00
		b. Booklet pane. Nos. 1217/20 with margins all round	2·20	
		c. Booklet pane. Nos. 1217/18 and 1221/2 with margins all round	2·50	
1218	**1134**	26p. multicoloured	45	30
1219	**1135**	29p. multicoloured	50	30
		a. Horiz pair. Nos. 1219/20	1·20	1·50
		b. Booklet pane. Nos. 1219/20 and 1223/4 with margins all round	3·75	
1220	**1136**	29p. multicoloured	50	30
1221	**1137**	40p. multicoloured	75	45
		a. Horiz pair. Nos. 1221/2	1·70	1·70
		b. Booklet pane. Nos. 1221/4 with margins all round	4·00	
1222	**1138**	40p. multicoloured	75	45
1223	**1139**	66p. multicoloured	1·25	70
		a. Horiz pair. Nos. 1223/4	2·75	2·75
		b. Booklet pane. Nos. 1223/4 with margins all round	2·50	
1224	**1140**	66p. multicoloured	1·25	70
1217/24	*Set of 8*		6·25	6·75
First Day Cover				7·50
Presentation Pack			7·50	
Set of 4 Gutter Pairs			13·00	

Plate Nos.: All values 1A (×4).
Sheets: 40 (2 panes 2×10). Nos. 1217/18, 1219/20, 1221/2 and 1223/4 were each printed together, *se-tenant*, as horizontal pairs in sheets containing two vertical columns of pairs separated by an illustrated and inscribed gutter.
Withdrawn: 5.5.2006.

1141 Bill Ivy and Phil Read **1142** Joey Dunlop and Ray McCullough

1143 Steve Hislop

1144 Carl Fogarty

1145 David Jefferies

1146 John McGuinness

50th Anniversary of Yamaha

(Des Ruth Sutherland. Litho Enschedé)

2005 (17 May). P 14 (C).

1225	**1141**	26p. multicoloured	50	55
		a. Sheetlet. Nos. 1225/30×2	11·50	
1226	**1142**	29p. multicoloured	60	65
1227	**1143**	40p. multicoloured	80	85
1228	**1144**	42p. multicoloured	85	90
1229	**1145**	68p. multicoloured	1·40	1·50
1230	**1146**	78p. multicoloured	1·60	1·70
1225/30 *Set of 6*			5·75	6·00
First Day Cover				6·75
Presentation Pack			6·75	
Carl Fogarty Folder (sheetlet & signed first day cover)			40·00	

Plate Nos.: All values 1A (×4) (sheets of 25 only).
Sheets: 25 (5×5) or 12 (2 columns 6×1). Nos. 1225/30 were issued in separate sheets of 25 and *se-tenant* in sheetlets of 12 containing two vertical columns separated by an illustrated gutter. Withdrawn: 16.5.2006.

1147 Paul Harris (founder)

1148 Planting Tree, Children grouped and Child drinking

1149 Child being immunised and Boy with Leg Braces and Crutches

1150 Food Preparations

1151 Supply Truck, Children with Volunteer and loading Cases

1152 Child having Eye Test, Group under Rotary Banner and Family

Centenary of Rotary International and Europa Gastronomy

(Des The Agency Ltd. Litho Cartor)

2005 (15 June). P 13½×14 (C).

1231	**1147**	26p. multicoloured	50	55
1232	**1148**	29p. multicoloured	60	65
1233	**1149**	40p. multicoloured	80	85
1234	**1150**	42p. multicoloured	85	90
1235	**1151**	64p. multicoloured	1·30	1·40
1236	**1152**	68p. multicoloured	1·40	1·50
1231/6 *Set of 6*			5·25	5·75
First Day Cover				6·75
Presentation Pack			6·75	

The 42p. value includes the 'EUROPA 2005' emblem.
Plate Nos.: All values 1A (×4).
Sheets: 25 (5×5); 42p. also 10 (2×5).
Withdrawn: 14.6.2006.

1153 Guttin' Herrin'

1154 Pickin' Spuds

1155 J. C. Kelly, Master Butcher

1156 Winckles, Foxdale

1157 Palace Ballroom

1158 Land Army

1159 Farmyard, Glen Maye

1160 Eva Kane, Summer Season Stars

1161 Donkey Rides

1162 Alfie Gilmour, 'Give us a go Mister!'

'Time to Remember'

(Des The Agency Ltd. Litho Lowe-Martin)

2005 (12 Aug).

(a) PVA gum. P 12½×13 (C)

1237	**1153**	26p. multicoloured	45	30
		a. Horiz strip of 5. Nos. 1237/41	2·50	2·50
1238	**1154**	26p. multicoloured	45	30
1239	**1155**	26p. multicoloured	45	30
1240	**1156**	26p. multicoloured	45	30
1241	**1157**	26p. multicoloured	45	30
1242	**1158**	29p. multicoloured	50	30
		a. Horiz strip of 5. Nos. 1242/6	3·50	3·75
1243	**1159**	29p. multicoloured	50	30
1244	**1160**	29p. multicoloured	50	30
1245	**1161**	29p. multicoloured	50	30
1246	**1162**	29p. multicoloured	50	30
1237/46 *Set of 10*			6·00	6·00
First Day Cover				6·75
Presentation Pack			6·75	

(b) Self-adhesive. P 12½×13

1247	1153	26p. multicoloured	50	55
		a. Horiz strip of 5. Nos. 1247/51	2·50	
		b. Die cut P 10½	50	55
		ba. Booklet pane. Nos. 1247b/51b, each×2	5·00	
1248	1154	26p. multicoloured	50	55
		b. Die-cut P 10½	50	55
1249	1155	26p. multicoloured	50	55
		b. Die-cut P 10½	50	55
1250	1156	26p. multicoloured	50	55
		b. Die-cut P 10½	50	55
1251	1157	26p. multicoloured	50	55
		b. Die-cut P 10½	50	55
1252	1158	29p. multicoloured	60	65
		a. Horiz strip of 5. Nos. 1252/6	3·75	
		b. Die-cut P 10½	60	65
		ba. Booklet pane. Nos. 1252b/6b, each×2	5·75	
1253	1159	29p. multicoloured	60	65
		b. Die-cut P 10½	60	65
1254	1160	29p. multicoloured	60	65
		b. Die-cut P 10½	60	65
1255	1161	29p. multicoloured	60	65
		b. Die-cut P 10½	60	65
1256	1162	29p. multicoloured	60	65
		b. Die-cut P 10½	60	65
1247/56 *Set of 10*			6·00	6·00

Nos. 1247b/51b and 1252b/6b were only available from £2.60 and £2.90 booklets, Nos. SB62/3.

Plate Nos.: All values 1A (×5).

Sheets: 50 (5×10). Nos. 1237/41, 1242/6, 1247/51 and 1252/6 were each printed together, *se-tenant*, in horizontal strips of five stamps throughout the sheets.

Withdrawn: 11.8.2006.

1163 Obelisk in St. Peter's Square (42p.); St. Peter's Basilica (£1.50) (*Illustration reduced. Actual size 170×75 mm*)

20th World Youth Day

(Des E. Cassidy. Litho BDT)

2005 (15 Aug). Sheet 170×75 mm. P 14×15 (C).

MS1257	1163	42p. multicoloured; £1.50 multicoloured	4·00	4·00
First Day Cover				5·00
Presentation Pack			5·00	

The stamps within No. MS1257 each have labels at left showing Pope John Paul II (42p.) and Pope Benedict XVI (£1.50).

Withdrawn: 14.8.2006.

1164 Harry Potter

1165 Harry Potter, Hermione, Ron Weasley and Goblet of Fire

1166 Trophy

1167 Hungarian Horntail Dragon

1168 Hogwarts Coat of Arms

1169 Murcus, Chieftainess of the Merpeople

Harry Potter and the Goblet of Fire (film)

(Des The Agency. Litho BDT)

2005 (21 Oct). P 13½ (C).

1258	1164	26p. multicoloured	65	55
1259	1165	29p. multicoloured	70	65
1260	1166	33p. multicoloured	80	70
1261	1167	64p. multicoloured	1·50	1·40
1262	1168	68p. multicoloured	1·60	1·50
1263	1169	75p. multicoloured	1·75	1·60
1258/63 *Set of 6*			6·50	6·25
First Day Cover				7·00
Presentation Pack			7·00	
Collectors Folder (complete sheets & special first day cover (silver post mark))			50·00	

Plate Nos.: All values 1A (×5).

Sheets: 5 (1×5) with enlarged illustrated right margins.

Withdrawn: 20.10.2006.

1170 Death of Nelson (Gibraltar £1); Arrival of Nelson's funeral procession at St. Paul's Cathedral, London (£1) (*Illustration reduced. Actual size 170×75 mm*)

Death Bicentenary of Admiral Lord Nelson

(Des and litho Lowe-Martin, Canada)

2005 (21 Oct). Sheet 170×75 mm. P 13½ (C).

MS1264	1170	Gibraltar £1 multicoloured; £1 multicoloured	4·50	4·50
First Day Cover				5·25
Presentation Pack			5·25	
Collectors Folder (MS1264, Gibraltar miniature sheet, Isle of Man & Gibraltar first day covers)			35·00	

The miniature sheet contains a £1 Gibraltar stamp and a £1 Isle of Man stamp. A similar miniature sheet, but inscribed 'issued by Gibraltar Post' was issued by Gibraltar.

Withdrawn: 20.10.2006.

1171 Mary and Jesus

1172 Angel with the Crown of Glory

1173 Shepherds worshipping Christ Child

1174 Nativity   **1175** Three Kings

Christmas. Stained-glass Windows from Manx Churches

(Des E. Cassidy. Litho Cartor)

2005 (7 Nov). P 13½×13 (C).
1265	**1171**	26p. multicoloured	50	55
1266	**1172**	29p. multicoloured	60	65
1267	**1173**	42p. multicoloured	85	90
1268	**1174**	60p. multicoloured	1·20	1·30
1269	**1175**	68p. multicoloured	1·40	1·50
1265/9 *Set of 5*			4·50	4·75
First Day Cover				5·75
Presentation Pack			5·75	

Nos. 1265/7 show windows from St. German's Cathedral, Peel and Nos. 1268/9 windows from Kirk Christ, Rushen.
Plate Nos.: All values 1A (×4).
Sheets: 50 (10×5) .
Withdrawn: 6.11.2006.

Year Folder 2005

2005 (7 Nov). Comprises Nos. 1191/246 and **MS**1257/69 (price £35).
Year Folder		70·00

Sold out: By 12.2006.

Year Pack 2005

2005 (7 Nov). Comprises Nos. 1191/246 and **MS**1257/69 (price £43).
Year Pack		85·00

Sold out: By 12.2006.

Post Office Yearbook

2005 (7 Nov). Comprises Nos. 1191/246, **MS**1257/69 and 'Time to Remember' CD including booklets SB62/3 (price £35).
Yearbook		70·00

Sold out: By 8.2008.

1176 Princess Elizabeth aged Five with Duke and Duchess of York and Princess Margaret, 1931

1177 Princess Elizabeth wearing ATS Uniform, c. 1944

1178 Queen Elizabeth wearing Diadem, 1952

1179 With Princes Philip, Andrew, Edward, Charles and Princess Anne, 1972

1180 With Prince Philip at Balmoral on Silver Wedding Anniversary, 1972

1181 With Regalia in Throne Room, Buckingham Palace, 2001

1182 With Prince William on Buckingham Palace Balcony

1183 With Crowd at Aylesbury, Buckinghamshire on Golden Jubilee Tour, 2002

80th Birthday of Queen Elizabeth II (1st issue)

(Des The Agency. Litho Austrian State Ptg Wks, Vienna)

2006 (16 Jan). P 14 (C).
1270	**1176**	20p. multicoloured	40	30
		a. Horiz strip of 4. Nos. 1270/3	1·70	1·70
1271	**1177**	20p. multicoloured	40	30
1272	**1178**	20p. multicoloured	40	30
1273	**1179**	20p. multicoloured	40	30
1274	**1180**	80p. multicoloured	1·60	1·00
		a. Horiz strip of 4. Nos. 1274/7	6·75	6·75
1275	**1181**	80p. multicoloured	1·60	1·00
1276	**1182**	80p. multicoloured	1·60	1·00
1277	**1183**	80p. multicoloured	1·60	1·00
1270/7 *Set of 8*			8·00	8·50
First Day Cover				9·25
Presentation Pack			9·50	
Collectors Folder (complete sheets)			32·00	
Set of 2 Gutter Strips			16·00	

See also No. **MS**1294.
Plate Nos.: Both values 1A (×4).
Sheets: 16 (2 blocks 2×4). Nos. 1270/3 and 1274/7 were each printed together, *se-tenant*, as horizontal strips of four stamps in sheets containing two blocks of eight separated by a large illustrated gutter.
Withdrawn: 15.1.2007.

1184 Jurby Chalice and Jurby Church

1185 Viking Period Gold Pin Head and Peel Castle

1186 Fragment of Early Neolithic Bowl and Meayll Hill, Rushen

1187 Manx Stoat and Cronk Sumark Late Iron Age Hill Fort

1188 Hen Harrier and South Barrule Hill, Malew

1189 Fossil Ammonite, Scarlett Point and Castletown

Manx—Study Isle of Man Natural History and Antiquarian Society

(Des Icon Imaging. Litho Enschedé)

2006 (15 Feb). P 14 (C).

1278	**1184**	26p. multicoloured	50	55
1279	**1185**	29p. multicoloured	60	65
1280	**1186**	64p. multicoloured	1·30	1·40
1281	**1187**	68p. multicoloured	1·40	1·50
1282	**1188**	78p. multicoloured	1·60	1·70
1283	**1189**	97p. multicoloured	1·90	2·00
1278/83	Set of 6		7·75	7·75
First Day Cover				8·50
Presentation Pack			9·50	

Plate Nos.: All values 1A (×4).
Sheets: 25 (5×5).
Withdrawn: 14.2.2007.

1190 Peregrine Falcon

1191 Puffin

1192 Manx Shearwater

1193 Chough

1194 Guillemot

1195 Whinchat

1196 Hen Harrier

1197 Goldcrest

(image of Grey Wagtail)
1198 Grey Wagtail

(image of Wren)
1199 Wren

Manx Bird Atlas

(Des Dr. J. Paul and The Agency. Litho Cartor)

2006 (17 Apr).

(a) PVA gum. P 12½ (C)

1284	**1190**	28p. multicoloured	55	35
		a. Horiz strip of 5. Nos. 1284/8	3·00	3·00
1285	**1191**	28p. multicoloured	55	35
1286	**1192**	28p. multicoloured	55	35
1287	**1193**	28p. multicoloured	55	35
1288	**1194**	28p. multicoloured	55	35
1289	**1195**	31p. multicoloured	60	40
		a. Horiz strip of 5. Nos. 1289/93	3·50	3·25
1290	**1196**	31p. multicoloured	60	40
1291	**1197**	31p. multicoloured	60	40
1292	**1198**	31p. multicoloured	60	40
1293	**1199**	31p. multicoloured	60	40
1284/93	Set of 10		6·50	6·25
First Day Cover				7·00
Presentation Pack			7·25	

(b) Self-adhesive. P 12½ (die-cut)

1293a	**1190**	28p. multicoloured	55	60
		ab. Horiz strip of 5. Nos. 1293a/e	5·50	5·50
1293b	**1191**	28p. multicoloured	55	60
1293c	**1192**	28p. multicoloured	55	60
1293d	**1193**	28p. multicoloured	55	60
1293e	**1194**	28p. multicoloured	55	60
1293f	**1195**	31p. multicoloured	60	65
		fa. Horiz strip of 5. Nos. 1293f/j	6·00	6·00
1293g	**1196**	31p. multicoloured	60	65
1293h	**1197**	31p. multicoloured	60	65
1293i	**1198**	31p. multicoloured	60	65
1293j	**1199**	31p. multicoloured	60	65
1293a/j	Set of 10		10·00	10·00

Nos. 1293a/j include the RSPB logo in the margin.
Plate Nos.: Both values 1A (×4).
Sheets: 50 (5×10). Nos. 1284/8, 1289/93, 1293a/e and 1293f/j
were each printed together, *se-tenant*, in horizontal strips of five
stamps throughout the sheets.
Withdrawn: 16.4.2007.

1200 Queen Elizabeth II at Tynwald Ceremony, 2003 (£1); In 1972
(£1) (*Illustration reduced. Actual size 120×78 mm*)

80th Birthday of Queen Elizabeth II (2nd issue)

(Des The Agency. Litho BDT)

2006 (21 Apr). Sheet 120×78 mm. P 14 (C).

MS1294	**1200**	£1×2 multicoloured	4·00	4·25
First Day Cover				5·50
Presentation Pack			5·50	

Withdrawn: 20.4.2007.

1201 West German Player

1202 West German Team

1203 Bobby Moore (England
captain) with Trophy and Alf
Ramsey (manager)

1204 Bobby Moore holding
Trophy aloft

1205 West German Players   **1206** Victorious England Team

World Cup Football Championship, Germany. 40th Anniversary of England's World Cup Victory

(Des Mannin Design. Litho Lowe-Martin, Canada)

2006 (2 May). P 12½×13 (C).

1295	**1201**	28p. multicoloured	55	60
1296	**1202**	31p. multicoloured	60	65
1297	**1203**	44p. multicoloured	90	95
1298	**1204**	72p. multicoloured	1·40	1·50
1299	**1205**	83p. multicoloured	1·70	1·80
1300	**1206**	94p. multicoloured	1·90	2·00
1295/300	*Set of 6*		7·00	7·50
First Day Cover				8·50
Presentation Pack			8·50	

Nos. 1295/1300 each contained a circle of gold imitation perforations.
Plate Nos. All values 1A (×5).
Sheets: 20 (4×5).
Withdrawn: 1.5.2007.

1207 1977 Isle of Man 10p. Europa Stamp (42p.); 1990 Isle of Man 15p. Europa Stamp (83p.) (*Illustration reduced. Actual size 170×75 mm*)

50th Anniversary of First Europa Stamp

(Des D. Clague. Litho Enschedé)

2006 (2 May). Sheet 170×75 mm. P 13½×14 (C).

MS1301	**1207**	42p. multicoloured; 83p multicoloured	2·50	2·75
First Day Cover				4·00
Presentation Pack			4·00	

Withdrawn: 1.5.2007.

1208 Letitia Tyler (First Lady 1841–2)   **1209** Joseph Gurney 'Czar' Cannon (Speaker of House of Representatives 1903–11)

1210 Matthew Quay (Civil War hero and Republican Party National Committee chairman)   **1211** Mary Clemmer (19th-century journalist)

1212 Ewan Clague (economist)   **1213** Henry 'Marse' Watterson (advisor to Pres. Roosevelt)

Manx Links with Washington

(Des Fusion Design. Litho BDT)

2006 (23 May). P 14 (C).

1302	**1208**	28p. multicoloured	55	60
1303	**1209**	31p. multicoloured	60	65
1304	**1210**	45p. multicoloured	90	95
1305	**1211**	50p. multicoloured	1·00	1·10
1306	**1212**	76p. multicoloured	1·50	1·60
1307	**1213**	83p. multicoloured	1·70	1·80
1302/7	*Set of 6*		6·25	6·50
First Day Cover				7·75
Presentation Pack			7·75	

Nos. 1302/7 were issued to coincide with the Washington 2006 Stamp Exhibition.
Plate Nos.: All values 1A (×4).
Sheets: 25 (5×5).
Withdrawn: 22.5.2007.

1214 Peel P50   **1215** Trident

1216 Viking Sport   **1217** BMC GRP Mini

1218 Manxcar   **1219** P1000

Peel Cars

(Des Fusion Design. Litho Lowe-Martin, Canada)

2006 (23 July). P 13½ (C).

1308	**1214**	28p. multicoloured	55	60
1309	**1215**	31p. multicoloured	60	65
1310	**1216**	38p. multicoloured	75	80
1311	**1217**	41p. multicoloured	1·00	85
1312	**1218**	54p. multicoloured	1·50	1·20
1313	**1219**	94p. multicoloured	2·00	2·00
1308/13	*Set of 6*		6·00	6·00
First Day Cover				7·00
Presentation Pack			7·25	
Collectors Folder (top row of 5 and sheet top of each value)			35·00	

Plate Nos.: All values 1A (×4).
Sheets: 25 (5×5).
Withdrawn: 21.7.2007.

1220 'Ewan Christian'

1221 'Dame Agatha Christie' (John Gay)

1222 'Sir Hall Caine' (Harry Furniss)

1223 'William Bligh' John Condé, after John Russell)

1224 'Lady Maria Callcott' (Sir Thomas Lawrence)

1225 'John Martin' (Henry Warren)

1226 'Sir John Betjeman' (Stephen Hyde)

1227 'Sir Edward Elgar' (Herbert Lambert)

150th Anniversary of National Portrait Gallery, London

(Des The Agency. Litho Lowe-Martin, Canada)

2006 (25 Aug). P 13½ (C).

1314	1220	28p. multicoloured	55	60
1315	1221	31p. multicoloured	60	65
1316	1222	38p. multicoloured	75	80
1317	1223	41p. multicoloured	80	85
1318	1224	44p. multicoloured	90	95
1319	1225	54p. multicoloured	1·10	1·20
1320	1226	64p. multicoloured	1·30	1·40
1321	1227	96p. multicoloured	1·90	2·00
1314/21		Set of 8	7·75	8·25
First Day Cover				9·25
Presentation Pack			9·50	

Plate Nos.: All values 1A (×4).
Sheets: 25 (5×5).
Withdrawn: 24.8.2007.

1228 Christmas Tree and Gifts

1229 Tree with Three Legs of Mann Decoration at Top

1230 Tree with White Decorations

1231 Monkey-puzzle Tree and Three Legs of Mann Symbols

1232 Tree with Yellow Three Legs of Mann Decorations

1233 Tree with Brown Three Legs of Mann Decorations

Christmas. Trees

(Des Emma Cooke and The Agency. Litho and die-stamped BDT)

2006 (11 Oct).

(a) PVA gum. P 14 (C)

1322	1228	28p. multicoloured	55	60
1323	1229	31p. multicoloured	60	65
1324	1230	41p. multicoloured	80	85
1325	1231	44p. multicoloured	90	95
1326	1232	72p. multicoloured	1·40	1·50
1327	1233	94p. multicoloured	1·90	2·00
1322/7		Set of 6	6·00	6·50
First Day Cover				7·50
Presentation Pack			7·75	

(b) Size 28×39 mm. Self-adhesive booklet stamps. P 9×9½ (die-cut)

1328	1228	28p. multicoloured	55	60
		a. Booklet pane. No. 1328×10	5·50	
1329	1229	31p. multicoloured	60	65
		a. Booklet pane.No. 1329×10	6·00	

Nos. 1323, 1325 and 1329 include the 'EUROPA 2006' emblem.
Nos. 1328/9 were only available in £2.80 and £3.10 booklets, Nos. SB64/5.

Plate Nos.: All values 1A (×5).
Sheets: 25 (5×5); 31p., 44p. also 10 (5×2).
Withdrawn: 10.10.2007.

1234 Benjamin Bunny (28p.); Jemima Puddle-duck (50p.); Peter Rabbit (72p.); Jeremy Fisher (75p.) (*Illustration reduced. Actual size 170×75 mm*)

The Tales of Beatrix Potter

(Des The Agency. Litho Lowe-Martin, Canada)

2006 (11 Oct). Sheet 170×75 mm. P 13 (C).

MS1330	1234	28p. multicoloured; 50p. multicoloured; 72p. multicoloured; 75p. multicoloured	4·50	4·75
First Day Cover				6·00
Presentation Pack			6·00	

Withdrawn: 10.10.2007.

Belgica '06 International Stamp Exhibition, Brussels

2006 (11 Oct). Sheet 148×210 mm. P 12½ (C).

MS1331	Nos. 1284/93	8·50	10·00

The logos for Belgica '06 and the RSPB are included in the margin of **MS**1331.

Withdrawn: 10.10.2007.

Year Folder 2006

2006 (11 Oct). Comprises Nos. 1270/93, **MS**1294/1327 and **MS**1330 (price £33).

Year Folder	65·00

Sold out: By 5.2008.

Year Pack 2006

2006 (11 Oct). Comprises Nos. 1270/93, **MS**1294/1327 and **MS**1330 (price £40).

Year Pack	80·00

Sold out: By 5.2008.

Post Office Yearbook

2006 (11 Oct). Comprises Nos. 1270/93, **MS**1294/1327 and **MS**1330/1 (price £35).
Yearbook .... 70·00
　　Sold out: By 11.2007.

  (1236 Joey Dunlop, 1237 David Jefferies)

1235 Steve Hislop　　**1236** Joey Dunlop　　**1237** David Jefferies

1238 Dave Molyneux　**1239** John McGuinness　**1240** Stanley Woods

1241 Geoff Duke　　　**1242** Bob McIntyre

1243 Giacomo Agostini　　**1244** Mike Hailwood

Centenary of Isle of Man TT Motor Cycle Races

(Des Ruth Sutherland. Litho BDT)

2007 (1 Jan). P 14½ (C).

1332	**1235**	(31p.) multicoloured	65	50
		a. Horiz strip of 5. Nos. 1332/6	4·00	4·00
1333	**1236**	(31p.) multicoloured	65	50
1334	**1237**	(31p.) multicoloured	65	50
1335	**1238**	(31p.) multicoloured	65	50
1336	**1239**	(31p.) multicoloured	65	50
1337	**1240**	(44p.) multicoloured	85	80
		a. Horiz strip of 5. Nos. 1337/41	5·25	5·25
1338	**1241**	(44p.) multicoloured	85	80
1339	**1242**	(44p.) multicoloured	85	80
1340	**1243**	(44p.) multicoloured	85	80
1341	**1244**	(44p.) multicoloured	85	80
1332/41	*Set of 10*		9·25	9·25
First Day Cover				9·75
Presentation Pack			10·00	
Collectors Folder (complete sheets)			45·00	
Souvenir Book			60·00	
Set of 2 Gutter Strips			20·00	
Stamp Cards (pre-paid) (set of 10)			16·00	16·00
Deluxe Stamp Cards (set of 14 Nos. 1332/41 and				
4 TT trophy cards) (mint)			25·00	

　　Nos. 1332/6 are inscribed 'UK' and were sold at 31p. each. Nos. 1337/41 are inscribed 'E' and were sold at 44p. each.
　　Plate Nos.: Both values 1A (×4).
　　Sheets: 20 (2 blocks 5×2). Nos. 1332/6 and 1337/41 were each printed together, *se-tenant*, as horizontal strips of five stamps in sheets containing two blocks of ten separated by a large illustrated gutter. Withdrawn: 31.12.2007.

A hardback souvenir book (price £30) contained a set of Nos. 1332/41 in a smaller format and perf 15. Each stamp printed in two vertical strips of five includes a single label. The page was also available separately (price £5).
On 3 June 2013 No.1338 was issued in an illustrated sheetlet of 12 stamps (price £8.52).

1245 Scouts hiking near South Barrule　**1246** Scout Investiture on Douglas Beach　**1247** Backpacking below Cronk-ny-Arrey-Laa

1248 Manx Scouts on Parade at St. Johns　**1249** Sea kayaking off Laxey Beach　**1250** Manx Scouts operating the TT Scoreboard

1251 Two Scouts at Camp, 1913 (50p.); Scout Camp with Bell Tent and Open Fire, 1913 (£1.50) (*Illustration reduced. Actual size 135×85 mm*)

Europa. Centenary of Scouting

(Des M. J. Southall. Litho BDT)

2007 (22 Feb). P 14 (C).

1342	**1245**	28p. multicoloured	65	65
		a. Booklet pane. Nos. 1342/4 with margins all round	3·00	
		b. Booklet pane. Nos. 1342, 1344 and 1346 with margins all round	4·50	
1343	**1246**	31p. multicoloured	75	75
		a. Booklet pane. Nos. 1343, 1345 and 1347 with margins all round	6·00	
1344	**1247**	44p. multicoloured	1·00	1·00
1345	**1248**	72p. multicoloured	1·70	1·70
		a. Booklet pane. Nos. 1345/7 with margins all round	7·50	
1346	**1249**	83p. multicoloured	2·00	2·00
1347	**1250**	£1 multicoloured	2·40	2·40
1342/7	*Set of 6*		8·50	8·50
First Day Cover				9·00
Presentation Pack			9·00	
Collectors Folder			45·00	
MS1348	135×85 mm. **1251** 50p., £1.50 multicoloured		4·75	4·75
		a. Booklet pane. As No. **MS**1348, but 155×96 mm with additional margins showing Scout emblems and a line of roulettes at left	4·75	
First Day Cover				5·25
Presentation Pack			5·25	

　　Nos. 1343/4 include the 'EUROPA 2007' emblem.
　　Plate Nos.: All values 1A (×4).
　　Sheets: 25 (5×5); 31p., 44p. also 10 (5×2). Withdrawn: 21.2.2008.

1252 Wedding, 1947   **1253** Queen and Duke of Edinburgh, c. 1955   **1254** Queen and Duke of Edinburgh, c. 1965

1255 Queen and Duke of Edinburgh, c. 1977   **1256** Queen and Duke of Edinburgh, c. 1997   **1257** Queen and Duke of Edinburgh, c. 2002

Diamond Wedding of Queen Elizabeth II and Duke of Edinburgh

(Des EDL Design. Litho BDT)

2007 (22 Feb). P 14 (C).

1349	**1252**	60p. multicoloured	1·25	1·00
		a. Horiz strip of 6. Nos. 1349/54	8·50	8·50
1350	**1253**	60p. multicoloured	1·25	1·00
1351	**1254**	60p. multicoloured	1·25	1·00
1352	**1255**	60p. multicoloured	1·25	1·00
1353	**1256**	60p. multicoloured	1·25	1·00
1354	**1257**	60p. multicoloured	1·25	1·00
1349/54 Set of 6			8·50	8·50
First Day Cover				9·00
Presentation Pack			9·00	

Plate Nos.: 1A (x4).
Sheets: 30 (6×5). Nos. 1349/54 were printed together, *se-tenant*, as horizontal strips of six stamps in sheets of 30.
Withdrawn: 21.2.2008.

1258 'Headland, Cornaa'   **1259** 'Headland, Sound'

1260 'St Marks Church'   **1261** 'Castletown Harbour Moonlight'

1262 'Bridge House, Castletown'   **1263** 'Winter Sun'

1264 'In Ancient Times'   **1265** 'Bracken Mountain'

Watercolour Paintings by Norman Sayle

(Des EDL. Litho Lowe-Martin, Canada)

2007 (12 Apr).

(a) PVA gum. P 12½×13

1355	**1258**	28p. multicoloured	65	65
1356	**1259**	28p. multicoloured	65	65
1357	**1260**	31p. multicoloured	75	75
1358	**1261**	31p. multicoloured	75	75
1359	**1262**	42p. multicoloured	1·00	1·00
1360	**1263**	44p. multicoloured	1·00	1·00
1361	**1264**	65p. multicoloured	1·50	1·50
1362	**1265**	75p. multicoloured	1·70	1·70
1355/62 Set of 8			8·00	8·00
First Day Cover				8·50
Presentation Pack			8·50	

(b) Self-adhesive. Die-cut P 10

1363	**1258**	28p. multicoloured	85	85
		a. Booklet pane. Nos. 1363/4, each×5	8·50	
1364	**1259**	28p. multicoloured	85	85
1365	**1260**	31p. multicoloured	95	95
		a. Booklet pane. Nos. 1365/6, each×5	9·25	
1366	**1261**	31p. multicoloured	95	95
1363/6 Set of 4			3·50	3·50

Nos. 1363/4 and 1365/6 were only issued in £2.80 or £3.10 stamp booklets, Nos. SB67/8.
Plate Nos.: All values 1A (each×4).
Sheets: 25 (5×5).
Withdrawn: 11.4.2008.

1266 King John granting Royal Charter   **1267** Liverpool Cathedral and Liverpool Metropolitan Cathedral

1268 Statue of Capt. Noel Chavasse ('Liverpool war heroes')   **1269** St. George's Hall

1270 Port of Liverpool   **1271** The Wall of Fame

800th Anniversary of the Royal Charter of Liverpool

(Des Fusion Design. Litho BDT)

2007 (20 Apr). P 14 (C).

1367	**1266**	31p. multicoloured	70	70
1368	**1267**	48p. multicoloured	1·10	1·10
1369	**1268**	54p. multicoloured	1·30	1·30
1370	**1269**	74p. multicoloured	1·70	1·70
1371	**1270**	80p. multicoloured	1·90	1·90
1372	**1271**	£1 multicoloured	2·30	2·30
1367/72 Set of 6			9·00	9·00

First Day Cover... 9·50
Presentation Pack... 9·50
   The plate numbers for Nos. 1367/72 were omitted from the sheets in error.
   Sheets: 20 (5×4).
   Withdrawn: 18.4.2008.

1272 *Susan Constant* and Map showing Voyage from England to Virginia, 1607

1273 Capt. Christopher Newport and *Susan Constant*, *Godspeed* and *Discovery* on the James River

1274 James Fort and James River, 1607

1275 Algonquin Princess Pocahontas and Capt. John Smith

1276 Jamestown Settlement, 1607

1277 Powhatan Village

400th Anniversary of Jamestown, Virginia, USA

(Des Julia Ashby Smyth. Litho Cartor)

2007 (26 Apr). P 13½ (C).
1373	**1272**	28p. multicoloured.........................	65	65
1374	**1273**	31p. multicoloured.........................	75	75
1375	**1274**	44p. multicoloured.........................	1·00	1·00
1376	**1275**	54p. multicoloured.........................	1·30	1·30
1377	**1276**	78p. multicoloured.........................	1·90	1·90
1378	**1277**	90p. multicoloured.........................	2·20	2·20
1373/8	*Set of 6*..		7·75	7·75
First Day Cover..				8·25
Presentation Pack..			8·25	

   Plate Nos.: All values 1A (×4).
   Sheets: 15 (3×5) with enlarged illustrated right margins.
   Withdrawn: 25.4.2008.

1278 James Brown (25p.); Joseph Cunningham and Holiday Camp, c 1895 (40p.); William Gill and First Landing Stage at Liverpool, c 1857 (80p.); Dalrymple Maitland and 'Liverpool Echo' Newspaper (80p.) (*Illustration reduced. Actual size 170×75 mm*)

800 Years of Trade between Liverpool and the Isle of Man

(Des Fusion Design. Litho)

2007 (10 May). Sheet 170×75 mm. P 14 (C).
MS1379 **1278** 25p., 40p., 80p.×2 multicoloured............	5·50	6·00
First Day Cover..		7·00
Presentation Pack..	7·00	

   Withdrawn: 9.5.2008.

TT Race Winners

2007 (9 July). Sheet 180×235 mm. P 14½ (C).
MS1379a Nos. 1332/41....................................	11·50	12·00
TT Race Winners Folder...................................		

   Plate Nos. 1A (x4).
   Sheets: 10 (2 blocks 5×1). Nos. 1332/41 were printed together, *se-tenant*, as horizontal strips of five stamps in sheets containing two blocks of five stamps and five *se-tenant* labels separated by a large illustrated gutter.
   Withdrawn: 8.7.2008.

21st World Scout Jamboree, Chelmsford, England

2007 (26 July). No. MS1348 additionally inscr with jamboree emblem on the margin.
MS1380 50p., £1.50 multicoloured.....................	5·00	5·50
Stamp Cards (pre-paid) (Nos. 1342, 1344, 1346,		
as No. MS1380)..	9·00	9·00

   The miniature sheet depicted on the stamp card differs from Type **1251** and MS1380. The face value is omitted, the 'centenary of scouting 2007' inscription is at bottom left and the Jamboree emblem at top right.
   Withdrawn: 25.7.2008.

1279 Map by John Speed, 1605

1280 Map by Capt. Greenville Collins, 1693

1281 Map published by John Drinkwater based on Trigonometrical Survey, 1826

1282 Ordnance Survey County Series Map, 1870

1283 Six-inch Series Map based on National Grid, 1975

1284 1:100,000 Map, 2006

Maps of the Isle of Man

(Des Eddie Cassidy. Litho Lowe-Martin)

2007 (1 Aug). P 12½×13 (C).
1381	**1279**	28p. multicoloured.........................	65	65
1382	**1280**	31p. multicoloured.........................	75	75
1383	**1281**	44p. multicoloured.........................	1·10	1·10
1384	**1282**	48p. multicoloured.........................	1·10	1·10
1385	**1283**	75p. multicoloured.........................	1·80	1·80
1386	**1284**	88p. multicoloured.........................	2·10	2·10
1381/6	*Set of 6*..		7·50	7·50
First Day Cover..				8·00
Presentation Pack..			8·00	

   Plate Nos.: All values 1A (×4).
   Sheets: 20 (5×4).
   Imprint: Lower side margins.
   Withdrawn: 31.7.2008.

1285 Captain John Ross and *Victory* trapped in Ice

1286 Flares from *Victory* guide returning Exploration Parties

1287 *Victory's* Crew hunting
with Inuit

1288 Hunted Musk Ox

1289 Crew on 300 Mile Trek
after abandoning *Victory*

1290 Crew in Whaleboats
rescued by Whaler *Isabella*

**International Polar Year (1st issue). Voyage of the *Victory*
to the North Pole, 1829–33**

(Des Peter Hearsey. Litho Lowe-Martin)

2007 (20 Aug). P 12½×13 (C).

1387	**1285**	28p. multicoloured	65	65
1388	**1286**	31p. multicoloured	70	70
1389	**1287**	55p. multicoloured	1·30	1·30
1390	**1288**	75p. multicoloured	1·80	1·80
1391	**1289**	90p. multicoloured	2·10	2·10
1392	**1290**	117p. multicoloured	2·75	2·75
1387/92 *Set of 6*			9·25	9·25
First Day Cover				9·75
Presentation Pack			9·75	

Plate Nos.: All values 1A (×4).
Sheets: 25 (5×5).
Withdrawn: 19.8.2008.

1291 'Ben-my-Chree' Log Cabin, Tagish Lake, British Columbia
(50p.); Graham 'Jimmy' Oates taking Motorcycle and Sidecar
along Railroad Track to Hudson Bay, 1932 (50p.); Kermode
Bear (subspecies of Grizzly Bear) (75p.); Dog Sled and
Hudson Bay Post Office, 1931–61) (75p.) (*Illustration reduced.
Actual size 170×75 mm*)

**International Polar Year (2nd issue). Manx Connections with
Northern Canada**

(Des Kcreative. Litho Lowe-Martin)

2007 (20 Aug). Sheet 170×75 mm. P 13 (C).

MS1393 **1291** 50p.×2, 75p.×2 multicoloured		6·00	6·50
First Day Cover			9·50
Presentation Pack		9·50	

Withdrawn: 19.8.2008.

1292 Harold Leece
ploughing Manx Style

1293 John Costain with
1947 Ferguson Tractor
and Trailed Plough

1294 Jim Caine with
Digger Plough

1295 Herbie Moore with
Swing Plough

1296 Jack Clague
ploughing World Style

1297 Jean Burns
ploughing

European Vintage Ploughing Championships, Isle of Man (Sepac)

(Des Peter Hearsey and Eddie Cassidy. Litho Cartor)

2007 (1 Sept). P 13 (C).

1394	**1292**	28p. multicoloured (a)	65	65
1395	**1293**	31p. multicoloured (a)	70	70
1396	**1294**	48p. multicoloured (b)	1·10	1·10
1397	**1295**	71p. multicoloured (a)	1·70	1·70
1398	**1296**	90p. multicoloured (a)	2·10	2·10
1399	**1297**	£1.27 multicoloured (a)	3·00	3·00
1394/9 *Set of 6*			9·25	9·25
First Day Cover				9·75
Presentation Pack			9·75	

No. 1396 is inscr 'sepac'. This stamp was also available in a folder
with ten other 'sepac' logo stamps issued by other participating
administrations (cost £12.50).
Plate Nos.: All values 1A (×4).
Sheets: 25 (5×5).
Printings: (a) 1.9.07; (b) 1.10.07.
Withdrawn: 30.9.2008.

1298 Angel
playing Trumpet

1299 Angel
playing Lute

1300 Angel
wearing Crown

1301 Angel with
Harp

1302 Angel with
Hands clasped
in Prayer

Christmas. 'Hark the Herald Angels Sing'

(Des Julia Ashby Smyth. Litho Lowe-Martin, Canada)

2007 (19 Oct). Self-adhesive. Die-cut perf 13×13½.

1400	**1298**	28p. multicoloured	65	65
1401	**1299**	31p. multicoloured	75	75
1402	**1300**	69p. multicoloured	1·60	1·60
1403	**1301**	78p. multicoloured	1·80	1·80
1404	**1302**	£1.24 multicoloured	3·00	3·00
1400/4 *Set of 5*			7·75	7·75

First Day Cover .... 8·25
Presentation Pack.. 8·25
　　The backing paper of Nos. 1400/4 is divided into rectangles by lines of rouletting.
　　　　Plate Nos.: All values 1A (each×5).
　　　　Sheets: 20 (5×4).
　　　　Withdrawn: 17.10.2008.

Year Folder 2007

2007 (19 Oct). Comprises Nos. 1332/62, 1367/79 and 1381/1404 (price £40).
Year Folder .... 80·00

Year Pack 2007

2007 (19 Oct). Comprises Nos. 1332/62, 1367/79 and 1381/1404 (price £49).
Year Pack £100

Post Office Yearbook

　2007 (19 Oct). Comprises Nos. 1332/62, 1367/79 and 1381/1404 (price £40).
Yearbook .... 80·00

1303 Queen Elizabeth 2

1304 Queen Mary 2

1305 Queen Victoria

Cunard Ocean Liners

(Des Kcreative. Litho Enschedé)

2008 (13 Jan). P 14×13½ (C).
1405	**1303**	£1 multicoloured	3·00	3·50
1405a	**1304**	£1 multicoloured	3·00	3·50
1405b	**1305**	£1 multicoloured	3·00	3·50
1405/b		Set of 3...	7·00	8·00

MS1405c 170×75 mm. Nos. 1405/b................ 7·00　8·00
First Day Cover (**MS**1405c) .... 　　8·75
Presentation Pack (**MS**1405c) .... 8·75
QE2 Farewell Season Folder (full sheet of No. 1405 and special first day cover) .... 50·00
　Nos. 1405/b were only available from the Isle of Man Philatelic Bureau in complete sheetlets, sold for £10 each, or from the miniature sheet.
　　　　Plate Nos.: 1A (×6).
　　　　Sheets: 10 (2 columns 1×5). Nos. 1405/b were each printed in separate sheetlets of ten stamps and ten labels containing two vertical strips of stamps alternated with two columns of stamp-size labels showing the interior of the ship, so that each stamp is accompanied by a se-tenant label at left.
　　　　Withdrawn: 12.1.2009.

1306 H.P. 0/400 and Bristol F2B Fighter　　1307 Avro 504N and Westland Wapiti

1308 Hawker Hurricane and Short Sunderland

1309 Gloster Meteor and Westland Whirlwind

1310 Hawker Hunter and E.E. Canberra

1311 BAE Harrier and Lockheed Hercules

90th Anniversary of the Royal Air Force

(Des Keith Woodcock and Kcreative. Litho BDT)

2008 (15 Jan). P 13½ (C).
1406	**1306**	31p. multicoloured	60	60
		a. Horiz strip of 3. Nos. 1406/8.........	2·20	2·20
		b. Booklet pane. Nos. 1406/9 with margins all round	4·25	
		c. Booklet pane. Nos. 1406/7 and 1409/10 with margins all round..	5·75	
		d. Booklet pane. Nos. 1406/7 and 1410/11 with margins all round..	5·75	
1407	**1307**	31p. multicoloured	60	60
1408	**1308**	31p. multicoloured	60	60
		a. Booklet pane. Nos. 1408/11 with margins all round	7·25	
1409	**1309**	90p. multicoloured	1·70	1·70
		a. Horiz strip of 3. Nos. 1409/11.......	6·50	6·50
1410	**1310**	90p. multicoloured	1·70	1·70
1411	**1311**	90p. multicoloured	1·70	1·70
1406/11		Set of 6...	8·50	8·50

First Day Cover .... 10·00
Presentation Pack.. 10·00
Souvenir Folder (full sheets)............................. 35·00
　　　　Plate Nos.: All values 1A (each×4).
　　　　Sheets: 12 (2 blocks 3×2). Nos. 1406/8 and 1409/11 were each printed together, se-tenant, as horizontal strips of three stamps in sheets containing two blocks of six separated by a large illustrated gutter.
　　　　Withdrawn: 14.1.2009.

1312 The Pagan Lady of Peel　　1313 Ship Burial

1314 Godred Crovan ('King Orry')

1315 Gautr Bjornsson the Sculptor

1316 Sigurd the Dragon Slayer   **1317** Coming of Christianity

The Viking Age on the Isle of Man

(Des Victor Ambrus and Kcreative. Litho BDT)

2008 (18 Feb). P 13½ (C).

1412	**1312**	28p. multicoloured	65	65
1413	**1313**	31p. multicoloured	75	75
1414	**1314**	44p. multicoloured	1·00	1·00
1415	**1315**	54p. multicoloured	1·30	1·30
1416	**1316**	69p. multicoloured	1·60	1·60
1417	**1317**	£1.24 multicoloured	3·00	3·00
1412/17	*Set of 6*		8·25	8·25
First Day Cover				9·75
Presentation Pack			9·75	

Plate Nos.: All values 1A (each×4).
Sheets: 25 (5×5).
Withdrawn: 17.2.2009.

1318 Isle of Man Bank £1 Note, 1956   **1319** Isle of Man Govt £10 Note, 1972

1320 Manx Bank (1882–1900) £1 Note   **1321** Isle of Man Govt 50p. Decimal Note, 1969

1322 Isle of Man Govt £50 Note, 1983   **1323** Parr's Bank £1 Note, 1918

Bank Notes of the Isle of Man

(Des Kcreative. Litho BDT)

2008 (7 Apr).

(a) PVA gum. P 14

1418	**1318**	30p. multicoloured	70	70
1419	**1319**	31p. multicoloured	75	75
1420	**1320**	44p. multicoloured	1·00	1·00
1421	**1321**	56p. multicoloured	1·40	1·40
1422	**1322**	85p. multicoloured	2·00	2·00
1423	**1323**	114p. multicoloured	2·75	2·75
1418/23	*Set of 6*		8·50	8·50
First Day Cover				10·00
Presentation Pack			10·00	

(b) Self-adhesive. Die-cut perf 12×12½

1424	**1318**	30p. multicoloured	80	1·00
		a. Booklet pane. No. 1424×10	7·50	

No. 1424 was only issued in £3 stamp booklets, No. SB70.
Plate Nos.: All values 1A (each×4).
Sheets: 20 (2 columns 1×10). Nos. 1418/23 were each printed in separate sheetlets containing two vertical strips of stamps alternated with two columns of stamp-size labels so that each stamp is accompanied by a *se-tenant* label at left.
Withdrawn: 6.4.2009 (Nos. 1418/23), 3.2010 (No. 1424).

1324 Archery (1p.); Show-jumping (2p.); Cycling (3p.); Hand holding Olympic Torch (94p.) (*Illustration reduced. Actual size 170×75 mm*)

Olympic Games, Beijing

(Des Pobjoy Mint Studio and Solus Strategic Limited. Litho Lowe-Martin, Canada)

2008 (21 Apr). Sheet 170×75 mm. P 13½ (C).

MS1425	1p., 2p., 3p., 94p. multicoloured	2·40	3·00
First Day Cover			4·00
Presentation Pack		4·00	

Withdrawn: 20.4.2009.

1325 Cornish Flag   **1326** Isle of Man Flag

1327 Scottish Flag   **1328** Breton Flag

1329 Irish Flag   **1330** Flag of Asturias

1331 Welsh Flag   **1332** Flag of Galicia

Interceltique. Flags of Celtic Countries and Europa

(Des Pete Jones Design. Litho Lowe-Martin, Canada)

2008 (12 May–1 Aug). P 13½ (C).

1426	**1325**	20p. multicoloured	45	45
1427	**1326**	30p. multicoloured	70	70
1428	**1327**	31p. multicoloured	70	70
1429	**1328**	48p. multicoloured	1·10	1·10
1430	**1329**	50p. multicoloured	1·20	1·20
1431	**1330**	56p. multicoloured	1·30	1·30
1432	**1331**	72p. multicoloured	1·70	1·70
1433	**1332**	£1.13 multicoloured	2·75	2·75
1426/33	*Set of 8*		9·75	9·75

1430 *Leaning Trees*   **1431** *Old Laxey*

Watercolour Paintings by Archibald Knox (Sepac)

(Des Icon Imaging. Litho Lowe-Martin)

2009 (16 Sept). P 12½ (C).

1542	**1426**	32p. multicoloured	75	75
1543	**1427**	33p. multicoloured	75	75
1544	**1428**	56p. multicoloured	1·25	1·25
1545	**1429**	62p. multicoloured	1·60	1·60
1546	**1430**	81p. multicoloured	1·90	1·90
1547	**1431**	182p. multicoloured	4·25	4·25
1542/7 *Set of 6*			10·50	10·50
First Day Cover				12·00
Presentation Pack			12·00	

No. 1544 is inscr 'sepac'. This stamp was also available in a folder with ten other 'sepac' logo stamps issued by other participating administrations.

Plate Nos.: All values 1A (each×4).
Sheets: 15 (5×3).
Withdrawn: 15.9.2010.

1432 Captain James Teare and SS *Ellan Vannin*; SS *Ellan Vannin* in Ramsey Harbour (*Illustration reduced. Actual size 170×75 mm*)

Centenary of Sinking of the SS *Ellan Vannin* (steam packet)

(Des Peter Hearsey. Litho BDT)

2009 (1 Oct). Sheet 170×75 mm. P 14 (C).

MS1548	**1432**	£1·50×2 multicoloured	7·00	7·00
First Day Cover				8·50
Presentation Pack			8·50	

Withdrawn: 30.9.2010.

1433 Father Christmas putting Present into Stocking   **1434** Writing List   **1435** Carrying Sack of Toys

1436 Carrying Wrapped Present   **1437** With Archbishop's Staff, Mitre and Robes   **1438** With Christmas Pudding and Wine Goblet

Christmas. Father Christmas

(Des Casco Design Services. Litho BDT)

2009 (20 Oct).

(a) Ordinary gum. P 14 (C)

1549	**1433**	30p. multicoloured	70	70
1550	**1434**	33p. multicoloured	75	75
1551	**1435**	56p. multicoloured	1·25	1·25
1552	**1436**	62p. multicoloured	1·60	1·60
1553	**1437**	81p. multicoloured	1·75	1·75
1554	**1438**	90p. multicoloured	2·40	2·40
1549/54 *Set of 6*			8·25	8·25
First Day Cover				10·00
Presentation Pack			10·00	

(b) Self-adhesive. Size 26×37 mm. Die-cut perf 14

1555	**1433**	30p. multicoloured	70	70
1556	**1434**	33p. multicoloured	75	75

Plate Nos.: All values 1A (each×4).
Sheets: Nos. 1549/54 25 (5×5); Nos. 1555/6 30 (6×5).
Withdrawn: 19.10.2011.

Year Folder 2009

2009 (20 Oct). Comprises Nos. 1473/1500, 1505/34, 1535/40 and 1542/54 (price £53).

Year Folder		£100

Year Pack 2009

2009 (20 Oct). Comprises Nos. 1473/1500, 1505/34, 1535/40 and 1542/54 (price £62.50).

Year Pack		£110

Post Office Yearbook

2009 (20 Oct). Comprises Nos. 1473/1500, 1505/34, 1535/40 and 1542/54 (price £55).

Yearbook		£100

1439 Woman walking in Lane   **1440** Angler

1441 Yachtsman   **1442** Climber

1443 Children riding Ponies   **1444** Apple picking

1445 Unloading Kayak   **1446** Motorcyclist

1447 Children on Rocky Shore

1448 Horses Ploughing at Cregneash National Folk Museum

Island Life

(Des truly London. Litho Lowe-Martin)

2010 (12 Jan).

		(a) Ordinary gum. P 12½ (C)		
1557	**1439**	(32p.) multicoloured	75	75
		a. Horiz strip of 4. Nos. 1557/60	3·00	3·00
1558	**1440**	(32p.) multicoloured	75	75
1559	**1441**	(32p.) multicoloured	75	75
1560	**1442**	(32p.) multicoloured	75	75
1561	**1443**	(33p.) multicoloured	75	75
		a. Horiz strip of 4. Nos. 1561/4	3·00	3·00
1562	**1444**	(33p.) multicoloured	75	75
1563	**1445**	(33p.) multicoloured	75	75
1564	**1446**	(33p.) multicoloured	75	75
1565	**1447**	56p. multicoloured	1·25	1·25
1566	**1448**	90p. multicoloured	2·40	2·40
1557/66 *Set of 10*			9·50	9·50
First Day Cover				11·00
Presentation Pack			11·00	
		(b) Self-adhesive. Die-cut perf 13½×13		
1567	**1439**	(32p.) multicoloured	75	75
		a. Booklet pane. Nos. 1567/70, each×3	9·00	
1568	**1440**	(32p.) multicoloured	75	75
1569	**1441**	(32p.) multicoloured	75	75
1570	**1442**	(32p.) multicoloured	75	75
1571	**1443**	(33p.) multicoloured	75	75
		a. Booklet pane. Nos. 1571/4, each×3	9·00	
1572	**1444**	(33p.) multicoloured	75	75
1573	**1445**	(33p.) multicoloured	75	75
1574	**1446**	(33p.) multicoloured	75	75
1567/74 *Set of 10*			6·75	6·75

Nos. 1557/60 and 1567/70 were inscribed 'IOM RATE' and originally sold for 32p. each.

Nos. 1561/4 and 1571/4 were inscribed 'UK RATE' and originally sold for 33p. each.

Nos. 1567/70 and 1571/4 were only issued in separate booklets of 12 stamps, Nos. SB74/5.

Plate Nos.: All values 1A (each×4).

Sheets: 40 (8×5). Nos. 1557/60 and 1561/4 were each printed together, *se-tenant*, as horizontal strips of four throughout the sheets. Withdrawn: 11.1.2011.

1449 Two Rainbows

1450 Company of Rainbows and Leaders

1451 Brownies holding Badges

1452 Five Brownies

1453 Girl Guide

1454 Guides and Leaders on Parade

1455 Senior Section Members

1456 Queen Elizabeth II meeting Guide Leaders

1457 Manx Guide Leaders (£1.50); Trefoil Guild Members planting Tree, 1985 (£1.50) (*Illustration reduced. Actual size 170×75 mm*)

Centenary of Girlguiding

(Des Andrew Robinson. Litho BDT)

2010 (18 Feb). P. 14 (C).

1575	**1449**	32p. multicoloured	75	75
		a. Horiz pair. Nos. 1575/6	1·50	1·50
1576	**1450**	32p. multicoloured	75	75
1577	**1451**	33p. multicoloured	75	75
		a. Horiz pair. Nos. 1577/8	1·50	1·50
1578	**1452**	33p. multicoloured	75	75
1579	**1453**	56p. multicoloured	1·25	1·25
		a. Horiz pair. Nos. 1579/80	2·50	2·50
1580	**1454**	56p. multicoloured	1·25	1·25
1581	**1455**	£1 multicoloured	2·25	2·25
		a. Horiz pair. Nos. 1581/2	4·50	4·50
1582	**1456**	£1 multicoloured	2·25	2·25
1575/82 *Set of 8*			10·00	10·00
First Day Cover				11·00
Presentation Pack			11·00	
MS1583 170×75 mm. **1457** £1.50×2 multicoloured			7·00	7·00
First Day Cover				8·50
Presentation Pack			8·50	

Nos. 1577 and 1579 include the 'EUROPA' emblem.

Plate Nos.: All values 1A (each×4).

Sheets: 12 (2 blocks 2×3) 33p., 56p. also separate sheets of 10 (2×5). Nos. 1575/6, 1577/8, 1579/80 and 1581/2 were each printed together, *se-tenant*, as horizontal pairs in sheetlets of 12 containing two blocks of six separated by a large illustrated vertical gutter. Withdrawn: 17.2.2011.

1458 Messerschmitt BF109 and Defiant

1459 Spitfire and Messerschmitt BF109

1460 Junkers Ju87 and Hurricane

1461 Messerschmitt BF110 and Hurricane

1462 Blenheim I and Junkers 88

1463 Heinkel III and Spitfire

1464 1981 60th Anniversary of Royal British Legion 20p. Stamp and Ship crowded with Evacuated Troops, Dunkirk, 1940 (£1.50); 1990 50th Anniversary of Battle of Britain Pair of 24p. Stamps and Aircrew running for Planes (£1.50) (*Illustration reduced. Actual size 170×75 mm*)

70th Anniversary of the Battle of Britain

(Des Keith Woodcock (Nos. 1584/9) and Kcreative. Litho BDT)

2010 (20 Apr). P 13½ (C).

1584	**1458**	70p. multicoloured	1·60	1·60
		a. Horiz strip of 3. Nos. 1584/6	5·25	5·25
1585	**1459**	70p. multicoloured	1·60	1·60
1586	**1460**	70p. multicoloured	1·60	1·60
1587	**1461**	70p. multicoloured	1·60	1·60
		a. Horiz strip of 3. Nos. 1587/9	5·25	5·25
1588	**1462**	70p. multicoloured	1·60	1·60
1589	**1463**	70p. multicoloured	1·60	1·60
1584/9 *Set of 6*			10·00	10·00
First Day Cover				10·50
Presentation Pack			10·50	
Commemorative Folder (complete sheets)			40·00	
MS1590 170×75 mm. **1464** £1.50×2 multicoloured			7·00	7·00
First Day Cover				11·00
Presentation Pack			11·00	

MS1590 also commemorates the 70th anniversary of Operations Dynamo and Ariel (evacuation of troops from Dunkirk).

Plate Nos.: Both sheets 1A (each×4).
Sheets: 12 (2 blocks 3×2). Nos. 1584/6 and 1587/9 were each printed together, *se-tenant*, as horizontal strips of three stamps in sheets containing two blocks of six separated by a large illustrated horizontal gutter.
Withdrawn: 19.4.2011.

1465 King George V and Queen Mary at Grand Hall, Douglas, 1920 and Cast of Great Britain 1d. George V Stamp

1466 King George V and Queen Mary, Isle of Man, 1920 and Cape of Good Hope *Tête-Bêche* Pairs of 1861 1d. 'Hope' Stamps

1467 King George V and Queen Mary arriving at Queen's Pier, Ramsey, 1920 and Great Britain 1910 2d. Tyrian Plum Stamp

1468 King George V and Queen Mary with Nurses, Ramsey, and Oil Rivers Protectorate 1893 20s. on 1s. Stamp

1469 King George V planting Tree at Bishopscourt, 1920 and George V ½d. Green Stamp

1470 King George V and Queen Mary at Castletown and Mauritius 1847 2d. Deep Blue Stamp

Centenary of Accession of King George V

(Des Kcreative. Litho Enschedé)

2010 (6 May). P 14 (C).

1591	**1465**	55p. multicoloured	1·25	1·25
1592	**1466**	60p. multicoloured	1·50	1·50
1593	**1467**	67p. multicoloured	1·60	1·60
1594	**1468**	96p. multicoloured	2·50	2·50
1595	**1469**	97p. multicoloured	2·50	2·50
1596	**1470**	£1.10 multicoloured	3·00	3·00
1591/6 *Set of 6*			11·50	11·50
First Day Cover				12·00
Presentation Pack			12·00	
Set of 6 Pre-Paid Postcards			5·50	15·00

Plate Nos.: All values 1A (each×4).
Sheets: 25 (5×5).
Withdrawn: 5.5.2011.

1471 Model T Speedster, 1915

1472 Model T Coupe, 1926

1473 Model T 7cwt Van, 1923

1474 Model T Town Car, 1912

1475 Model T Charabanc, 1922

1476 Model T Tourer, 1912

50th Anniversary of Model T Ford Register

(Des Peter Hearsey and Eddie Cassidy. Litho BDT)

2010 (7 May). P 13½ (C).

1597	**1741**	35p. multicoloured	80	80
1598	**1742**	36p. multicoloured	85	85
1599	**1743**	60p. multicoloured	1·50	1·50
1600	**1744**	74p. multicoloured	1·75	1·75
1601	**1745**	97p. multicoloured	2·25	2·25
1602	**1746**	172p. multicoloured	4·00	4·00
1597/602 *Set of 6*			11·00	11·00
First Day Cover				12·00
Presentation Pack			12·00	

Plate Nos.: 1A (each×4).
Sheets: 25 (5×5).
Withdrawn: 6.5.2011.

1477 Lord Derby Halfpenny, 1709 and Castle Rushen

1478 Matthew Boulton 'Cartwheel' Copper Penny, 1798 and Soho Mint, Birmingham

1479 Victorian Manx Farthing, 1839 and View of Douglas

1480 Revestment Act Bicentenary Gold Coin, 1965 and Manx Flag over Castle Rushen, c. 1760

1481 Decimal 5p. Coin, 1971 and Tower of Refuge

1482 £5 Coin, 2010 and Laxey Wheel

History of Manx Coins.

(Des Mike J. Southall. Litho Lowe-Martin)

2010 (24 June). P 13 (C).

1603	**1477**	35p. multicoloured	60	60
1604	**1478**	36p. multicoloured	65	65
1605	**1479**	55p. multicoloured	90	90
1606	**1480**	60p. multicoloured	1·00	1·00
1607	**1481**	67p. multicoloured	1·25	1·25
1608	**1482**	£1.87 multicoloured	6·50	6·50
1603/8 *Set of 6*			10·50	10·50
First Day Cover				12·00
Presentation Pack			12·00	

Plate Nos.: All values 1A (each×4).
Sheets: 25 (5×5).
Withdrawn: 23.6.2011.

1483 Steam Locomotive *Caledonia* with Trailer No. 57 at Snaefell Summit, 1995

1484 Steam Locomotive *Sutherland* and Manx Electric Railway Car No. 1, Laxey Station, 1998

1485 Steam Locomotive *Caledonia* with MER Trailer No. 58 at Bulgham

1486 Steam Locomotive *Loch* with Trailers No. 57 and 58 at Skinscoe on MER Line

1487 Manx Electric Railway Car No. 33 at Keristal on Steam Railway Line

1488 Steam Locomotives No. 4 *Loch* and No. 11 *Maitland*, 1993

Isle of Man Railways and Tramways

(Des Kcreative. Litho BDT)

2010 (24 June). P 14 (C).

1609	**1483**	35p. multicoloured	65	65
1610	**1484**	36p. multicoloured	70	70
1611	**1485**	55p. multicoloured	95	95
1612	**1486**	88p. multicoloured	1·25	1·25
1613	**1487**	£1.32 multicoloured	1·40	1·40
1614	**1488**	£1.46 multicoloured	6·50	6·50
1609/14 *Set of 6*			11·00	11·00
First Day Cover				13·00
Presentation Pack			13·00	
MS1615 150×210 mm. Nos. 1609/14 and three stamp-size labels			11·00	11·00

Plate Nos.: All values 1A (each×4).
Sheets: 15 (3×5).
Withdrawn: 23.6.2011.

Girlguiding UK Centenary Camp

2010 (31 July). P 14 (C).

MS1616 170×75 mm.	**1457**	£1.50×2 multicoloured	7·00	7·00
First Day Cover				9·00

No. **MS**1583 additionally inscr with 'GIRLGUIDING UK CENTENARY CAMP Harewood House 31 July - 7 August 2010' and emblem on the upper left sheet margin.
Plate Nos.: All values 1A (each×4).
Sheets: 15 (3×5).
Withdrawn: 30.7.2011.

1489 Cardinal Newman (*Illustration reduced. Actual size 170×75 mm*)

State Visit of Pope Benedict XVI to the United Kingdom and Beatification of Cardinal Newman

(Litho BDT)

2010 (11 Aug). Sheet 170×75 mm. P 13 (C).

MS1617 **1489**		£1.50×2 multicoloured	7·00	7·00
First Day Cover				8·75
Presentation Pack			8·75	

Withdrawn: 10.8.2011.

1490 *Three-Legged Postman* (Bertram), 1940

1491 *Peveril Camp, Peel* (Herbert Kaden), 1940

1492 *Life at Palace Camp, Douglas* (Imre Goth), 1941

1493 *Douglas, Isle of Man* (linocut) (Hermann Fechenbach), 1941

1494 *Violinist at Onchan Camp* (Ernst Eisenmayer), 1941

1495 *Portrait of Klaus E. Hinrichsen* (Kurt Schwitters), 1941

Isle of Man Internment Art History (1st series)

(Des Kcreative. Litho Lowe-Martin)

2010 (24 Sept). P 13½ (C).

1618	**1490**	35p. multicoloured	90	90
1619	**1491**	36p. multicoloured	95	95
1620	**1492**	55p. multicoloured	1·40	1·40
1621	**1493**	67p. multicoloured	1·90	1·90
1622	**1494**	£1.32 multicoloured	2·75	2·75
1623	**1495**	£1.72 multicoloured	4·00	4·00
1618/23 *Set of 6*			11·50	11·50
First Day Cover				13·00
Presentation Pack			13·00	

See also Nos. 1682/**MS**1690.
Plate Nos.: All values 1A (each×4).
Sheets: 25 (5×5).
Withdrawn: 23.9.2011.

1496 Nativity ('Jesus is born', 'Shepherds hear first', 'The Magi see a star') (*Illustration reduced. Actual size 170×75 mm*)

Friends and Heroes (animated TV series). The Christmas Story

(Litho Enschedé)

2010 (1 Oct). Sheet 170×75 mm. Multicoloured. P 13½×14 (C).

MS1624 **1496** £1×3 multicoloured		7·00	7·00
First Day Cover			8·50
Presentation Pack		8·50	

Withdrawn: 30.9.2011.

1497 Old Braddan Church

1498 The Braaid

1499 The Dhoon Glen

1500 The Dhoon Beach

1501 Cronk ny Arree Laa

1502 St. Patrick's Isle in Snow

Christmas. 'Let it Snow'

(Des Kcreative. Litho BDT)

2010 (20 Oct). P 13 (C).

1625	**1497**	35p. multicoloured	70	70
1626	**1498**	36p. multicoloured	75	75
1627	**1499**	60p. multicoloured	1·75	1·75
1628	**1500**	88p. multicoloured	2·10	2·10
1629	**1501**	97p. multicoloured	2·40	2·40
1630	**1502**	£1.46 multicoloured	3·25	3·25
1625/30 *Set of 6*			10·50	10·50
First Day Cover				12·50
Presentation Pack			12·50	

Plate Nos.: All values 1A (each×4).
Sheets: 50 (5×10).
Withdrawn: 19.10.2011.

1503 Prince William (*Illustration reduced. Actual size 170×75 mm*)

Engagement of Prince William and Miss Catherine Middleton

(Des Emma Cooke. Litho BDT)

2010 (26 Nov). Sheet 170×75 mm. P 14½×14 (C).

MS1631 **1503** £1.50×2 multicoloured		7·00	7·00
First Day Cover			9·00
Presentation Pack		9·00	

Withdrawn: 25.11.2011.

Year Folder 2010

2010 (20 Oct). Comprises Nos. 1557/66, 1575/1614 and **MS**1617/30 (price £54).
Year Folder £110

Year Pack 2010

2010 (20 Oct). Comprises Nos. 1557/66, 1575/1614 and **MS**1617/30 (price £63).
Year Pack £125

Post Office Yearbook 2010

2010 (20 Oct). Comprises Nos. 1557/66, 1575/1614 and **MS**1617/30 (price £57.50).
Yearbook £115

1504 Queen Elizabeth II, 1953

1505 Queen and Prince Philip, Diamond Wedding Anniversary, November 2007, Broadlands, Romsey

1506 Princess Elizabeth and Prince Philip on Honeymoon at Broadlands, 1949

1507 On Buckingham Palace Balcony after Trooping the Colour, 1971

1508 Watching Golden Jubilee Parade, London, June 2002

1509 Prince Philip, 1953

1510 Queen Elizabeth II and Prince Philip, 1970s
(*Illustration reduced. Actual size 110×70 mm*)

Queen Elizabeth II and Prince Philip: 'Lifetime of Service'

(Litho BDT)

2011 (6 Feb). P 13½ (C).

1632	**1504**	35p. multicoloured	90	90
1633	**1505**	36p. multicoloured	95	95
1634	**1506**	55p. multicoloured	1·50	1·50
1635	**1507**	60p. multicoloured	1·75	1·75
1636	**1508**	£1.14 multicoloured	2·50	2·50
1637	**1509**	£1.46 multicoloured	3·25	3·25
1632/7 Set of 6			10·50	10·50
First Day Cover				12·00
Presentation Pack			12·00	

Special Commemorative Folder (½ sheets of Nos. 1632, 1634/5, 1637, complete sheets of Nos. 1633, 1636, and **MS**1638/9)... 50·00

MS1638 110×70 mm. **1510** £3 multicoloured		7·25	7·25

MS1639 175×164 mm. Nos. 1632/7 and three stamp-size labels .... 11·00 11·00

First Day Cover (**MS**1638) .... 9·00

Presentation Pack (**MS**1638) .... 9·00

Nos. 1632/7 have blackish lilac borders, but stamps from **MS**1639 have deep dull purple borders.

No. **MS**1639 forms a diamond-shape but with the left, right and top corners removed.

Sheets: 8 containing top and bottom rows of three stamps and centre row of two stamps.

Withdrawn: 4.2.2012.

1511 'Baptisms'

1512 'School Days'

1513 'Working Life'

1514 'Weddings'

1515 'Family Album'

1516 'Emigration'

1517 'Memorials'

1518 'Family Tree'

Genealogy

(Des Emma Cooke. Litho Lowe-Martin)

2011 (18 Feb). P 13½ (C).

1640	**1511**	35p. multicoloured	90	90
1641	**1512**	35p. multicoloured	90	90

1642	**1513**	36p. multicoloured	95	95
1643	**1514**	36p. multicoloured	95	95
1644	**1515**	67p. multicoloured	1·75	1·75
1645	**1516**	67p. multicoloured	1·75	1·75
1646	**1517**	£1.10 multicoloured	2·40	2·40
1647	**1518**	£1.10 multicoloured	2·40	2·40
1640/7	*Set of 8*		12·00	12·00
	First Day Cover			13·00
	Presentation Pack		13·00	

Plate Nos.: All values 1A (each×4).
Sheets: 24 (2 blocks, 3×4) Nos. 1640/1, 1642/3, 1644/5 and 1646/7 were printed in sheets containing the two designs of each value in separate blocks of 12 separated by a central gutter. Withdrawn: 17.2.2012.

1519 Wall Butterfly (*Lasiommata megera*)   **1520** Small Tortoiseshell (*Aglais urticae*)

1521 Dark Green Fritillary (*Argynnis aglaja*)   **1522** Common Blue (*Polyommatus icarus*)

1523 Comma (*Polygonia c-album*)   **1524** Green-veined White (*Pieris napi*)

1525 Red Admiral (*Vanessa atalanta*)   **1526** Speckled Wood (*Pararge aegeria*)

The Isle of Man Butterfly Collection

(Des Richard Lewington and Emma Cooke. Litho Lowe-Martin)

2011 (1 Apr).

		(a) Ordinary gum. P 13 (C)		
1648	**1519**	37p. multicoloured	90	90
1649	**1520**	37p. multicoloured	90	90
1650	**1521**	38p. multicoloured	1·00	1·00
1651	**1522**	38p. multicoloured	1·00	1·00
1652	**1523**	58p. multicoloured	1·50	1·50
1653	**1524**	58p. multicoloured	1·50	1·50
1654	**1525**	£1.15 multicoloured	2·40	2·40
1655	**1526**	£1.15 multicoloured	2·40	2·40
1648/55	*Set of 8*		12·00	12·00
	First Day Cover			13·00
	Presentation Pack		13·00	
MS1656	210×250 mm. Nos. 1648, 1650, 1652 and			
	1654, each×4		22·00	22·00
		(b) Self-adhesive. Die-cut perf 13		
1657	**1520**	37p. multicoloured	90	90
		a. Booklet pane. No. 1657×12..........	10·00	

No. 1657 was issued in £4.44 booklets, No. SB76.
Plate Nos.: All values 1A (each×4).
Sheets: 50 (5×10).
Withdrawn: 31.3.2012.
One stamp of each value incorporates the WWF emblem.

1527 Senior TT Stanley Woods v. Jimmy Guthrie, 1935   **1528** Senior TT Mike Hailwood v. Giacomo Agostini, 1967

1529 Senior TT Tom Herron v. John Williams, 1976   **1530** Sidecar TT Race A George O'Dell v. Dick Greasley, 1977

1531 Classic TT Alex George v. Mike Hailwood, 1979   **1532** Senior TT Steve Hislop v. Carl Fogarty, 1992

1533 Formula 1 TT Joey Dunlop v. David Jefferies, 2000   **1534** Senior TT John McGuinness v. Cameron Donald, 2008

1535 Sidecar TT Klaus Klaffenbock v. John Holden, 2010   **1536** Superstock TT Ian Hutchinson v. Ryan Farquhar, 2010

1537 Senior TT Steve Hislop v. Carl Fogarty, 1992 (*Illustration reduced. Actual size* 110×85 *mm*)

TT2011 Centenary of the Mountain Course. Greatest TT Races of All Time.

(Des Pete Jones Design. Litho BDT)

2011 (1 Apr). P 14 (1658/67) or 14×15 (**MS**1668) (C).

1658	**1527**	38p. multicoloured	90	90
		a. Horiz strip of 5. Nos. 1658/62	4·50	4·50
1659	**1528**	38p. multicoloured	90	90
1660	**1529**	38p. multicoloured	90	90
1661	**1530**	38p. multicoloured	90	90
1662	**1531**	38p. multicoloured	90	90
1663	**1532**	68p. multicoloured	1·60	1·60
		a. Horiz strip of 5. Nos. 1663/7	8·00	8·00
1664	**1533**	68p. multicoloured	1·60	1·60
1665	**1534**	68p. multicoloured	1·60	1·60
1666	**1535**	68p. multicoloured	1·60	1·60
1667	**1536**	68p. multicoloured	1·60	1·60
1658/67		*Set of 10*	12·50	12·50
First Day Cover				14·00
Presentation Pack			14·00	

Special Commemorative Folder (complete sheetlets and
MS1668) .... 40·00

MS1668 110×85 mm.	**1537** £3 multicoloured	7·25	7·25
First Day Cover			9·00
Presentation Pack		14·00	

Plate Nos.: All values 1A (each×4).
Sheets: 20 (5×4) Nos. 1658/62 and 1663/7 were each printed together, *se-tenant*, as horizontal strips of five stamps throughout the sheets.
Withdrawn: 31.3.2012.

1537a Miss Catherine Middleton

1537b Prince William

1538 Miss Catherine Middleton; Prince William (*Illustration reduced. Actual size 170×75 mm*)

Royal Wedding

(Des Emma Cooke. Litho BDT)

2011 (15 Apr–27 May). P 14½×14 (C).

1668a	**1537a**	£1 multicoloured	2·25	2·25
1668b	**1537b**	£1 multicoloured	2·25	2·25
MS1669 170×75 mm.	**1538** £1×2 multicoloured	4·75	4·75
First Day Cover (**MS**1669)			6·50
Presentation Pack (**MS**1669)		6·50	

Special Folder (sheetlet of Nos. 1668a/b, each×5,
MS1669 *and* **MS**1631 .... 40·00

Nos. 1668a/b were only available from the Isle of Man Philatelic Bureau in sheetlets of ten stamps (five of each design) and ten labels, issued on 27 May 2011 and sold for £10 each, or from the miniature sheet.

Nos. 1668a/b were re-issued on 1 July 2013 for the Birth of Prince George of Cambridge in sheetlets of eight (four of each design) and four labels announcing the birth, sold for £8. This sheetlet was also sold in a souvenir folder with a first day cover for £25 and a 'Celebration Folder' (complete sheetlet) for £16.50.

Sheets: 10. Nos. 1668a/b were printed together in sheetlets of ten stamps and ten labels containing two blocks of five stamps and five labels separated by an illustrated gutter, so that each stamp has a *se-tenant* label at either right or left.
Withdrawn: 14.4.2012.

1539 The Southern Hundred, 1955

1540 "I'm staking my claim on the sands at Douglas", early 1950s

1541 Over the Water – "I must get me a bigger horse", 1955

1542 Will Uncle Sam provide the 'Third Leg?', 1940

1543 Bob a Job Week, 1954

1544 'Well Councillor – did you vote for evening meetings?'

Cartoons by Harold 'Dusty' Miller

(Des EJC Design. Litho Lowe-Martin)

2011 (10 May). P 13 (C).

1670	**1539**	37p. multicoloured	90	90
1671	**1540**	38p. multicoloured	90	90
1672	**1541**	68p. multicoloured	1·60	1·60
1673	**1542**	76p. multicoloured	1·90	1·90
1674	**1543**	£1.10 multicoloured	2·75	2·75
1675	**1544**	£1.65 multicoloured	4·00	4·00
1670/5		*Set of 6*	12·00	12·00
First Day Cover				13·00
Presentation Pack		13·00	

Plate Nos.: All values 1A (each×4).
Sheets: 25 (5×5).
Withdrawn: 9.5.2012.

1545 Manx Cats holding Coat of Arms

1546 Three Manx Cats and Coat of Arms

1547 Tabby Manx Cat on Wall

1548 Tabby Manx Cat

1549 Two Manx Cats and Coat of Arms

1550 Manx Cat on Quayside standing on Coat of Arms

Tales of the Tailless (Manx Cats)

(Des Kcreative. Litho Cartor)

2011 (23 June). P 13×13½ (C).

1676	**1545**	37p. multicoloured	90	90
1677	**1546**	38p. multicoloured	90	90
1678	**1547**	58p. multicoloured	1·50	1·50
1679	**1548**	76p. multicoloured	1·90	1·90
1680	**1549**	£1.15 multicoloured	2·40	2·40
1681	**1550**	£1.65 multicoloured	4·00	4·00
1676/81		*Set of 6*	11·50	11·50
First Day Cover				13·00
Presentation Pack		13·00	

Plate Nos.: All values 1A (each×4).
Sheets: 20 (4×5).
Withdrawn: 22.6.2012.

1551 South Lancashire Brigade on Peel Harbour, August 1908   **1552** Postcard with King Edward VII 1/2d. Stamp with 1908 Knockaloe Camp Cancellation

1553 Knockaloe Camp (from postcard designed by internee, 1915)   **1554** Alien's Detention Camp Letter with Pair of King George V Profile Head 1/2d. Stamps, cancelled 1914

1555 Easter Postcard published by Knockaloe Camp Printer's Workshop and Peace Dove   **1556** King George V 3d. Registered Envelope with 1915 Knockaloe Camp Cancellation

1557 Knockaloe Camp (from postcard designed and printed within camp)   **1558** Letter with Internee Produced Stamp (for internal camp mail)

1559 Postcard of Huts at Knockaloe Camp, 1916 (50p.); Official Prisoners of War Envelope with King George V 1d. Stamp with The Camp Knockaloe Cancellation, 1915 (50p.); Easter Postcard and 1915 The Camp Knockaloe Cancellation (£1); King George V 3d. Registered Envelope with 1915 The Camp Knockaloe Cancellations (£1) (*Illustration reduced. Actual size 171×76 mm*)

Isle of Man Internment (2nd series). Postal History of Knockaloe Camp

(Des Kcreative. Litho Cartor)

2011 (8 Aug). P 13×13½ (C).

1682	**1551**	37p. multicoloured	90	90
		a. Horiz pair. Nos. 1682/3	1·75	1·75
1683	**1552**	37p. multicoloured	90	90
1684	**1553**	38p. multicoloured	90	90
		a. Horiz pair. Nos. 1684/5	1·75	1·75
1685	**1554**	38p. multicoloured	90	90
1686	**1555**	58p. multicoloured	1·50	1·50
		a. Horiz pair. Nos. 1686/7	3·00	3·00
1687	**1556**	58p. multicoloured	1·50	1·50
1688	**1557**	£1.15 multicoloured	2·75	2·75
		a. Horiz pair. Nos. 1688/9	5·50	5·50

1689	**1558**	£1.15 multicoloured	2·75	2·75
1682/9 *Set of 8*			12·00	12·00
First Day Cover				13·00
Presentation Pack			13·00	
MS1690 171×76 mm. **1559** 50p.×2 multicoloured;				
£1×2 multicoloured			7·25	7·25
First Day Cover				9·00
Presentation Pack			9·00	

Nos. 1682/3, 1684/5, 1686/7 and 1688/9 were each printed together, *se-tenant*, as horizontal pairs in sheets of 20.

Plate Nos.: All values 1A (each×4).

Sheets: 20 (4×5).

Withdrawn: 7.8.2012.

1560 Narcissus (*Illustration reduced. Actual size 124×184 mm*)

Narcissus

(Des Yang Xiaomei. Litho Cartor)

2011 (1 Sept). Sheet 124×184 mm. P 13½×13 (C).

MS1691 **1560** 5p.×2, 10p.×2, 35p.×2 multicoloured		2·50	2·50
First Day Cover			4·00
Presentation Pack		4·00	

No. **MS**1691 was released to commemorate the 27th Asian International Stamp Exhibition, Wuxi, Jiangsu, China.

Withdrawn: 31.8.2012.

T **1561** and Nos. 1692/6 are vacant.

1562 Games Mascot Tosha; Badminton; Boxing; Rugby 7; Cycling; Gymnastics; Athletics; Swimming (*Illustration reduced. Actual size 170×76 mm*)

Fourth Commonwealth Youth Games, Isle of Man

(Des Isle of Man Advertising & PR Ltd. Litho BDT)

2011 (1 Sept). Sheet 170×76 mm. P 14×14½ (C).

MS1697 **1562** 38p.×8 multicoloured		7·25	7·25
First Day Cover			9·00
Presentation Pack		9·00	

Withdrawn: 31.8.2012.

1563 Robin   **1564** Redwing

1565 Goldfinches   **1566** Siskins

1567 Waxwings   **1568** Long-tailed Tits

Christmas. Birds in Winter (Europa) (Sepac)

(Des Jeremy Paul and EJC Design. Litho Lowe-Martin)

2011 (28 Sept).

(a) Ordinary gum. P 13 (C)

1698	**1563**	(37p.) multicoloured	90	90
1699	**1564**	(38p.) multicoloured	90	90
1700	**1565**	58p. multicoloured	1·40	1·40
1701	**1566**	68p. multicoloured	1·75	1·75
		a. Perf 12½×13	1·75	1·75
1702	**1567**	76p. multicoloured	1·90	1·90
1703	**1568**	£2 multicoloured	4·75	4·75
1698/703 *Set of 6*			11·50	11·50
First Day Cover				13·00
Presentation Pack			13·00	

(b) Self-adhesive. Roul

1704	**1563**	(37p.) multicoloured	90	90
1705	**1564**	(38p.) multicoloured	90	90

Nos. 1698 and 1704 were inscr 'IOM' and originally sold for 37p.
Nos. 1699 and 1705 were inscr 'UK' and originally sold for 38p.
No. 1700 was inscr 'sepac'.
No. 1701/a include the 'EUROPA' emblem.
No. 1701a only comes from 'EUROPA' sheetlets of ten.
  Plate Nos.: All values 1A (each×4).
  Sheets: 50 (5×10), 68p. also 10 (2×5).
  Withdrawn: 27.9.2012.

No. 1700 was also available in a folder with 11 other 'sepac' logo stamps issued by other participating postal administrations. Cost £15.

1569 Triumph Herald Sailboat

1570 Citroen Grand Design

1571 Polar Hilux   **1572** Hammerhead Eagle i-Thrust

1573 Robin Reliant Space Shuttle

1574 Caravan Airship

Top Gear Challenges

(Des Dave Macdonald. Litho Lowe-Martin)

2011 (5 Nov).

(a) Ordinary gum. P 13 (C)

1706	**1569**	37p. multicoloured	90	90
1707	**1570**	38p. multicoloured	90	90
1708	**1571**	58p. multicoloured	1·40	1·40
1709	**1572**	68p. multicoloured	1·75	1·75
1710	**1573**	£1.10 multicoloured	2·40	2·40
1711	**1574**	£1.82 multicoloured	4·25	4·25
1706/11 *Set of 6*			11·50	11·50
First Day Cover				13·50
Presentation Pack			13·50	
Special Folder (containing Nos. 1706/11, 1712/13 and sheetlet of stickers)			40·00	

(b) Self-adhesive. Roul

1712	**1573**	£1.10 multicoloured	2·40	2·40
1713	**1574**	£1.82 multicoloured	4·25	4·25

The top edge of sheetlet (No. 1712×5) was cut around in the shape of a space shuttle and sheetlet (No. 1713×5) was cut around in the shape of a airship.
  Plate Nos.: All values 1A (each×4).
  Sheets: 20 (5×4).
  Withdrawn: 31.11.2012.

Year Folder 2011

2011 (5 Nov). Comprises Nos. **MS**1631/8, 1640/55, 1658/68 and **MS**1669/1703 (price £62).
Year Folder   £120

Year Pack 2011

2011 (5 Nov). Comprises Nos. **MS**1631/8, 1640/55, 1658/68 and **MS**1669/1703 (price £74).
Year Pack   £140

Post Office Yearbook

2011 (5 Nov). Comprises Nos. **MS**1631/8, 1640/55, 1658/68 and **MS**1669/1703 (price £62).
Yearbook   £120

1575 Sailing

1576 Cycling

1577 Swimming

1578 Tennis

1579 Rowing

1580 Athletics

1581 Shooting

1582 Cycling *(Illustration reduced. Actual size 120×78 mm)*

Olympic Games, London

(Des Sir Paul Smith. Litho The Lowe-Martin Group)

2012 (1 Jan). P 13 (C).

1714	**1575**	37p. multicoloured	....	90	90
1715	**1576**	38p. multicoloured	....	90	90
1716	**1577**	58p. multicoloured	....	1·40	1·40
1717	**1578**	68p. multicoloured	....	1·75	1·75
1718	**1579**	76p. multicoloured	....	1·90	1·90
1719	**1580**	£1 multicoloured	....	2·40	2·40
1720	**1581**	£1.15 multicoloured	....	2·50	2·50

1714/20 *Set of 7*	11·50	11·50
First Day Cover...		13·00
Presentation Pack..	13·00	
Collectors Book Stamp Panes (set of 8) (price £27.60)	55·00	
Collectors Book Postcard Panes (set of 8)....................	16·00	
Special Collectors Book (containing sets of 8 stamp		
panes and 8 postcard panes) (price £50)...................	£100	
Set of 8 *Pre-paid Stamp Cards*	9·00	20·00
MS1721 120×78 mm. **1582** £3 multicoloured.................	8·00	8·00
First Day Cover...		8·50
Presentation Pack..	8·50	
MS1722 210×230 mm. Nos. 1714/20, each×2	23·00	23·00

Nos. 1714/20 and **MS**1721 were also issued in Collectors Book stamp panes, 218×220 mm, containing five stamps of the same design (1714/20) or **MS**1721 in purple margins. These were available from the Philatelic Bureau individually or as a set.

A Gold Medal Winners Men's Team Pursuit commemorative sheet issued on 3 September 2012 contained stamps as No. 1715 and the £3 stamp within **MS**1721, both×3, with *se-tenant* labels. The sheet was sold for £10.

Plate Nos.: All values 1A (each×4).
Sheets: 5 (1×5).
Withdrawn: 31.12.2012.

1583 Queen Elizabeth II in 1990

1584 Queen Elizabeth II Trooping the Colour, 1979

1585 Queen Elizabeth II at Film Premiere, 1955

1586 Queen Elizabeth II in Tuvalu, 1982

1587 Queen Elizabeth II, 1968

1588 Queen Elizabeth II at the Derby, Epsom, 2008

1589 Queen Elizabeth II, c. 2005 *(Illustration reduced. Actual size 110×70 mm)*

Diamond Jubilee (1st issue)

(Des Casco and EJC Design. Litho BDT)

2012 (6 Feb-21 Apr). P 13 (C).

1723	**1583**	37p. multicoloured		90	90
1724	**1584**	38p. multicoloured		90	90
1725	**1585**	58p. multicoloured		1·40	1·40
1726	**1586**	68p. multicoloured		1·75	1·75
1727	**1587**	£1.10 multicoloured		2·40	2·40
1728	**1588**	£1.82 multicoloured		4·25	4·25
1723/8 *Set of 7*				11·50	11·50
First Day Cover					13·00
Presentation Pack				13·00	
Special Folder (price £30)				60·00	
Stamp and Coin Pack (price £15)					30·00

MS1729 174×164 mm. Nos. 1723/8 and three stamp-
size labels.. 11·50 11·50
MS1730 110×70 mm. **1589** £3 multicoloured (21 Apr) 7·25 7·25
First Day Cover .... 8·50
Presentation Pack .... 8·50

No. **MS**1729 forms a diamond-shape but with the left, right and top corners removed.

See also Nos. **MS**1755/**MS**1758.

Sheets: 8 containing top and bottom rows of three stamps and centre row of two stamps.
Withdrawn: 5.2.2013.

1590 Frost Arbory (oil on canvas), 1931

1591 A Colby Mill (watercolour), 1954

1592 Landing the Catch, Port St. Mary (watercolour), c. 1913

1593 Early Spring (oil on canvas), 1910

1594 Port Erin Bay (oil on canvas), 1937

Paintings by William Hoggatt

(Des EJC Design. Litho BDT)

2012 (20 Feb). P 14 (C).

1731	**1590**	38p. multicoloured		90	90
		a. Horiz strip of 5. Nos. 1731/5		4·50	4·50
1732	**1591**	38p. multicoloured		90	90

1733	**1592**	38p. multicoloured		90	90
1734	**1593**	38p. multicoloured		90	90
1735	**1594**	38p. multicoloured		90	90
1731/5 *Set of 5*				4·50	4·50
First Day Cover					6·00
Presentation Pack				6·00	

Plate Nos.: 1A (×4).
Sheets: 20 (5×4). Nos. 1731/5 were printed together, *se-tenant*, in horizontal strips of five throughout the sheets.
Withdrawn: 19.2.2013.

1595 Titanic

1596 Interior of Titanic

1597 Captain Edward Smith, Lifebelt and Letter

1598 Lifebelt and Titanic Sinking

1599 Survivors in Lifeboats

1600 Passengers and Titanic

Centenary of the Sinking of the Titanic

(Des IoM Advertising & PR. Litho BDT)

2012 (2 Apr). P 13 (C).

1736	**1595**	37p. multicoloured		90	90
		a. Horiz strip of 3. Nos. 1736/8		3·50	3·50
1737	**1596**	38p. multicoloured		90	90
1738	**1597**	68p. multicoloured		1·75	1·75
1739	**1598**	76p. multicoloured		2·00	2·00
		a. Horiz strip of 3. Nos. 1739/41		8·25	8·25
1740	**1599**	£1.15 multicoloured		2·40	2·40
1741	**1600**	£1.65 multicoloured		4·00	4·00
1736/41 *Set of 6*				11·50	11·50
First Day Cover					13·00
Presentation Pack				13·00	

*Special Folder (**MS**1742 and set of 6 PHQ cards) (price £20)* .... 40·00

MS1742 210×297 mm. Nos. 1736/8 and Nos. 1739/41×2.. 25·00 25·00

Plate Nos.: 1A (each×4).
Sheets: 15 (3×5). Nos. 1736/8 and 1739/41 were each printed together, *se-tenant*, in horizontal strips of three throughout the sheets, each strip forming a composite background design.
Withdrawn: 1.4.2013.

1601 Castletown Harbour Lighthouse

1602 Douglas Harbour Lighthouse

1603 Peel Harbour Lighthouse

1604 Laxey Harbour Lighthouse

1605 Ramsey Harbour
Lighthouse

1606 Port St. Mary Harbour
Lighthouse

Harbour Lights. Minor Lighthouses of the Isle of Man (Europa)

(Des Tracey Dean. Litho BDT)

2012 (2 Apr). P 13½ (C).				
1743	**1601**	1p. multicoloured	10	10
1744	**1602**	68p. multicoloured	1·75	1·75
1745	**1603**	75p. multicoloured	2·00	2·00
1746	**1604**	£1 multicoloured	2·40	2·40
1747	**1605**	£1.30 multicoloured	2·50	2·50
1748	**1606**	£1.60 multicoloured	4·00	4·00
1743/8 Set of 6			12·50	12·50
First Day Cover			14·00	
Presentation Pack				14·00
MS1722 210×230 mm. Nos. 1714/20, each×2			23·00	23·00

No. 1744 includes the Europa emblem.
Plate Nos.: All values 1A (each×4).
Sheets: 20 (4×5), 68p also 10 (5×2).
Withdrawn: 1.4.2013.

1607 Goss China Manx Cottage

1608 Crown Devon Model of
Early Manx Racing Car

1609 Royal Doulton Spittoon
showing Postman at Maughold

1610 Willow Art China Model of
Three-legged Manx Dog "Prince
Toby Orry"

1611 China Plate showing Cat
"Ginger-Manx of Glen Orry",
1962

1612 Enamelled Silver Freemasons
Founder's Jewel showing Tower of
Refuge, Douglas Bay

The Kelly Collection of Manx Memorabilia

(Des The Agency Ltd. Litho BDT)

2012 (8 May). P 14½×14 (C).				
1749	**1607**	(38p.) multicoloured	90	90
1750	**1608**	(41p.) multicoloured	95	95
1751	**1609**	58p. multicoloured	1·10	1·10
1752	**1610**	68p. multicoloured	1·75	1·75
1753	**1611**	£1.10 multicoloured	2·40	2·40
1754	**1612**	£1.82 multicoloured	4·25	4·25
1749/54 Set of 6			11·00	11·00
First Day Cover				13·00
Presentation Pack			13·00	

No. 1749 was inscr 'IOM' and originally sold for 38p.
No. 1750 was inscr 'UK' and originally sold for 41p.
Plate Nos.: All values 1A (each×4).
Sheets: 20 (5×4).
Withdrawn: 7.5.2013.

1613 Thames Diamond Jubilee Pageant (*Illustration reduced. Actual
size 170×75 mm*)

Diamond Jubilee (2nd issue). Thames Diamond Jubilee Pageant

(Des EJC Design. Litho BDT)

2012 (3-5 June). Multicoloured. P 14 (**MS**1755/6), 13½ (**MS**1757) or 13
(**MS**1758) (all comb).

MS1755 170×75 mm. **1613** 50p. *Gloriana* (royal row barge); 50p. Lifeboat from TSS *Lady of Mann*; 50p. *Vital Spark* (replica Viking longboat); £1.50 Royal Barge *Spirit of Chartwell* (85×29 mm)	7·25	7·25
MS1756 210×298 mm 50p.×3 *Gloriana* (royal row barge); 50p.×3 Lifeboat from TSS *Lady of Mann*; 50p.×3 *Vital Spark* (replica Viking longboat); £1.50×3 Royal Barge *Spirit of Chartwell* (85×29 mm) and nine stamp-size labels	20·00	20·00
MS1757 210×298 mm. Nos. 1632/4, each×2, 1635×3, 1636×2, 1637 and £3 multicoloured (as stamp within **MS**1638) and 12 stamp-size labels (4 June)	25·00	25·00
MS1758 210×298 mm. Nos. 1723/6, each×2, 1727/8, £3 multicoloured (as stamp within **MS**1730) and 18 stamp-size labels (5 June)	22·00	22·00
First Day Cover (**MS**1755)	8·50	
Presentation Pack (**MS**1755)	8·50	
Commemorative Folder (**MS**1756/8) (10 July) (*price £30*)	60·00	

Nos. **MS**1756/8 were sold as "commemorative sheets" by the Isle of
Man Post Office.
Withdrawn: 1.6.2013.

1614 Mark Cavendish
celebrating Win in Scratch Race,
2006 Commonwealth Games

1615 Winning Scheldeprijs
Vlaanderen, Belgium, 2007

1616 Winning Milan – San
Remo Classic, Italy, 2009

1617 Wearing Green Jersey at
end of Tour de France, Paris,
2011

1618 Winning World Road Race
Championships, Copenhagen,
September 2011

1619 Wearing Medal and
Rainbow Jersey of World Road
Race Champion

1620 At Kuurne-Brussels-Kuurne Race, 2012 618 Winning World Road Race Championships, Copenhagen, September 2011

Victories of Mark Cavendish (cyclist)

(Des Ruth Sutherland. Litho Lowe-Martin)

2012 (19-30 June). P 13 (C).

1759	**1614**	38p. multicoloured		90	90
1760	**1615**	41p. multicoloured		95	95
1761	**1616**	65p. multicoloured		1·50	1·50
1762	**1617**	71p. multicoloured		1·60	1·60
1763	**1618**	80p. multicoloured		1·90	1·90
1764	**1619**	105p. multicoloured		2·40	2·40
1765	**1620**	116p. multicoloured		2·50	2·50
1759/65 Set of 7				11·50	11·50
First Day Cover					13·50

MS1766 210×296 mm. Nos. 1759/62, each×2, 1763 and 1764/5, each×2, and seven stamp-size labels (30 June) .... 16·00 16·00

Presentation Pack .... 13·50

Stamp and Coin Pack (Nos. 1759/65 and 50p commemorative coin) .... 30·00

Special Folder (Nos. 1759/**MS**1766, first day cover and 50p. commemorative coin) (price £30) .... 60·00

No. **MS**1766 is an "augmented reality" commemorative sheet. If the 105p. stamp and adjoining label at bottom left are scanned with the Lowe-Martin app a video of Mark Cavendish winning the World Championship will be displayed on a smartphone.

Plate Nos.: All values 1A (each×4)
Sheets: 20 (5×4).
Withdrawn: 18.6.2013.

1621 Colletes succinctus

1622 Epeolus variegatus

1623 Osmia rufa

1624 Halictus rubicundus

1625 Bombus monticola

1626 Apis mellifera

1627 Colletes succinctus

1628 Epeolus variegatus

Bee Fauna of the Isle of Man

(Des Richard Lewington and Emma Cooke. Litho Cartor (1767/72) or BDT (1773/4))

2012 (8 Aug).

(a) Ordinary gum. P 13 (C)

1767	**1621**	38p. multicoloured		90	90
1768	**1622**	41p. multicoloured		95	95
1769	**1623**	£1 multicoloured		2·40	2·40

1770	**1624**	£1.05 multicoloured		2·40	2·40
1771	**1625**	£1.30 multicoloured		2·50	2·50
1772	**1626**	£1.47 multicoloured		3·25	3·25
1767/72 Set of 6				12·00	12·00
First Day Cover					14·00
Presentation Pack				14·00	

(b) Self-adhesive. Die-cut perf 13×12½

1773	**1627**	38p. multicoloured		90	90
		a. Booklet pane. No. 1773×10		9·00	90
1774	**1628**	41p. multicoloured		95	95
		a. Booklet pane. No. 1774×10		9·50	1·75

Nos. 1773/4 were only issued in £3.80 and £4.10 stamp booklets, Nos. SB77/8.
Nos. 1767/72 are honey-scented.
Plate Nos.: All values 1A (each×4).
Sheets: 50 (5×10).
Withdrawn: 7.8.2013.

1629 AW FK.8 B5773 (1918)

1630 MS Type L 3253 (1915)

1631 DH.2 5964 (1916)

1632 Sopwith Camel B5648 (1918)

1633 RAF BE.2C 4359 (1917)

1634 Short S.32 402 (1912)

Centenary of the Royal Flying Corps

(Des Arvo Vercamer and EJC Design. Litho Cartor)

2012 (20 Sept). P 13½ (C).

1775	**1629**	38p. multicoloured		90	90
1776	**1630**	41p. multicoloured		95	95
1777	**1631**	65p. multicoloured		1·50	1·50
1778	**1632**	80p. multicoloured		1·90	1·90
1779	**1633**	£1.37 multicoloured		2·75	2·75
1780	**1634**	£1.91 multicoloured		4·25	4·25
1775/80 Set of 6				12·00	12·00
First Day Cover					14·50
Presentation Pack				14·50	

Plate Nos.: All values 1A (each×5).
Sheets: 25 (5×5).
Withdrawn: 19.9.2013.

1635 Terra Nova at the ice foot of Cape Evans, 5 January 1911; Memorial Cairn erected at Site of Scott's Tent, 1912 (Illustration reduced. Actual size 170×75 mm)

Centenary of Captain Robert Scott's South Pole Expedition, 1910-13

(Des EJC Design. Litho Lowe-Martin)

2012 (2 Oct). Sheet 170×75 mm. P 13 (C).
MS1781 **1635** £1.50×2 black, grey and lavender .... 7·25 7·25

First Day Cover .... 8·50
Presentation Pack .... 8·50
Withdrawn: 1.10.2013.

1636 Ramsey Christmas Lights

1637 Glen Auldyn

1638 Castletown Police Station

1639 Sulby Glen

1640 Martin's Sweet Shop, Ramsey

1641 Lake Lane, Peel

Christmas Scenes. 'A Time Gone By.' Paintings by Michael Starkey

(Des EJC Design. Litho Cartor)

2012 (20 Oct). P 13 (C).

(a) Ordinary gum. P 13 (C)

1782	**1636**	38p. multicoloured	90	90
1783	**1637**	41p. multicoloured	95	95
1784	**1638**	71p. multicoloured	1·60	1·60
1785	**1639**	£1.05 multicoloured	2·40	2·40
1786	**1640**	£1.16 multicoloured	2·50	2·50
1787	**1641**	£1.73 multicoloured	4·00	4·00
1782/7		Set of 6	12·00	12·00
		First Day Cover		14·50
		Presentation Pack	14·50	

(b) Self-adhesive. Die-cut perf 11

1788	**1636**	38p. multicoloured	90	90
1789	**1637**	41p. multicoloured	95	95

Plate Nos.: All values 1A (each×4).
Sheets: Nos. 1782/7 20 (4×5); Nos. 1788/9 25 (5×5).
Withdrawn: 19.10.2013.

Year Folder 2012

2012 (20 Oct). Comprises Nos. 1714/21, 1723/8, **MS**1730/41, 1743/55, 1759/65, 1767/72 and 1775/87 (price £60)
Year Folder £120

Year Pack 2012

2012 (20 Oct). Comprises Nos. 1714/21, 1723/8, **MS**1730/41, 1743/55, 1759/65, 1767/72 and 1775/87 (price £72)
Year Pack £140

Post Office Yearbook

2012 (20 Oct). Comprises Nos. 1714/21, 1723/8, **MS**1730/41, 1743/55, 1759/65, 1767/72 and 1775/87 (price £62)
Yearbook £120

1642 Knight

1643 King

1644 Warder

1645 Bishop

1646 Queen

1647 Pawn

The Chronicles of Man and the Lewis Chessmen

(Des EJC Design. Litho Cartor)

2013 (11 Jan). P 13½ (C).

1790	**1642**	38p. multicoloured	90	90
1791	**1643**	41p. multicoloured	95	95
1792	**1644**	71p. multicoloured	1·60	1·60
1793	**1645**	80p. multicoloured	1·90	1·90
1794	**1646**	130p. multicoloured	2·75	2·75
1795	**1647**	191p. multicoloured	4·25	4·25
1790/5		Set of 6	12·00	12·00
		First Day Cover		14·50
		Presentation Pack	14·50	

Plate Nos.: All values 1A (each×4).
Sheets: 40 (4×10).

1648 Queen Victoria

1649 King Edward VII and Queen Alexandra

1650 Souvenir of Visit of King George V and Queen Mary to Manchester, 2013

1651 King George VI, Queen Elizabeth, Princess Elizabeth and Princess Margaret

1652 Arms and Photo of Queen Elizabeth II

1653 Queen Elizabeth II and Duke of Edinburgh (Coronation souvenir)

1654 Coronation Photograph (*Illustration reduced. Actual size 110×70 mm*)

60th Anniversary of the Coronation. 'A Celebration of Coronation Commemoratives' (Coronation memorabilia)

(Des Casco and EJC Design. Litho BDT)

2013 (6 Feb–21 Apr). P 14½×14 (**MS**1802) or 14 (others) (both comb).

1796	**1648**	38p. multicoloured	90	90
1797	**1649**	41p. multicoloured	95	95
1798	**1650**	65p. multicoloured	1·50	1·50
1799	**1651**	£1.05 multicoloured	2·40	2·40
1800	**1652**	£1.37 multicoloured	2·75	2·75
1801	**1653**	£1.73 multicoloured	4·00	4·00
1796/801 *Set of 6*			12·00	12·00
First Day Cover				14·50
Presentation Pack			14·50	

Special Folder (complete sheet No. 1801, ½ sheets (5 stamps+label) others) (price £30)........... 60·00

MS1802 110×70 mm. **1654** £3 multicoloured (21 Apr) .... 7·25   7·25

First Day Cover .... 8·50

Presentation Pack .... 8·50

    Plate Nos.: All values 1A (each×4).
    Sheets: 8 (3×3) with central label.

1655 Year of the Snake (*Illustration reduced. Actual size 171×75 mm*)

Chinese New Year. Year of the Snake

(Des Siobhan McDevitt and EJC Design. Litho Beijing Stamp Printing Co (**MS**1803, **MS**184) or BDT (**MS**1803a, **MS**1804a))

2013 (8 Feb–4 Mar). P 12 (C).

MS1803 171×75 mm. **1655** 5p. Multicoloured coiled snake; 20p. Chinese letter containing fish; 20p. Chinese letter containing two cranes; 20p. Chinese letter containing deer; 20p. Chinese letter containing magpie and flowers; £2.15 Coiled yellow snake with flower and foliage pattern .... 7·25   7·25

   a. Perf 14½ (4 Mar) .... 7·25   7·25

MS1804 170×211 mm. 5p. Multicoloured coiled snake×16; 20p. Chinese letter containing fish; 20p. Chinese letter containing deer; 20p. Chinese letter containing two cranes; 20p. Chinese letter containing magpie and flowers .... 4·00   4·00

   a. Perf 14½ (4 Mar) .... 4·00   4·00

First Day Cover (**MS**1803) .... 8·50

First Day Cover (**MS**1803a) .... 8·50

Presentation Pack (**MS**1803) .... 8·50

Presentation Pack (**MS**1803a) .... 8·50

1656 Early and Modern Uniforms   **1657** Early Police Motorbikes and Modern Car and Motorcycle ('Vehicles')

1658 German Shepherd Dogs tracking Suspect and in Training and Springer Spaniel Sniffer Dog   **1659** Control Room Computers and Police with Radios ('Communications')

1660 Police Constable at Door and Police talking to Children ('Community')   **1661** Early and Current Police Stations

150th Anniversary of the Isle of Man Constabulary

(Des Emma Cooke. Litho BDT)

2013 (20 Feb). P 14 (C).

1805	**1656**	38p. multicoloured	90	90
1806	**1657**	41p. multicoloured	95	95
1807	**1658**	71p. multicoloured	1·60	1·60
1808	**1659**	80p. multicoloured	1·90	1·90
1809	**1660**	£1.47 multicoloured	3·25	3·25
1810	**1661**	£1.82 multicoloured	4·25	4·25
1805/10 *Set of 6*			12·50	12·50
First Day Cover				14·50
Presentation Pack			14·50	

    Plate Nos.: All values 1A (each×4).
    Sheets: 15 (3×5).

1662 Fire Engine (*Illustration reduced. Actual size 170×75 mm*)

Isle of Man Fire and Rescue Service

(Des Emma Cooke. Litho Cartor)

2013 (20 Feb). Sheet 170×75 mm. P 13½×14 (C).

MS1811 **1662** £3 multicoloured .... 7·25   7·25

First Day Cover .... 8·50

Presentation Pack .... 8·50

1663 Three Legs of Man wearing Armour   **1664** Arms with Three Legs of Man

1665 Three Legs of Man with Crown   **1666** Three Legs of Man in Stained Glass Window

1667 Three Legs of Man wearing Spurs

1668 Arms with Three Legs of Man, Peregrine Falcon, Raven and Crown

1669 Symbolic Three Legs of Man

1670 Three Legs of Man on Wall, Douglas

The Three Legs of Man

(Des Emma Cooke (EJC Design). Litho BDT)

2013 (3 Apr).

		(a) Ordinary gum. P 13 (C)		
1812	**1663**	5p. multicoloured	10	10
1813	**1664**	10p. multicoloured	25	25
1814	**1665**	40p. multicoloured	95	95
1815	**1666**	42p. multicoloured	95	95
1816	**1667**	69p. multicoloured	1·60	1·60
1817	**1668**	73p. multicoloured	1·60	1·60
1818	**1669**	£1.19 multicoloured	2·50	2·50
1819	**1670**	£2 multicoloured	4·25	4·25
1812/19 *Set of 8*			12·00	12·00
First Day Cover				14·50
Presentation Pack			14·50	

		(b) Self-adhesive. Die-cut perf 12½×13		
1820	**1665**	40p. multicoloured	95	95
		a. Booklet pane. No. 1820×10	9·50	
1821	**1666**	42p. multicoloured	95	95
		a. Booklet pane. No. 1821×10	9·50	

Plate Nos. All values 1A (each×4).
Sheets: 40 (8×5).

1671 *Robin's Reign, 1970*

1672 *How Old are you?, 1983*

1673 *Secret Agent, 1984*

1674 *Walls Have Eyes, 1985*

1675 *Magnet, 2003*

1676 *Robin Gibb Live, 2005*

1677 *Titanic Requiem (composed with R. J. Gibb, performed by Royal Philharmonic Orchestra), 2012*

1678 *50 St. Catherine's Drive*

Robin Gibb (singer and songwriter) Commemoration. Album Covers

(Des EJC Design. Litho Lowe-Martin)

2013 (24 Apr). P 13 (C).

1822	**1671**	2p. multicoloured	10	10
1823	**1672**	40p. multicoloured	95	95
1824	**1673**	42p. multicoloured	95	95
1825	**1674**	50p. multicoloured	1·25	1·25
1826	**1675**	69p. multicoloured	1·60	1·60
1827	**1676**	73p. multicoloured	1·60	1·60
1828	**1677**	120p. multicoloured	2·50	2·50
1829	**1678**	178p. multicoloured	4·00	4·00
1822/9 *Set of 8*			12·50	12·50
First Day Cover				14·50
Presentation Pack			14·50	
Retail Pack (first day cover and presentation pack)			28·00	
*Special Folder (**MS**1830, No. 1829 on special envelope and dvd) (price £30)*			60·00	
MS1830 211×298 mm. Nos. 1822/5 and Nos. 1826/9×2 .			25·00	25·00

Plate Nos.: All values 1A (each×4).
Sheets: 20 (4×5).

1679 Dubs Steam Locomotive *Caledonia*, Douglas Station, July 2009

1680 Manx Electric Railway Tramcar No. 6 at Halfway House Crossing, August 2012

1681 Beyer Peacock Steam Locomotive No. 10 *G. H. Wood* leaving Douglas Station, July 2009

1682 Manx Electric Railway Tramcar No. 5, Baldrine, September 2012

1683 Beyer Peacock Steam Locomotive No. 13 *Kissack*, Ellenbrook, July 2012

1684 Manx Electric Railway Tramcar No. 7 arriving at Laxey Station, May 2012

Isle of Man Railways. 140th Anniversary of the Isle of Man Steam Railway and 120th Anniversary of the Manx Electric Railway Douglas to Groudle Line. Modern Isle of Man Railways Posters

(Des EJC Design. Litho BDT)

2013 (17 May). P 14 (C).

1831	**1679**	40p. multicoloured	95	95
1832	**1680**	42p. multicoloured	95	95
1833	**1681**	69p. multicoloured	1·60	1·60
1834	**1682**	119p. multicoloured	2·50	2·50
1835	**1683**	160p. multicoloured	3·75	3·75
1836	**1684**	161p. multicoloured	3·75	3·75
1831/6 *Set of 6*			13·00	13·00
First Day Cover				14·50
Presentation Pack			14·50	

Plate Nos.: All values 1A (each×4).
Sheets: 15 (5×3).

1685 Eugène Christophe, 1919

1686 Mark Cavendish, 2011

1687 Brian Robinson, 1960

1688 Miguel Indurain, 1992

1689 Jacques Anquetil, 1963

1690 Eddy Merckx, 1970

1691 Bernard Hinault, 1979

1692 Bradley Wiggins, 2012 Centenary of the Tour de France (cycle race)

Centenary of the Tour de France (cycle race)

(Des EJC Design. Litho BDT)

2013 (19 June). P 13 (C).

1837	**1685**	1p. multicoloured	10	10
1838	**1686**	40p. multicoloured	95	95
1839	**1687**	42p. multicoloured	95	95
1840	**1688**	69p. multicoloured	1·60	1·60
1841	**1689**	73p. multicoloured	1·60	1·60
1842	**1690**	108p. multicoloured	2·40	2·40
1843	**1691**	119p. multicoloured	2·50	2·50
1844	**1692**	120p. multicoloured	2·50	2·50
1837/44 *Set of 8*			12·00	12·00
First Day Cover				14·50
Presentation Pack			14·50	
Gift Pack (presentation pack and maximum cards)			30·00	
Postcards			12·00	
Maximum Cards				19·50

Plate Nos.: All values 1A (each×4).
Sheets: 25 (5×5).

1693 The Last Flight of Concorde, 2003

1694 England win the World Cup, 1966

1695 Isle of Man Postal Independence, 1973

1696 Queen Elizabeth II's State Visit to China, 1986

1697 President Kennedy Assassinated in Dallas, 1963

1698 Man Lands on the Moon, 1969

225th Anniversary of the *Times of London*. Newspaper Headlines (Europa)

(Des EJC Design. Litho BDT)

2013 (4 July). P 14½×14 (C).

1845	**1693**	40p. multicoloured	95	95
1846	**1694**	42p. multicoloured	95	95
1847	**1695**	73p. multicoloured	1·60	1·60
1848	**1696**	108p. multicoloured	2·40	2·40
1849	**1697**	141p. multicoloured	3·25	3·25
1850	**1698**	179p. multicoloured	4·25	4·25
1845/50 *Set of 6*			13·00	13·00
First Day Cover				14·50
Presentation Pack			14·50	

Plate Nos.: All values 1A (each×4).
Sheets: 15 (5×3), 73p. also 10 (5×3), each stamp with a 41×12 mm *se-tenant* label at the top showing 'THE TIMES' title. No. 1847 includes the Europa emblem.

For details of Royal Wedding stamps with Prince George labels, issued 31 July 2013, see Nos. 1668a/b.

1699 Murals from St. Thomas' Church, Douglas (*Illustration reduced. Actual size 170×76 mm*)

St. Thomas' Church Murals by John Miller Nicholson

(Des EJC Design. Litho Cartor)

2013 (8 Aug). Sheet 170×76 mm. Multicoloured. P 13×13½ (C).

MS1851	170×76 mm. **1699** £1 Angels; £2 Saints	7·25	7·25
First Day Cover			8·50
Presentation Pack		8·50	

1700 Lion

1701 Snow Leopard

1702 Tiger

1703 Cheetah

1704 Leopard

1705 Jaguar

Big Cats by Jeremy Paul (Sepac)

(Des Dr. Jeremy Paul (illustrations) and EJC Design. Litho Lowe-Martin)

2013 (13 Sept). P 13 ½ (C).

1852	**1700**	40p. multicoloured	95	95
1853	**1701**	42p. multicoloured	95	95
1854	**1702**	69p. multicoloured	1·60	1·60
1855	**1703**	120p. multicoloured	2·50	2·50
1856	**1704**	160p. multicoloured	3·75	3·75
1857	**1705**	161p. multicoloured	3·75	3·75
1852/7 *Set of 6*			13·00	13·00
First Day Cover				14·50
Presentation Pack			14·50	

No. 1854 includes the 'sepac' emblem and was also available in a folder with 11 other 'sepac' emblem stamps issued by other participating postal administrations. Cost £15.

Plate Nos.: All values 1A (each×4).

Sheets: 20 (5×4).

1706 Baboon; Rhinoceros; Giraffes; Kudu (*Illustration reduced. Actual size 170×75 mm*)

A Journey through Africa with Jeremy Paul

(Des Dr. Jeremy Paul (illustrations) and EJC Design. Litho Cartor)

2013 (13 Sept). Sheet 170×75 mm. P 13½×13 (vert) or 13×13½ (horiz) (both comb).

MS1858 **1706** 75p.×4 multicoloured		7·25	7·25
First Day Cover			8·50
Presentation Pack		8·50	

1707 Girl posting Letter (Christmas 1990)

1708 The Three Kings ('Love Came Down at Christmas' 1991)

1709 Angel with the Crown of Glory (Stained Glass Windows, 2005)

1710 Robin (Christmas 1988)

1711 St. Catherine's Church, Port Erin ('Winter in Mann', 1995)

1712 Christmas Tree and Gifts (Christmas Trees, 2006)

A Christmas Stamp Gallery. Designs adapted from previous Christmas Stamps

(Des EJC Design. Litho BDT)

2013 (17 Oct).

		(a) Ordinary gum. P 13 (C)		
1859	**1707**	40p. multicoloured	95	95
1860	**1708**	42p. multicoloured	95	95
1861	**1709**	73p. multicoloured	1·60	1·60
1862	**1710**	108p. multicoloured	2·40	2·40
1863	**1711**	119p. multicoloured	2·50	2·50
1864	**1712**	178p. multicoloured	4·25	4·25
1859/64 *Set of 6*			12·00	12·00
First Day Cover				14·50
Presentation Pack			14·50	

		(b) Self-adhesive. Die-cut perf 11		
1865	**1707**	40p. multicoloured	95	95
1866	**1708**	42p. multicoloured	95	95

Plate Nos.: All values 1A (each×4).

Sheets: 20 (5×4) Nos. 1859/64; 25 (5×5) Nos. 1865/6.

Year Folder 2013

2013 (17 Oct). Comprises Nos. 1790/803, 1805/19, 1822/9 and 1831/64 (price £72).

Year Folder	£140

Year Pack 2013

2013 (17 Oct). Comprises Nos. 1790/803, 1805/19, 1822/9 and 1831/64 (price £83).

Year Pack	£165

Post Office Yearbook

2013 (17 Oct). Comprises Nos. 1790/803, 1805/19, 1822/9 and 1831/64 (price £72).

Yearbook	£140

1713 Visual Arts

1714 Drama

1715 Literature

1716 Film

1717 Music

1718 Craft

1719 Dance

1720 Design

Island of Culture 2014

(Des Juan Moore. Litho Lowe-Martin Group, Canada)

2014 (6 Jan). P 13 (C).

1867	**1713**	(40p.) multicoloured	95	95
1868	**1714**	(40p.) multicoloured	95	95
1869	**1715**	(42p.) multicoloured	95	95
1870	**1716**	(42p.) multicoloured	95	95
1871	**1717**	(73p.) multicoloured	1·60	1·60
1872	**1718**	(£1.19) multicoloured	2·50	2·50
1873	**1719**	(£1.19) multicoloured	2·50	2·50
1874	**1720**	(£1.19) multicoloured	2·50	2·50
1867/74 Set of 8			11·50	11·50
First Day Cover				14·00
Presentation Pack			14·00	
Gift Pack (Presentation Pack and Postcards)			32·00	
Postcards			10·50	

Nos. 1867/8 were inscr 'IOM' and originally sold for 40p., Nos. 1869/70 were inscr 'UK' and sold for 42p., No. 1871 was inscr 'EU' and sold for 73p. and Nos. 1872/4 were inscr 'ROW' and sold for £1.19.
Plate Nos.: All values 1A (×4)
Sheets: 20 No. 1871 also 10 (5×2))

1721 Winter Berries and Flowers

Winter Flora

(Des Catherine James (illustration) and EJC Design. Litho Lowe-Martin)

2014 (6 Jan). Sheet 130×90 mm. Multicoloured. P 13 (C).

First Day Cover			8·00
Presentation Pack		8·00	
MS1875 1721 75p.×4 Ivy berries; Fir cones; Hellebore flowers; Rose hips		7·25	7·25

1722 Communications

1723 Sappers

1724 Trenches

1725 Horses

1726 Christmas Truce

1727 Officers' Dugout

1728 Detail from German Christmas card produced in Knockaloe Internment Camp, 1917

Centenary of World War I (1st issue). Life in the Trenches

(Litho BDT)

2014 (19 Feb). P 14 (1876/81) or 15×14 (MS1882) (both comb).

1876	**1722**	40p. multicoloured	95	95
1877	**1723**	42p. multicoloured	95	95
1878	**1724**	69p. multicoloured	1·60	1·60
1879	**1725**	£1.08 multicoloured	2·40	2·40
1880	**1726**	£1.41 multicoloured	3·25	3·25
1881	**1727**	£1.60 multicoloured	3·75	3·75
1876/81 Set of 6			11·50	11·50
First Day Cover				13·00
Presentation Pack			13·00	
Folder (complete sheets and MS1882) (price £30)			60·00	
MS1882 1728 £3.00 110×70 mm. multicoloured			7·25	7·25
First Day Cover				8·00
Presentation Pack			8·00	

Nos. 1876/81 were each printed in sheetlets of eight stamps with a central stamp-size label inscr "Safe, Though All Safety's Lost..." (Rupert Brooke).
Plate Nos.:
Sheets: 8 (3×3) with a central label

1729 Four Red Arrows

1730 Red Arrows flying in Formation

1731 Two Red Arrows

1732 Two Red Arrows

1733 Four Red Arrows   **1734** View from Cockpit

50th Display Season of Royal Air Force Red Arrows

(Des EJC Design. Litho BDT)

2014 (19 Feb).

(a) Ordinary gum. P 13 (C)

1883	**1729**	40p. multicoloured	95	95
1884	**1730**	42p. multicoloured	1·00	1·00
1885	**1731**	69p. multicoloured	1·60	1·60
1886	**1732**	73p. multicoloured	1·75	1·75
1887	**1733**	108p. multicoloured	2·50	2·50
1888	**1734**	265p. multicoloured	6·25	6·25
1883/8 Set of 6			12·50	12·50
First Day Cover				13·50
Presentation Pack			13·50	

(b) Self-adhesive. Die-cut perf 13½

1889	**1729**	40p. multicoloured	95	95
		a. Booklet pane. Nos. 1889/91	3·50	
		b. Booklet pane. Nos. 1889/94	13·50	
1890	**1730**	42p. multicoloured	1·00	1·00
1891	**1731**	69p. multicoloured	1·60	1·60
1892	**1732**	73p. multicoloured	1·75	1·75
		a. Booklet pane. Nos. 1892/4	10·50	
1893	**1733**	108p. multicoloured	2·50	2·50
1894	**1734**	265p. multicoloured	6·25	6·25
1889/94 Set of 6			13·50	13·50

Nos. 1889/94 were issued in £11.94 booklets, No. SB81.
Plate Nos.: All values 1A (each×5)
Sheets: 20 (5×4).

1735 'Deer's Cry'   **1736** 'To the Virtue of His Crucifixion'

1737 'In Splendour of Fire'   **1738** 'God's Wisdom to Guide Me'

1739 'In Compactness of Rock'   **1740** 'God's Shield to Protect Me'

1741 'His Ascension'   **1742** 'In the Creator of the Universe'

1743 'God's Way to Lie Before Me'   **1744** 'I Bind Myself Today'

150th Birth Anniv of Archibald Knox (1864–1933, artist and designer). Images from his Illuminated Manuscript *Deer's Cry*

(Des EJC Design. Litho LM Group)

2014 (4 Apr).

(a) Ordinary gum. P 13×12½ (C)

1895	**1735**	42p. multicoloured	1·00	1·00
		a. Horiz strip of 5. Nos. 1895/9	5·00	5·00
1896	**1736**	42p. multicoloured	1·00	1·00
1897	**1737**	42p. multicoloured	1·00	1·00
1898	**1738**	42p. multicoloured	1·00	1·00
1899	**1739**	42p. multicoloured	1·00	1·00
1900	**1740**	75p. multicoloured	1·75	1·75
		a. Horiz strip of 5. Nos. 1900/4	8·75	8·75
1901	**1741**	75p. multicoloured	1·75	1·75
1902	**1742**	75p. multicoloured	1·75	1·75
1903	**1743**	75p. multicoloured	1·75	1·75
1904	**1744**	75p. multicoloured	1·75	1·75
1895/904 Set of 10			13·50	13·50
First Day Cover				13·50
Presentation Pack			13·50	

(b) Self-adhesive. Die-cut perf 13½

1905	**1735**	42p. multicoloured	1·00	1·00
		a. Booklet pane. Nos. 1905×3, 1906×2, 1907×3 and 1908/9×2	4·50	
1906	**1737**	42p. multicoloured	1·00	1·00
1907	**1739**	42p. multicoloured	1·00	1·00
1908	**1736**	42p. multicoloured	1·00	1·00
1909	**1738**	42p. multicoloured	1·00	1·00
1905/9 Set of 5			4·50	4·50

Nos. 1895/9 and 1900/4 were each printed together, *se-tenant*, as horizontal strips of five stamps in sheets of 20 (5×4).
Nos. 1905/9 were issued in £5.04 booklets, No. SB82.
Plate Nos.: 1A (×4)
Sheets: 20 (5×4).

1745 Brodir the Warrior   **1746** The Battle of Clontarf   **1747** Eithne weaves the Raven Banner

1748 Clontarf Warrior   **1749** King Brian Boru   **1750** Fight for the Raven Banner

Millennium of the Battle of Clontarf (between King Brian Boru of Ireland and the Norse)

(Des Victor G. Ambrus. Litho BDT)

2014 (15 Apr). P 14 (C).

1910	**1745**	2p. multicoloured	10	10
1911	**1746**	42p. multicoloured	1·00	1·00
1912	**1747**	90p. multicoloured	2·25	2·25

1913	**1748**	£1 multicoloured	2·40	2·40
1914	**1749**	£1.60 multicoloured	3·75	3·75
1915	**1750**	£2.30 multicoloured	5·50	5·50
1910/15		Set of 6	13·50	13·50
First Day Cover				13·50
Presentation Pack				14·50

Plate Nos.: All values 1A (each×4)
Sheets: 15 (5×3)

1751 Manx Loaghtan Ram; Northern Dairy Shorthorn Cattle; Cotswold Sheep; Exmoor Ponies; Gloucestershire Old Spot Pig; Irish Moiled Cattle

The Manx Ark. 40th Anniv of the Rare Breeds Survival Trust and Centenary of Southern District Agricultural Society

(Des Dr. Jeremy Paul (illustration) and EJC Design. Litho Cartor)

2014 (16 Apr). Sheet 170×75 mm. P 13×13½ (C).

First Day Cover		6·50
Presentation Pack	6·50	
MS1916 1751	38p.×6 multicoloured	5·50	5·50

Centenary of Howard Pixton's Victory in International Schneider Trophy Seaplane Race, Monacoy

(Des R. Carter. Litho BDT)

2014 (20 Apr). P 14 (C).

| *Special Folder* (**MS1916** perforate and imperf and signed cover) (price £35) | 70·00 |
| **MS1916a** 148×210 mm. 75p. As Type **710**×4 with five stamp-size labels | 7·25 | 7·25 |

No. **MS1916a** was sold as a "commemorative sheet" by Isle of Man Post. It contains stamps as Type **710** (1997 Manx Aircraft), but revalued and with 2014 imprint date. An imperforate version of the commemorative sheet was sold for £7.50 by Isle of Man Post.

1752 Tank leaving Landing Craft

1753 Troops on Landing Beach

1754 Tank

1755 Tanks on Road

1756 Veteran

1757 Troops in Normandy

70th Anniversary of D-Day. A Manxman's Journey

(Des EJC Design. Litho BDT)

2014 (8 May). P 14 (C).

1917	**1752**	42p. multicoloured	1·00	1·00
1918	**1753**	75p. multicoloured	1·75	1·75
1919	**1754**	90p. multicoloured	2·25	2·25
1920	**1755**	110p. multicoloured	2·75	2·75
1921	**1756**	144p. multicoloured	3·50	3·50
1922	**1757**	182p. multicoloured	4·25	4·25
1917/22		Set of 6	14·00	14·00

First Day Cover		15·00
Presentation Pack	15·00	
MS1922a 210×296 mm. As Nos. 1131/8 and Winston Churchill and Soldiers with Guidebook designs from **MS1139** but with 2014 imprint dates	21·00	21·00
Commemorative Folder (MS1922a, signed first day cover of Nos. 1917/22 and D-Day crown) (price £35)	70·00

Plate Nos.: 1A×4
Sheets: 15 (3×5)

1757a Hellebore Flowers

sepac. Winter Flora

(Des Catherine James (illustration) and EJC Design. Litho Lowe-Martin Group)

2014 (16 July). P 13 (C).

1923	**1757a**	75p. multicoloured	1·75	1·75
First Day Cover				3·25
Presentation Pack			3·25	

No. 1923 is as the 75p. hellebore flowers stamp in the Winter Flora miniature sheet, No. **MS1875**, but with the addition of a 'sepac' inscription at top left.

Plate Nos.: 1A×4
Sheets: 28 (4×7)

1758 Liner *Queen Elizabeth* in Panama Canal

Centenary of the Panama Canal

(Des Isle of Man Advertising. Litho BDT)

2014 (8 Aug). Sheet 110×70 mm. P 14 (C).

First Day Cover		9·50
Presentation Pack	9·50	
MS1924 1758 £3.50 multicoloured	8·50	8·50

1759 Peel Castle and Douglas Light House

1760 Douglas Iron Pier and View of Douglas

1761 Webbs Louvre, Douglas

1762 Bradda Head and Douglas Lighthouse

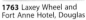

1763 Laxey Wheel and Fort Anne Hotel, Douglas

1764 Groudle Wheel

History of Manx Playing Cards

(Des EJC Design. Litho Lowe-Martin)

2014 (8 Aug). P 13×12½ (C).

1925	**1759**	42p. multicoloured	1·00	1·00
1926	**1760**	75p. multicoloured	1·75	1·75
1927	**1761**	90p. multicoloured	2·25	2·25
1928	**1762**	110p. multicoloured	2·75	2·75
1929	**1763**	121p. multicoloured	3·00	3·00
1930	**1764**	182p. multicoloured	4·25	4·25
1925/30	*Set of 6*		13·50	13·50
First Day Cover				14·50
Presentation Pack			14·50	

Plate Nos.: All values 1A (each×4)
Sheets: 20

1765 Orion seen from Niarbyl

1766 Leo seen from Port Erin

1767 Cygnus and the Milky way seen from Fort Island

1768 Pegasus and Andromeda seen from Langness

Dark Sky Discovery

(Des Isle of Man Advertising. Litho BDT)

2014 (1 Sept). P 14 (C).

1931	**1765**	42p. multicoloured	1·00	1·00
1932	**1766**	164p. multicoloured	4·00	4·00
1933	**1767**	182p. multicoloured	4·25	4·25
1934	**1768**	230p. multicoloured	5·50	5·50
1931/4	*Set of 4*		13·50	13·50
First Day Cover				14·50
Presentation Pack			14·50	

Plate Nos.: All values 1A (×5)
Sheets: 20

1769 David Callister in Studio (Mannin Line)

1770 Presenter John Kennaugh with Sheep (Countryside)

1771 Stormy Sea (Weather Reports)

1772 Alan Jackson and Children (Jackson's Jollybodys)

1773 House of Keys (Mandate)

1774 Jim Caine playing Piano (Jazz Hour)

1775 Peter Kneale commentating (Radio TT)

1776 Visit of Queen Elizabeth, 1979 (Outside Broadcasts)

50th Anniversary of Manx Radio

(Des Mainstream Marketing & Communications. Litho Lowe-Martin)

2014 (1 Oct). P 13 (C).

1935	**1769**	42p. multicoloured	1·00	1·00
1936	**1770**	42p. multicoloured	1·00	1·00
1937	**1771**	50p. multicoloured	1·25	1·25
1938	**1772**	50p. multicoloured	1·25	1·25
1939	**1773**	75p. multicoloured	1·75	1·75
1940	**1774**	75p. multicoloured	1·75	1·75
1941	**1775**	£1.20 multicoloured	3·00	3·00
1942	**1776**	£1.20 multicoloured	3·00	3·00
1935/42	*Set of 8*		12·50	12·50
First Day Cover				13·50
Presentation Pack			13·50	

Plate Nos.: 1A (each×4)
Sheets: 20

1777 Port St. Mary Town Banner

Isle of Man Guild of Silk Painters Town Banners

(Des EJC Design. Litho LM Group)

2014 (23 Oct). Sheet 170×75 mm. P 13 (C).
First Day Cover... 8·25
Presentation Pack... 8·25
MS1943 **1777** £3 multicoloured .... 7·25 7·25

1778 Billy flying with Snowman and Snowdog

1779 Father Christmas, Snowman and Snowdog

1780 Snowman and Snowdog

1781 Snowdog

1782 Billy and Snowdog in Sledge and Snowman Skiing

1783 Snowman, Billy and Snowdog

Christmas. *The Snowman and the Snowdog* (**film**)

(Litho Cartor)

2014 (23 Oct).

(a) Ordinary gum. P 13 (C)
1944	**1778**	42p. multicoloured	1·00	1·00
1945	**1779**	42p. multicoloured	1·00	1·00
1946	**1780**	75p. multicoloured	1·75	1·75
1947	**1781**	90p. multicoloured	2·25	2·25
1948	**1782**	£1.21 multicoloured	3·00	3·00
1949	**1783**	£2.21 multicoloured	5·25	5·25

1944/9 Set of 6... 13·00 13·00
First Day Cover... 14·00
Presentation Pack... 14·00
(b) Self-adhesive. Die-cut perf 11
1950	**1778**	42p. multicoloured	1·00	1·00
1951	**1779**	42p. multicoloured	1·00	1·00

Plate Nos.: 1A×4
Sheets: 20 (5×4) (1944/9), 25 (5×5) (1950/1)

Year Folder 2014

2014 (1 Nov). Comprises Nos. 1867/88, 1895/904, 1910/**MS**1916, 1917/22 and 1923/49 (price £75)
Year Folder £150

YearPack 2014

2014 (1 Nov). Comprises Nos. 1867/88, 1895/904, 1910/**MS**1916, 1917/22 and 1923/49 (price £86.25)
Year Pack £175

Post Office Yearbook

2014 (1 Nov). Comprises Nos. 1867/88, 1895/904, 1910/**MS**1916, 1917/22 and 1923/49 (price £77.50)
Year Book... £150

1784 Sheep

1785 Year of the Sheep

Chinese New Year. Year of the Sheep

(Des Guo Zhenshan (10p.) or Du Xiaoxiao (£3). Litho)

2015 (2 Jan). P 13 (C).
1952 **1784** 10p. multicoloured 25 25
First Day Cover... 8·50
Presentation Pack... 8·50
MS1953 171×75 mm. **1785** 10p. multicoloured; £3 multicoloured .... 7·50 7·50
Plate Nos.: 1A (×4)
Sheets: (4×5)

No. 1952 was printed in sheetlets of 16 stamps with four stamp-size labels showing calligraphy at the four corners of the sheetlet.

1786 Winston Churchill aged 19 in Uniform of Fourth Queen's Own Hussars

1787 Winston Churchill, c. 1890s

1788 On Stage

1789 In Study, writing

1790 Giving V for Victory Sign

1791 In Front of Microphones

1792 Painting   **1793** Laying Bricks

50th Death Anniversary of Winston Churchill

(Des Isle of Man Advertising & PR Ltd. Litho Cartor)

2015 (2 Jan). P 13½ (C).

1954	**1786**	42p. multicoloured	1·00	1·00
		a. Vert pair. Nos. 1954/5	2·00	2·00
1955	**1787**	42p. multicoloured	1·00	1·00
1956	**1788**	75p. multicoloured	1·75	1·75
		a. Vert pair. Nos. 1956/7	3·50	3·50
1957	**1789**	75p. multicoloured	1·75	1·75
1958	**1790**	90p. multicoloured	2·25	2·25
		a. Vert pair. Nos. 1958/9	4·50	4·50
1959	**1791**	90p. multicoloured	2·25	2·25
1960	**1792**	110p. multicoloured	2·75	2·75
		a. Vert pair. Nos. 1960/1	5·50	5·50
1961	**1793**	110p. multicoloured	2·75	2·75
1954/61 *Set of 8*			15·00	15·00
First Day Cover				16·00
Presentation Pack			16·00	

Plate Nos.: All values 1A (each×5)
Sheets: 20 (5×4).

Nos. 1954/5, 1956/7, 1958/9 and 1960/1 were each printed together, *se-tenant*, as vertical pairs throughout the sheets.

1794 Palestine   **1795** Home Front

1796 Western Front   **1797** Eastern Front

1798 Gallipoli   **1799** Italy

Centenary of World War I (2nd issue). Battle Fronts

(Des CASCO. Litho BDT)

2015 (17 Feb). P 14 (C).

1962	**1794**	42p. multicoloured	1·00	1·00
1963	**1795**	42p. multicoloured	1·00	1·00
1964	**1796**	75p. multicoloured	1·75	1·75
1965	**1797**	£1.10 multicoloured	2·75	2·75
1966	**1798**	£1.44 multicoloured	3·50	3·50
1967	**1799**	£1.64 multicoloured	4·00	4·00
1962/7 *Set of 6*			12·50	12·50
First Day Cover				13·50
Presentation Pack			13·50	
Commemorative Folder (sheets of 8 42p.×2, 75p,. partial				
sheets (5 stamps) £1.10, £1.44, £1.64) (price £30)			60·00	

Plate Nos.: None
Sheets: 8 (3×3) with central label. Sheets of 15 (3×5) were for post office use

1800 Penny Black   **1801** Two Pence Blue

1802 Penny Red   **1803** Edward Stanley Gibbons and Gibbons Stamp Monthly

1804 William Mulready and Mulready Envelope   **1805** Rowland Hill and Letter with Postmarked Penny Black

175th Anniversary of the Penny Black

(Des Leanne Sherliker. Litho BDT)

2015 (17 Feb). P 13½.

1968	**1800**	1p. multicoloured	10	10
1969	**1801**	42p. multicoloured	1·00	1·00
1970	**1802**	90p. multicoloured	2·25	2·25
1971	**1803**	£1.20 multicoloured	3·00	3·00
1972	**1804**	£1.60 multicoloured	3·75	3·75
1973	**1805**	£2.30 multicoloured	5·50	5·50
1968/73 *Set of 6*			14·00	14·00
First Day Cover				15·00
Presentation Pack			15·00	
*Penny Black Mulready Special Folder (1971/3, **MS**1974,*				
2 reproduction Mulready envelopes, 4 caricature				
envelopes) (price £20)			40·00	
MS1974 No. 1968×16 and Nos. 1969/70, each×2			7·00	7·00

Plate Nos.: All values 1A (each×4)
Sheets: 20 (4×5)

1806 VJ Day

1807 VE Day

70th Anniversary of the End of World War II

(Litho BDT)

2015 (26 Feb). Multicoloured. P 13½ (C).

First Day Cover		8·75
Presentation Pack	8·75	
MS1975 121×55 mm. 1806 £1 Gurkha soldier; £1 Soldier	4·75	4·75
MS1976 55×54 mm. 1807 £1.50 'VE DAY' newspaper headline and medal	3·50	3·50

1808 Duke of Wellington and Manxman Caesar Bacon (Ensign (later Major) in 23rd Light Dragoons, fought at Waterloo)

Bicentenary of the Battle of Waterloo (1st issue)

(Des Paul Hannon (artwork) and EJC Design. Litho)

2015 (9 Mar). P 13 (C).

1977	1808	£1 multicoloured	2·40	2·40
First Day Cover				3·75
Presentation Pack			3·75	

Plate Nos.: 1A×4
Sheets: 25 (5×5)

1809 The Viking Arrival

1810 Manx Bill of Rights

1811 Tourist Industry

1812 Spuds 'n Herring (traditional Manx meal)

1813 Manx Nobby (herring fishing boat, 1890s)

1814 TT Races

1815 Steam Railway, Manx Electric Railway and Bus

1816 Old House of Keys, Castletown

1817 Women campaigning for Women's Suffrage, Ramsey Beach

1818 Tynwald Hill

Millennium of Tynwald Tapestry

(Des EJC Design. Litho)

2015 (10 Apr).

(a) Ordinary gum. P 14 (C)

1978	1809	(42p.) multicoloured	1·00	1·00
		a. Horiz strip of 5. Nos. 1978/82	5·00	5·00
1979	1810	(42p.) multi-coloured	1·00	1·00
1980	1811	(42p.) multicoloured	1·00	1·00
1981	1812	(42p.) multicoloured	1·00	1·00
1982	1813	(42p.) multicoloured	1·00	1·00
1983	1814	(75p.) multicoloured	1·75	1·75
		a. Horiz strip of 5. Nos. 1983/7	8·75	8·75
1984	1815	(75p.) multicoloured	1·75	1·75
		a. Larger Queen's head	1·75	1·75
1985	1816	(75p.) multicoloured	1·75	1·75
1986	1817	(75p.) multicoloured	1·75	1·75
1987	1818	(75p.) multicoloured	1·75	1·75
1978/87 *Set of 10*			13·50	13·50
First Day Cover				14·50
Presentation Pack			14·50	

(b) Self-adhesive. Die-cut perf 13½

1988	1809	(42p.) multicoloured	1·00	1·00
		a. Booklet pane. Nos. 1988×3, 1989×2, 1990×3 and 1991/2 each×2	9·50	
1989	1810	(42p.) multicoloured	1·00	1·00
1990	1811	(42p.) multi-coloured	1·00	1·00
1991	1812	(42p.) multicoloured	1·00	1·00
1992	1813	(42p.) multicoloured	1·00	1·00

Nos. 1978/82 and 1988/92 were inscr '1ST' and originally sold for 42p. each.

Nos. 1983/7 were inscr 'EU' and originally sold for 75p. each.

Nos. 1988/92 were issued in booklets of 12 stamps, No. SB83, originally sold for £5.04.

Plate Nos.: 1A (×4)

Sheets: 50 (5×10) 1983a also 10 (5×2). Nos. 1978/82 and 1983/7 were each printed together, *se-tenant*, as horizontal strips of five stamps throughout the sheets.

No. 1983a has a larger Queen's head and comes from Europa sheetlets of ten.

1818a Gurkha Soldier

The Gurkhas 200 Years of Service to the Crown

(Litho BDT)

2015 (24 Apr). P 13½.

1993	1818a	£1 multicoloured	2·40	2·40

No. 1993 was only available from commemorative sheetlets of ten stamps and ten labels, sold from the Isle of Man Philatelic Bureau for £10 per sheet, or from MS1975.

1819 'TIME TO TALK ORGAN DONATION'

1820 'SUPPORTING MANX DAIRY FARMERS'

1821 'WOMEN DEMAND EQUAL PAY'

1822 'PLEASE TAKE LITTER HOME'

1823 WI Members with Campaign Placards

1824 WI Members with Campaign Placards from 1983

Centenary of the Women's Institute

(Des Isle of Man Advertising. Litho Lowe-Martin)

2015 (25 Apr.). P 13 (C).

1994	**1819**	(42p.) multicoloured	1·00	1·00
1995	**1820**	(42p.) multicoloured	1·00	1·00
1996	**1821**	£1 multicoloured	2·40	2·40
1997	**1822**	£1 multicoloured	2·40	2·40
1998	**1823**	£1.75 multicoloured	4·25	4·25
1999	**1824**	£1.75 multicoloured	4·25	4·25
1994/9	*Set of 6*		14·00	14·00
First Day Cover				15·00
Presentation Pack			15·00	

Nos. 1994/5 were inscr. '1ST' and originally sold for 42p. each.
Plate Nos.: All values 1A (each×4)
Sheets: 20 (5×4)
Nos. 1994/9 have rose-scented lacquer.

1825 John Halsall's Maritime History

Maritime History

(Des John Halsall (illustration) and Isle of Man Advertising. Litho)

2015 (1 May). Sheet 171×75 mm. Multicoloured. P 13½ (C).

MS2000 **1825** 75p. *Master Frank*; 75p. HMS *Ramsey*; £1 HMS *Ben my Chree*; £1 *Lusitania* and *Wanderer*....	8·50	8·50
First Day Cover		9·50
Presentation Pack	9·50	

1826 Wellington on Horseback inspecting troops (William Barnes Wollen)

1827 Battle of Quatre-Bras (Richard Knotel)

1828 Fighting at La Haye-Sainte (Richard Knotel)

1829 Napoleon ordering the advance of the Imperial Guard

1830 Defence of Chateau de Hougoumont (Denis Dighton)

1831 Wellington defeats Ney at Quatre-Bras (Vereker M. Hamilton)

1832 Wellington and Blücher (after Daniel Maclise)

1833 Col Halkett calling on the Imperial Guard to surrender

Bicentenary of the Battle of Waterloo (2nd issue)

(Des MM&C. Litho Lowe-Martin)

2015 (8 May). P 12½ (C).

2001	**1826**	75p. multicoloured	1·75	1·75
		a. Horiz pair. Nos. 2001/2	3·50	3·50
2002	**1827**	75p. multicoloured	1·75	1·75
2003	**1828**	75p. multicoloured	1·75	1·75
		a. Horiz pair. Nos. 2003/4	3·50	3·50
2004	**1829**	75p. multicoloured	1·75	1·75
2005	**1830**	90p. multicoloured	2·25	2·25
		a. Horiz pair. Nos. 2005/6	4·50	4·50
2006	**1831**	90p. multicoloured	2·25	2·25
2007	**1832**	90p. multicoloured	2·25	2·25
		a. Horiz pair. Nos. 2007/8	4·50	4·50
2008	**1833**	90p. multicoloured	2·25	2·25
2001/8	*Set of 8*		15·00	15·00
First Day Cover				16·00
Presentation Pack			16·00	

Special Folder (No. 1977 and complete sheets of Nos. 2001/8) (price £30) .... 60·00

Sheets: 8 (2×4). Nos. 2001/2, 2003/4, 2005/6 and 2007/8 were each printed together, *se-tenant*, in horizontal pairs throughout the sheets.

1834 Coronation

1835 Investiture of Prince Charles as Prince of Wales

1836 Silver Jubilee

1837 Queen Elizabeth II in Garter Robes

1838 Trooping the Colour

1839 Golden Jubilee

1840 Diamond Jubilee **1841** Opening of Parliament

Pomp and Circumstance. The Reign of Queen Elizabeth II

(Des The fresh Group. Litho BDT)

2015 (18 June). (a) Ordinary gum. P 14×14½ (C)

2009	**1834**	44p. multicoloured	1·10	1·10
2010	**1835**	44p. multicoloured	1·10	1·10
2011	**1836**	77p. multicoloured	1·90	1·90
2012	**1837**	77p. multicoloured	1·90	1·90
2013	**1838**	93p. multicoloured	2·25	2·25
2014	**1839**	93p. multicoloured	2·25	2·25
2015	**1840**	£1.24 multicoloured	3·00	3·00
2016	**1841**	£1.24 multicoloured	3·00	3·00
2009/16 Set of 8			15·00	15·00
First Day Cover				16·00
Presentation Pack			16·00	

(b) Self-adhesive. Die-cut perf 11½ (9 Sept)

2017	**1834**	44p. multicoloured	1·10	1·10
		a. Booklet pane. Nos. 2017/18	2·25	
		b. Booklet pane. Nos. 2017/24	15·00	
2018	**1835**	44p. multicoloured	1·10	1·10
2019	**1836**	77p. multicoloured	1·90	1·90
		a. Booklet pane. Nos. 2019/21	6·00	
2020	**1837**	77p. multicoloured	1·90	1·90
2021	**1838**	93p. multicoloured	2·25	2·25
2022	**1839**	93p. multicoloured	2·25	2·25
		a. Booklet pane. Nos. 2022/4	8·25	
2023	**1840**	£1.24 multicoloured	3·00	3·00
2024	**1841**	£1.24 multicoloured	3·00	3·00
2009/16 Set of 8			15·00	15·00

Nos. 2017/24 were issued in £13.52 booklets, No. SB84.
Plate Nos.: All values 1A (each×5)
Sheets: 20 (5×4)

1842 Humboldt Penguin **1843** Red Panda **1844** Ruffed Lemur

1845 Waldrapp Ibis **1846** Fishing Cat **1847** Rodrigues Fruit Bat

50th Anniversary of The Curraghs Wildlife Park

(Des Home Strategic. Litho Cartor)

2015 (3 July). P 13½ (C).

2025	**1842**	44p. multicoloured	1·10	1·10
2026	**1843**	44p. multicoloured	1·10	1·10
2027	**1844**	93p. multicoloured	2·25	2·25
2028	**1845**	£1.13 multicoloured	2·75	2·75
2029	**1846**	£1.24 multicoloured	3·00	3·00
2030	**1847**	£2.38 multicoloured	5·75	5·75
2025/30 Set of 6			14·50	14·50

First Day Cover		16·00
Presentation Pack	16·00	
Postcards (set of 6)	8·75	

Plate Nos.: All values 1A (each×4)
Sheets: 18 (3×6)

1848 Douglas Corporation Transport Leyland Cub KPZ1 **1849** Isle of Man Road Services Leyland/MCW Olympic HR40

1850 Isle of Man Road Services Leyland Tiger PS1 **1851** Douglas Corporation Transport Daimler CWA6

1852 Isle of Man Road Services Leyland Titan PD1 **1853** Douglas Corporation Transport AEC Regent I

Manx Buses (2nd series)

(Des Peter Hearsey (illustrations) and EJC Design. Litho Cartor)

2015 (15 July). P 13 (C).

2031	**1848**	44p. multicoloured	1·10	1·10
2032	**1849**	60p. multicoloured	1·40	1·40
2033	**1850**	77p. multicoloured	1·90	1·90
2034	**1851**	93p. multicoloured	2·25	2·25
2035	**1852**	147p. multicoloured	3·50	3·50
2036	**1853**	186p. multicoloured	4·50	4·50
2031/6 Set of 6			13·00	13·00
First Day Cover				14·00
Presentation Pack			14·00	

Plate Nos.: All values 1A (each×4)
Sheets: 25 (5×5)

1854 Isle of Man Bank Limited

1855 The Isle of Man Steam Packet Company Limited

1856 The Finch Hill Pavilion and Bowling Club Limited

1857 Heron and Brearley Limited

1858 Farmers Combine Limited

1859 Peel Golf Club Limited

150th Anniversary of the Isle of Man Companies Act

(Des Emma Cooke. Litho BDT)

2015 (28 Sept). P 13 (C).

2037	**1854**	44p. multicoloured	1·10	1·10
2038	**1855**	77p. multicoloured	1·90	1·90
2039	**1856**	93p. multicoloured	2·25	2·25
2040	**1857**	113p. multicoloured	2·75	2·75
2041	**1858**	154p. multicoloured	3·75	3·75
2042	**1859**	165p. multicoloured	4·00	4·00
2037/42	*Set of 6*		14·00	14·00
First Day Cover				15·00
Presentation Pack			15·00	

Plate Nos.: All values 1A (each×4)
Sheets: 15 (3×5)

1860 Self Portrait, 1954

1861 Pendulum, 1964

1862 The Watcher, 1977

1863 Three Legs of Man, 1979

1864 Horse, 1985

1865 The Deemster Fish, 1996

1866 Captain Quilliam, 2005

1867 Illiam Dhone, 2006

1868 Triton III, 2009

1869 Quince, 2015

Bryan Kneale – Six Decades

(Des IOM Advertising. Litho Lowe-Martin)

2015 (1 Oct). P 13×12½ (C).

2043	**1860**	44p. multicoloured	1·10	1·10
		a. Block of 10. Nos. 2043/52	10·50	10·50
2044	**1861**	44p. multicoloured	1·10	1·10
2045	**1862**	44p. multicoloured	1·10	1·10
2046	**1863**	44p. multicoloured	1·10	1·10
2047	**1864**	44p. multicoloured	1·10	1·10
2048	**1865**	44p. multicoloured	1·10	1·10
2049	**1866**	44p. multicoloured	1·10	1·10
2050	**1867**	44p. multicoloured	1·10	1·10
2051	**1868**	44p. multicoloured	1·10	1·10
2052	**1869**	44p. multicoloured	1·10	1·10
2043/52	*Set of 10*		10·50	10·50
First Day Cover				11·50
Presentation Pack			11·50	

Plate Nos.: 1A (×5)
Sheets: 30 (5×6).
Nos. 2043/52 were printed together, *se-tenant*, as blocks of ten stamps throughout the sheet.

1870 Wise Man and 'Niart'

1871 Virgin Mary and Baby Jesus and 'Grayse'

1872 Peace Dove and 'Shee'

1873 Angel and 'Graih'

1874 Cross and 'Credjue'

Christmas. 250th Anniversary of First Prayer Book in Manx Gaelic

(Des Julia Ashby Smyth (illustrations) and EJC Design. Litho Lowe Martin Group)

2015 (23 Oct). Self-adhesive. Die-cut perf 13½.

2053	**1870**	44p. multicoloured	1·10	1·10
		a. Booklet pane. No. 2053×10	10·00	
2054	**1871**	77p. multicoloured	1·90	1·90
2055	**1872**	93p. multicoloured	2·25	2·25
2056	**1873**	124p. multicoloured	3·00	3·00
2057	**1874**	320p. multicoloured	7·75	7·75
2053/7 *Set of 5*			14·50	14·50
First Day Cover				16·00
Presentation Pack			16·00	

No. 2053 was also issued in £4.40 booklets, No. SB85.

Plate Nos.: All values 1A (each×4)

Sheets: 25 (5×5)

Year Folder 2015

2015 (15 Nov). Comprises Nos. **MS**1953/1987, 1994/2016 and 2025/57 (*price £85*)

Year Folder	£175

Year Pack 2015

2015 (15 Nov). Comprises Nos. **MS**1953/1987, 1994/2016 and 2025/57 (*price £97*)

Year Pack	£200

Post Office Yearbook

2015 (15 Nov). Comprises Nos. Nos. **MS**1953/1987, 1994/2016 and 2025/57 (£87.50)

Year Book	£175

SOUVENIR POSTAL STATIONERY POSTCARDS

The following postcards were issued by the Isle of Man Postal Authority often in connection with various philatelic exhibitions and, with the exception of Nos. PC8, PC11 and PC15/16 show imprinted stamp designs.

'San Marino 82'

1982 (1 Sept). Card showing imprinted stamp design as No. 217. Sold at 30p.

PC1	19½p. multicoloured	1·00	1·20

Withdrawn: 30.4.84.

'Tembal 83', Basel

1983 (21 May). Card showing imprinted stamp design as No. 250. Sold at 30p.

PC2	20½p. multicoloured	1·00	1·60

Withdrawn: 20.5.84.

'Espana 84', Madrid

1984 (27 Apr). Card showing imprinted stamp design as No. 266. Sold at 30p.

PC3	20½p. multicoloured	1·50	1·70

Withdrawn: 26.4.85.

'Ausipex 84', Melbourne

1984 (21 Sept). Card showing imprinted stamp design as No. 278. Sold at 40p.

PC4	33p. multicoloured	1·50	2·75

Withdrawn: 20.9.85.

'Italia 85', Rome

1985 (25 Oct). Card showing imprinted stamp designs as Nos. 292/3. Sold at 40p.

PC5	14p. +14p. multicoloured	1·50	3·25

Withdrawn: 24.10.86.

'Ameripex 86', Chicago

1986 (22 May). Card showing imprinted stamp design as No. 302. Sold at 40p.

PC6	34p. multicoloured	2·20	2·75

Withdrawn: 21.5.87.

'Stockholmia 86', Stockholm

1986 (28 Aug). Card showing imprinted stamp designs as Nos. 305/6. Sold at 40p.

PC7	15p. +15p. multicoloured	1·20	2·00

Withdrawn: 27.8.87.

'Hafnia 87', Copenhagen

1987 (16 Oct). Card with Nos. 358/9 affixed. Sold at 50p.

PC8	12p. +15p. multicoloured	1·20	1·70

Withdrawn: 15.10.88.

'Finlandia 88', Helsinki

1988 (1 June). Card showing imprinted stamp designs as Nos. 371 and 375. Sold at 50p.

PC9	14p. +18p. multicoloured	1·20	1·50

Withdrawn: 31.5.89.

'Sydpex 88', Sydney

1988 (30 July). Card showing imprinted stamp designs as Nos. 386/7. Sold at 60p.

PC10	29p. +31p. multicoloured	1·50	1·70

Withdrawn: 29.7.89.

'Filacept 88', The Hague

1988 (18 Oct). Card with Nos. 383/4 affixed. Sold at 50p.

PC11	22p. +22p. multicoloured	1·20	2·00

Withdrawn: 17.10.89.

'Belgica 90', Brussels

1990 (2 June). Card showing imprinted stamp designs as Nos. 442 and 446. Sold at 50p.

PC12	1p. +37p. multicoloured	1·20	1·50

Withdrawn: 2.93.

'Essen 94', Centenary of Picture Postcards

1994 (5 May). Cards showing imprinted stamp design as No. 338. Sold at 80p. the pair.

PC13	31p. multicoloured (Douglas)	1·20	1·50
PC14	31p. multicoloured (Ramsey)	1·20	1·50

Withdrawn: 4.5.95.

'Jakarta 95'

1995 (19 Aug). Sold at 15p.

PC15	Komodo Dragon	75	1·00

Withdrawn: 6.98.

'Beijing 95'

1995 (16 Sept). Sold at 15p.

PC16	Great Wall of China	75	1·00

Withdrawn: 6.98.

Isle of Man T.T. Races and 50th Anniversary of Honda

1998 (1 June). Card showing imprinted stamp design as No. 809. Sold at 50p.

PC17	25p. multicoloured	1·00	1·20

Withdrawn: 6.99.

'Espana 2000', Madrid

2000 (6 Oct). Card showing imprinted stamp design as No. 910.

PC18	45p. multicoloured	1·50	1·50

Withdrawn: 6.2002.

'Sindelfingen', Germany

2000 (6 Oct). Card showing imprinted stamp design as No. 911.

PC19	65p. multicoloured	1·50	1·50

Withdrawn: 6.2002.

Joey Dunlop (motorcycle champion) Commemoration

2001 (17 May). Cards showing stamp designs and enlarged photographs on the front and Douglas postage paid impression on the reverse. Sold at £5.71.

PC20/5 *Set of 6 cards*		11·50	11·50

Withdrawn: 16.5.2002.

MANX POSTAL MUSEUM POSTCARDS

1987 (23 Mar). Sold at 10p.
PM1   Reopening of Regent Street Post Office,
      Douglas 30   1·00
      Sold out: By 2.90.

1989 (28 Apr). Sold at 15p.
PM2   Bicentenary of the Mutiny on the *Bounty*.......... 40   1·50
      Sold out: By 1.93.

1990 (10 Apr). Sold at 18p.
PM3   CUNARD 150 Exhibition, Liverpool. Sinking of
      Lusitania (as No. 191) 50   1·50
      Sold out: By 2.94.

POSTAGE DUE STAMPS

D **1**   D **2**

(Des and litho Questa)

1973 (5 July). P 14×13½ (C).
D1	D **1**	½p. red, black and bistre-yellow (ab)....	1·50	1·10
D2		1p. red, black and cinnamon (ab)	50	60
D3		2p. red, black and lt apple-green (ab)	15	20
		a. Positive offset of red ptg on back.		
D4		3p. red, black and grey (ab).....................	20	20
D5		4p. red, black and carmine-rose (ab).....	30	35
D6		5p. red, black and cobalt (ab).................	30	35
D7		10p. red, black and light lavender (ab).	40	40
D8		20p. red, black and pale turq-grn (ab) ..	75	60
D1/8 *Set of 8*...			3·75	3·50
Presentation Pack (ptg b)			5·00	

    Prices quoted above are for printing (b), which can be identified by the letter 'A' added after 1973 at the foot of the stamp. Collectors should beware of spurious examples with the 'A' removed. Price for set of 8 from printing (a) £24 mint or used.
    Printings: (a) 5.7.73; (b) 1.9.73. Examples of printing (b) are known used from mid-August onwards.
    Plate Nos.: All values 1A, 1B (each×3).
    Sheets: 100 (10×10).
    Imprint: Right-hand corner, bottom margin, and left-hand corner, top margin.
    Sold out: Printing (a) between 13.8.73 and 10.9.73. Printing (b) ½p. by 12.74; 1p. by 2.75; 2p. and 3p. by 5.75; others by 31.12.75.

(Des and litho Questa)

1975 (8 Jan). P 14×13½ (C).
D9	D **2**	½p. black, red and greenish yellow.......	10	10
D10		1p. black, red and flesh...........................	10	10
D11		4p. black, red and rose-lilac...................	10	15
D12		7p. black, red and lt greenish blue........	15	20
D13		9p. black, red and brownish grey...........	25	30
D14		10p. black, red and bright mauve...........	25	20
D15		50p. black, red and orange-yellow.........	90	90
D16		£1 black, red and turquoise-green	1·50	1·60
D9/16 *Set of 8*...			3·00	3·25
First Day Cover...				4·50
Presentation Pack..			3·50	

    Plate Nos.: All values 1A, 1B (each×3).
    Sheets: 100 (10×10).
    Imprint: Left-hand corner, bottom margin.
    Withdrawn: 31.12.82 (1p. to £1); 31.12.85 ½p.

D **3** Badge of Post   D **4**
Office Authority

(Litho BDT)

1982 (5 Oct). Centres multicoloured; background colour given. P 14½×14 (C).
D17	D **3**	1p. turquoise-green...	10	10
D18		2p. mauve..	10	10

D19		5p. greenish blue..	10	10
D20		10p. reddish lilac...	20	25
D21		20p. grey..	40	45
D22		50p. buff..	90	1·10
D23		£1 salmon...	1·60	2·10
D24		£2 bright blue..	3·25	4·25
D17/24 *Set of 8*...			6·00	7·75
First Day Cover...				12·00
Presentation Pack Plate...			8·00	

    Plate Nos.: All values 1A, 1B (×5).
    Sheets: 50 (10×5).
    Imprint: Right-hand corner, bottom margin.

(Des Colleen Corlett. Litho BDT)

1992 (18 Sept). P 13×13½ (C).
D25	D **4**	£5 multicoloured	8·00	8·50
First Day Cover...			8·00	8·50
Presentation Pack..			9·50	

    Plate Nos.: 1A, 1B (each×4).
    Sheets: 50 (10×5).
    Imprint: Right-hand corner, bottom margin.

STAMP BOOKLETS

PRICES are given for complete booklets. All booklets to No. SB7 are stitched.

B **1** Derbyhaven

1973 (5 July–17 Oct). Coloured covers as Type B **1**, 49×51 mm, printed in black Type B **1**. Yellow cover.
SB1   10p. booklet containing 2×2½p. (No. 16), 2×2p.
         (No. 15) and 2×½p (No. 12) (ab) .... 12·00

              Ballaugh Church. Green cover
SB2   25p. booklet containing 10×2½p. (No. 16) (ab).......... 3·00

              Peel Castle. Stone cover
SB3   30p. booklet containing 10×3p (No. 17) (a).................. 15·00
SB3*a*   As SB3 but cover in buff (b) .... 14·00

        Quayside, Douglas. Lavender-grey cover
SB4   50p. booklet containing 8×2½p. (No. 16) and
         10×3p. (No. 17) (a)... 6·00
SB4*a*   As SB4 but grey-green cover (b)............................... 5·50
    Nos. SB1/4 were made up from ordinary sheets, the stamps being in vertical pairs with stitching through the side margins. Stamps from both sides of the sheets were used, so that panes come either upright or inverted.
    Printings: (a) 5.7.73: (b) 17.10.73.

STAMP SACHETS. These are cardboard covers, with stamps loose inside, contained in clear plastic sachets.

ISLE OF MAN
10p
3 at 2½p
5 at ½p
POST OFFICE STAMPS

B **2**

1973 (5 July–1 Nov). Stamp Sachets. Covers as Type B **2**, 51×32 mm, 10p. sachet containing 5×½p (No. 12) and 3×2½p (No. 16) 10p. sachet containing 2×½p (No. 12) and 3×3p (No. 17) (1 Nov) (Price 1·00 each).

B **3** Old Laxey Bridge (*Illustration reduced. Actual size 89×51 mm*)

1974 (1 Apr*). Coloured covers as Type B **3** printed in black as Type B **3**. Buff cover.

SB5   30p. booklet containing 8×½p. (No. 12), 4×3p. (No. 17) and 4×3½p. (No. 18) .... 2·00

Monk's Bridge, Ballasalla. Green cover

SB6   40p. booklet containing 4×½p. (No. 12), 8×3p. (No. 17) and 4×3½p. (No. 18) .... 2·00

St. Michael's Chapel, Langness. Red cover

SB7   50p. booklet containing 12×3p. (No. 17) and 4×3½p. (No. 18) .... 2·00

Nos. SB5/7 contain panes of four, and were produced in the same way as Nos. SB1/4. 3p. panes from SB5/7 exist with either shiny or matt gum. ½p. panes are shiny gum and 3½p. panes matt gum only (see note after No. 33).

*The booklets were placed on sale at the Interpex stamp exhibition in New York on 22 March 1974 and panes and covers exist cancelled with this date.

1974 (29 July–19 June). Stamp Sachets. Cover designs as Nos. SB5/7, 98×56 mm, but inscriptions redrawn. Contents unchanged.

   30p. sachet. Pink cover (Price 1·50) ....

   40p. sachet. Green cover (Price 1·60) ....

   50p. sachet. Yellow cover (Price 1·90) ....

1975 (25 Apr–16 June). Stamp Sachets. Blue cover showing Post Office badge.

   20p. sachet containing 3×2p. (No. 15) and 4×3½p. (No. 18) attached to cover by the selvedge (Price 2·20) ....

   20p. sachet containing 1×½p. (No. 12), 2×1½p. (No. 14) and 3×5½p. (No. 22), loose or attached to selvedge (28 May) (Price 2·70) ....

   20p. sachet containing 4×½p. (No. 12), 2×1½p. (No. 14) and 3×5p. (No. 21), loose or attached to selvedge (16 June) (Price 2·70) ....

1976 (20 Sept)–79. Stamp Sachet. Blue cover similar to Type B **3**, 82×49 mm, showing Rushen and Castletown Harbour.

   20p. sachet containing 2×1p. (No. 13) and 3×6p. (No. 23) (Price 1·10) ....

   20p. sachet containing 2×1p. (No. 13) and 3×6p. (No. 139) (3.79) (Price 2·40) ....

B **4** Viking Longship (*Illustration reduced. Actual size 89×49 mm*)

Millennium of Tynwald

1979 (16 May). Folded card covers as Type B **4**.

SB8   20p. booklet containing 4×3p. and 2×4p. (No. 150ab) (blue cover) .... 1·00

SB9   40p. booklet containing 8×3p. and 4×4p. (No. 150a×2) (pink cover) .... 1·20

SB10 60p. booklet containing 12×3p. and 6×4p. (No. 150a×3) (yellow cover) .... 1·50

SB8 is also known with a single pane (No. 150a). SB9 and SB10 also exist with at least one pane 150ab.

   Withdrawn: 28.9.80.

1980 (29 Sept). Folded card covers as Type B **4**, 83×49 mm.

SB11 40p. booklet containing 2×1p., 4×3p., 4×4p. and 2×5p. (Nos. 150ba and 188a) (pink cover showing Manx Loaghtyn Ram) .... 1·00

SB12 80p. booklet containing 4×1p., 8×3p., 8×4p. and 4×5p. (Nos. 150ba and 188a each×2) (green cover showing Peregrine Falcon) .... 1·50

   Withdrawn: 9.4.86.

1985 (12 June). Booklet No. SB11 with cover surcharged 50p. and an additional loose 10p. stamp inside.

SB13 50p. booklet containing Nos. 150ba, 188a and one 10p. (No. 236) .... 4·50

   Withdrawn: 9.4.86.

B **5** Celtic Cross Logo (*Illustration reduced. Actual size 48×80 mm*)

Manx Heritage Year

1986 (10 Apr). Folded card covers as Type B **5**.

SB14 50p. booklet containing 2×1p., 2×4p., 2×5p. and 3×10p. (Nos. 188a and 316a) olive-green cover) .... 1·40

SB15 £1.14 booklet containing 2×1p., 2×2p., 4×3p., 4×4p., 2×5p. and 7×10p. (Nos. 150ba, 188a, 315a and 316a) (greenish blue cover) .... 2·50

   Withdrawn: 25.3.87.

B **6** Loch Promenade (*Illustration reduced. Actual size 82×48 mm*)

Victorian Douglas

1987 (26 Mar). Folded card covers as Type B **6**.

SB16 50p. booklet containing either No. 334a or 334ab (orange-brown and deep yellow-green cover Type B **6**) .... 1·50

SB17 £1.10 booklet containing either Nos. 334a or 334ab, and 334b or 334ba (orange-brown and bright scarlet cover showing The Breakwater) .... 2·50

   Withdrawn: 15.3.88.

B **7** Baldwin Reservoir Tramway Steam Locomotive *Injebreck*
(*Illustration reduced. Actual size 82×48 mm*)

Manx Railways and Tramways

1988 (16 Mar). Folded multicoloured card covers as Type B **7**.
SB18   50p. booklet containing No. 367a (cover Type B **7**)...   2·00
SB19   £1.99 booklet containing Nos. 367a and 370a
                  (cover showing Manx Electric Railway train at
                  Maughold Head) ....   5·00
Withdrawn: 15.10.89.

B **8** 'Mutineers casting Bligh adrift' (Robert Dodd)
(*Illustration reduced. Actual size 155×100 mm*)

Bicentenary of The Mutiny on the *Bounty*

(Des C. Abbott)

1989 (28 Apr). Multicoloured cover as Type B **8**. Booklet contains text
and Illustrations on interleaving pages. Stitched.
SB20   £5.30 booklet containing Nos. 408a/b, 410a and
                  MS415a..   10·00
Examples of No. MS415 from the booklet have wider margins than
the normal miniature sheets.
            Withdrawn: 2.92.

Manx Railways and Tramways

1989 (16 Oct). Folded multicoloured covers as Type B **7**, 82×48 mm.
SB21   50p. booklet containing No. 367b (cover showing
                  Port Erin Breakwater Tramway Locomotive
                  Henry B. Loch) ....   1·50
SB22   £2.09 booklet containing Nos. 367b and 371a (cover
                  showing Douglas Cable Tramway) ....   4·50
            Withdrawn: 13.2.90.

Manx Railways and Tramways

1990 (14 Feb). Folded multicoloured covers as Type B **7**, 82×48 mm.
SB23   50p. booklet containing No. 372a (cover showing
                  Marine Drive Tramway) ....   2·00
SB24   £1.74 booklet containing No. 372b (cover showing
                  Ramsey Harbour Tramway).........................   4·50
            Withdrawn: 8.1.91.

B **9** Penny Black (*Illustration reduced. Actual size 125×75 mm*)

**150th Anniversary of the Penny Black and 'Stamp World London
90' International Stamp Exhibition, London**

(Des Colleen Corlett)

1990 (3 May). Black and ochre cover as Type B **9**. Booklet contains
text and Illustrations on interleaving pages. Stapled.
SB25   £3.50 booklet containing Nos. 442c, 443a and MS447a   9·00
            Withdrawn: 23.9.93.

Manx Railway and Tramways

1991 (9 Jan). Folded multicoloured covers as Type B **7**.
SB26   50p. booklet containing No. 367ca (cover,
                  80×48 mm, showing Groudle Glen Railway
                  steam locomotive *Polar Bear*).....................   3·00
SB27   £1 booklet containing No. 367cb (cover,
                  56×43 mm, showing I.M.R. No. 11 *Maitland*
                  pulling Royal Train, 1963)..........................   2·75
            Withdrawn: 7.1.92.

B **10** Three Kings (*Illustration reduced. Actual size
150×105 mm*)

Christmas

(Des D. Swinton)

1991 (14 Oct). Deep violet cover as Type B **10**. Stitched.
SB28   £4.16 booklet containing No. 500a×2.....................   10·00
            Withdrawn: 23.9.93.

Manx Railways and Tramways

1992 (8 Jan). Folded multicoloured covers as Type B **7**, but
56×43 mm.
SB29   £1 booklet containing No. 375ab (cover showing
                  double-decker horse tram, Douglas).....................   3·00
SB30   £2 booklet containing No. 375ac (cover showing
                  T.P.O. Special) ....   5·00
            Withdrawn: 3.1.93.

B **11** Union Pacific No. 119, 1869 (*Illustration reduced. Actual size
119×74 mm*)

Construction of Union Pacific Railroad

1992 (22 May). Multicoloured cover as Type B **11**. Pane attached by
selvedge.
SB31   £4.38 booklet containing pane No. 522b.....................   8·50
            Withdrawn: 27.4.94.

B **12** *Francis Drake* (ketch)

Ships

1993 (4 Jan). Multicoloured covers as Type B **12**. Panes attached by selvedge.

SB32   £1.10 booklet containing pane No. 543a (cover
                Type B **12**).. 3·00
SB33   £2.20 booklet containing pane No. 543b (cover
                showing *Tynwald I*)... 5·00
        Withdrawn: 20.4.96.

B **13** No. 9 Tunnel Car and Crew (*Illustration reduced. Actual size 160×98 mm*)

Centenary of Manx Electric Railway

(Des A. Theobald)

1993 (3 Feb). Multicoloured cover as Type B **13**. Stitched.
SB34   £4.44 booklet containing pane No. 559a×4.................... 10·00
        Withdrawn: 27.4.94.

B **14** (*Illustration reduced. Actual size 62×95 mm*)

Christmas

1993 (12 Oct). Folded multicoloured covers as Type B **14**. Panes attached by selvedge.
SB35   £1.90 booklet containing No. 578×10 (cover
                Type B **14**).. 3·50
SB36   £2.30 booklet containing No. 579×10 (cover showing
                No. 579)... 5·00
        Withdrawn: 10.10.95.

B **15** (*Illustration reduced. Actual size 134×85 mm*)

Manx Tourism Centenary

1994 (18 Feb). Multicoloured cover as Type B **15**. Pane attached by selvedge.
SB37   £2.40 booklet containing pane No. 590a and pane of
                12 (3×4) greetings labels... 5·00
        Sold out: By 9.95.

B **16** Postman Pat, Jess, Ferry and Aircraft (*Illustration reduced. Actual size 152×85 mm*)

Postman Pat visits the Isle of Man

(Des Coleen Corlett)

1994 (14 Sept). Multicoloured cover as Type B **16** cut out to show stamps from first pane. Booklet contains text and Illustrations on labels attached to panes. Stitched.
SB38   £4.04 booklet containing Nos. 614a/19a, **MS**620a
                and pane of 8 character labels................................. 9·00
        Withdrawn: By 2.97.

B **17** Car and Passengers at Snaefell Summit (*Illustration reduced. Actual size 162×97 mm*)

Centenary of Snaefell Mountain Railway

(Des A. Theobald)

1995 (8 Feb). Black, scarlet and grey cover as Type B **17**. Booklet contains text and Illustrations on labels attached to panes. Stitched.
SB39   £4.63 booklet containing No. 634a×3 and **MS**638a..... 10·00
        Withdrawn: By 2.97.

B **18** Thomas the Tank Engine (*Illustration reduced. Actual size 151×80 mm*)

50th Anniversary of Thomas the Tank Engine Stories by Revd. Awdry. 'Thomas the Tank Engine's Dream'

(Des O. Bell)

1995 (15 Aug). Multicoloured cover as Type B **18** cut out to show stamps from first pane. Stitched.
SB40   £3.92 booklet containing Nos. 656a/b, 657a, 658a,
                659a and 660a .... 8·50
        Withdrawn: By 2.97.

B **19** Aerial view of Langness Lighthouse
(*Illustration reduced. Actual size* 130×82 *mm*)

Lighthouses

(Des D. Swinton)

1996 (24 Jan). Multicoloured cover as Type B **19**. Booklet contains text and Illustrations on interleaving pages. Stitched.
SB41   £4.74 booklet containing Nos. 672a/5a.............................   12·00
  Withdrawn: By 5.97.

Ships

1996 (21 Apr). Multicoloured cover as Type B **12**, 54×42 mm. Pane attached by selvedge.
SB42   96p. booklet containing pane No. 687a (cover
           showing *Sir Winston Churchill*)....................................   10·00
  Sold out: 5.97.

B **20** (*Illustration reduced. Actual size* 118×81 *mm*)

Dogs

(Des Coleen Corlett)

1996 (18 Sept). Multicoloured cover as Type B **20**. Booklet contains text and Illustrations on interleaving pages. Stitched.
SB43   £4.71 booklet containing Nos. 719a, 720a, 721a and
           MS725a...   12·00
  Withdrawn: 17.9.97.

B **21** Tawny Owl (*Illustration reduced. Actual size* 152×80 *mm*)

Owls

(Des Isle of Man P.O.)

1997 (12 Feb). Multicoloured cover as Type B **21**. Booklet contains text and Illustrations on interleaving pages. Stitched.
SB44   £4.62 booklet containing Nos. 734a/6a and
           MS740a...   10·00
  Withdrawn: 11.2.98.

Ships

1997 (14 May). Multicoloured cover as Type B **12**, 55×42 mm. Pane attached by selvedge.
SB45   £1 booklet containing pane No. 541a (cover
           showing Royal Yacht *Britannia*)................................   5·00
        a. With extra loose 4p. stamp and optd inside
           front cover ....   6·00
  No. SB45a was issued from booklet machines until 1 July 1997 when the postal rates were revised. The overprint inside the front cover was applied by handstamp.
    Withdrawn: 31.12.97 No. SB45a; 30.11.98 No. SB45.

B **22** King Edward Bay Golf and Country Club (*Illustration reduced. Actual size* 160×98 *mm*)

Golf

(Des L. Bridge)

1997 (29 May). Multicoloured cover as Type B **22**. Booklet contains text and Illustrations on panes and interleaving pages. Stitched.
SB46   £4.54 booklet containing Nos. 755a/7a and
           MS759a...   10·00
  Withdrawn: 28.5.98.

B **23** Cushag

Flowers

1998 (12 Feb). Multicoloured cover as Type B **23**. Pane attached by selvedge.
SB47   £1 booklet containing No. 775a ....   3·50
  Withdrawn: 31.8.99.

B **24** Basking Shark (*Illustration reduced. Actual size* 157×105 *mm*)

U.N.E.S.C.O. International Year of the Ocean

(Des Isle of Man P.O.)

1998 (16 Mar). Multicoloured cover as Type B **24**. Booklet contains text and Illustrations on interleaving pages. Stitched.
SB48   £3.62 booklet containing No. 798a/b...............................   9·00
  The price (£3.92) and content details of SB48 are incorrectly stated on the back cover.
    Withdrawn: 13.3.99.

B **25** Steam Train at Douglas Station (*Illustration reduced. Actual size* 157×105 *mm*)

125th Anniversary of Isle of Man Steam Railway

(Des A. Peck)

1998 (2 May). Multicoloured cover as Type B **25**. Booklet contains text and Illustrations on interleaving pages. Stitched.
SB49   £4.05 booklet containing Nos. 803a×2 and **MS**807a...   9·00
Sold out: 6.2000.

B **26** *Manchester & Salford, 1868–1887 (Illustration reduced. Actual size 158×108 mm)*

175th Anniversary of Royal National Lifeboat Institution

(Des Mainstream Media)

1999 (4 Mar). Multicoloured cover as Type B **26**. Booklet contains text and Illustrations on interleaving pages. Stitched.
SB50   £4.64 booklet containing Nos. 832a/b and
          MS839a...   15·00
Withdrawn: 3.3.2000.

Flowers

1999 (26 Apr). Multicoloured cover as Type B **23**, 54×41 mm. Pane attached by selvedge.
SB51   £1 booklet containing pane No. 775ba (cover
          showing Dog Rose)...   3·00
Sold out: By 31.8.2004.

B **27** *Bus Radiator and Headlights (Illustration reduced. Actual size 158×100 mm)*

Manx Buses

(Des P. Hearsey)

1999 (18 June). Multicoloured cover as Type B **27**. Booklet contains text and Illustrations on panes and interleaving pages. Stitched.
SB52   £4.78 booklet containing panes Nos. 845a/d.................   13·00
Sold out: 8.2001.

B **28** *Flags, Weapons and Military Headgear (Illustration reduced. Actual size 180×75 mm)*

Isle of Man at War

(Des The Agency Ltd)

2000 (22 May). Multicoloured cover as Type B **28**. Booklet contains text and Illustrations on interleaving pages. Stitched.
SB53   £4.99 booklet containing Nos. 887a/b and **MS**893a....   12·00
Sold out: By 6.2003.

B **29** *'The Coronation, 1953' (Terence Cuneo) (Illustration reduced. Actual size 165×95 mm)*

Golden Jubilee

(Des The Agency Ltd)

2002 (6 Feb). Multicoloured cover as Type B **29**. Booklet contains text and Illustrations on panes and interleaving pages. Stitched.
SB54   £5.87 booklet containing panes Nos. 959a, 962a,
          970b, 973b and **MS**975b...............................   13·00
Withdrawn: 30.4.2004.

B **30** *Aspects of the Isle of Man (Illustration reduced. Actual size 105×70 mm)*

Photography–'The People's Choice

2002 (1 Oct). Multicoloured covers as Type B **30**. Self-adhesive.
SB55   £2.30 booklet containing No. 1021a.....................   7·00
SB56   £2.70 booklet containing No. 1031a.....................   8·50
Withdrawn: 30.4.2004.

B **31** *Henry Bloom Noble and Original Villa Marina (Illustration reduced. Actual size 104×70 mm)*

Centenary of Henry Bloom Noble Trust

2003 (1 Oct). Multicoloured covers as Type B **31**. Self-adhesive.
SB57   £2.30 booklet containing No. 1101a.....................   6·00
SB58   £2.70 booklet containing No. 1106a.....................   10·00
Withdrawn: 31.12.2004.

B **32** Soldier, Viking, Miner, Spinner and Fisherman (*Illustration reduced. Actual size 102×70 mm*)

Manx National Heritage The Story of Mann

2004 (3 Aug). Multicoloured covers as Type B **32**. Self-adhesive.
SB59	(£2.50) booklet containing pane No. 1167a (cover as Type B **32**)	10·00
SB60	(£2.80) booklet containing pane No. 1172a (cover showing Cregneash, Calf of Man, Castle Rushen, Laxey Wheel and Peel Castle)	12·00

Withdrawn: 2.8.2005.

B **33** 'Mona's Queen' (Arthur Burgess) (*Illustration reduced. Actual size 165×95 mm*)

175th Anniversary of Steam Packet Company

(Des Tracy Harding)

2005 (6 May). Multicoloured cover as Type B **33**. Booklet contains text and Illustrations on interleaving pages. Stitched.
SB61	£7.80 booklet containing panes Nos. 1217b/c, 1219b, 1221b and 1223b	14·00

Withdrawn: 5.5.2006.

B **34** Traditional Scenes (*Illustration reduced. Actual size 107×76 mm*)

'Time to Remember'

2005 (12 Aug). Multicoloured covers as Type B **34** showing portions of the stamp designs within. Self-adhesive.
SB62	£2.60 booklet containing pane No. 1247b (cover as Type B **34**)	5·50
SB63	£2.90 booklet containing pane No. 1252b (cover showing scenes from stamps)	6·00

Sold out: By 12.2006.

B **35** Christmas Tree with Lights (*Illustration reduced. Actual size 150×70 mm*)

Christmas

2006 (11 Oct). Multicoloured covers as Type B **35**. Self-adhesive.
SB64	£2.80 booklet containing pane No. 1328a (Type B **35**)	5·50
SB65	£3.10 booklet containing pane No. 1329a (cover showing tree with Three Legs of Mann decoration at top)	6·00

Withdrawn: 10.10.2007.

B **36** Scouts hiking near South Barrule (*Illustration reduced. Actual size 165×96 mm*)

Centenary of Scouting

(Des M. Southall)

2007 (22 Feb). Multicoloured cover as Type B **36**. Booklet contains text and Illustrations on interleaving pages. Stitched.
SB66	£9.16 booklet containing panes Nos. 1342a/b, 1343a, 1345a and **MS**1348a	20·00

Withdrawn: 21.2.2008.

B **37** 'Headland, Cornaa' (*Illustration reduced. Actual size 132×67 mm*)

Watercolour Paintings by Norman Sayle

2007 (12 Apr). Multicoloured covers as Type B **37**. Self-adhesive.
SB67	£2.80 booklet containing pane No. 1363a (Type B **37**)	8·50
SB68	£3.10 booklet containing pane No. 1365a (cover showing St. Mark"s Church)	9·25

B **38** Aircraft (*Illustration reduced. Actual size 156×96 mm*)

90th Anniversary of the Royal Air Force

(Des Kcreative)

2008 (15 Jan). Multicoloured cover as Type B **38**. Booklet contains text and Illustrations on panes and interleaving pages. Stitched.
SB69   £9.68 booklet containing panes Nos. 1406b/d and
                1408a .... 23·00

B **39** Isle of Man Bank £1 Note (*Illustration reduced. Actual size 98×63 mm*)

Bank Notes of the Isle of Man

2008 (7 Apr). Multicoloured cover as Type B **39**. Self-adhesive.
SB70   £3 booklet containing pane No. 1424a...................... 7·00
Withdrawn: 3.2010.

B **40** Biplane (*Illustration reduced. Actual size 167×95 mm*)

Centenary of Naval Aviation

(Des Kcreative)

2009 (15 Jan). Multicoloured cover as Type B **40**. Booklet contains text and Illustrations on panes and interleaving pages. Stitched.
SB71   £10.26 booklet containing panes Nos. 1473b/d and
                1475a .... 23·00

B **41** Ballakilley Farm (*Illustration reduced. Actual size 119×83 mm*)

Mills and Millers. Photographs by Chris Kilip

2009 (1 Apr). Grey and black covers as Type B **41**. Self-adhesive.
SB72   £3.20 booklet containing pane No. 1501a...................... 7·00
SB73   £3.30 booklet containing pane No. 1503a (cover
                showing *Mr. Cubbon*)... 7·00

B **42** Horses Ploughing at Cregneash National Folk Museum (*Illustration reduced. Actual size 102×72 mm*)

Island Life

2010 (12 Jan). Multicoloured covers as Type B **42**. Self-adhesive.
SB74   (£3.84) booklet containing pane No. 1567a (cover as
                Type B **42**)... 9·00
SB75   (£3.96) booklet containing pane No. 1571a (cover
                showing unloading of kayak)................................... 9·00

B **43** Painted Lady Butterfly (*Illustration reduced. Actual size 125×70 mm*)

The Isle of Man Butterfly Collection.

2011 (1 Apr). Multicoloured cover as Type B **43**. Self-adhesive.
SB76   £4.44 booklet containing pane No. 1657a...................... 10·00

B **44** Colletes succinctus (*Illustration reduced. Actual size 76×59 mm*)

Bee Fauna of the Isle of Man

2012 (8 Aug). Multicoloured covers as Type B **44**. Self-adhesive.
SB77   £3.80 booklet containing pane No. 1773a
                (Type B **44**)... 9.00
SB78   £4.10 booklet containing pane No. 1774a (cover
                showing *Epeolus variegatus*)................................... 9.50

B **45** Three Legs of Man with Crown (*Illustration reduced. Actual size 76×58 mm*)

The Three Legs of Man

2013 (3 Apr). Multicoloured as Type B **45**. Self-adhesive.
SB79	£4 booklet containing pane No. 1820a (Type B **45**)	9·50
SB80	$4.20 booklet containing pane No. 1821a (cover showing Three Legs of Man in stained glass)	9·50

B **46** Red Arrows

50th Display Season of Royal Air Force Red Arrows

2014 (19 Feb). Multicoloured cover, 210×136 mm, as Type B **46**. Self-adhesive
SB81	£11.94 booklet containing panes Nos. 1889a/b and 1892a.............................	13·50

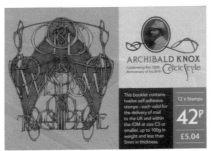

B **47** Inscription 'GOD WISDOM'

150th Birth Anniv of Archibald Knox (1864–1933, artist and designer).

2014 (4 Apr). Multicoloured cover, 110×76 mm, as Type B **47**. Self-adhesive.
SB82	£5.04 booklet containing pane No. 1905a	4·50

B **48** The Viking Arrival

Millennium of Tynwald Tapestry

2015 (10 Apr). Multicoloured cover, 101×69 mm, as Type B **48**. Self-adhesive.
SB83	(£5.04) booklet containing pane No. 1988a.......	9·50

B **49** Queen Elizabeth II

Pomp and Circumstance. The Reign of Queen Elizabeth II

2015 (9 Sept). Multicoloured cover, 200×135 mm, as Type B **49**. Self-adhesive.
SB84	£13.52 booklet containing panes Nos. 2017a/b, 2019a and 2022a..............	30·00

B **50** Wise Man

Christmas. 250th Anniversary of First Prayer Book in Manx Gaelic

2015 (23 Oct). Multicoloured cover, 80×120 mm, as Type B **50**. Self-adhesive.
SB85	£4.40 booklet containing pane No. 2045a.......	10·00

COMMEMORATIVE SHEETS

The following commemorative sheets have been issued; they are outside the scope of this catalogue.

1.2.2008	Royal Air Force	2014	John McGuiness
2.6.2008	Money	2014	Schneider Trophy
15.4.2009	Europa Astronomy	2014	D-Day Anniversary
1.5.2010	Railways and Tramways	2014	Tour de France
19.10.2012	Flying Corps	2015	Birth of HRH Princess Charlotte

Jersey

THE GERMAN OCCUPATION

1940–1945

Soon after the commencement of the occupation of Jersey by German forces on 1 July 1940 orders were given by the German Commandant to the Islands Postmaster for stocks of the currently available stamps to be forwarded to the Jersey printers, J. T. Bigwood, for overprinting with a swastika and 'JERSEY 1940'. All values of the 1937–8 definitives from ½d. to 10s., excluding the 1d., were so overprinted as were the 1940 Postal Centenary stamps, excluding the 1d., but whilst this was in progress the Bailiff of Jersey protested to the German Commandant who referred the matter to Berlin and was ordered to destroy the stocks. Four complete sets to 1s., and a few singles, however, are known to exist. At the same time Bigwoods prepared a local 1d. stamp incorporating the ams of Jersey and the words 'ETATS DE JERSEY'. These were printed in imperforate sheets of 30 (10×3) and are known with and without a swastika and '1940' overprint. These also were destroyed with the exception of two sheets of each which have been cut up for collectors and a damaged sheet with the overprint which is complete. There is also a complete sheet of the unoverprinted stamp in the British Postal Museum & Archive.

Jersey eventually issued locally printed ½d. and 1d. stamps, the 1d. on 1 April 1941 and the ½d. on 29 January 1942. No distinct shades exist though both values come on newsprint paper and, in addition, the 1d. is known on chalk-surfaced paper.

In June 1943 a pictorial set of six stamps from ½d. to 3d. was issued, the designer being the well-known Jersey artist Edmund Blampied. Two values, the 1d. and 2½d., are known on newsprint paper.

Both these and the earlier issues remained on sale until 13 April 1946 after which date they could no longer be used.

1   **2**

The Swastika Overprints

1940. Prepared for use but not issued. Stamps of Great Britain overprinted by J. T. Bigwood, States Printers.

(a) On 1937–9 definitive issue

Cat. No.	Type No.		Unused
SW1	**1**	½d. green	£3500
SW2		1½d. red-brown	£3500
SW3		2d. orange	£3500
SW4		2½d. ultramarine	£3500
SW5		3d. violet	£3500
SW6		4d. grey-green	£3500
SW7		5d. brown	£3500
SW8		6d. purple	£3500
SW9		7d. emerald-green	£3500
SW10		8d. bright carmine	£3500
SW11		9d. deep olive-green	£3500
SW12		10d. turquoise-blue	£3500
SW13		1s. bistre-brown	£3500

(b) On 1940 Stamp Centenary issue

SW14	**2**	½d. green	£3500
SW15		1½d. red-brown	£3500
SW16		2d. orange	£3500
SW17		2½d. ultramarine	£3500
SW18		3d. violet	£3500

Collectors should note that these overprints have been extensively forged.

3   **4**

(Des R. W. Cutland. Typo J. T. Bigwood)

1940. Prepared for use but not issued. No wmk. Imperforate.

SW19	**3**	1d. scarlet	£3250
SW20	**4**	1d. scarlet	£3250

5 Arms of Jersey

Stamps issued during the German Occupation

(Des Major N. V. L. Rybot. Typo Jersey Evening Post, St. Helier)

1941–43. White paper. No wmk. P 11 (L).

1	**5**	½d. bright green (29.1.42)	8·00	6·00
		a. Imperf between (vertical pair)	£900	
		b. Imperf between (horizontal pair)	£800	
		c. Imperf (pair)	£300	
		d. On greyish paper (1.43)	12·00	12·00
2		1d. scarlet (1.4.41)	8·00	5·00
		a. Imperf between (vertical pair)	£900	
		b. Imperf between (horizontal pair)	£800	
		c. Imperf (pair)	£325	
		d. On chalk-surfaced paper (9.41)	55·00	48·00
		e. On greyish paper (1.43)	14·00	14·00
1	First Day Cover (plain)			7·50
2	First Day Cover (plain)			8·00

Sheets: 60 (6×10).
Imprint: ½d. 'EVENING POST', JERSEY, JANUARY, 1942.
1d. 'EVENING POST', JERSEY, 17/3/41.
Quantities printed: ½d. 703,500; 1d. 1,030,620.
Withdrawn and invalidated: 13.4.46.

6 Old Jersey Farm   **7** Portelet Bay

8 Corbière Lighthouse   **9** Elizabeth Castle

10 Mont Orgueil Castle   **11** Gathering Vraic (seaweed)

Pictorial Issue

(Des E. Blampied. Eng H. Cortot.
Typo French Govt Printing Works, Paris)

1943 (1 June)–**44.** No wmk. P 13½ (C).

3	**6**	½d. green	12·00	12·00
		a. Rough, grey paper (6.10.43)	15·00	14·00
4	**7**	1d. scarlet	3·00	50
		a. On newsprint (28.2.44)	3·50	75
5	**8**	1½d. brown (8.6.43)	8·00	5·75
6	**9**	2d. orange-yellow (8.6.43)	7·50	2·00
7	**10**	2½d. blue (29.6.43)	3·00	1·00
		a. On newsprint (25.2.44)	1·00	1·75
		ba. Thin paper (design shows through on reverse)	£225	
8	**11**	3d. violet (29.6.43)	3·00	2·75
3/8	Set of 6		30·00	21·00
	First Day Covers (3)			36·00
	Set of 6 Gutter Pairs		80·00	

Printings: The sheets of the various printings were dated in the sheet corners as follows:

½d.	1st Printing	1/5/43
	2nd Printing	3/5/43
	3rd Printing	6/10/43
1d.	1st Printing	7/5/43
	2nd Printing	8/5/43
	3rd Printing	7/10/43
	4th Printing	28/2/44
1½d.	1st Printing	17/5/43
	2nd Printing	18/5/43
2d.	1st Printing	20/5/43
	2nd Printing	21/5/43
2½d.	1st Printing	31/5/43
	2nd Printing	25/2/44
3d.	1st Printing	4/6/43
	2nd Printing	5/6/43

Sheets: 60 (2 panes 3×10).
Imprint: None.
Quantities printed: ½d. (No. 3) 360,000; ½d. (No. 3a) 120,000; 1d. (No. 4) 960,000; 1d. (No. 4a) 240,000; 1½d. 360,000; 2d. 360,000; 2½d. (No. 7) 360,000; 2½d. (Nos. 7a/b) 360,000; 3d. 360,000.
Withdrawn and invalidated: 13.4.46.

REGIONAL ISSUES

Although specifically issued for regional use, these issues were initially valid for use throughout Great Britain. However, they ceased to be valid for use in Jersey and Guernsey from 1 October 1969 when these islands each established their own independent postal administration and introduced their own stamps.

DATES OF ISSUE. Conflicting dates of issue have been announced for some of the regional issues, partly explained by the stamps being released on different dates by the Philatelic Bureau in Edinburgh or the Philatelic Counter in London and in the regions. We have adopted the practice of giving the earliest known dates, since once released the stamps could have been used anywhere in the U.K.

INVALIDATION. The regional issues of Jersey were invalidated for use in Jersey and Guernsey on 1 November 1969 (although Guernsey granted a further extension for British and regional stamps till the end of March 1970). The stamps continued to be valid for use in the rest of the United Kingdom until 29 February 1972. Those still current remained on sale at philatelic sales counters until 30 September 1970.

11a Multiple Crowns   12   13

(Des E. Blampied (Type **12**), W. Gardner (Type **13**). Portrait by Dorothy Wilding Ltd. Photo Harrison)

1958–67. Wmk Type **11a**. P 15×14 (C).

9	**12**	2½d. carmine-red (8.6.64)	75	1·00
		a. Imperf three sides (pair)	£3250	
10	**13**	3d. deep lilac (18.8.58)	30	40
		p. One centre phosphor band (9.6.67)	15	15
11		4d. ultramarine (7.2.66)	25	30
		p. Two phosphor bands (5.9.67)	15	25
9/11	Set of 3		80	1·25
9	First Day Cover			30·00
10	First Day Cover			20·00
11	First Day Cover			10·00

Cylinder Nos.: 2½d. 1; 3d. (ord) 1, 2; 3d. (phos) 2; 4d. (ord) 1; 4d. (phos) 1.
Sheets: 240 (12×20).
Quantities sold (ordinary only); 2½d. 4,770,000; 3d. 35,169,720; 4d. 6,623,040.
Withdrawn: 31.8.66 2½d.
Sold out: 10.67 3d. (ordinary); 11.67 4d. (ordinary); 10.68 3d. and 4d. (phosphor).

1968–69. No wmk. Chalk-surfaced paper. One centre phosphor band (4d. values) or two phosphor bands (5d.). P 15×14 (C).

12	**13**	4d. olive-sepia (4.9.68)	15	25
		Ey. Phosphoe omitted	£1000	
13		4d. bright vermilion (26.2.69)	15	25
14		5d. Royal blue (4.9.68)	15	50
12/14	Set of 3		40	90
12, 14	First Day Cover			3·00

Cylinder Nos.: 4d. (olive-sepia) 1; 4d. (bright vermilion) 1; 5d. 1.
Withdrawn: 30.9.69 (locally), 30.9.70 (British Philatelic Counters) 4d. olive-sepia, 4d. bright vermilion and 5d.

INDEPENDENT POSTAL ADMINISTRATION

Jersey established their own independent postal administration on 1 October 1969 and introduced their own stamps.

NO WATERMARK. All the following issues are on unwatermarked paper.

14 Elizabeth Castle

15 La Hougue Bie (Prehistoric Tomb)

16 Portelet Bay

17 La Corbière Lighthouse

18 Mont Orgueil Castle by Night

19 Arms and Royal Mace

20 Jersey Cow

21 Chart of the English Channel

22 Mont Orgueil Castle by Day

23 Queen Elizabeth II (after Cecil Beaton)

24 Jersey Airport

25 Legislative Chamber

26 The Royal Court

27 Queen Elizabeth II (after Cecil Beaton)

(Des V. Whiteley. Photo Harrison (½d. to 1s.9d.), Courvoisier (others))

1969 (1 Oct)–**70**. Granite paper (2s.6d. to £1). Multicoloured; frame colours given. P 14 (½d. to 1s.9d.) or 12 (others), all comb.

15	**14**	½d. ochre (a)	10	60
		a. Thick paper (a)	30	60
16	**15**	1d. brown (abc)	10	10
		a. Booklet stamp with blank margins* (a)	75	
		b. Thick paper (a)	80	90
17	**16**	2d. claret (a)	10	10
		a. Thinner paper (bc)	50	50
18	**17**	3d. ultramarine (a)	10	10
		a. Thinner paper (d)	75	75
		b. Orange omitted	£425	
19	**18**	4d. yellow-olive (a)	10	10
		a. Booklet stamp with blank margins* (a)	50	
		b. Thinner paper (c)	50	50
		c. Gold omitted	1·90	
20	**19**	5d. bistre (a)	10	10
		a. Thinner paper (c)	50	50
		b. Gold omitted	†	—
21	**20**	6d. yellow-brown (ab)	10	10
		a. Thinner paper (e)	9·00	9·00
22	**21**	9d. orange-brown (a)	10	20
		a. Thinner paper (d)	2·75	2·75
23	**22**	1s. reddish lilac (a)	25	25
		a. Thinner paper (c)	2·00	2·00
24	**21**	1s.6d. myrtle-green (a)	80	80
		a. Thinner paper (d)	3·50	3·50
25	**23**	1s.9d. pale myrtle-green (a)	1·00	1·00
		a. Thinner paper (c)	15·00	15·00
26	**24**	2s.6d. black and pale mauve (a)	1·60	1·60
27	**25**	5s. black and pale blue (a)	6·50	6·50
28	**26**	10s. black and pale slate-blue (a)	14·00	14·00
		a. Error. Green border †	£5500	
29	**27**	£1 pale bistre (af) ††	1·90	1·90
15/29 *Set of 15*			20·00	20·00
First Day Cover				20·00
15/29 *Presentation Packs* (3)			24·00	

*Nos. 16a and 19a are on medium paper. No. 16b on thick paper comes from 7s. and 10s. booklets.

†During the final printing of the 10s. a sheet was printed in the colours of the 50p., No. 56, ie. green border instead of slate.

††Printing (f) is the decimal issue which can be positively distinguished by the inscriptions in the left sheet margin which read 'Sheet value £25' at bottom and 'Value per row £5' at top instead of 'Sheet value £25 0s. 0d.' and 'Value per row £5 0s. 0d.' respectively. It exists with more blue in the Queen's dress and less red in the drapery but this printing also includes intermediate shades close to printing (a).

The thinner paper varieties result from a deliberate change as the thicker paper did not adhere well. The two types may be further distinguished by the gum which is creamy on the thicker paper and white on the thinner.

There are a number of shades in this issue which are in part due to the variation in the paper.

There was no postal need for the ½d. value as the ½d. coin had been withdrawn prior to its issue in anticipation of decimalisation.

The presentation packs contained, respectively, low values to 9d., middle values (1s.–2s.6d.) and high values (5s.–£1). The low value pack exists in two forms; with the ½d. stamp (dark blue cover) or without the ½d. (purple cover). The low value packs are 217×119 mm, the middle and high value packs are 101×140 mm. All four packs were issued with wrap covers and no punched holes. The price is for a set of three – either low value pack.

Printings: (a) 1.10.69; (b) 18.2.70; (c) 15.4.70; (d) 5.5.70; (e) 27.5.70; (f) 3.73.

Cylinder Nos.: ½d., 1D, 2d., 4d., 5s. 1A (×5); 3d. 1A (37); 5d., 6d., 9d., 1s.6d., 1s.9d. 1A (×6); 2s.6d. to £1 None.

Sheets: 60 (6×10) ½d. to 1s.6d.; (10×6) 1s.9d.; 25 (5×5) 2s.6d. to £1

Quantities sold: ½d. 999,439; 1d. 1,050,124; 2d. 726,837; 3d. 635,019; 4d. 7,148,849; 5d. 4,886,016; 6d. 550,766; 9d. 954,649; 1s. 577,086; 1s.6d. 419,872; 1s.9d. 306,674; 2s.6d. 244,894; 5s. 206,629; 10s. 179,981; £1 271,194.

Withdrawn: 14.2.72 (except ½d., sold out 10.69, and £1 withdrawn 31.8.77).

Invalidated: 14.2.72 (except £1).

28 First Day Cover

Inauguration of Post Office

(Des R. Sellar. Photo Harrison)

1969 (1 Oct). Multicoloured; background colours given. P 14 (C).

30	**28**	4d. magenta	10	15
31		5d. new blue	20	10
32		1s.6d. red-brown	50	75
33		1s.9d. bright emerald	80	1·00
30/3 *Set of 4*			1·40	1·80
First Day Cover				4·00
Presentation Pack			2·00	

Cylinder Nos.: All values 1A (×4).

Sheets: 60 (6×10).

Quantities sold: 4d. 1,483,686; 5d. 742,820; 1s.6d. 272,155; 1s.9d. 238,856.

Withdrawn: 1.10.70.

Invalidated: 14.2.72.

29 'Lord Coutanche' (Sir James Gunn)

30 'Sir Winston Churchill' (Van Praag)

31 'Liberation' (Edmund Blampied)

32 S.S. *Vega* (unknown artist)

25th Anniversary of Liberation

(Des Rosalind Dease from paintings. Photo Courvoisier)

1970 (9 May). Granite paper. P 11½ (C).

34	**29**	4d. multicoloured	20	20
35	**30**	5d. multicoloured	20	20
36	**31**	1s.6d. multicoloured	90	1·00
37	**32**	1s.9d. multicoloured	90	1·00
34/7 *Set of 4*			2·00	2·00
First Day Cover				4·00
Presentation Pack			2·75	

A special Presentation Pack in gold, red and blue-green on olive was given to Jersey schoolchildren (Price £15). The normal Presentation Pack is printed in gold and blue-green.

Sheets: 50 (10×5) 4d., 5d.; (5×10) 1s.6d., 1s.9d.

Quantities sold: 4d. 1,617,751; 5d. 1,296,678; 1s.6d. 334,468; 1s.9d. 319,893.

Withdrawn: 9.5.71.

Invalidated: 14.2.72.

33 'A Tribute to Enid Blyton'

34 'Rags to Riches'

35 'Gourmet's Delight'

36 'We're the Greatest'

'Battle of Flowers' Parade

(Des Jennifer Toombs. Photo Courvoisier)

1970 (28 July). Granite paper. P 11½ (C).

38	**33**	4d. multicoloured		20	10
39	**34**	5d. multicoloured		20	20
40	**35**	1s.6d. multicoloured		2·50	2·20
41	**36**	1s.9d. multicoloured		2·75	2·20
38/41		Set of 4		5·00	4·25
		First Day Cover			5·00
		Presentation Pack		6·50	

Sheets: 50 (5×10).
Quantities sold: 4d. 1,905,109; 5d. 1,498,301; 1s.6d. 262,072; 1s.9d. 231,077.
Withdrawn: 27.7.71.
Invalidated: 14.2.72.

37 Martello Tower, Archirondel

Decimal Currency

(Des V. Whiteley. Photo Harrison (½ to 9p.), Courvoisier (others)).

1970–74. Designs as Type **37** etc., but with values inscribed in decimal currency and new design (6p.). Chalk-surfaced paper (4½p., 5½p., 8p.), granite paper (10p., 20p., 50p.).

42	**14**	½p. multicoloured (bgk)		10	10
		a. Booklet stamp with blank margins (b)		20	
43	**17**	1p. multicoloured (bn)		10	10
		a. Orange omitted		£500	
44	**20**	1½p. multicoloured (b)		10	10
45	**18**	2p. multicoloured (b)		10	10
		a. Booklet stamp with blank margins		60	
46	**19**	2½p. multicoloured (bk)		10	10
		a. Booklet stamp with blank margins (b)		60	
		ab. Gold (Mace) omitted		£775	
		ac. Gold (Mace) ptg double		£575	
47	**15**	3p. multicoloured (bch)		10	10

		a. Booklet stamp with blank margins (e)		60	
48	**16**	3½p. multicoloured (bh)		10	10
		a. Booklet stamp with blank margins (h)		25	
49	**21**	4p. multicoloured (bfimo)		10	10
49a	**19**	4½p. multicoloured (j)*		75	75
		ab. Uncoated paper		£400	
50	**22**	5p. multicoloured (blmo)		10	10
50a	**20**	5½p. multicoloured (j)		75	75
51	**37**	6p. multicoloured (b)		20	10
52	**21**	7½p. multicoloured (b)		50	50
52a	**18**	8p. multicoloured (j)		75	75
53	**23**	9p. multicoloured (b)		70	70
54	**24**	10p. multicoloured (adh)		40	30
55	**25**	20p. multicoloured (adh)		90	80
56	**26**	50p. multicoloured (al)		1·50	1·20
42/56		Set of 18		4·50	4·50
		First Day Covers (3) 42/56, 29			6·50
		Presentation Packs (4)		6·75	

Gum: From 1974 printings appeared with dextrin added to the PVA gum giving a bluish-green tinge and mottled appearance. The ½p., 1p., 2½p., 3p., 3½p., 4p., 5p. and 8p. all exist both PVA and PVA dextrin. The 4½p. and 5½p. only come with dextrin, and the 10, 20 and 50p. only with gum arabic.

The original three presentation packs were issued with wrap covers and no punched holes. The original low value pack (½p. to 4p.) measured 223×115 mm, the medium value (5p. to 9p.) and high value pack (10p. to £1) each measured 110×140 mm. All three packs were reprinted (with two punched holes) in the larger size, 223×115 mm. The new medium value pack contained three additional values, 4½p., 5½p. and 8p.

Printings: (a) 1.10.70; (b) 15.2.71; (c) 1.8.72; (d) 15.11.72; (e) 1.12.72; (f) 1.10.73; (g) 3.12.73; (h) 1.7.74; (i) 12.8.74; (j) 31.10.74; (k) 1.11.74; (l) 28.1.75; (m) 1.4.75; (n) 21.4.75; (o) 30.10.75.

Plate Nos.: ½p., 2p., 3½p., 6p., 8p. 1A (×5); 1p. 1A (×7), 2A–1A (×6) (n); 1½p., 2½p., 4½p., 5½p., 7½p., 9p. 1A (×6); 3p. 1A (×5), 1A (×4)–2A (h); 4p. 1A (×6), 2A–1A (×5) (mo); 5p. 1A (×5), 2A–1A (×4) (mo); 10p. to 50p. None.

Sheets: 50 (5×10) ½p. to 8p.; (10×5) 9p.; 25 (5×5) 10p. to 50p.

Quantities sold: ½p. 2,247,128; 1p. 1,654,860; 1½p. 817,871; 2p. 2,305,239; 2½p. 5,096,912; 3p. 4,780,836; 3½p. 2,069,095; 4p. 3,908,727; 4½p. 349,157; 5p. 3,593,226; 5½p. 333,125; 6p. 1,072,224; 7½p. 538,810; 8p. 329,361; 9p. 458,977; 10p. 862,524; 20p. 765,524; 50p. 490,675.

Withdrawn: 31.1.77 (½p. to 9p.); 31.8.77 (others).

38 White-eared Pheasant

39 Thick-billed Parrot

40 Western Black and White Colobus Monkey

41 Ring-tailed Lemur

Wildlife Preservation Trust (1st series)

(Des Jennifer Toombs. Photo Courvoisier)

1971 (12 Mar). Granite paper. P 11½ (C).

57	**38**	2p. multicoloured		20	10
58	**39**	2½p. multicoloured		20	15
59	**40**	7½p. multicoloured		1·75	1·75
60	**41**	9p. multicoloured		2·50	2·50
57/60		Set of 4		4·00	4·00
		First Day Cover			8·00
		Presentation Pack		5·00	

See also Nos. 73/6, 217/21, 324/9, 447/51 and 824/9.
Sheets: 50 (5×10) 2p., 9p.; (10×5) others.
Quantities sold: 2p. 1,025,544; 2½p. 1,363,427; 7½p. 233,147; 9p. 220,710.
Withdrawn: 11.3.72.

42 Royal British Legion Badge   **43** Poppy Emblem and Field

44 Jack Counter VC, and Victoria Cross   **45** Crossed Tricolour and Union Jack

50th Anniversary of Royal British Legion

(Des G. Drummond. Litho Questa)

1971 (15 June). P 14 (C).

61	**42**	2p. multicoloured	20	10
62	**43**	2½p. multicoloured	20	10
63	**44**	7½p. multicoloured	1·00	1·10
64	**45**	9p. multicoloured	1·00	1·10
61/4 *Set of 4*			2·00	2·10
First Day Cover				3·50
Presentation Pack			2·50	

Plate Nos.: 2p., 2½p. 1A, 1B (each×4); others 1A, 1B (each×5).
Sheets: 50 (5×10).
Imprint: Right-hand corner, bottom margin.
Quantities sold: 2p. 1,381,873; 2½p. 1,529,866; 7½p. 239,477; 9p. 226,407.
Withdrawn: 14.6.72.

46 'Tante Elizabeth' (E. Blampied)   **47** 'English Fleet in the Channel' (P. Monamy)

48 'The Boyhood of Raleigh' (Millais)   **49** 'The Blind Beggar' (W. W. Ouless)

Jersey Artists (1st series). Paintings

(Des and photo Courvoisier)

1971 (5 Oct). Granite paper. P 11½ (C).

65	**46**	2p. multicoloured	15	10
66	**47**	2½p. multicoloured	20	10
67	**48**	7½p. multicoloured	95	95
68	**49**	9p. multicoloured	1·10	1·10
65/8 *Set of 4*			2·00	2·00
First Day Cover				4·75
Presentation Pack			2·50	

See also Nos. 115/18, 213/16, 320/3, 344/9, 352/6, 397/401 and 428/32.
Sheets: 50 (5×10) 2p., 9p.; (10×5) others.
Quantities sold: 2p. 1,243,198; 2½p. 1,490,595; 7½p. 264,532; 9p. 251,770 .
Withdrawn: 4.10.72.

50 Jersey Fern   **51** Jersey Thrift

52 Jersey Orchid   **53** Jersey Viper's Bugloss

Wild Flowers of Jersey

(Des G. Drummond. Photo Courvoisier)

1972 (18 Jan). Granite paper. P 11½ (C).

69	**50**	3p. multicoloured	20	10
70	**51**	5p. multicoloured	30	20
71	**52**	7½p. multicoloured	95	95
72	**53**	9p. multicoloured	1·00	1·00
69/72 *Set of 4*			2·00	2·00
First Day Cover				3·50
Presentation Pack			2·50	

Sheets: 50 (5×10).
Quantities sold: 3p. 1,124,878; 5p. 332,764; 7½p. 202,404; 9p. 196,998.
Withdrawn: 17.1.73.

54 Cheetah   **55** Rothschild's Mynah

56 Spectacled Bear   **57** Tuatara

Wildlife Preservation Trust (2nd series)

(Des Jennifer Toombs. Photo Courvoisier)

1972 (17 Mar). Granite paper. P 11½ (C).

73	**54**	2½p. multicoloured	30	10
74	**55**	3p. multicoloured	25	20
75	**56**	7½p. multicoloured	50	70
76	**57**	9p. multicoloured	80	90
73/6 *Set of 4*			1·60	1·70
First Day Cover				4·50
Presentation Pack			2·50	

Sheets: 50 (10×5) 3p.; (5×10) others.
Quantities sold: 2½p. 1,223,916; 3p. 1,631,752; 7½p. 279,935; 9p. 235,968.
Withdrawn: 16.3.73.

58 Artillery Shako

59 Shako
(2nd North Regt)

60 Shako (5th
South-West Regt)

61 Helmet (3rd
Jersey Light Infantry)

Royal Jersey Militia (1st series)

(Des and photo Courvoisier)

1972 (27 June). Granite paper. P 11½ (C).

77	**58**	2½p. multicoloured	10	10
78	**59**	3p. multicoloured	10	10
79	**60**	7½p. multicoloured	30	30
80	**61**	9p. multicoloured	50	60
77/80 *Set of 4*			90	90
First Day Cover				3·00
Presentation Pack			1·70	

See also Nos. 1253/7.
Sheets: 50 (10×5).
Quantities sold: 2½p. 1,240,393; 3p. 1,857,224; 7½p. 300,554; 9p. 271,832.
Withdrawn: 26.6.73.

62 Princess Anne

63 Queen Elizabeth and Prince Philip

64 Prince Charles

65 The Royal Family

Royal Silver Wedding

(Des G. Drummond from photographs by D. Groves.
Photo Courvoisier)

1972 (1 Nov). Granite paper. P 11½ (C).

81	**62**	2½p. multicoloured	10	10
82	**63**	3p. multicoloured	10	10
83	**64**	7½p. multicoloured	35	35
84	**65**	20p. multicoloured	35	35
81/4 *Set of 4*			80	80
First Day Cover				1·50
Presentation Pack			1·10	

Sheets: 25 (5×5).
Quantities sold: 2½p. 1,743,240; 3p. 1,638,566; 7½p. 424,029; 20p. 418,824.
Sold out: by 23.1.73 (7½p., 20p.); 16.5.73 (3p.).
Withdrawn: 31.10.73 (2½p.).

66 Silver Wine Cup and Christening Cup

67 Gold Torque

68 Royal Seal of Charles II

69 Armorican Bronze Coins

Centenary of La Sociètè Jersiaise

(Des G. Drummond. Photo Courvoisier)

1973 (23 Jan). Granite paper. P 11½ (C).

85	**66**	2½p. violet-blue, new blue and black	10	10
86	**67**	3p. bright cerise, orange-yellow and black	10	10
87	**68**	7½p. multicoloured	25	25
88	**69**	9p. multicoloured	30	30
85/8 *Set of 4*			70	60
First Day Cover				1·20
Presentation Pack			1·20	

Sheets: 50 (10×5) 3p., 7½p.; (5×10) others.
Quantities sold: 2½p. 2,008,923; 3p. 2,437,421; 7½p. 363,543; 9p. 327,917.
Sold out: by 31.10.73 (7½p.).
Withdrawn: 22.1.74. (2½p, 3p., 9p.).

70 Balloon *L'Armee de La Loire* and Letter, Paris, 1870

71 Astra Seaplane, 1912

72 Supermarine Sea Eagle

73 de Havilland DH.86 Dragon Express *Giffard Bay*

Jersey Aviation History (1st series)

(Des and photo Courvoisier)

1973 (16 May). Granite paper. P 11½ (C).

89	**70**	3p. multicoloured	10	10
90	**71**	5p. multicoloured	10	10
91	**72**	7½p. multicoloured	35	35
92	**73**	9p. multicoloured	45	45
89/92 *Set of 4*			90	90
First Day Cover				1·50
Presentation Pack			1·20	

See also Nos. 340/3, 409/13, 530/4, 618/23, 807/12, 962/7, 1074/MS1080, 1326/MS1332, 1410/MS1416, 1643/MS1649.
Sheets: 50 (5×10).
Quantities sold: 3p. 3,085,497; 5p. 641,583; 7½p. 368,069; 9p. 356,379.
Sold out: by 31.10.73 (7½p.).
Withdrawn: 15.5.74 (3p., 5p., 9p.).

74 *North Western*, built 1870

75 *Calvados*, 1873

76 *Carteret* at Grouville Station, 1898

77 *Caesarea*, 1873, and Route Map

Jersey Railway History (1st series). Centenary of Jersey Eastern Railway

(Des G. Drummond. Photo Courvoisier)

1973 (6 Aug). Granite paper. P 11½ (C).

93	**74**	2½p. multicoloured	10	10
94	**75**	3p. multicoloured	10	10
95	**76**	7½p. multicoloured	35	35
96	**77**	9p. multicoloured	45	45
93/6 *Set of 4*			90	90
First Day Cover				1·40
Presentation Pack			1·20	

See also Nos. 365/9 and 1433/**MS**1439.

Sheets: 50 (5×10).

Quantities sold: 2½p. 1,591,063; 3p. 3,051,097; 7½p. 396,919; 9p. 365,310.

Sold out: by 31.10.73 (7½p.).

Withdrawn: 5.8.74. (2½p, 3p., 9p.).

78 Princess Anne and Captain Mark Phillips

Royal Wedding

(Des and photo Courvoisier)

1973 (14 Nov). Granite paper. P 11½ (C).

97	**78**	3p. multicoloured	10	10
98		20p. multicoloured	50	50
97/8 *Set of 2*			60	60
First Day Cover				80
Presentation Pack			95	

Sheets: 25 (5×5).

Quantities sold: 3p. 1,988,407; 20p. 522,793.

Withdrawn: 30.11.74.

79 Spider Crab

80 Conger Eel

81 Lobster

82 Tuberculate Ormer

Marine Life (1st series)

(Des Jennifer Toombs. Photo Courvoisier)

1973 (15 Nov). Granite paper. P 11½ (C).

99	**79**	2½p. multicoloured	10	10
100	**80**	3p. multicoloured	10	10
101	**81**	7½p. multicoloured	30	35
102	**82**	20p. multicoloured	40	45
99/102 *Set of 4*			80	90
First Day Cover				1·20
Presentation Pack			1·40	

See also Nos. 670/3, 864/9, 947/**MS**953, 1163/**MS**1169, 1264/**MS**1270, 1444/9, 1525/**MS**1531 and 1567/**MS**1573.

Sheets: 50 (5×10).

Quantities sold: 2½p. 1,596,526; 3p. 1,243,541; 7½p. 501,541; 20p. 517,440.

Sold out: by 28.2.74 (7½p.).

Withdrawn: 30.11.74 (2½p., 3p., 20p.).

83 Freesias

84 Anemones

85 Carnations and Gladioli

86 Daffodils and Iris

Spring Flowers

(Des G. Drummond. Photo Courvoisier)

1974 (13 Feb). Granite paper. P 11½ (C).

103	**83**	3p. multicoloured	10	10
104	**84**	5½p. multicoloured	15	15
105	**85**	8p. multicoloured	25	30
106	**86**	10p. multicoloured	30	35
103/6 *Set of 4*			70	80
First Day Cover				1·20
Presentation Pack			1·20	

Sheets: 50 (10×5).

Quantities sold: 3p. 1,239,968; 5½p. 590,376; 8p. 475,665; 10p. 507,542.

Withdrawn: 28.2.75.

87 First U.K. Pillar-box and Contemporary Cover

88 Jersey Postmen, 1862 and 1969

89 Modern Pillar-box and Cover

90 Mail Transport, 1874 and 1974

Centenary of Universal Postal Union

(Des G. Drummond. Photo Courvoisier)

1974 (7 June). Granite paper. P 11½ (C).

107	**87**	2½p. multicoloured	10	10
108	**88**	3p. multicoloured	10	15
109	**89**	5½p. multicoloured	25	25
110	**90**	20p. multicoloured	35	40
107/10 *Set of 4*			70	75
First Day Cover				1·00
Presentation Pack			1·20	

Sheets: 50 (5×10).
Quantities sold: 2½p. 461,174; 3p. 1,380,018; 5½p. 421,674; 20p. 386,348.
Withdrawn: 30.6.75.

91 John Wesley

92 Sir William Hillary

93 Canon Wace

94 Sir Winston Churchill

Anniversaries. Events described on stamps

(Des recess and litho DLR)

1974 (31 July). P 13×14 (C).

111	**91**	3p. agate and light cinnamon	10	10
112	**92**	3½p. blackish violet & light azure	10	10
113	**93**	8p. blue-black and pale rose-lilac	20	25
114	**94**	20p. black and pale buff	45	50
		a. Pale buff (background omitted)		
111/14 *Set of 4*			75	80
First Day Cover				1·00
Presentation Pack			1·20	

Plate Nos.: 3p. and 20p. 1A–1A, 1B–1B; 3½p. and 8p. 1A–1A, 1B–1B, 2A–1A, 2B–1B.
Sheets: 50 (10×5).
Imprint: Right-hand corner, bottom margin.
Quantities sold: 3p. 908,852; 3½p. 2,355,391; 8p. 338,397; 20p. 409,291.
Withdrawn: 31.7.75.

95 *Catherine* and *Mary* (royal yachts)

96 French Two-decker

97 Dutch Vessel

98 Battle of Cap La Hague, 1692

Jersey Artists (2nd series). Marine Paintings by Peter Monamy

(Des and photo Courvoisier)

1974 (22 Nov). Granite paper. P 11½ (C).

115	**95**	3½p. multicoloured	10	10
116	**96**	5½p. multicoloured	15	10
117	**97**	8p. multicoloured	25	30
118	**98**	25p. multicoloured	55	60
115/18 *Set of 4*			95	1·00
First Day Cover				2·00
Presentation Pack			1·70	

Sheets: 50 (10×5) 8p.; (5×10) others.
Quantities sold: 3½p. 1,670,994; 5½p. 448,137; 8p. 416,296; 25p. 415,991.
Withdrawn: 30.11.75.

99 Potato Digger

100 Cider Crusher

101 Six-Horse Plough

102 Hay Cart

Nineteenth-Century Farming

(Des G. Drummond. Photo Courvoisier)

1975 (25 Feb). Granite paper. P 11½ (C).

119	**99**	3p. multicoloured	10	10
120	**100**	3½p. multicoloured	10	10
121	**101**	8p. multicoloured	20	25
122	**102**	10p. multicoloured	35	40
119/22 *Set of 4*			70	75
First Day Cover				90
Presentation Pack			1·00	

Sheets: 50 (5×10).
Quantities sold: 3p. 588,185; 3½p. 1,025,295; 8p. 432,432; 10p. 457,196.
Withdrawn: 28.2.76.

103 H.M. Queen Elizabeth, the Queen Mother (photograph by Cecil Beaton)

Royal Visit

(Des and photo Courvoisier)

1975 (30 May). Granite paper. P 11½ (C).

123	**103**	20p. multicoloured	50	50
First Day Cover				1·70
Presentation Pack			1·00	

Cylinder Nos.: A1–1–1–1–1, B1–1–1–1–1.
Sheets: 25 (5×5).
Quantity sold: 572,675.
Withdrawn: 31.5.76.

104 Nautilus Shell

105 Parasol

106 Deckchair

107 Sandcastle with flags of Jersey and the U.K.

Jersey Tourism

(Des A. Games. Photo Courvoisier)

1975 (6 June). Designs based on holiday posters. Granite paper. P 11½ (C).

124	**104**	5p. multicoloured	10	10
125	**105**	8p. multicoloured	15	15
126	**106**	10p. multicoloured	30	30
127	**107**	12p. multicoloured	40	40
124/7	*Set of 4*		80	80
First Day Cover				1·10
Presentation Pack			1·70	
MS128 147×69 mm. Nos. 124/7			90	1·10
First Day Cover				4·00

Cylinder Nos.: All values A1–1–1–1–1, B1–1–1–1–1.
Sheets: 50 (10×5).
Quantities sold: 5p. 1,377,519; 8p. 368,521; 10p. 467,278; 12p. 389,574; miniature sheet 298,689.
Withdrawn: 30.6.76.

108 Common Tern

109 British Storm Petrel

110 Brent Geese

111 Shag

Sea Birds

(Des Jennifer Toombs. Photo Courvoisier)

1975 (28 July). Granite paper. P 11½ (C).

129	**108**	4p. multicoloured	10	10
130	**109**	5p. multicoloured	15	10
131	**110**	8p. multicoloured	40	30
132	**111**	25p. multicoloured	70	70
129/32	*Set of 4*		1·00	1·00

First Day Cover		1·25
Presentation Pack	1·60	

Sheets: 50 (10×5).
Quantities sold: 4p. 872,260; 5p. 2,871,390; 8p. 384,550; 25p. 362,160.
Withdrawn: 31.7.76.

112 Armstrong Whitworth Siskin IIIA

113 Supermarine Southampton I Flying Boat

114 Supermarine Spitfire Mk I

115 Folland Fo. 144 Gnat T.1

50th Anniversary of Royal Air Forces Association, Jersey Branch

(Des A. Theobald. Photo Courvoisier)

1975 (30 Oct). Granite paper. P 11½ (C).

133	**112**	4p. multicoloured	10	10
134	**113**	5p. multicoloured	15	15
135	**114**	10p. multicoloured	40	30
136	**115**	25p. multicoloured	70	60
133/6	*Set of 4*		1·20	1·00
First Day Cover				1·60
Presentation Pack			1·50	

Cylinder Nos.: All values A1–1–1–1–1, B1–1–1–1–1.
Sheets: 50 (5×10).
Quantities sold: 4p. 1,496,640; 5p. 1,805,624; 10p. 581,627; 25p. 407,423.
Withdrawn: 30.10.76.

116 Map of Jersey Parishes

117 Zoological Park

118 St. Mary's Church

119 Seymour Tower

120 La Corbière Lighthouse

121 St. Saviour's Church

122 Elizabeth Castle

123 Gorey Harbour

124 Jersey Airport

125 Grosnez Castle

126 Bonne Nuit Harbour

127 Le Hocq Tower

128 Morel Farm

129 Parish Arms and Island Scene

130 Flag and Map

131 Postal H.Q. and Badge

132 Parliament, Royal Court and Arms

133 Lieutenant-Governor's Flag and Government House

134 Queen Elizabeth II (photograph by Alex Wilson)

Parish Arms and Views

(Des Courvoisier (£2), G. Drummond (others). Litho Questa (½p. to 15p.). Photo Courvoisier (others))

1976–80. Granite paper (20p. to £2). P 14½ (½p. to 15p.) or 12 (others), all comb.

137	116	½p. multicoloured (af)	10	10
138	117	1p. multicoloured (af)	10	10
		a. Booklet pane of 4 (No. 13832 plus 2 se-tenant labels) (b)	70	
		b. Booklet pane. No. 138×4 (begh)	80	
139	118	5p. multicoloured (ad)	10	10
		a. Booklet pane of 4 (b)	40	
140	119	6p. multicoloured (ad)	10	10
		a. Booklet pane of 4 (eg)	40	
141	120	7p. multicoloured (ad)	10	10
		a. Booklet pane of 4 (bh)	40	
142	121	8p. multicoloured (ad)	15	10
		a. Booklet pane of 4 (eg)	80	

143	122	9p. multicoloured (a)	15	10
		a. Booklet pane of 4 (h)	60	
144	123	10p. multicoloured (af)	20	10
145	124	11p. multicoloured (af)	25	25
146	125	12p. multicoloured (a)	25	20
147	126	13p. multicoloured (a)	25	20
148	127	14p. multicoloured (a)	30	20
149	128	15p. multicoloured (a)	30	25
150	129	20p. multicoloured (c)	45	45
151	130	30p. multicoloured (c)	55	50
152	131	40p. multicoloured (c)	80	80
153	132	50p. multicoloured (c)	1·00	1·00
154	133	£1 multicoloured (c)	3·00	3·00
155	134	£2 multicoloured (d)	4·00	4·00
137/55 *Set of 19*			11·00	11·00
First Day Covers (4)				12·00
Presentation Packs (4)			12·00	

Printings: (a) 29.1.76; (b) 5.4.76; (c) 20.8.76; (d) 16.11.77; (e) 28.2.78; (f) 31.8.78; (g) 1.10.79; (h) 6.5.80.

Plate or cylinder Nos.: ½p. to 9p., 13p., 14p. 1A, 1B, 1C, 1D (each×4); 10p. 1A, 1B, 1C, 1D (each×4), 1B–1B–1B–2B, 2A–1A–1A–2A, 2B–1B–1B–2B, 2C–1C–1C–2C, 2D.1D.1D.2D.; 11p. 1A, 1B, 1C, 1D (each×5); 12p. 1A, 1B, 1C, 1D (each×4), 1A–1A–2A–2A, 1B–1B–2B–2B, 1C–1C–2C–2C, 1D–1D–2D–2D; 15p. 1A, 1B, 1C, 1D (each×4), 1A–2A–1A–1A, 1B–2B–1B–1B, 1C–2C–1C–1C, 1D–2D–2D–1D, 1A–3A–2A–1A, 1B–3B–2B–1B, 1C–3C–2C–1C, 1D–3D––2D–1D.; 20p. A1–1–1–1–1, B1–1–1–1–1, C1–1–1–1–1, D1–1–1–1–1; 30p. £1 A1–1–1–1–1, B1–1–1–1––1; 40p, 50p. A1–1–1–1, B1–1–1–1; £2 A1–1–1–1–1–1–1–1, B1–1–1–1–1–1–1, C1–1–1–1–1–1–1–1, D1–1–1–1–1–1–1–1.

Sheets: 50 (5×10) ½p. to 15p.; 25 (5×5) others.

Imprint: Right-hand corner, bottom margin (½p. to 15p.); central, bottom margin (others).

Withdrawn: 27.2.82 ½p. to 9p. (sheets); 20.4.82 1p., 5p. to 9p. (booklets); 31.7.82 10p. to 15p.; 28.2.83 20p. to £1; 31.3.92 £2.

135 Sir Walter Raleigh and Map of Virginia

136 Sir George Carteret and Map of New Jersey

137 Philippe D'Auvergne and Long Island Landing

138 John Copley and Sketch

Bicentenary of American Independence

(Des M. Orbell. Photo Courvoisier)

1976 (29 May). Granite paper. P 11½ (C).

160	135	5p. multicoloured	10	10
161	136	7p. multicoloured	15	10
162	137	11p. multicoloured	40	40
163	138	13p. multicoloured	50	50
160/3	*Set of 4*		1·00	1·00
First Day Cover				1·20
Presentation Pack			1·40	

Cylinder Nos.: 5p. 11p. A1–1–1–1, B1–1–1–1; others
A1–1–1–1, B1–1–1–1.
Sheets: 25 (5×5).
Quantities sold: 5p. 980,029; 7p. 1,352,629; 11p. 582,706; 13p.
435,561.
Withdrawn: 31.5.77.

139 Dr. Grandin and Map of
China

140 Sampan on the Yangtze

141 Overland Trek

142 Dr. Grandin at Work

Birth Centenary of Dr. Lilian Grandin (medical missionary)

(Des Jennifer Toombs. Photo Courvoisier)

1976 (25 Nov). Granite paper. P 11½ (C).

164	139	5p. multicoloured	10	10
165	140	7p. lt yellow, yellow-brown & blk	10	10
166	141	11p. multicoloured	35	30
167	142	13p. multicoloured	50	50
164/7	*Set of 4*		95	90
First Day Cover				1·20
Presentation Pack			1·40	

Cylinder Nos.: 7p. A1–1–1, B1–1–1; 13p. A1–1–1–1, B1–1–1–1–1;
others A1–1–1–1, B1–1–1–1.
Sheets: 50 (5×10).
Quantities sold: 5p. 757,843; 7p. 1,043,198; 11p. 384,436; 13p.
354,096.
Withdrawn: 30.11.77.

143 Coronation, 1953
(photograph by Cecil
Beaton)

144 Visit to Jersey, 1957

145 Queen Elizabeth II
(photograph by Peter
Grugeon)

Silver Jubilee

(Des G. Drummond. Photo Courvoisier)

1977 (7 Feb). Granite paper. P 11½ (C).

168	143	5p. multicoloured	15	10
169	144	7p. multicoloured	20	15
170	145	25p. multicoloured	40	55
168/70	*Set of 3*		70	70
First Day Cover				1·20
Presentation Pack			1·20	

Cylinder Nos.: All values A1–1–1–1, B1–1–1–1.
Sheets: 25 (5×5).
Imprint: Central, bottom margin.
Quantities sold: 5p. 1,220,986; 7p. 1,212,639; 25p. 681,241.
Withdrawn: 28.2.78.

146 Coins of 1871 and 1877

147 One-twelfth Shilling, 1949

148 Silver Crown, 1966

149 £2 Piece, 1972

Centenary of Currency Reform

(Des D. Henley. Litho Questa)

1977 (25 Mar). P 14 (C).

171	146	5p. multicoloured	10	10
172	147	7p. multicoloured	15	10
173	148	11p. multicoloured	30	30
174	149	13p. multicoloured	40	40
171/4	*Set of 4*		80	75
First Day Cover				1·10
Presentation Pack			1·40	

Plate Nos.: 7p. 1A, 1B (each×5); 1A–2A–1A (×3); 1B–2B–1B (×3);
others 1A, 1B (each×5).
Sheets: 50 (5×10).
Imprint: Right-hand corner, bottom margin.
Quantities sold: 5p. 1,029,661; 7p. 923,950; 11p. 383,834; 13p.
368,249.
Withdrawn: 31.3.78.

150 Sir William Weston and
Santa Anna, 1530

151 Sir William Drogo and
Ambulance, 1877

152 Duke of Connaught and
Rolls-Royce Ambulance, 1917

153 Duke of Gloucester and Stretcher-team, 1977

St. John Ambulance Centenary

(Des A. Theobald. Litho Questa)

1977 (24 June). P 14×13½ (C).

175	**150**	5p. multicoloured	10	10
176	**151**	7p. multicoloured	10	10
177	**152**	11p. multicoloured	25	25
178	**153**	13p. multicoloured	40	40
175/8 *Set of 4*			75	75
First Day Cover				1·10
Presentation Pack			1·20	

Plate Nos.: 5p. 1A, 1B, 1C (each×5); 7p., 11p. 1A, 1B, 1C (each×6); 13p. 1A, 1B, 1C (each×5), 1B–2B–1B–1B–1B.
Sheets: 40 (8×5).
Imprint: Bottom corner, right-hand margin.
Quantities sold: 5p. 849,532; 7p. 1,089,526; 11p. 421,039; 13p. 370,887.
Withdrawn: 30.6.78.

154 Arrival of Queen Victoria, 1846

155 Victoria College, 1852

156 Sir Galahad Statue, 1924

157 College Hall

125th Anniversary of Victoria College

(Des R. Granger Barrett. Litho Questa)

1977 (29 Sept). P 14½ (C).

179	**154**	7p. multicoloured	15	10
180	**155**	10½p. multicoloured	20	15
		a. Black ptg double		
181	**156**	11p. multicoloured	25	25
182	**157**	13p. multicoloured	40	40
179/82 *Set of 4*			90	90
First Day Cover				1·10
Presentation Pack			1·40	

Plate Nos.: 7p. 1A, 1B (each×6); 1A–1A–2A–1A–1A–1A, 1B–1B–2B–1B–1B–1B; 13p. 1A, 1B (each×6); others 1A, 1B (each×5).
Sheets: 50 (5×10) 7 and 10½p., (10×5) others.
Imprint: Right-hand corner, bottom margin.
Quantities sold: 7p. 1,496,997; 10½p. 906,669; 11p. 528,293; 13p. 371,251.
Withdrawn: 30.9.78.

158 Harry Vardon Satuette and Map of Royal Jersey Course

159 Harry Vardon's Grip and Swing

160 Harry Vardon's Putt

161 Golf Trophies and Book by Harry Vardon

Jersey Golf (1st series). Centenary of Royal Jersey Golf Club

(Des Jennifer Toombs. Litho Questa)

1978 (28 Feb). P 14 (C).

183	**158**	6p. multicoloured	10	10
184	**159**	8p. multicoloured	15	10
185	**160**	11p. multicoloured	35	35
186	**161**	13p. multicoloured	40	40
183/6 *Set of 4*			90	75
First Day Cover				1·10
Presentation Pack			1·40	

See also Nos. 1035/9.
Plate Nos.: 6p. 1A, 1B (each×5); 8p., 11p. 1A, 1B (each×4); 13p. 1A, 1B (each×4), 2A–1A–1A–1A, 2B–1B–1B–1B.
Sheets: 50 (5×10).
Imprint: Right-hand corner, bottom margin.
Quantities sold: 6p. 837,427; 8p. 851,904; 11p. 466,343; 13p. 368,648.
Withdrawn: 28.2.79.

162 Mont Orgueil Castle

163 St. Aubin's Fort

164 Elizabeth Castle

Europa Monuments. Castles from Paintings by Thomas Phillips

(Des from paintings by Thomas Philips. Photo Courvoisier)

1978 (1 May). Granite paper. P 11½ (C).

187	**162**	6p. multicoloured	10	10
188	**163**	8p. multicoloured	15	15
189	**164**	10½p. multicoloured	35	40
187/9 *Set of 3*			55	55
First Day Cover				70
Presentation Pack			80	

Cylinder Nos.: All values A1–1–1–1, B1–1–1–1, C1–1–1–1, D1–1–1–1.
Sheets: 20 (5×4).
Imprint: Central, bottom margin.
Quantities sold: 6p. 2,602,412; 8p. 2,592,722; 10½p. 2,564,535.
Withdrawn: 31.5.79.

165 'Gaspé Basin' (P. J. Ouless)

166 Map of Gaspé Peninsula Ouless)

167 *Century* (brigantine)

168 Early Map of Jersey

169 St. Aubin's Bay, Town and Harbour

Links with Canada

(Des R. Granger Barrett. Litho Questa)

1978 (9 June). P 14½ (C).
190	**165**	6p. multicoloured	10	10
191	**166**	6p. multicoloured	15	10
192	**167**	10½p. multicoloured	20	20
193	**168**	11p. multicoloured	40	35
194	**169**	13p. multicoloured	45	45
190/4 *Set of 5*			1·10	1·00
First Day Cover				1·25
Presentation Pack			1·50	

There is considerable variation in the background colour of No. 193.
Plate Nos.: 6p. 1A, 1B, 1C, 1D (each×5); others 1A, 1B, 1C, 1D (each×6).
Sheets: 50 (5×10).
Imprint: Right-hand corner, bottom margin.
Quantities sold: 6p. 1,047,825; 8p. 1,095,489; 10½p. 999,002; 11p. 443,932; 13p. 367,472.
Withdrawn: 30.6.79.

170 Queen Elizabeth and Prince Philip

171 Hallmarks of 1953 and 1977

25th Anniversary of Coronation

(Des and photo Courvoisier)

1978 (26 June). Granite paper. P 11½ (C).
195	**170**	8p. silver, black and cerise	20	10
196	**171**	25p. silver, black and new blue	50	60
195/6 *Set of 2*			60	60
First Day Cover				90
Presentation Pack			1·00	

Cylinder Nos.: Both values A1–1–1, B1–1–1.
Sheets: 50 (10×5).
Quantities sold: 8p. 1,060,259; 25p. 459,558.
Withdrawn: 30.6.79.

172 Mail Cutter, 1778–1827

173 *Flamer*, 1831–37

174 *Diana*, 1877–90

175 *Ibex*, 1891–1925

176 *Caesarea*, 1960–75

Bicentenary of England–Jersey Government Mail Packet Service

(Des Jersey P.O. Litho Harrison)

1978 (18 Oct). P 14½×14 (C).
197	**172**	6p. black, yellow-brown and greenish yellow	10	10
198	**173**	8p. black, dull yellowish green and pale yellow-green	15	10
199	**174**	10½p. black, ultramarine & cobalt	30	25
200	**175**	11p. blk, purple & pale rose-lilac	35	35
201	**176**	13p. black, Venetian red and pink	40	45
197/201 *Set of 5*			1·10	1·10
First Day Cover				1·40
Presentation Pack			1·50	

Plate Nos.: All values 1A, 1B (each×3).
Sheets: 50 (5×10).
Imprint: Right-hand corner, bottom margin.
Quantities sold: 6p. 1,157,597; 8p. 1,149,500; 10½p. 528,170; 11p. 468,589; 13p. 371,210.
Withdrawn: 31.10.79.

177 Jersey Calf

178 'Ansom Designette' (calf presented to the Queen, 27 June 1978)

Ninth World Jersey Cattle Bureau Conference

(Des Jersey P.O. and Questa. Litho Questa)

1979 (1 Mar). P 13½ (C).
202	**177**	6p. multicoloured	10	10
		a. Gold ptg double	£400	
203	**178**	25p. multicoloured	50	60
		a. Gold ptg double	£400	
202/3 *Set of 2*			60	65
First Day Cover				1·00
Presentation Pack			1·10	

Plate Nos.: Both values 1A, 1B, 1C, 1D, 1E, 1F (each×8).
Sheets: 20 (4×5).
Imprint: Right-hand corner, bottom margin.
Withdrawn: 29.2.80.

179 Jersey Pillar Box, c.1860

180 Clearing a Modern Jersey Post Box

181 Telephone Switchboard, c. 1900

182 Modern S.P.C. Telephone System

Europa. Communications

(Des Jennifer Toombs. Litho Questa)

1979 (1 Mar). Thin paper. P 14 (C).
204	**179**	8p. multicoloured	15	15
		a. Horiz pair. Nos. 204/5	50	60
		b. Thick paper	40	40
		ba. Horiz pair. Nos. 204b/5b	80	90
		c. Perf 14½ (thick paper)	30	30
		ca. Horiz pair. Nos. 204c/5c	60	70
		cb. Yellow omitted*		
205	**180**	8p. multicoloured	15	15
		b. Thick paper	40	40
		c. Perf 14½ (thick paper)	30	30
		cb. Pale rose-red omitted*		

206	**181**	10½p. multicoloured	15	15
		a. Horiz pair. Nos. 206/7.......................	50	70
		b. Thick paper	70	70
		ba. Horiz pair. Nos. 206b/7b...................	1·40	1·60
		c. Perf 14½	70	70
		ca. Horiz pair. Nos. 206c/7c....................	1·40	1·60
207	**182**	10½p. multicoloured	15	15
		b. Thick paper	70	70
		c. Perf 14½	70	70
		ca. Greenish blue omitted........................		

204/7 *Set of 4*	90	90
First Day Cover (Nos. 204/5, 206c/7c)...........		1·20
First Day Cover (Nos. 204/7)		
Presentation Pack (either perforation)	1·30	

Although both perforations were supplied to Jersey at the same time the 8p. perforated 14½ is not known used before early April.

*Nos. 204cb and 205cb appear to have only five arcs of colour in the background instead of the usual eight. They come from the same sheet.

Plate Nos.: Both values 1A, 1B, 1C, 1D, 1E, 1F, 1G, 1H (each×8).
Sheets: 20 (4×5) the two designs of each value were printed together, *se-tenant*, in horizontal pairs throughout
Imprint: Central, bottom margin.
Quantities sold: 8p. 5,149,852; 10½p. 3,047,039.
Withdrawn: 29.2.80.

183 Percival Mew Gull *Golden City*

184 de Havilland DHC-1 Chipmunk

185 Druine D.31 Turbulent

186 de Havilland DH.82A Tiger Moth

187 North American AT-6 Harvard

25th Anniversary of International Air Rally

(Des A. Theobald. Photo Courvoisier)

1979 (24 Apr). Granite paper. P 11½ (C).

208	**183**	6p. multicoloured	10	10
209	**184**	8p. multicoloured	25	20
210	**185**	10½p. multicoloured	25	30
211	**186**	11p. multicoloured	30	30
212	**187**	13p. multicoloured	40	40
208/12 *Set of 5*	1·10	1·10
First Day Cover		1·50
Presentation Pack...	1·60	

Cylinder Nos.: 13p. A1–1–1–1–1, B1–1–1–1–1, C1–1–1–1–1, D1–1–1–1–1; others A1–1–1–1, B1–1–1–1, C1–1–1–1, D1–1–1–1.
Sheets 20 (5×4).
Imprint: Central, bottom margin.
Quantities sold: 6p. 1,327,279; 8p. 1,338,234; 10½p. 433,127; 11p. 457,566; 13p. 426,528.
Withdrawn: 30.4.80.

188 'My First Sermon'

189 'Orphans'

190 'The Princes in the Tower'

191 'Christ in the House of His Parents'

Jersey Artists (3rd series). International Year of the Child and 150th Birth Anniversary of Sir John Millais (painter)

(Des Jersey P.O. and Courvoisier. Photo Courvoisier)

1979 (13 Aug). Granite paper. P 12×12½ (25p.) or 12×11½ (others), all comb.

213	**188**	8p. multicoloured	20	15
214	**189**	10½p. multicoloured	30	30
215	**190**	11p. multicoloured	30	30
216	**191**	25p. multicoloured	50	60
213/16 *Set of 4*	1·20	1·20
First Day Cover		1·50
Presentation Pack...	1·60	

Cylinder Nos.: 25p. A1–1–1–1, B1–1–1–1; others A1–1–1–1, B1–1–1–1, C1–1–1–1, D1–1–1–1.
Sheets: 20 (4×5) 25p. or (5×4) others.
Quantities sold: 8p. 1,187,969; 10½p. 953,826; 11p. 508,316; 25p. 463,234.
Withdrawn: 30.8.80.

192 Pink Pigeon

193 Orang-utan

194 Waldrapp Ibis

195 Lowland Gorilla

196 Rodriguez Flying Fox

Wildlife Preservation Trust (3rd series)

(Des Jennifer Toombs. Photo Courvoisier)

1979 (8 Nov). Granite paper. P 11½ (C).

217	**192**	6p. multicoloured	10	10
218	**193**	8p. multicoloured	20	15
219	**194**	11½p. multicoloured	30	30
220	**195**	13p. multicoloured	45	40
221	**196**	15p. multicoloured	45	40
217/21 *Set of 5*	1·20	1·20
First Day Cover		1·40
Presentation Pack...	1·60	

Cylinder Nos.: All values A1–1–1–1–1, B1–1–1–1–1, C1–1–1–1–1, D1–1–1–1–1.
Sheets: 20 (11½p. 4×5; others 5×4).
Imprint: Right-hand corner, bottom margin.
Quantities sold: 6p. 1,128,144; 8p. 1,080,889; 11½p. 559,534; 13p. 443,140; 15p. 433,115.
Withdrawn: 30.11.80.

197 Plan of Mont Orgueil

198 Plan of La Tour de St. Aubin

199 Plan of Elizabeth Castle

200 Map of Jersey showing Fortresses

Jersey Fortresses. Drawings by Thomas Phillips

(Litho Enschedé)

1980 (5 Feb). P 13×13½ (25p.) or 13½×13 (others), all comb.

222	**197**	8p. multicoloured	20	15
223	**198**	11½p. multicoloured	30	30
224	**199**	13p. multicoloured	30	30
225	**200**	25p. multicoloured	50	60
222/5 Set of 4			1·20	1·20
First Day Cover				1·40
Presentation Pack			1·60	

Pack Sheets: 20 (4×5).
Imprint: Right-hand corner, bottom margin.
Quantities sold: 8p. 665,647; 11½p. 363,246; 13p. 415,790; 25p. 379,743.
Withdrawn: 28.2.81.

201 Sir Walter Raleigh and Paul Ivy (engineer)

202 discussing Elizabeth Castle

203 Sir George Carteret receiving rights to Smith's Island, Virginia, from King Charles II

204 Lady Carteret, maid Jean Chevalier

Europa. Personalities. Links with Britain

(Des Jersey Post Office and Questa. Litho Questa)

1980 (6 May). P 14 (C).

226	**201**	9p. multicoloured	20	15
		a. Horiz pair. Nos. 226/7	40	50
227	**202**	9p. multicoloured	20	15
228	**203**	13½p. multicoloured	30	30
		a. Horiz pair. Nos. 228/9	60	80
229	**204**	13½p. multicoloured	30	30
226/9 Set of 4			90	1·20
First Day Cover				1·40
Presentation Pack			1·60	

Plate Nos.: Both values 1A, 1B, 1C, 1D, 1E, 1F (each×4).
Sheets: 20 (4×5). The two designs of each value were printed together, *se-tenant*, in horizontal pairs throughout, forming composite designs.
Imprint: Central, left-hand margin.
Quantities sold: 9p. 4,793,980; 13½p. 2,638,136.
Withdrawn: 31.5.81.

205 Planting   **206** Digging   **207** Weighbridge

Centenary of Jersey Royal Potato

(Des R. Granger Barrett. Litho Questa)

1980 (6 May). P 14 (C).

230	**205**	7p. multicoloured	20	20
231	**206**	15p. multicoloured	30	30
232	**207**	17½p. multicoloured	40	40
230/2 Set of 3			80	80
First Day Cover				1·00
Presentation Pack			1·20	

Plate Nos.: All values 1A, 1B, 1C, 1D, 1E, 1F (each×6).
Sheets: 20 (4×5).
Imprint: Central, left-hand margin.
Quantities sold: 7p. 1,379,048; 15p. 383,956; 17½p. 375,082.
Withdrawn: 31.5.81.

208 Three Lap Event

209 Jersey International Road Race

210 Motocross Scrambling

211 Sand Racing (saloon cars)

212 National Hill Climb

60th Anniversary of Jersey Motor-cycle and Light Car Club

(Des A. Theobald. Photo Courvoisier)

1980 (24 July). Granite paper. P 11½ (C).

233	**208**	7p. multicoloured	15	15
234	**209**	9p. multicoloured	20	15
235	**210**	13½p. multicoloured	30	30
236	**211**	15p. multicoloured	30	35
237	**212**	17½p. multicoloured	35	40
233/7 Set of 5			1·20	1·20
First Day Cover				1·60
Presentation Pack			1·70	

Cylinder Nos.: 7p., 15p. A1–1–1–1–1, B1–1–1–1–1, C1–1–1–1–1, D1–1–1–1–1; others A1–1–1–1, B1–1–1–1, C1–1–1–1, D1–1–1–1.
Sheets: 20 (5×4).
Imprint: Left-hand corner, bottom margin.
Quantities sold: 7p. 1,452,280; 9p. 1,426,548; 13½p. 384,861; 15p. 350,608; 17½p. 338,658.
Withdrawn: 31.7.81.

213 *Eye of the Wind*

214 Diving from Inflatable Dinghy

215 Exploration of Papua New Guinea

216 Captain Scott's *Discovery*

217 Using Aerial Walkways, Conservation Project, Sulawesi

218 *Eye of the Wind*, and Goodyear Aerospace Airship *Europa*

Operation Drake and 150th Anniversary of Royal Geographical Society (14p.)

(Des G. Drummond. Litho Questa)

1980 (1 Oct). P 14 (C).

238	**213**	7p. multicoloured		15	15
239	**214**	9p. multicoloured		20	20
240	**215**	13½p. multicoloured		30	30
241	**216**	14p. multicoloured		30	35
242	**217**	15p. multicoloured		35	40
		a. Black (face value and inscr) ptg double			
243	**218**	17½p. multicoloured		40	40
		a. Black (face value and inscr) ptg double			
238/43 *Set of 6*				1·50	1·70
First Day Cover					2·00
Presentation Pack				2·10	

Plate Nos.: All values 1A, 1B, 1C, 1D, 1E, 1F (each×6).
Sheets: 20 (5×4).
Imprint: Upper left-hand margin.
Quantities sold: 7p. 1,631,558; 9p. 1,071,684; 13½p. 432,201; 14p. 357,109; 15p. 357,922; 17½p. 351,215.
Withdrawn: 31.10.81.

219

220

221

222

Bicentenary of Battle of Jersey. Details of painting 'The Death of Major Peirson' by J. S. Copley

(Photo Courvoisier)

1981 (6 Jan). Granite paper. P 12½×12 (C).

244	**219**	7p. multicoloured		15	15
245	**220**	10p. multicoloured		25	25
246	**221**	15p. multicoloured		35	40
247	**222**	17½p. multicoloured		40	40
244/7 *Set of 4*				1·00	1·20
					1·40
First Day Cover					1·50
Presentation Pack				1·40	
MS248 144×97 mm. Nos. 244/7				1·40	1·60
First Day Cover					7·00

Stamps from No. **MS**248 are without white margins.
Cylinder Nos.: All values A1–1–1–1, B1–1–1–1.
Sheets: 20 (5×4).
Imprint: Right-hand corner, bottom margin.
Quantities sold: 7p. 997,416; 10p. 1,107,456; 15p. 367,971; 17½p. 359,794; miniature sheet 469,953.
Withdrawn: 31.1.82.

223 De Bagot

224 De Carteret

225 La Cloche

226 Dumaresq

227 Payn

228 Janvrin

229 Poingdestre

230 Pipon

231 Marett

232 Le Breton

233 Le Maistre

234 Bisson

235 Robin

236 Herault

237 Messervy

238 Fiott

239 Malet

240 Mabon

241 De St. Martin

242 Hamptonne

243 Badier   **244** L'Arbalestier   **245** Journeaulx   **246** Lempriere

247 Auvergne   **248** Remon

249 Jersey Crest and Map of Channel   **250** 'Queen Elizabeth II' (Norman Hepple)

Arms of Jersey Families

(Des Courvoisier (£5), G. Drummond (others). Litho Questa (½p. to £1). Photo Courvoisier (£5))

1981 (24 Feb)–**88**. Granite paper (£5). P 15×14 (16p., 17p., 18p., 19p., 26p., 75p.), 12½×12 (£5) or 14 (others), all comb.

249	223	½p. black, silver & turq-grn (a)	20	20
250	224	1p. multicoloured (a)	10	10
		a. Booklet pane of 6 (acf)	40	
		b. Perf 15×14 (o)	30	30
251	225	2p. multicoloured (a)	10	10
		a. Booklet pane of 6 (cf)	70	
		b. Perf 15×14 (io)	20	20
		ba. Booklet pane of 6 (l)	1·00	
252	226	3p. multicoloured (a)	10	15
		a. Booklet pane of 6 (a)	80	
		b. Perf 15×14 (ik)	15	15
		ba. Booklet pane of 6 (h)	1·00	
253	227	4p. black, silver and mauve (a)	15	15
		a. Perf 15×14 (k)	20	20
		ab. Booklet pane of 6 (mq)	1·00	
254	228	5p. multicoloured (a)	15	15
		a. Perf 15×14 (k)	30	30
255	229	6p. multicoloured (a)	20	20
		a. Perf 15×14 (k)	40	40
256	230	7p. multicoloured (a)	25	25
		a. Booklet pane of 6 (ac)	1·40	
257	231	8p. multicoloured (a)	30	30
		a. Booklet pane of 6 (f)	1·70	
258	232	9p. multicoloured (ae)	30	25
		a. Perf 15×14 (h)	40	40
		ab. Booklet pane of 6 (h)	2·50	
		ac. 'Ghost impression' from No. 261a*		
259	233	10p. multicoloured (a)	25	25
		a. Booklet pane of 6 (ac)	1·50	
		b. Perf 15×14 (l)	40	40
		ba. Booklet pane of 6 (l)	2·00	
260	234	11p. multicoloured (be)	30	30
		a. Booklet pane of 6 (f)	1·90	
		b. Perf 15×14 (m)	45	45
		ba. Booklet pane of 6 (m)	2·50	
261	235	12p. multicoloured (be)	35	30
		a. Perf 15×14 (hq)	50	50
		ab. Booklet pane of 6 (hq)	3·00	
262	236	13p. multicoloured (b)	35	35
		a. Perf 15×14 (i)	50	50
263	237	14p. multicoloured (b)	40	40
		a. Perf 15×14 (i)	40	40
		ab. Booklet pane of 6 (l)	2·40	
264	238	15p. multicoloured (b)	40	40
		a. Perf 15×14 (mo)	45	45
		ab. Booklet pane of 6 (m)	2·50	

265	239	16p. multicoloured (jo)	35	35
		a. Booklet pane of 6 (q)	2·20	
266	240	17p. multicoloured (j)	45	45
266a	241	18p. multicoloured (p)	50	50
266b	242	19p. multicoloured (p)	60	60
267	243	20p. black, silver and lemon (b)	50	50
		a. Perf 15×14 (k)	80	80
268	244	25p. black and dull blue (d)	45	45
268a	223	26p. black, silver and carmine (p)	50	50
269	245	30p. multicoloured (d)	50	60
		a. Perf 15×14 (k)	1·00	1·00
270	246	40p. multicoloured (d)	80	80
		a. Perf 15×14 (m)	1·50	1·40
271	247	50p. multicoloured (d)	1·00	1·00
		a. Perf 15×14 (m)	1·90	1·90
272	248	75p. multicoloured (n)	1·50	1·50
273	249	£1 multicoloured (d)	2·00	2·00
274	250	£5 multicoloured (g)	8·00	8·00
249/74 Set of 29..			18·00	18·00
First Day Covers (7)				20·00
Presentation Packs (4)			20·00	

*Examples of No. 258ac show an impression of the blue (shield) plate from the 12p. value. The error was caused by an impression of the 12p. plate remaining on the transfer roller.

No. 258a only occurs in the £2.16 stamp booklet issued 27 April 1984, No. 259b from the £3.12 booklet of 1 April 1986, No. 260b from the £3.60 booklet of 6 April 1987 and No. 261a from the £2.16 booklet of 27 April 1984 and the £3.84 booklet of 17 May 1988.

No. 252b first occurred in the £2.16 stamp booklet of 27 April 1984, but was subsequently issued in sheets.

Printings: (a) 24.2.81; (b) 28.7.81; (c) 1.12.81; (d) 23.2.82; (e) 11.6.82; (f) 19.4.83; (g) 17.11.83; (h) 27.4.84; (i) 15.11.84; (j) 25.10.85; (k) 4.3.86; (l) 1.4.86; (m) 6.4.87; (n) 23.4.87; (o) 12.1.88; (p) 26.4.88; (q) 17.5.88.

Plate and Cylinder Nos.: ½p., 20p. 1A, 1B, 1C, 1D, 1E, 1F, 1G, 1H (each×3); 6p., 11p., 12p., 13p., 14p., 50p., 75p. 1A, 1B, 1C, 1D, 1E, 1F, 1G, 1H (each×3); 10p. 1A, 1B, 1C, 1D, 1F, 1G, 1H (each×5), 2A–1A (×4), 2B–1B (×4), 2C–1C (×4), 2D–1D. (×4), 2E–1E (×4), 2F–1F (×4), 2G–1G (×4), 2H–1H (×4); 25p. 1A–1A, 1B–1B, 1C–C, 1D–1D., 1E–1E, 1F–1F, 1G–1G, 1H–1H; 26p. 1A, 1B, 1C, 1D, 1F, 1G, 1H (each×3); £1 1A, 1B, 1C, 1D, 1E, 1F, 1G, 1H (each×6); £5 A1–1–1–1, B1–1–1–1, C1–1–1–1, D1–1–1–1; others 1A, 1B, 1C, 1D, 1E, 1G, 1H (each×4).

Sheets: £1 25 (5×5); £5 10 (5×2); others 50 (10×5).

Imprint: Right–hand corner, bottom margin.

Withdrawn: 31.12.85 ½p.; 30.4.87 £1; 31.3.90 1p. to 10p.; 31.1.91 11p. to 20p.; 31.3.91 25p. to 75p.; 30.4.97 £5.

251 Knight of Hambye slaying Dragon   **252** Servant slaying Knight and awaiting Execution

253 St. Brelade celebrating Easter on Island   **254** Island revealing itself as Huge Fish

Europa. Folklore

(Des Jennifer Toombs. Litho Questa)

1981 (7 Apr). P 14½ (C).

275	251	10p. multicoloured	25	15
		a. Horiz pair. Nos. 275/6	60	70
276	252	10p. multicoloured	25	15
277	253	18p. multicoloured	30	30
		a. Horiz pair. Nos. 277/8	1·00	1·20
278	254	18p. multicoloured	30	30
275/8 Set of 4			1·40	1·70
First Day Cover				1·90
Presentation Pack			2·00	

Legends: 10p., Slaying of the Dragon of Lawrence by the Knight of Hambye; 18p. Voyages of St. Brelade.

Plate Nos.: 10p. 1A, 1B, 1C, 1D, 1E, 1F, 1G, 1H (each×6); 18p. 1A, 1B, 1C, 1D, 1E, 1F, 1G, 1H (each×5).

Sheets: 20 (4×5). The two designs of each value were each printed together, se-tenant, in horizontal pairs throughout .

Imprint: Central, left-hand margin.

Quantities sold: 10p. 3,459,902; 18p. 2,494,444.

Withdrawn: 30.4.82.

255 The Harbour by Gaslight

256 The Quay

257 Royal Square

258 Halkett Place

259 Central Market

150th Anniversary of Gas Lighting in Jersey

(Des R. Granger Barrett. Photo Courvoisier)

1981 (22 May). Granite paper. P 11½ (C).

279	**255**	7p. multicoloured	20	15
280	**256**	10p. multicoloured	25	25
281	**257**	18p. multicoloured	40	40
282	**258**	22p. multicoloured	45	45
283	**259**	25p. multicoloured	60	60
279/83 *Set of 5*			1·70	1·70
First Day Cover				1·90
Presentation Packs			2·00	

Cylinder Nos.: All values A1–1–1–1–1, B1–1–1–1–1, C1–1–1–1–1, D1–1–1–1–1.
Sheets: 20 (5×4).
Imprint: Left-hand corner, bottom margin.
Quantities sold: 7p. 1,433,090; 10p. 1,416,051; 18p. 384,043; 22p. 417,191; 25p. 333,402.
Withdrawn: 31.5.82.

260 Prince Charles and Lady Diana Spencer

Royal Wedding

(Des Jersey P.O. and Courvoisier. Photo Courvoisier)

1981 (28 July). Granite paper. P 11½ (C).

284	**260**	10p. multicoloured	20	20
285		25p. multicoloured	70	80
284/5 *Set of 2*			85	90
First Day Cover				2·25
Presentation Packs			2·00	

Cylinder Nos.: Both values A1–1–1–1–1, B1–1–1–1–1.
Sheets: 20 (5×4).
Imprint: Left-hand corner, bottom margin.
Quantities sold: 10p. 935,571; 25p. 580,597.
Withdrawn: 31.7.82.

261 Christmas Tree in Royal Square

262 East Window, Parish Church, St. Helier

263 Boxing Day Meet of Jersey Drag Hunt

Christmas

(Des A. Copp. Litho Questa)

1981 (29 Sept). P 14½ (C).

286	**261**	7p. multicoloured	25	20
287	**262**	10p. multicoloured	35	30
		a. Black (face value, inscr and choir) printed double	£180	
288	**263**	18p. multicoloured	50	50
286/8 *Set of 3*			1·00	90
First Day Cover				1·50
Presentation Pack			1·20	
Postcards (set of 3)			1·10	2·50

Plate Nos.: All values 1A, 1B, 1C, 1D, 1E, 1F, 1G, 1H (each×5).
Sheets: 20 (4×5).
Imprint: Central, left-hand margin.
Quantities sold: 7p. 1,437,626; 10p. 1,386,934; 18p. 422,693.
Withdrawn: 30.9.82.

264 Jersey, 16,000 B.C.

265 10,000 B.C.

266 7,000 B.C.

267 4,000 B.C.

Europa. History. Formation of Jersey

(Des A. Copp. Litho Questa)

1982 (20 Apr). P 14 (C).

289	**264**	11p. multicoloured	20	20
290	**265**	11p. multicoloured	20	20
291	**266**	19½p. multicoloured	50	50
292	**267**	19½p. multicoloured	50	50
289/92 *Set of 4*			1·20	1·20
First Day Cover				1·50
Presentation Pack			1·50	

Plate Nos.: All values 1A, 1B, 1C, 1D, 1E, 1F (each×6), 11p. (No. 289) also 1G, 1H (each×6).
Sheets: 20 (Nos. 289, 292, 4×5; others 5×4).
Imprint: Central, left-hand margin.
Quantities sold: 11p. (both designs) 3,414,424; 19½p. (both designs) 2,307,769.
Withdrawn: 30.4.83.

268 Rollo, Duke of Normandy, William the Conqueror and 'Clameur de Haro'

269 John of England, Philippe Auguste of France and Siege of Rouen

270 Jean Martell (brandy merchant), early Still and view of Cognac

271 Victor Hugo 'Le Rocher des Proscrits' (rock where he used to meditate) and Marine Terrace

272 Pierre Teilhard de Chardin (philosopher) and 'Maison Saint Louis' (science institute)

273 Père Charles Rey (scientist), anemotachymeter and The Observatory, St. Louis

Links with France

(Des R. Granger Barrett. Litho Questa)

1982 (11 June–7 Sept). P 14 (C).

293	**268**	8p. multicoloured	20	15
		a. Horiz pair. Nos. 293/4	50	60
		b. Booklet pane. Nos. 293/4 each×2 (7.9.82)	1·00	
294	**269**	8p. multicoloured	20	15
295	**270**	11p. multicoloured	30	20
		a. Horiz pair. Nos. 295/6	60	70
		b. Booklet pane. Nos. 295/6 each×2 (7.9.82)	1·50	
296	**271**	11p. multicoloured	30	20
297	**272**	19½p. multicoloured	45	30
		a. Horiz pair. Nos. 297/8	90	1·00
		b. Booklet pane. Nos. 297/8 each×2 (7.9.82)	2·20	
		c. Black (face value and inscr) printed double		
298	**273**	19½p. multicoloured	45	30
		c. Black (face value and inscr) printed double		
293/8	*Set of 6*		1·70	2·00
First Day Cover				2·25
Presentation Pack			2·40	

Each booklet pane has margins all round and text, in English or French, printed on the binding selvedge.

Nos. 297c and 298c come from an example of booklet pane No. 297b.

Plate Nos.: All values 1A, 1B, 1C, 1D (each×4).

Sheets: 20 (4×5). The two designs of each value were printed together, *se-tenant*, in horizontal pairs throughout.

Imprint: Central, left-hand margin.

Quantities sold (sheet stamps): 8p. (both designs) 2,019,854; 11p. (both designs) 1,914,536; 19½p. (both designs) 828,272.

Withdrawn: 30.6.83 (sheets).

274 Sir William Smith and Proclamation of King George V, Jersey, 1910

275 Sir William Smith and Lord Baden-Powell at Boys' Brigade Display, 1903

276 Boys' Brigade Band, Jersey Liberation Parade, 1945

277 Lord and Lady Baden-Powell in St. Helier, 1924

278 Scouts in Summer Camp, Jersey

Youth Organizations

(Des A. Theobald. Photo Courvoisier)

1982 (18 Nov). Granite paper. P 11½ (C).

299	**274**	8p. multicoloured	20	20
300	**275**	11p. multicoloured	20	20
301	**276**	24p. multicoloured	45	50
302	**277**	26p. multicoloured	60	60
303	**278**	29p. multicoloured	75	70
299/303 Set of 5			2·00	2·00
First Day Cover				2·50
Presentation Pack			2·40	

Nos. 299/303 were issued on the occasion of the 75th anniversary of the Boy Scout Movement, the 125th birth anniversary of Lord Baden-Powell and the centenary of the Boys' Brigade (1983).

Cylinder Nos.: All values A1–1–1–1–1, B1–1–1–1–1, C1–1–1–1–1, D1–1–1–1–1.

Sheets: 20 (11p., 26p. 5×4; others 4×5).

Imprint: Lower left-hand margin.

Quantities sold: 8p. 1,006,110; 11p. 1,006,206; 24p. 242,482; 26p. 255,359; 29p. 244,746.

Withdrawn: 30.11.83.

279 H.M.S. *Tamar* with H.M.S. *Dolphin* at Port Egmont

280 H.M.S. *Dolphin* and H.M.S. *Swallow* off Magellan Strait

281 Discovering Pitcairn Island

282 Carteret taking possession of English Cove, New Zealand

283 H.M.S. *Swallow* sinking a Pirate Ship, Macassar Strait

284 H.M.S. *Endymion* leading Convoy from West Indies

Jersey Adventurers (1st series). 250th Birth Anniv of Philippe de Carteret

(Des R. Granger Barrett. Litho Questa)

1983 (15 Feb). P 14×14½ (C).

304	**279**	8p. multicoloured	20	15
		a. Black (face value and inscr) printed double		
305	**280**	11p. multicoloured	25	15
		a. Black (face value and inscr) printed double		
306	**281**	19½p. multicoloured	40	40
307	**282**	24p. multicoloured	45	50
		a. Black (face value and inscr) printed double		
308	**283**	26p. multicoloured	50	50
		a. Black (face value and inscr) printed double		
309	**284**	29p. multicoloured	65	65
304/9 Set of 6			2·20	2·10

First Day Cover .... 2·75
Presentation Pack .... 3·50
   See also Nos. 417/21 and 573/8.
   Plate Nos.: All values 1A, 1B, 1C, 1D, 1E, 1F (each×6).
   Sheets: 20 (4×5).
   Imprint: Central, left-hand margin.
   Quantities sold: 8p. 983,227; 11p. 979,640; 19½p. 377,535; 24p. 264,595; 26p. 279,424; 29p. 254,023.
   Withdrawn: 29.2.84.

285 1969 5s. Legislative Chamber Definitive   **286** Royal Mace

287 1969 10s. Royal Court Definitive showing Green Border Error   **288** Bailiff's Seal

Europa. Great Works of Human Genius

(Des G. Drummond. Litho Questa)

1983 (19 Apr). P 14½ (C).
310	**285**	11p. multicoloured	25	30
		a. Horiz pair. Nos. 310/11	80	90
311	**286**	11p. multicoloured	25	30
312	**287**	19½p. multicoloured	35	40
		a. Horiz pair. Nos. 312/13	90	1·10
313	**288**	19½p. multicoloured	35	40
310/13	*Set of 4*		1·50	1·80
	First Day Cover			2·00
	Presentation Pack		2·20	

   Plate Nos.: Both values 1A, 1B, 1C, 1D, 1E, 1F (each×6).
   Sheets: 20 (4×5). The two designs of each value were printed together, *se-tenant*, in horizontal pairs throughout,
   Imprint: Central, left-hand margin.
   Quantities sold: 11p. (both designs) 2,973,691; 19½p. (both designs) 1,301,579.
   Withdrawn: 30.4.84.

289 Charles Le Geyt and Battle of Minden (1759)   **290** London to Weymouth Mail Coach

291 P.O. Mail Packet *Chesterfield* attacked by French Privateer   **292** Mary Godfray and the Hue Street Post Office

293 Mail Steamer leaving St. Helier Harbour

World Communications Year and 250th Birth Anniversary of Charles Le Geyt (first Jersey postmaster)

(Des A. Copp. Litho Questa)

1983 (21 June). P 14 (C).
314	**289**	8p. multicoloured	20	20
315	**290**	11p. multicoloured	30	30
316	**291**	24p. multicoloured	55	55
317	**292**	26p. multicoloured	65	65
318	**293**	29p. multicoloured	80	80
314/18	*Set of 5*		2·20	2·20
	First Day Cover			2·50
	Presentation Pack		2·75	

   Plate Nos.: All values 1A, 1B, 1C, 1D (each×5).
   Sheets: 20 (4×5).
   Imprint: Central, left-hand margin.
   Quantities sold: 8p. 1,136,008; 11p. 961,725; 24p. 244,690; 26p. 247,654; 29p. 230,325.
   Withdrawn: 30.6.84.

294 Assembly Emblem

13th General Assembly of the A.I.P.L.F. (Association Internationale des Parlementaires de Langue Francaise)

(Des A. Copp. Litho Questa)

1983 (21 June). P 14½ (C).
319	**294**	19½p. multicoloured	75	75
	First Day Cover			1·25
	Presentation Pack		1·20	

   Plate Nos.: 1A, 1B, 1C, 1D (each×5).
   Sheets: 20 (4×5).
   Imprint: Central, left-hand margin.
   Quantity sold: 312,304.
   Withdrawn: 30.6.84.

295 'Cardinal Newman'   **296** 'Incident in the French Revolution'   **297** 'Thomas Hardy'

298 'David with the Head of Goliath'

Jersey Artists (4th series). 50th Death Anniversary of Walter Ouless (artist)

(Des and photo Courvoisier)

1983 (20 Sept). Granite paper. P 11½ (C).
320	**295**	8p. multicoloured	30	30
321	**296**	11p. multicoloured	50	50
322	**297**	20½p. multicoloured	75	75
323	**298**	31p. multicoloured	1·00	1·00
320/3	*Set of 4*		2·40	2·40
	First Day Cover			2·75
	Presentation Pack		3·00	

   Cylinder Nos.: All values A1, B1 (each×5).
   Sheets: 20 (4×5) 31p. or (5×4) others.
   Imprint: Central, left-hand margin.
   Quantities sold: 8p. 1,054,200; 11p. 1,055,429; 20½p. 424,049; 31p. 216,128.
   Withdrawn: 30.9.84.

299 Golden Lion Tamarin   **300** Snow Leopard   **301** Jamacian Boa

302 Road Island Gecko   **303** Coscoroba Swan   **304** St. Lucia Amazon

Wildlife Preservation Trust (4th series)

(Des W. Oliver. Litho Questa)

1984 (17 Jan). P 13½×14 (C).

324	**299**	9p. multicoloured		25	25
325	**300**	12p. multicoloured		25	25
326	**301**	20½p. multicoloured		60	60
327	**302**	26p. multicoloured		75	75
328	**303**	28p. multicoloured		80	80
329	**304**	31p. multicoloured		1·00	1·00
324/9 *Set of 6*				3·25	3·25
First Day Cover					4·00
Presentation Pack				3·75	

Plate Nos.: 20½p. 1B, 1C, 1E, 1F (each×4); 28p. 1B, 1C, 1D, 1E, 1F (each×4); others 1A, 1B, 1C, 1D, 1E, 1F (each×4).
Sheets: 20 (5×4).
Imprint: Central, left-hand margin.
Quantities sold: 9p. 1,229,713; 12p. 1,365,973; 20½p. 266,444; 26p. 239,180; 28p. 255,205; 31p. 221,422.
Withdrawn: 31.1.85.

305 C.E.P.T. 25th Anniversary Logo

Europa

(Des J. Larrivière. Litho Questa)

1984 (12 Mar). P 14½×15 (C).

330	**305**	9p. cobalt, ultramarine & black		40	40
331		12p. light green, green and black		50	50
332		20½p. rose-lilac, dp magenta & blk		90	90
330/2 *Set of 3*				1·70	1·70
First Day Cover					2·00
Presentation Pack				2·00	

Plate Nos.: All values 1A, 1B, 1C, 1D, 1E, 1F (each×3).
Sheets: 20 (4×5).
Imprint: Central, left-hand margin.
Quantities sold: 9p. 1,352,245; 12p. 1,388,802; 20½p. 742,046.
Withdrawn: 31.3.85.

306 Map showing Commonwealth

Links with the Commonwealth

(Des A. Copp. Litho Questa)

1984 (12 Mar). Sheet 108×74 mm. P 15×14½ (C).

MS333	**306**	multicoloured	2·00	2·00
First Day Cover				2·50
Presentation Pack			2·75	

Quantity sold: 215,566.
Withdrawn: 31.3.85.

307 *Sarah Bloomshoft* at Demie de Pas Light, 1906   **308** *Hearts of Oak* and *Maurice Georges'* 1949

309 *Elizabeth Rippon* and *Hanna*, 1949

311 *Elizabeth Rippon* and *Bacchus*, 1973   **312** *Thomas James King* and *Cythara*, 1983

310 *Elizabeth Rippon* and *Santa Maria*, 1951

Jersey Lifeboats (1st series). Centenary of the Jersey R.N.L.I. Lifeboat Station

(Des G. Palmer. Litho Questa)

1984 (1 June). P 14½ (C).

334	**307**	9p. multicoloured		25	20
335	**308**	9p. multicoloured		25	20
336	**309**	12p. multicoloured		35	35
337	**310**	12p. multicoloured		35	35
338	**311**	20½p. multicoloured		60	70
339	**312**	20½p. multicoloured		60	70
334/9 *Set of 6*				2·10	2·30
First Day Cover					3·00
Presentation Pack				3·25	
Postcard (as No. 339)				1·20	2·20

See also Nos. 890/1.
Plate Nos.: All values 1A, 1B, 1C, 1D, 1E, 1F (each×5).
Sheets: 20 (4×5).
Imprint: Central, left-hand margin.
Quantities sold: 9p. (No. 3×4) 485,538; 9p. (No. 3×5) 435,647; 12p. (No. 336) 534,920; 12p. (No. 337) 518,807; 20½p. (No. 338) 298,935; 20½p. (No. 339) 290, 945.
Withdrawn: 30.6.85.

313 Bristol Type 170 Freighter Mk 32   **314** Airspeed A.S. 57 Ambassador 2

315 de Havilland DH.114 Heron 1B

316 de Havilland DH.89A Dragon Rapide

Jersey Aviation History (2nd series). 40th Anniversary of International Civil Aviation Organization

(Des G. Drummond. Litho Questa)

1984 (24 July). P 14 (C).

340	**313**	9p. multicoloured	20	15
341	**314**	12p. multicoloured	35	35
342	**315**	26p. multicoloured	75	75
343	**316**	31p. multicoloured	1·00	1·00
340/3	*Set of 4*		2·10	2·00
First Day Cover				2·75
Presentation Pack			3·25	

Plate Nos.: All values 1A, 1B, 1C, 1D (each×4).
Sheets: 20 (4×5).
Imprint: Central, left-hand margin.
Quantities sold: 9p. 563,394; 12p. 751,072; 26p. 262,640; 31p. 193,703.
Withdrawn: 31.7.85.

317 'Robinson Crusoe leaves the Wreck'

318 'Edinburgh Castle'

319 'Maori Village'

320 'Australian Landscape'

321 'Waterhouse's Corner, Adelaide'

322 'Captain Cook at Botany Bay'

Jersey Artists (5th series). Paintings by John Alexander Gilfillan. Links with Australia

(Des R. Granger Barrett. Photo Courvoisier)

1984 (21 Sept). Granite paper. P 11½×12 (C).

344	**317**	9p. multicoloured	25	20
345	**318**	12p. multicoloured	30	20
346	**319**	20½p. multicoloured	60	60
347	**320**	26p. multicoloured	70	70
348	**321**	28p. multicoloured	80	80
349	**322**	31p. multicoloured	80	80
344/9	*Set of 6*		3·00	3·00
First Day Cover				3·75
Presentation Pack			3·75	
Postcards (Set of 3 as Nos. 347/9)			1·70	4·50

Cylinder Nos.: All values A1, B1 (each×6).
Sheets: 20 (4×5).
Imprint: Central, left-hand margin.
Quantities sold: 9p. 541,384; 12p. 635,192; 20½p. 210,119; 26p. 234,836; 28p. 188,052; 31p. 192,353.
Withdrawn: 30.9.85.

323 'B.L.C. St. Helier'   **324** 'Oda Mt Bingham'

Christmas. Jersey Orchids (1st series)

(Photo Courvoisier)

1984 (15 Nov). Granite paper. P 12×11½ (C).

350	**323**	9p. multicoloured	40	40
351	**324**	12p. multicoloured	70	70
350/1	*Set of 2*		1·00	1·00
First Day Cover				1·50
Presentation Pack			1·50	

See also Nos. 433/7, 613/17, 892/7, 1143/**MS**1149, 1372/**MS**1378 and 1577/**MS**1538.
Cylinder Nos.: Both values A1, B1, C1, D1 (each×6).
Sheets: 20 (4×5).
Imprint: Central, left-hand margin.
Quantities sold: 9p. 1,197,796; 12p. 1,116,097.
Withdrawn: 30.11.85.

325 '*Hebe* off Corbière, 1874'

326 'The *Gaspe* engaging the *Diomede*'

327 'The Paddle-steamer *London* entering Naples, 1856'

328 'The *Rambler* entering Cape Town, 1840'

329 'St. Aubin's Bay from Mount Bingham, 1871'

Jersey Artists (6th series). Death Centenary of Philip John Ouless

(Photo Harrison)

1985 (26 Feb). P 14×15 (C).

352	**325**	9p. multicoloured	25	20
353	**326**	12p. multicoloured	30	30
354	**327**	22p. multicoloured	65	65
355	**328**	31p. multicoloured	1·00	1·00
356	**329**	34p. multicoloured	1·20	1·20
352/6 *Set of 5*			3·00	3·00
First Day Cover				3·50
Presentation Pack			4·00	

Cylinder Nos.: 31p. 1B (×5); others 1A, 1B (each×5) 9p. also 2A-2A-1A-2A-1A.
Sheets: 20 (4×5).
Imprint: Central, left-hand margin.
Quantities sold: 9p. 463,589; 12p. 405,133; 22p. 407,598; 31p. 193,772; 34p. 185,467.
Withdrawn: 28.2.86.

330 John Ireland (composer) and Faldouet Dolmen

331 Ivy St. Helier (actress) and His Majesty's Theatre, London

332 Claude Debussy (composer) and St. Aubin Fort

Europa. European Music Year

(Des Jennifer Toombs. Litho Questa)

1985 (23 Apr). P 14 (C).

357	**330**	10p. multicoloured	30	30
358	**331**	13p. multicoloured	40	40
359	**332**	22p. multicoloured	70	70
357/9 *Set of 3*			1·20	1·20
First Day Cover				1·60
Presentation Pack			2·00	

Nos.: 10p. 1A, 1B, 1C, 1D, 1E, 1F (each×5); 13p. 1A, 1C, 1D, 1E, 1F (each×5); 22p. 1A, 1B, 1D, 1E, 1F (each×5).
Sheets: 20 (4×5).
Imprint: Central, left-hand margin.
Quantities sold: 10p. 916,040; 13p. 766,179; 22p. 620,375.
Withdrawn: 30.4.86.

333 Girls' Brigade **334** Girl Guides (75th anniversary) **335** Prince Charles and Jersey Youth Service Activities Base

336 Sea Cadet Corps **337** Air Training Corps

International Youth Year

(Des A. Theobald. Litho Questa)

1985 (30 May). P 14½×14 (C).

360	**333**	10p. multicoloured	30	30
361	**334**	13p. multicoloured	40	40
362	**335**	29p. multicoloured	80	80
363	**336**	31p. multicoloured	90	90
364	**337**	34p. multicoloured	1·10	1·10
360/4 *Set of 5*			3·25	3·25
First Day Cover				3·50
Presentation Pack			3·75	

Plate Nos.: All values 1A, 1B, 1C, 1D, 1E, 1F (each×5).
Sheets: 20 (5×4).
Imprint: Central, left-hand margin.
Quantities sold: 10p. 943,351; 13p. 944,724; 29p. 175,365; 31p. 183,551; 34p. 175,842.
Withdrawn: 30.5.86.

338 *Duke of Normandy* at Cheapside **339** *Saddletank* at First Tower

340 *La Moye* at Millbrook **341** *St. Heliers* at St. Aubin

342 *St. Aubyns* at Corbière

Jersey Railway History (2nd series). Centenary of the first train to Corbière

(Des G. Palmer. Photo Courvoisier)

1985 (16 July). Granite paper. P 11½ (C).

365	**338**	10p. multicoloured	35	35
366	**339**	13p. multicoloured	40	40
367	**340**	22p. multicoloured	80	80
368	**341**	29p. multicoloured	95	95
369	**342**	34p. multicoloured	1·00	1·00
365/9 *Set of 5*			3·25	3·25
First Day Cover				3·50
Presentation Pack			4·00	

Cylinder Nos.: 10p., 13p. A1, B1 (each×5); others A1 (×5).
Sheets: 20 (4×5).
Imprint: Central, left-hand margin.
Quantities sold: 10p. 708,912; 13p. 706,189; 22p. 249,659; 29p. 179,849; 34p. 179,977.
Withdrawn: 31.7.86.

343 Memorial Window to Revd. James Hemery (former Dean) and St. Helier Parish Church

344 Judge Francis Jeune, Baron St. Helier, and Houses of Parliament

345 Silverware by Pierre Amiraux

346 Francis Voisin (merchant) and Russian Port

347 Robert Brohier, Schweppes Carbonation Plant and Bottles

348 George Ingouville, V.C., R.N., and Attack on Viborg

300th Anniversary of Huguenot Immigration

(Des R. Granger Barrett. Litho Questa)

1985 (10 Sept). P 14 (C).

370	**343**	10p. multicoloured	30	30
		a. Booklet pane of 4	1·20	
371	**344**	10p. multicoloured	30	30
		a. Booklet pane of 4	1·20	
372	**345**	13p. multicoloured	40	40
		a. Booklet pane of 4	1·60	
373	**346**	13p. multicoloured	40	40
		a. Booklet pane of 4	1·60	
		ab. Black (face value and inscr) printed double	55	50
374	**347**	22p. multicoloured	55	50
		a. Booklet pane of 4	2·20	
		b. Black (inscr) printed double		
375	**348**	22p. multicoloured	55	50
		a. Booklet pane of 4	2·20	
370/5 *Set of 6*			2·20	2·20
First Day Cover				2·50
Presentation Pack			2·75	

Each booklet pane has margins all round and text printed on the binding selvedge.
Plate Nos.: 13p. (No. 372) 1A, 1B, 1C, 1D (each×4); 22p. (No. 375) 1A, 1C, 1D (each×5); others 1A, 1B, 1C, 1D (each×5).

Sheets: 20 (4×5).
Imprint: Central, left-hand margin.
Quantities sold (sheets): 10p. (No. 370) 308,085; 10p. (No. 371) 310,475; 13p. (No. 372) 488,224; 13p. (No. 373) 477,764; 22p. (No. 374) 259,921; 22p. (No. 375) 253,607.
Withdrawn: 30.9.86 (sheets).

349 Howard Davis Hall, Victoria College

350 Racing Schooner *Westward*

351 Howard Davis Park, St. Helier

352 Howard Davis Experimental Farm, Trinity

Thomas Davis (philanthropist) Commemoration

(Des A. Copp. Litho Cartor)

1985 (25 Oct). P 13½ (C).

376	**349**	10p. multicoloured	35	35
377	**350**	13p. multicoloured	50	50
378	**351**	31p. multicoloured	80	80
379	**352**	34p. multicoloured	90	90
376/9 *Set of 4*			2·30	2·30
First Day Cover				2·75
Presentation Pack			3·00	

Plate Nos.: 10p. 1A, 1B, 1C, 1D (each×5); 13p. 2A, 2B, 2C, 2d. (each×5); 31p. 3A, 3B, 3C, 3D. (each×5); 34p. 4A, 4B, 4C, 4D. (each×5).
Sheets: 20 (4×5).
Imprint: Central, left-hand margin.
Quantities sold: 10p. 939,104; 13p. 831,351; 31p. 170,020; 34p. 156,653.
Withdrawn: 31.10.86.

353 *Amaryllis belladonna* (Pandora Sellars)

354 'A Jersey Lily' (Lily Langtry) (Sir John Millais)

Jersey Lilies

(Des C. Abbott. Litho Questa)

1986 (28 Jan). P 15×14½ (C).

380	**353**	13p. multicoloured	45	45
381	**354**	34p. multicoloured	1·00	1·10
380/1	*Set of 2*		1·40	1·50
First Day Cover				2·00
Presentation Pack			2·20	
MS382	140×96 mm. Nos. 380×4 and 381		2·75	3·00
First Day Cover				6·50
Presentation Pack			4·00	

Plate Nos.: 13p. 1A, 1B, 1C, 1D, 1E, 1F, 1G, 1H (each×6); 34p. 1A, 1B, 1C, 1D (each×5).
Sheets: 20 (4×5); (5×4) 34p.
Imprint: Central, left-hand margin.
Quantities sold: 13p. 444,175; 34p. 169,811; miniature sheet 157,575.
Withdrawn: 31.1.87.

355 King Harold, Wiliam of Normandy and Halley's Comet, 1066 (from Bayeux Tapestry)

356 Lady Carteret, Edmond Halley, Map and Comet

357 Aspects of Communications in 1910 and 1986 on TV Screens

Appearance of Halleys Comet

(Des Jennifer Toombs. Litho Cartor)

1986 (4 Mar). P 13½×13 (C).

383	**355**	10p. multicoloured	35	35
384	**356**	22p. multicoloured	75	75
385	**357**	31p. multicoloured	90	1·10
383/5	*Set of 3*		1·80	2·00
First Day Cover				2·40
Presentation Pack			2·75	

Plate Nos.: 10p., 22p. 1A, 1B, 1C, 1D (each×5); 31p. 1A, 1B, 1C, 1D (each×6).
Sheets: 20 (4×5).
Imprint: Central, left-hand margin.
Quantities sold: 10p. 552,062; 22p. 245,111; 31p. 182,390.
Withdrawn: 31.3.87.

358 Dwarf Pansy

359 Sea Stock

360 Sand Crocus

Europa. Environmental Conservation

(Des Pandora Sellars. Litho Questa)

1986 (21 Apr). P 14½×14 (C).

386	**358**	10p. multicoloured	35	35
387	**359**	14p. multicoloured	45	45
388	**360**	22p. multicoloured	70	70
386/8	*Set of 3*		1·40	1·40
First Day Cover				1·70
Presentation Pack			2·20	

Plate Nos.: 22p. 1A, 1B, 1C, 1E, 1F (each×5); others 1A, 1B, 1C, 1D, 1E, 1F (each×5).
Sheets: 20 (5×4).
Imprint: Central, left-hand margin.
Quantities sold: 10p. 892,977; 14p. 892,631; 22p. 612,513.
Withdrawn: 30.4.87.

361 Queen Elizabeth II (from photo by Karsh)

60th Birthday of Queen Elizabeth II

(Photo Courvoisier)

1986 (21 Apr). Granite paper. P 14½ (C).

389	**361**	£1 multicoloured	2·50	2·75
First Day Cover				3·25
Presentation Pack			3·00	

No. 389 was retained in use as part of the current definitive series until replaced by No. 500.
For a £2 value in this design see No. 491b.
Cylinder Nos.: A1, B1, C1, D1 (each×6).
Sheets: 20 (4×5).
Imprint: Central, left-hand margin.
Quantity sold: 431,591.
Withdrawn: 31.5.90.

362 Le Rât Cottage

363 The Elms (Trust Headquarters)

364 Morel Farm

365 Quétivel Mill

366 La Vallette

50th Anniversary of the National Trust for Jersey

(Des A. Copp. Litho Cartor)

1986 (17 June). P 13½×13 (C).

390	**362**	10p. multicoloured	25	20
391	**363**	14p. multicoloured	35	30
392	**364**	22p. multicoloured	65	65
393	**365**	29p. multicoloured	80	80
394	**366**	31p. multicoloured	90	90
390/4	*Set of 5*		2·60	2·60

First Day Cover .... 3·00
Presentation Pack .... 3·75
    Plate Nos.: All values 1A, 1B, 1C, 1D (each×5).
    Sheets: 20 (4×5).
    Imprint: Central, left-hand margin.
    Quantities sold: 10p. 946,735; 14p. 919,823; 22p. 427,370; 29p. 173,763; 31p. 178,353.
    Withdrawn: 30.6.87.

367 Prince Andrew and Miss Sarah Ferguson

Royal Wedding

(Des A. Copp. Litho Cartor)

1986 (23 July). P 13½ (C).

395	**367**	14p. multicoloured	35	35
396		40p. multicoloured	1·10	1·10

395/6 *Set of 2* .... 1·30   1·30
First Day Cover .... 2·00
Presentation Pack .... 2·20
    Plate Nos.: Both values 1A, 1B, 1C, 1D (each×6).
    Sheets: 20 (5×4).
    Imprint: Central, left-hand margin.
    Quantities sold: 14p. 991,943; 40p. 267,312.
    Withdrawn: 31.7.87.

368 'Gathering Vraic'   **369** 'Driving Home in the Rain'

370 'The Miller'   **371** 'The Joy Ride'

372 'Tante Elizabeth'

Jersey Artists (7th series). Birth Centenary of Edmund Blampied

(Des A. Copp. Litho Questa)

1986 (28 Aug). P 14 (C).

397	**368**	10p. multicoloured	25	25
398	**369**	14p. black, brownish grey & lt bl..........	40	40
399	**370**	29p. multicoloured	75	75
400	**371**	31p. black, brownish grey and pale orange	90	90
401	**372**	34p. multicoloured	95	95

397/401 *Set of 5* .... 3·00   3·00
First Day Cover .... 3·75
Presentation Pack .... 4·00
    Plate Nos.: 14p., 31p. 1A, 1B, 1C, 1D (each×3); others 1A, 1B, 1C, 1D (each×5).
    Sheets: 20 (4×5).
    Imprint: Central, left-hand margin.
    Quantities sold: 10p. 885,979; 14p. 675,290; 29p. 163,085; 31p. 157,559; 34p. 151,128.
    Withdrawn: 31.8.87.

373 Island Map on Jersey Lily, and Dove holding Olive Branch   **374** Mistletoe Wreath encircling European Robin and Dove

375 Christmas Cracker releasing Dove

Christmas. International Year of Peace

(Des G. Taylor. Litho Questa)

1986 (4 Nov). P 14½×14 (C).

402	**373**	10p. multicoloured	30	25
403	**374**	14p. multicoloured	50	40
404	**375**	34p. multicoloured	1·10	90

402/4 *Set of 3* .... 1·75   1·40
First Day Cover .... 2·00
Presentation Pack .... 2·00
    Plate Nos.: All values 1A, 1B, 1C, 1D, 1E, 1F (each×6).
    Sheets: 20 (5×4).
    Imprint: Central, left-hand margin.
    Quantities sold: 10p. 947,614; 14p. 940,123; 34p. 169,269.
    Withdrawn: 30.11.87.

Post Office Yearbook

1986 (4 Nov). Comprises Nos. 380/404 (price £11).
Yearbook .... 45·00
    Withdrawn: 31.1.88.

376 *Westward* under Full Sail   **377** T. B. Davis at the Helm

378 *Westward* overhauling *Britannia*

379 *Westward* fitting-out at St. Helier

Racing Schooner *Westward*

(Des A. Copp. Litho Cartor)

1987 (15 Jan). P 13½ (C).

405	**376**	10p. multicoloured	40	35
406	**377**	14p. multicoloured	50	55
407	**378**	31p. multicoloured	95	95
408	**379**	34p. multicoloured	95	95
405/8	*Set of 4*		2·50	2·50
	First Day Cover			2·75
	Presentation Pack		3·75	

Plate Nos.: All values 1A, 1B, 1C, 1D (each×5).
Sheets: 20 (4×5).
Imprint: Central, left-hand margin.
Quantites sold: 10p. 519,330; 14p. 370,229; 31p. 173,046; 34p. 158,754.
Withdrawn: 31.1.88.

380 de Havilland D.H.86 Dragon Express *Belcroute Bay*

381 Boeing 757 and Douglas DC-9-155

382 Britten Norman 'long nose' Trislander and Islander

383 Shorts 330 and Vickers Viscount 800

384 B.A.C. One Eleven 500 and Handley Page H.P.R.7 Dart Herald

Jersey Aviation History (3rd series). 50th Anniversary of Jersey Airport

(Des G. Palmer. Litho Questa)

1987 (3 Mar). P 14 (C).

409	**380**	10p. multicoloured	30	30
410	**381**	14p. multicoloured	45	45
411	**382**	22p. multicoloured	55	50
412	**383**	29p. multicoloured	90	90
413	**384**	31p. multicoloured	95	95
409/13	*Set of 5*		2·80	2·80
	First Day Cover			3·75
	Presentation Pack		3·75	

Plate Nos.: All values 1A, 1B, 1C, 1D (each×4).
Sheets: 20 (4×5).
Imprint: Central, left-hand margin.
Quantities sold: 10p. 313,733; 14p. 281,226; 22p. 368,486; 29p. 155,159; 31p. 167,709.
Withdrawn: 31.3.88.

385 St. Mary and St. Peter's Roman Catholic Church

386 Villa Devereux St. Brelade

387 Fort Regent Leisure Centre, St. Helier

Europa. Modern Architecture

(Des A. Copp. Litho Questa)

1987 (23 Apr). P 15×14 (C).

414	**385**	11p. multicoloured	30	30
415	**386**	15p. multicoloured	45	45
416	**387**	22p. multicoloured	70	75
414/16	*Set of 3*		1·30	1·40
	First Day Cover			2·00
	Presentation Pack		2·20	

Plate Nos.: 11p., 15p. 1A, 1B, 1C, 1D, 1E, 1F, 1G, 1H, 1I, 1J (each×6); 22p. 1A, 1B, 1C, 1D, 1E, 1F, 1G, 1H (each×6).
Sheets: 10 (2×5).
Imprint: Central, left-hand margin.
Quantities sold: 11p. 847,735; 15p. 883,825; 22p. 467,615.
Withdrawn: 30.4.88.

388 H.M.S. *Racehorse* and H.M.S. *Carcass* (bomb-ketches) trapped in Arctic

389 H.M.S. *Alarm* on Fire, Rhode Island

390 H.M.S. *Arethusa* wrecked off Ushant

391 H.M.S. *Rattlesnake* stranded on Isle de Trinidad

392 Mont Orgueil Castle and Fishing Boats

Jersey Adventurers (2nd series). Philippe D'Auvergne

(Des R. Granger Barrett. Litho Questa)

1987 (9 July). P 14 (C).

417	**388**	11p. multicoloured	30	30
418	**389**	15p. multicoloured	40	45
419	**390**	29p. multicoloured	70	75
420	**391**	31p. multicoloured	80	90
421	**392**	34p. multicoloured	85	95
417/21	*Set of 5*		2·75	3·00
	First Day Cover			3·25
	Presentation Pack		4·25	

See also Nos. 501/6 and 539/44.

Plate Nos.: All values 1A, 1B, 1C, 1D (each×4).
Sheets: 20 (4×5).
Imprint: Central, left-hand margin.
Quantities sold: 11p. 694,506; 15p. 897,162; 29p. 138,711; 31p. 144,518; 34p. 140,968.
Withdrawn: 31.7.88.

393 Grant of Lands to Normandy, 911 and 933

394 Edward the Confessor and Duke Robert I of Normandy landing on Jersey, 1030

395 King William's Coronation, 1066, and Fatal Fall, 1087

396 Death of William Rufus, 1100, and Battle of Tinchebrai, 1106

397 Civil War between Matilda and Stephen, 1135–41

398 Henry inherits Normandy, 1151: John asserts Ducal Rights in Jersey, 1213

900th Death Anniversary of William the Conqueror

(Des Jennifer Toombs, Litho Cartor)

1987 (9 Sept–16 Oct). P 13½ (C).

422	**393**	11p. multicoloured (a)	30	30
		a. Booklet pane of 4 (b)	1·20	
423	**394**	15p. multicoloured (a)	35	35
		a. Booklet pane of 4 (b)	1·40	
424	**395**	22p. multicoloured (a)	70	65
		a. Booklet pane of 4 (b)	2·75	
425	**396**	29p. multicoloured (a)	75	75
		a. Booklet pane of 4 (b)	3·00	
426	**397**	31p. multicoloured (a)	85	85
		a. Booklet pane of 4 (b)	3·25	
427	**398**	34p. multicoloured (a)	95	95
		a. Booklet pane of 4 (b)	3·75	
422/7 *Set of 6*			3·60	3·60
First Day Cover				3·75
Presentation Pack			4·50	

Each booklet pane has margins all round and text printed on the binding selvedge.
Printings: (a) 9.9.87; (b) 16.10.87.
Plate Nos.: All values 1A, 1B, 1C, 1D (each×6).
Sheets: 20 (4×5).
Imprint: Central, left-hand margin.
Quantities sold (sheets): 11p. 869,726; 15p. 968,815; 22p. 217,160; 29p. 139,905; 31p. 147,527; 34p. 143,684.
Withdrawn: 30.9.88 (sheets).

399 'Grosnez Castle'   **400** 'St. Aubin's Bay'

401 'Mont Orgueil Castle'   **402** 'Town Fort and Harbour, St. Helier'

403 'The Hermitage'

Christmas. Jersey Artists (8th series). Paintings by John Le Capelain

(Photo Courvoisier)

1987 (3 Nov). Granite paper. P 11½ (C).

428	**399**	11p. multicoloured	35	30
429	**400**	15p. multicoloured	50	50
430	**401**	22p. multicoloured	65	65
431	**402**	31p. multicoloured	90	80
432	**403**	34p. multicoloured	1·00	1·00
428/32 *Set of 5*			3·00	3·00
First Day Cover				3·75
Presentation Pack			4·00	

Cylinder Nos.: 11p., 15p., 22p. A1, B1 (each×6); 31p., 34p. A1 (×6).
Sheets: 20 (5×4).
Imprint: Central, left-hand margin.
Quantities sold: 11p. 951,916; 15p. 874,209; 22p. 371,992; 31p. 154,824; 34p. 145,550.
Withdrawn: 30.11.88.

Post Office Yearbook

1987 (3 Nov). Comprises Nos. 272 and 405/32 (price £11.50).
Yearbook .... 38·00
Withdrawn: 28.2.89.

404 *Cymbidium pontac*

405 Odontioda Eric Young

406 *Lycaste auburn* Seaford and Ditchling

407 *Odontoglossum* St. Brelade

408 *Cymbidium mavourneen* Jester

Jersey Orchids (2nd series)

(Litho Questa)

1988 (12 Jan). P 14 (C).

433	**404**	11p. multicoloured	30	35
434	**405**	15p. multicoloured	45	45
435	**406**	29p. multicoloured	75	75
436	**407**	31p. multicoloured	80	80
437	**408**	34p. multicoloured	95	95
433/7 *Set of 5*			3·00	3·00
First Day Cover				3·50
Presentation Pack			3·75	

Plate Nos.: All values 1A, 1B, 1C, 1D (each×5).
Sheets: 20 (4×5) 11p, 29p, 34p.; (5×4) 15p, 31p.
Imprint: Central, left-hand margin.
Quantities sold: 11p. 558,185; 15p. 374,117; 29p. 143,613; 31p. 162,096; 34p. 151,193.
Withdrawn: 31.1.89.

409 Labrador Retriever

410 Wire-haired Dachshund

411 Pekingese

412 Cavalier King Charles Spaniel

413 Dalmatian

Centenary of Jersey Dog Club

(Des P. Layton. Litho Questa)

1988 (2 Mar). P 14 (C).

438	**409**	11p. multicoloured	35	40
439	**410**	15p. multicoloured	45	60
440	**411**	22p. multicoloured	70	80
441	**412**	31p. multicoloured	90	1·00
442	**413**	34p. multicoloured	1·00	1·00
438/42 *Set of 5*			3·00	3·50
First Day Cover				3·75
Presentation Pack			4·25	

Plate Nos.: All values 1A, 1B, 1C, 1D (each×4).
Sheets: 20 (4×5).
Imprint: Central, left-hand margin.
Quantities sold: 11p. 371,583; 15p. 374,953; 22p. 178,132; 31p. 154,530; 34p. 146,628.
Withdrawn: 31.3.89.

414 de Havilland DHC-7 (Dash Seven), London Landmarks and Jersey Control Tower

415 Weather Radar and Jersey Airport Landing System

416 Hydrofoil, St. Malo, and Elizabeth Castle, St. Helier

417 Port Control Tower and Jersey Radio Maritime Communication Centre, La Moye

Europa. Transport and Communications

(Des A. Copp. Litho Cartor)

1988 (26 Apr). P 14×13½ (horiz) or 13½×14 (vert), both comb.

443	**414**	16p. multicoloured	40	45
444	**415**	16p. multicoloured	40	45
445	**416**	22p. multicoloured	75	75
446	**417**	22p. multicoloured	75	75
443/6 *Set of 4*			2·10	2·20
First Day Cover				2·50
Presentation Pack			3·00	

Plate Nos.: Nos. 443/4, 446 1A, 1B, 1C, 1D (each×5); No. 445 1A, 1B, 1C, 1D (each×6).
Sheets: 20 (4×5) Nos. 443, 445; (5×4) Nos. 444, 446.
Imprint: Central, left-hand margin.
Quantities sold: 16p. (No. 443) 881,324; 16p. (No. 444) 865,868; 22p. (No. 445) 509,086; 22p. (No. 446) 510,104.
Withdrawn: 30.4.89.

418 Rodriguez Fody

419 Volcano Rabbit

420 White-faced Marmoset

421 Ploughshare Tortoise

422 Mauritius Kestrel

Wildlife Preservation Trust (5th series)

(Des W. Oliver. Litho Cartor)

1988 (6 July). P 13½×14 (vert) or 14×13½ (horiz), both comb.

447	**418**	12p. multicoloured	40	45
448	**419**	16p. multicoloured	50	50
449	**420**	29p. multicoloured	90	1·00
450	**421**	31p. multicoloured	1·00	1·10
451	**422**	34p. multicoloured	1·10	1·20
447/51 *Set of 5*			3·50	3·75
First Day Cover				4·50
Presentation Pack			4·50	

Plate Nos.: All values 1A, 1B, 1C, 1D (each×6).
Sheets: 20 (5×4) 12p., 29p., 34p.; (4×5) 16p., 31p.
Imprint: Central, left-hand margin.
Quantities sold: 12p. 875,722; 16p. 969,800; 29p. 146,567; 31p. 155,348; 34p. 151,723.
Withdrawn: 31.7.89.

423 Rain Forest Leaf Frog, Costa Rica

424 Archaeological Survey, Peru

425 Climbing Glacier, Chile

426 Red Cross Centre, Solomon Islands

427 Underwater Exploration, Australia

428 *Zebu* (brigantine) returning to St. Helier

Operation Raleigh

(Des V. Ambrus. Photo Courvoisier)

1988 (27 Sept). Granite paper. P 12 (C).

452	**423**	12p. multicoloured	35	25
453	**424**	16p. multicoloured	40	40
454	**425**	22p. multicoloured	60	60
455	**426**	29p. multicoloured	75	75
456	**427**	31p. multicoloured	80	90
457	**428**	34p. multicoloured	1·00	1·00
452/7 *Set of 6*			3·50	3·50
First Day Cover				3·75
Presentation Pack			4·50	

No. 455 also commemorates the 40th anniversary of the World Health Organization.
Cylinder Nos.: All values A1 (×5).
Sheets: 20 (5×4).
Imprint: Central, left-hand margin.
Quantities sold: 12p. 706,594; 16p. 507,077; 22p. 226,791; 29p. 127,647; 31p. 127,658; 34p. 128,055.
Withdrawn: 30.9.89.

429 St. Clement

430 St. Ouen

431 St. Brelade

432 St. Lawrence

Christmas. Jersey Parish Churches (1st series)

(Des P. Layton. Litho BDT)

1988 (15 Nov). P 13½ (C).

458	**429**	12p. multicoloured	30	15
459	**430**	16p. multicoloured	45	30
460	**431**	31p. multicoloured	90	90
461	**432**	34p. multicoloured	95	95
458/61 *Set of 4*			2·20	2·20
First Day Cover				2·75
Presentation Pack			3·75	
Postcards (set of 4)			2·00	5·50

See also Nos. 535/8 and 597/600.
Plate Nos.: All values 1A, 1B, 1C, 1D (each×5).
Sheets: 20 (4×5).
Imprint: Central, left-hand margin.
Quantities sold: 12p. 964,161; 16p. 917,883; 31p. 170,477; 34p. 159,688.
Withdrawn: 30.11.89.

Post Office Yearbook

1988 (15 Nov). Comprises Nos. 266a/b, 268a and 433/61 (price £11.50).

Yearbook	42·00

Withdrawn: 23.10.89.

433 Talbot Type 4 CT Tourer, 1912

434 De Dion Bouton Type 1-D, 1920

435 Austin 7 'Chummy' 1926

436 Ford 'Model T', 1926

437 Bentley 8 Litre, 1930

438 Cadillac '452A-V16 Fleetwood Sports Phaeton', 1931

Vintage Cars (1st series)

(Des A. Copp. Litho Questa)

1989 (31 Jan). P 14 (C).

462	**433**	12p. multicoloured	35	30
463	**434**	16p. multicoloured	50	45
464	**435**	23p. multicoloured	65	55
		a. Black (inscr etc) printed double		
465	**436**	30p. multicoloured	90	80
466	**437**	32p. multicoloured	90	1·00
467	**438**	35p. multicoloured	1·00	1·00
462/7 Set of 6			3·75	3·75
First Day Cover				4·25
Presentation Pack			4·50	

See also Nos. 591/6, 905/10 and 1532/7.
Plate Nos.: 12p., 30p. 1A, 1B (each×4); 16p., 32p. 1C, 1D (each×4); 23p., 35p. 1A, 1B, 1C, 1D (each×4).
Sheets: 20 (4×5).
Imprint: Central, left-hand margin.
Quantities sold: 12p. 253,257; 16p. 230,695; 23p. 228,895; 30p. 130,974; 32p. 144,798; 35p. 148,189.
Withdrawn: 31.1.90.

439 Belcroute Bay

440 High Street, St. Aubin

441 Royal Jersey Golf Course

442 Portelet Bay

443 Les Charrières D'Anneport

444 St. Helier Marina

445 Sand Yacht Racing, St. Ouen's Bay

446 Rozel Harbour

447 St. Aubin's Harbour

448 Jersey Airport

449 Corbière Lighthouse

450 Val de la Mare

451 Elizabeth Castle

452 Greve de Lecq

453 Samarès Manor

454 Bonne Nuit Harbour

455 Grosnez Castle

456 Augrès Manor

457 Central Market

458 St. Brelades Bay

459 St. Ouen's Manor

460 La Hougue Bie

461 Mont Orgueil Castle

462 Royal Square, St. Helier

463 Queen Elizabeth II (from photo by Karsh)

464 Arms of King George VI

Jersey Scenes

(Des G. Drummond (1p. to 75p.). Photo Courvoisier (£2), Litho Questa (£4), BDT (others))

1989 (21 Mar)–**95**. P 11½×12 (£2), 15×14 (£4) or 13×13½ (others), all comb.

468	**439**	1p. multicoloured (a)	10	10
469	**440**	2p. multicoloured (a)	10	10
470	**441**	4p. multicoloured (a)	10	10
		a. Booklet pane of 6 with margins all round (d)	60	
471	**442**	5p. multicoloured (a)	10	15
		a. Booklet pane of 6 with margins all round (f)	75	
472	**443**	10p. multicoloured (a)	30	30
473	**444**	13p. multicoloured (a)	40	45
474	**445**	14p. multicoloured (ae)	40	45
		a. Booklet pane of 6 with margins all round (d)	2·40	
		b. Booklet pane of 8 with margins all round (i)	3·20	
475	**446**	15p. multicoloured (ae)	45	50
		a. Booklet pane of 6 with margins all round (f)	2·50	
476	**447**	16p. multicoloured (ah)	50	55
		a. Booklet pane of 8 with margins all round (i)	3·50	
477	**448**	17p. multicoloured (aj)	50	55
478	**449**	18p. multicoloured (akm)	55	60
		a. Booklet pane of 6 with margins all round (d)	3·00	
479	**450**	19p. multicoloured (ano)	55	60
480	**451**	20p. multicoloured (ae)	45	45
		a. Booklet pane of 6 with margins all round (f)	2·50	
481	**452**	21p. multicoloured (b)	50	55
482	**453**	22p. multicoloured (bh)	45	50
		a. Booklet pane of 8 with margins all round (i)	3·50	
483	**454**	23p. multicoloured (bjkmo)	75	55
484	**455**	24p. multicoloured (b)	60	60
485	**456**	25p. multicoloured (b)	70	75
486	**457**	26p. multicoloured (bh)	75	80
487	**458**	27p. multicoloured (b)	80	90
488	**459**	30p. multicoloured (c)	85	90
489	**460**	40p. multicoloured (c)	1·00	1·00
490	**461**	50p. multicoloured (c)	1·20	1·40
491	**462**	75p. multicoloured (c)	2·00	1·50
491b	**463**	£2 multicoloured (g)	4·00	3·25
491c	**464**	£4 multicoloured (l)	7·00	6·75
468/91c Set of 26			22·00	22·00
First Day Covers (5)				28·00
Presentation Packs (5)			27·00	

For £1 value as No. 491b see No. 389.
Printings: (a) 21.3.89; (b) 16.1.90; (c). 13.3.90; (d) 3.5.90; (e) 13.11.90; (f) 12.2.91; (g) 19.3.91; (h) 7.1.92; (i) 22.5.92; (j) 11.1.93; (k) 18.2.94; (l) 24.1.95; (m) 21.3.95; (n) 1.9.95; (o) 12.11.96.

Cylinder or Plate Nos.: £2 A1, B1, C1, D1 (each×6); £4 1A (×5); others 1A, 1B, 1C, 1D, 1E, 1F (each×4).
Sheets: £2 20 (4×5); £4 10 (5×2); others 50 (5×10).
Imprint: Left-hand corner, bottom margin (£4) or central, left-hand margin (others).
Withdrawn: 31.3.99 (1p. to £2), 30.11.2009 (£4).

465 Agile Frog (*Rana dalamantina*)

466 Large Chequered Skipper (*Heteropterus morpheus*)

467 Barn Owl (*Tyto alba*)

468 Green Lizard (*Lacerta viridis*)

Jersey Rare Fauna (1st series)

(Des W. Oliver. Litho Cartor)

1989 (25 Apr.). P 13½×13 (Nos. 492 and 495), 13×13½ (No. 493) or 13½×14 (No. 494), all comb.

492	**465**	13p. multicoloured	60	65
493	**466**	13p. multicoloured	60	65
494	**467**	17p. multicoloured	80	85
495	**468**	17p. multicoloured	80	85
492/5 *Set of 4*			2·50	2·75
First Day Cover				3·50
Presentation Pack			3·50	

See also Nos. 1158/**MS**1162.
Plate Nos.: All designs 1A, 1B, 1C, 1D (each×5).
Sheets: 20 (4×5) Nos. 492 and 495; (5×4) Nos. 493/4.
Imprint: Central, left-hand margin.
Quantities sold: 13p. (No. 492) 650,061; 13p. (No. 493) 589,329; 17p. (No. 494) 552,582; 17p. (No. 495) 515,262.
Withdrawn: 30.4.90.

469 Toddlers' Toys

470 Playground Games

471 Party Games

472 Teenage Sports

Europa. Children's Toys and Games

(Des from clay plaques by Clare Luke. Litho Questa)

1989 (25 Apr.). P 14 (C).

496	**469**	17p. multicoloured	50	50
497	**470**	17p. multicoloured	50	50
498	**471**	23p. multicoloured	75	75
499	**472**	23p. multicoloured	75	75
496/9 *Set of 4*			2·25	2·25

First Day Cover		2·75
Presentation Pack	3·00	

Plate Nos.: All designs 1A, 1B, 1C, 1D, 1E, 1F (each×4).
Sheets: 20 (4×5).
Imprint: Central, left-hand margin.
Quantities sold: 17p. (No. 496) 473,930; 17p. (No. 497) 471,124; 23p. (No. 498) 424,212; 23p. (No. 499) 424,340.
Withdrawn: 30.4.90.

473 Queen Elizabeth II and Royal Yacht *Britannia* in Elizabeth Harbour

Royal Visit

(Des A. Copp. Litho Questa)

1989 (24 May). P 14½ (C).

500	**473**	£1 multicoloured	2·75	2·75
First Day Cover				3·00
Presentation Pack			3·00	

No. 500 was retained in use as part of the current definitive series until replaced by No. 634.
Sheets: 20 (4×5).
Imprint: Central, left-hand margin.
Withdrawn: 30.6.94.

474 Philippe d'Auvergne presented to Louis XVI, 1786

475 Storming the Bastille, 1789

476 Marie de Boullion and Revolutionaries, 1790

477 D'Auvergne's Headquarters at Mont Orgueil, 1795

478 Landing Arms for Chouan Rebels, 1796

479 The Last Chouan Revolt, 1799

Bicentenary of the French Revolution. Philippe D'Auvergne

(Des V. Ambrus. Litho Cartor)

1989 (7 July). P 13½ (C).

501	**474**	13p. multicoloured	40	30
		a. Booklet pane of 4	1·60	
502	**475**	17p. multicoloured	50	40
		a. Booklet pane of 4	2·00	
503	**476**	23p. multicoloured	60	50
		a. Booklet pane of 4	2·25	
504	**477**	30p. multicoloured	95	1·00
		a. Booklet pane of 4	3·75	
505	**478**	32p. multicoloured	1·00	1·10
		a. Booklet pane of 4	4·00	
506	**479**	35p. multicoloured	1·20	1·30
		a. Booklet pane of 4	4·50	
501/6 *Set of 6*			4·25	4·00
First Day Cover				4·25
Presentation Pack			4·50	

Each booklet pane has margins all round and text printed on the binding selvedge.

See also Nos. 539/44.

Plate Nos.: All values 1A, 1B, 1C, 1D (each×4).

Sheets: 20 (5×4).

Imprint: Central, left-hand margin.

Quantities sold: 13p. 637,422; 17p. 840,904; 23p. 408,967; 30p. 133,642; 32p. 148,474; 35p. 151,639.

Withdrawn: 31.7.90.

480 *St. Helier* off Elizabeth Castle

481 *Caesarea II* off Corbière Lighthouse

482 *Reindeer* in St. Helier Harbour

483 *Ibex* racing *Frederica* off Portelet

484 *Lynx* off Noirmont

Centenary of Great Western Railway Steamer Service to Channel Islands

(Des G. Palmer. Litho Questa)

1989 (5 Sept). P 13½×14 (C).

507	**480**	13p. multicoloured	30	30
508	**481**	17p. multicoloured	35	35
509	**482**	27p. multicoloured	80	80
510	**483**	32p. multicoloured	95	95
511	**484**	35p. multicoloured	1·10	1·10
507/11	Set of 5		3·25	3·25
First Day Cover				3·50
Presentation Pack			3·75	

Plate Nos.: 13p., 27p. 1A, 1B (each×4); 17p., 32p. 1C, 1D (each×4); 35p. 1A, 1B, 1C, 1D (each×4).

Sheets: 20 (4×5).

Imprint: Central, left-hand margin.

Quantities sold: 13p. 265,382; 17p. 294,992; 27p. 135,226; 32p. 128,966; 35p. 134,800.

Withdrawn: 28.9.90.

485 Gorey Harbour

486 La Corbière

487 Grève de Lecq

488 Bouley Bay

489 Mont Orgueil

150th Birth Anniversary of Sarah Louisa Kilpack (artist)

(Litho Enschedé)

1989 (24 Oct). P 13×12½ (C).

512	**485**	13p. multicoloured	25	25
513	**486**	17p. multicoloured	30	30
514	**487**	23p. multicoloured	70	75
515	**488**	32p. multicoloured	85	85
516	**489**	35p. multicoloured	90	1·00
512/16	Set of 5		2·75	2·75
First Day Cover				3·25
Presentation Pack			4·00	

Plate Nos.: 13p., 17p., 1A, 1B, 1C (each×5); 23p., 32p., 35p. 1A, 1B (each×5).

Sheets: 20 (4×5).

Imprint: Central, left-hand margin.

Quantities sold: 13p. 649,308; 17p. 571,503; 23p. 159,487; 32p. 138,562; 35p. 137,950.

Withdrawn: 31.10.90.

Post Office Yearbook

1989 (24 Oct). Comprises Nos. 462/80 and 492/516 (price £12).

Yearbook		38·00

Sold out: 12.11.90.

490 Head Post Office, Broad Street, 1969

491 Postal Headquarters, Mont Millais, 1990

492 Hue Street Post Office, 1815

493 Head Post Office, Halkett Place, 1890

Europa. Post Office Buildings

(Des P. Layton. Litho Cartor)

1990 (13 Mar). P 13½×14 (vert) or 14×13½ (horiz), both comb.

517	**490**	18p. multicoloured	50	50
518	**491**	18p. multicoloured	50	50
519	**492**	24p. multicoloured	65	65
520	**493**	24p. multicoloured	65	65
517/20	*Set of 4*		2·10	2·00
First Day Cover				2·50
Presentation Pack			3·00	

Plate Nos.: All designs 1A, 1B, 1C, 1D (each×5).
Sheets: 20 (5×4) 18p.; (4×5) 24p.
Imprint: Central, left-hand margin.
Quantities sold: 18p. (No. 517) 596,221; 18p. (No. 518) 595,918; 24p. (No. 519) 400,441; 24p. (No. 520) 406,656.
Withdrawn: 31.3.91.

494 'Battle of Flowers' Parade

495 Sports

496 Mont Orgueil Castle and German Underground Hospital Museum

497 Salon Culinaire

Festival of Tourism

(Des A. Copp. Litho Enschedé)

1990 (3 May). P 14×13½ (C).

521	**494**	18p. multicoloured	55	55
522	**495**	24p. multicoloured	70	70
523	**496**	29p. multicoloured	85	85
524	**497**	32p. multicoloured	90	90
521/4	*Set of 4*		2·75	2·75
First Day Cover				3·25
Presentation Pack			4·00	
MS525	151×100 mm. Nos. 521/4		2·75	3·00
First Day Cover				6·50
Presentation Pack			4·50	

Plate Nos.: 18p. 1A, 1B, 1C, 1D, 1E (each×5); 24p. 1A, 1B, 1C, 1D (each×5); 29p. 1A (×5); 32p. 1A, 1B (each×5).
Sheets: 20 (5×4).
Imprint: Central, left-hand margin.
Quantities sold: 18p. 630,610; 24p. 252,670; 29p. 168,528; 32p. 127,334; miniature sheet 110,177.
Withdrawn: 31.5.91.

498 Early Printing Press and Jersey Newspaper Mastheads

499 Modern Press, and Offices of *Jersey Evening Post* in 1890 and 1990

500 Radio Jersey Broadcaster

501 Channel Television Studio Cameraman

International Literacy Year. Jersey News Media

(Des A. Copp. Litho Cartor)

1990 (26 June). P 13½ (C).

526	**498**	14p. multicoloured	45	45
527	**499**	18p. multicoloured	45	45
528	**500**	34p. multicoloured	90	90
529	**501**	37p. multicoloured	95	95
526/9	*Set of 4*		2·50	2·50
First Day Cover				2·75
Presentation Pack			3·50	

Plate Nos.: All values 1A, 1B, 1C, 1D (each×4).
Sheets: 20 (4×5).
Imprint: Central, left-hand margin.
Quantities sold: 14p. 926,906; 18p. 795,733; 34p. 121,842; 37p. 129,468.
Withdrawn: 30.6.91.

502 British Aerospace Hawk T.1

503 Supermarine Spitfire

504 Hawker Hurricane Mk I

505 Vickers-Armstrong Wellington

506 Avro Lancaster

Jersey Aviation History (4th series). 50th Anniversary of Battle of Britain

(Des G. Palmer. Litho Questa)

1990 (4 Sept). P 14 (C).

530	**502**	14p. multicoloured	40	45
531	**503**	18p. multicoloured	55	60
532	**504**	24p. multicoloured	85	85
533	**505**	34p. multicoloured	1·50	1·60
534	**506**	37p. multicoloured	1·60	1·60

530/4 *Set of 5* .... 4·50   4·50
First Day Cover .... 5·25
Presentation Pack .... 5·25

Plate Nos.: 14p., 34p. 1A, 1B (each×5); 18p., 37p. 1C, 1D (each×5); 24p. 1A, 1B, 1C, 1D (each×5).
Sheets: 20 (4×5).
Imprint: Central, left-hand margin.
Quantities sold: 14p. 495,815; 18p. 519,684; 24p. 206,541; 34p. 136,330; 37p. 134,747.
Withdrawn: 30.9.91.

507 St. Helier   **508** Grouville

509 St. Saviour   **510** St. John

Christmas. Jersey Parish Churches (2nd series)

(Des P. Layton. Litho BDT)

1990 (13 Nov). P 13½ (C).

535	**507**	14p. multicoloured	45	40
536	**508**	18p. multicoloured	45	40
		a. Deep blue-green (Queen's head, value and 'JERSEY') omitted	£1500	
537	**509**	34p. multicoloured	1·00	1·00
538	**510**	37p. multicoloured	1·20	1·20

535/8 *Set of 4* .... 3·00   3·00
First Day Cover .... 3·50
Presentation Pack .... 4·00
Postcards (set of 4) .... 2·20   5·00

Plate Nos.: All values 1A, 1B, 1C, 1D (each×5).
Sheets: 20 (4×5).
Imprint: Central, left-hand margin.
Quantities sold: 14p. 948,076; 18p. 690,282; 34p. 141,514; 37p. 147,768.
Withdrawn: 30.11.91.

Post Office Yearbook

1990 (13 Nov). Comprises Nos. 481/91 and 517/38 (price £12.50).
Yearbook .... 35·00
Withdrawn: 30.11.91.

511 Prince's Tower, La Hougue Bie   **512** D'Auvergne's Arrest in Paris

513 D'Auvergne plotting against Napoleon   **514** Execution of George Cadoudal

515 H.M.S. *Surly* (cutter) attacking French Convoy   **516** D'Auvergne's Last Days in London

175th Death Anniversary of Philippe D'Auvergne

(Des V. Ambrus. Litho Cartor)

1991 (22 Jan). P 13½ (C).

539	**511**	15p. multicoloured	45	40
540	**512**	20p. multicoloured	55	55
541	**513**	26p. multicoloured	70	75
542	**514**	31p. multicoloured	90	90
543	**515**	37p. multicoloured	1·10	1·10
544	**516**	44p. multicoloured	1·20	1·20

539/44 *Set of 6* .... 4·50   4·50
First Day Cover .... 4·75
Presentation Pack .... 5·00

Plate Nos.: All values 1A, 1B, 1C, 1D (each×4).
Sheets: 20 (4×5).
Imprint: Central, left-hand margin.
Quantities sold: 15p. 709,403; 20p. 454,921; 26p. 159,902; 31p. 140,379; 37p. 341,103; 44p. 153,157.
Withdrawn: 31.1.92.

517 'Landsat 5' and Thematic Mapper Image over Jersey   **518** 'ERS-1' Earth Resources Remote Sensing Satellite

519 'Meteosat' Weather Satellite   **520** 'Olympus' Direct Broadcasting Satellite

Europa. Europe in Space

(Des A. Copp. Litho Enschedé)

1991 (19 Mar). P 14½×13 (C).

545	**517**	20p. multicoloured	50	50
546	**518**	20p. multicoloured	50	50
547	**519**	26p. multicoloured	80	85
548	**520**	26p. multicoloured	80	85

545/8 *Set of 4* .... 2·40   2·40
First Day Cover .... 2·75
Presentation Pack .... 3·00

Plate Nos.: All designs 1A, 1B, 1C (each×5).
Sheets: 20 (5×4).
Imprint: Central, left-hand margin.
Quantities sold: 20p. (No. 545) 682,799; 20p. (No. 546) 690,871; 26p. (No. 547) 442,476; 26p. (No. 548) 439,415.
Withdrawn: 31.3.92.

521 1941 1d. Stamp (50th anniv of first Jersey postage stamp)

522 Steam Train (centenary of Jersey Eastern Railway extension to Gorey Pier)

523 Jersey Cow and Herd Book (125th anniv of Jersey Herd Book)

524 Stone-laying Ceremony (painting by P. Ouless) (150th anniv of Victoria Harbour)

525 Marie Bartlett and Hospital (250th anniversary of Marie Bartlett's hospital bequest)

Anniversaries

(Des A. Copp. Litho Cartor)

1991 (16 May). P 13½ (C).

549	**521**	15p. multicoloured	30	30
550	**522**	20p. multicoloured	50	55
551	**523**	26p. multicoloured	60	70
552	**524**	31p. multicoloured	75	80
553	**525**	53p. multicoloured	1·70	1·70
549/53 *Set of 5*			3·50	3·75
First Day Cover				4·25
Presentation Pack			4·50	

Plate Nos.: All values 1A, 1B, 1C, 1D (each×4).
Sheets: 20 (5×4).
Imprint: Central, left-hand margin.
Quantities sold: 15p. 618,479; 20p. 608,585; 26p. 245,772; 31p. 133,604; 53p. 135,394.
Withdrawn: 30.5.92.

526 *Melitaea cinxia*

527 *Euplagia quadripunctaria*

528 *Deilephilia porcellus*   **529** *Inachis io*

Butterflies and Moths (1st series)

(Des W. Oliver. Litho Enschedé)

1991 (9 July). P 13×12½ (C).

554	**526**	15p. multicoloured	35	35
555	**527**	20p. multicoloured	45	30
556	**528**	37p. multicoloured	1·40	1·50
557	**529**	57p. multicoloured	1·70	1·90
554/7 *Set of 4*			3·50	3·75
First Day Cover				4·50
Presentation Pack			4·50	

See also Nos. 1279/**MS**1285 and 1651/**MS**1657.
Plate Nos.: All values 1A, 1B, 1C (each×4).
Sheets: 20 (4×5).
Imprint: Central, left-hand margin.
Quantities sold: 15p. 489,632; 20p. 646,607; 37p. 130,494; 57p. 142,646.
Withdrawn: 31.7.92.

530 Drilling for Water, Ethiopia

531 Building Construction, Rwanda

532 Village Polytechnic, Kenya

533 Treating Leprosy, Tanzania

534 Ploughing, Zambia

535 Immunisation Clinic, Lesotho

Overseas Aid

(Des A. Theobald. Litho BDT)

1991 (3 Sept). P 13½×14 (C).

558	**530**	15p. multicoloured	45	40
559	**531**	20p. multicoloured	50	45
560	**532**	26p. multicoloured	70	70
561	**533**	31p. multicoloured	85	90
562	**534**	37p. multicoloured	1·10	1·10
563	**535**	44p. multicoloured	1·20	1·40
558/63 *Set of 6*			4·50	4·50
First Day Cover				5·00
Presentation Pack			5·00	

Plate Nos.: All values 1A, 1B (each×4).
Sheets: 20 (4×5).
Imprint: Central, left-hand margin.
Quantities sold: 15p. 517,917; 20p. 644,721; 26p. 177,179; 31p. 115,769; 37p. 111,112; 44p. 142,024.
Withdrawn: 30.9.92.

536 'This is the Place for Me'

537 'The Island Come True'

538 'The Never Bird'

539 'The Great White Father'

Christmas. Illustrations by Edmund Blampied for J. M. Barrie's 'Peter Pan'

(Litho Questa)

1991 (5 Nov). P 14 (C).

564	**536**	15p. multicoloured	40	40
565	**537**	20p. multicoloured	65	65
566	**538**	37p. multicoloured	1·20	1·20
567	**539**	53p. multicoloured	1·60	1·60
564/7 *Set of 4*			3·50	3·50
First Day Cover				4·00
Presentation Pack			4·50	

Plate Nos.: All values 1A, 1B (each×5).
Sheets: 20 (5×4).
Imprint: Central, left-hand margin.
Quantities sold: 15p. 917,860; 20p. 693,203; 37p. 128,585; 53p. 117,877.
Withdrawn: 30.11.92.

Post Office Yearbook

1991 (5 Nov). Comprises Nos. 491*b* and 539/67 (price £13.50).

Yearbook		32·00

Sold out: By 9.93.

540 Pied Wagtail

541 Firecrest

542 Common Snipe

543 Northern Lapwing

544 Fieldfare

Winter Birds

(Des W. Oliver. Litho Cartor)

1992 (7 Jan). P 13½×14 (C).

568	**540**	16p. multicoloured	50	25
569	**541**	22p. multicoloured	70	55
570	**542**	28p. multicoloured	80	85
571	**543**	39p. multicoloured	1·20	1·20
572	**544**	57p. multicoloured	1·70	1·70
568/72 *Set of 5*			4·50	4·25
First Day Cover				5·25
Presentation Pack			5·50	

See also Nos. 635/9.
Plate Nos.: All values 1A, 1B, 1C, 1D (each×4).
Sheets: 20 (5×4).
Imprint: Central, left-hand margin.
Quantities sold: 16p. 481,678; 22p. 462,647; 28p. 268,973; 39p. 151,671; 57p. 132,065.
Withdrawn: 30.1.93.

545 Shipping at Shanghai, 1860

546 Mesny's Junk running Taiping Blockade, 1862

547 General Mesny outside River Gate, 1874

548 Mesny in Burma, 1877

549 Mesny and Governor Chang, 1882

550 Mesny in Mandarin's Sedan Chair, 1886

Jersey Adventures (3rd series). 150th Birth Anniversary of William Mesny

(Des V. Ambrus. Litho Cartor)

1992 (25 Feb). P 13½ (C).

573	**545**	16p. multicoloured	40	45
		a. Black printed double	1·50	
		b. Booklet pane of 4	1·50	
574	**546**	16p. multicoloured	40	45
		a. Booklet pane of 4	1·50	
575	**547**	22p. multicoloured	65	65
		a. Booklet pane of 4	2·00	
576	**548**	22p. multicoloured	65	65
		a. Booklet pane of 4	2·00	
577	**549**	33p. multicoloured	90	95
		a. Booklet pane of 4	3·00	
578	**550**	33p. multicoloured	90	95
		a. Booklet pane of 4	3·00	
573/8 *Set of 6*			3·50	3·75
First Day Cover				4·25
Presentation Pack			4·50	

Each booklet pane has margins all round and text printed on the binding selvedge.
Plate Nos.: All values 1A, 1B, 1C, 1D (each×4).
Sheets: 20 (4×5).
Imprint: Central, left-hand margin.
Quantities sold: 16p. (No. 573) 346,732; 16p. (No. 574) 336,655; 22p. (No. 575) 377,299; 22p. (No. 576) 360,220; 33p. (No. 577) 129,904; 33p. (No. 578) 130,637.
Withdrawn: 27.2.93 (sheets).

551 *Tickler* (brigantine)

552 *Hebe* (brig)

553 *Gemini* (barque)

554 *Percy Douglas* (full-rigged ship)

Jersey Shipbuilding

(Des A. Copp. Litho Questa)

1992 (14 Apr). P 14 (C).

579	**551**	16p. multicoloured		45	40
580	**552**	22p. multicoloured		70	75
581	**553**	50p. multicoloured		1·40	1·50
582	**554**	57p. multicoloured		1·60	1·70
579/82 *Set of 4*				3·75	4·00
First Day Cover					4·50
Presentation Pack				4·50	
MS583 148×98 mm. Nos. 579/82				4·00	4·25
First Day Cover					4·50
Presentation Pack				4·50	

Plate Nos.: 16p. 1A, 1B, 1C, 1D, 1E, 1F (each×4); 22p., 57p. 1A, 1B, 1C, 1D (each×4); 50p. 1A, 1B (each×4).
Sheets: 20 (5×4).
Imprint: Central, left-hand margin.
Quantities sold: 16p. 673,830; 22p. 462,972; 50p. 138,158; 57p. 111,044; miniature sheet 126,594.
Withdrawn: 30.4.93.

555 John Bertram (ship owner) and Columbus

556 Sir George Carteret (founder of New Jersey)

557 Sir Walter Ralegh (founder of Virginia)

Europa. 500th Anniversary of Discovery of America by Columbus

(Des V. Ambrus. Litho Questa)

1992 (14 Apr). P 14×14½ (C).

584	**555**	22p. multicoloured		65	50
585	**556**	28p. multicoloured		75	80
586	**557**	39p. multicoloured		1·10	1·40
584/6 *Set of 3*				2·20	2·40
First Day Cover					3·00
Presentation Pack				3·25	

Plate Nos.: 22p. 1A, 1B (each×5); 28p. 1A, 1B, 1C, 1D (each×5); 39p. 1C, 1D (each×5).
Sheets: 20 (4×5).
Imprint: Central, left-hand margin.
Quantities sold: 22p. 459,817; 28p. 664,537; 39p. 298,597.
Withdrawn: 30.4.93.

558 'Snow Leopards' (Allison Griffiths)

559 'Three Elements' (Nataly Miorin)

560 'Three Men in a Tub' (Amanda Crocker)

561 'Cockatoos' (Michelle Millard)

Batik Designs

(Litho Questa)

1992 (23 June). P 14½ (C).

587	**558**	16p. multicoloured		45	40
588	**559**	22p. multicoloured		65	45
589	**560**	39p. multicoloured		1·10	1·20
590	**561**	57p. multicoloured		1·50	1·70
587/90 *Set of 4*				3·25	3·50
First Day Cover					4·00
Presentation Pack				4·25	

Plate Nos.: 16p., 39p. 1A, 1B (each×4); 22p., 57p. 1C, 1D (each×4).
Sheets: 20 (5×4).
Imprint: Central, left-hand margin.
Quantities sold: 16p. 427,970; 22p. 472,443; 39p. 112,188; 57p. 113,465.
Withdrawn: 30.6.93.

562 Morris Cowley 'Bullnose', 1925

563 Rolls-Royce 20/25, 1932

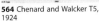

564 Chenard and Walcker T5, 1924

565 Packard 900, series Light Eight, 1932

566 Lanchester 21, 1927

567 Buick 30 Roadster, 1913

Vintage Cars (2nd series)

(Des A. Copp. Litho Enschedè)

1992 (8 Sept). P 13×12½ (C).

591	**562**	16p. multicoloured		30	30
592	**563**	22p. multicoloured		45	45
593	**564**	28p. multicoloured		70	75

594	**565**	33p. multicoloured	90	95
595	**566**	39p. multicoloured	1·00	1·10
596	**567**	50p. multicoloured	1·50	1·70
591/6 *Set of 6*			4·50	4·75
First Day Cover				5·00
Presentation Pack			5·25	

Plate Nos.: All values 1A, 1B (each×4).
Sheets: 20 (4×5).
Imprint: Central, left-hand margin.
Quantities sold: 16p. 434,984; 22p. 426,734; 28p. 290,202; 33p. 134,477; 39p. 124,759; 50p. 127,917.
Withdrawn: 30.9.93.

568 Trinity

569 St. Mary

570 St. Martin

571 St. Peter

Christmas. Jersey Parish Churches (3rd series)

(Des P. Layton. Litho BDT)

1992 (3 Nov). P 13½ (C).

597	**568**	16p. multicoloured	40	30
598	**569**	22p. multicoloured	55	50
599	**570**	39p. multicoloured	1·10	1·10
600	**571**	57p. multicoloured	1·50	1·50
597/600 *Set of 4*			3·25	3·25
First Day Cover				3·75
Presentation Pack			4·00	
Postcards (set of 4)			2·00	5·00

Plate Nos.: All values 1A, 1B, 1C, 1D (each×5).
Sheets: 20 (4×5).
Imprint: Central, left-hand margin.
Quantities sold: 16p. 894,098; 22p. 729,413; 39p. 93,764; 57p. 95,936.
Withdrawn: 30.11.93.

Post Office Yearbook

1992 (3 Nov). Comprises Nos. 568/600 (price £14.50).

Yearbook		32·00

Sold out: By 10.95.

572 Farmhouse

573 Trinity Church

574 Daffodils and Cows

575 Jersey Cows

576 Sunbathing

577 Windsurfing

578 Crab (Queen's head at left)

579 Crab (Queen's head at right)

580 'Singin' in the Rain' Float

581 'Dragon Dance' Float

582 'Bali, Morning of the world' Float

583 'Zulu Fantasy' Float

Booklet Stamps

(Des A. Copp. Litho BDT)

1993 (11 Jan). P 13 (C).

601	**572**	(17p.) multicoloured	60	70
		a. Booklet pane. Nos. 601/4, each×2, with margins all round	5·00	
602	**573**	(17p.) multicoloured	60	70
603	**574**	(17p.) multicoloured	60	70
604	**575**	(17p.) multicoloured	60	70
605	**576**	(23p.) multicoloured	70	60
		a. Booklet pane. Nos. 605/8, each×2, with margins all round	5·50	
606	**577**	(23p.) multicoloured	70	60
607	**578**	(23p.) multicoloured	70	60
608	**579**	(23p.) multicoloured	70	60
609	**580**	(28p.) multicoloured	85	80
		a. Booklet pane. Nos. 609/12, each×2, with margins all round	7·00	
610	**581**	(28p.) multicoloured	85	80
611	**582**	(28p.) multicoloured	85	80
612	**583**	(28p.) multicoloured	85	80
601/12 *Set of 12*			7·75	7·50
First Day Cover				16·00
Presentation Pack			10·00	

The above do not show face values, but are inscribed 'BAILIWICK POSTAGE PAID' (Nos. 601/4), 'U.K. MINIMUM POSTAGE PAID' (Nos. 605/8) or 'EUROPE POSTAGE PAID' (Nos. 609/12). They were initially sold at 17p., 23p. or 28p., but Nos. 601/4 and 609/12 were increased to 18p. and 30p. on 10 January 1994 and Nos. 601/4 to 19p. on 4 July 1995. On 10 March 1997 Nos. 601/4 were increased to 20p., Nos. 605/8 to 24p. and Nos. 609/12 to 31p.
Withdrawn: 30.9.99.

584 *Phragmipedium* Eric Young 'Jersey'

585 *Odontoglossum* Augres 'Trinity'

586 *Miltonia* St. Helier 'Colomberie'

587 *Phragmipedium* pearcei

588 *Calanthe* Grouville 'Gorey'

Jersey Orchids (3rd series)

(Litho Enschedé)

1993 (26 Jan). P 14×13 (C).

613	**584**	17p. multicoloured	45	35
		a. *Black* printed double		
614	**585**	23p. multicoloured	70	65
		a. *Black* printed double		
615	**586**	28p. multicoloured	80	75
		a. *Black* printed double		
616	**587**	39p. multicoloured	1·20	1·40
617	**588**	57p. multicoloured	1·70	1·90
		a. *Black* printed double		
613/17 *Set of 5*			4·50	4·50

First Day Cover.. 5·00
Presentation Pack.. 5·25
    Plate Nos.: 17p., 23p. 1A, 1B, 1C (each×5); 28p., 39p., 57p. 1A, 1B
    (each×5).
    Sheets: 20 (5×4).
    Imprint: Central, left-hand margin.
    Quantities sold: 17p. 391,802; 23p. 391,444; 28p. 188,149; 39p.
    141,610; 57p. 141,463.
    Withdrawn: 31.1.94.

589 Douglas Dakota

590 Wight Seaplane

591 Avro Shackleton A.E.W.2

592 Gloster Meteor Mk III and de Havilland D.H.100 Vampire FB.5

593 BAe Harrier GR.1A

594 Panavia Tornado F.3

Jersey Aviation History (5th series). 75th Anniversary of Royal Air Force

(Des A. Theobald. Litho Questa)

1993 (1 Apr.) P 14 (C).

618	**589**	17p. multicoloured	45	30
619	**590**	23p. multicoloured	60	65
620	**591**	28p. multicoloured	70	70
621	**592**	33p. multicoloured	80	85
622	**593**	39p. multicoloured	1·00	1·10
623	**594**	57p. multicoloured	1·50	1·60

618/23 *Set of 6*.. 4·50 4·75
First Day Cover.. 6·00
Presentation Pack.. 5·25
MS624 147×98 mm. Nos. 619 and 623......... 4·50 4·75
First Day Cover.. 6·00
Presentation Pack.. 5·25
    Nos. 618/24 also commemorate the 50th anniversary of the Royal
Air Force Association and the 40th anniversary of the first air display
on Jersey.
    Plate Nos.: 17p., 23p. 1A, 1B, 1C, 1D (each×4); 28p., 33p., 39p.,
    57p. 1A, 1B (each×4).
    Sheets: 20 (5×4).
    Imprint: Central, left-hand margin.
    Quantities sold: 17p., 578,871; 23p. 581,661; 28p. 184,066; 33p.
    140,430; 39p. 144,522; 57p. 159,447; miniature sheet 113,236.
    Withdrawn: 30.4.94.

595 'Jersey's Opera House' (Ian Rolls)

596 'The Ham and Tomato Bap' (Jonathan Hubbard)

597 'Vase of Flowers' (Neil Mackenzie)

Europa. Contemporary Art

(Litho Cartor)

1993 (1 Apr.) P 13½×14 (C).

625	**595**	23p. multicoloured	60	60
626	**596**	28p. multicoloured	70	70
627	**597**	39p. multicoloured	1·10	1·10

625/7 *Set of 3* .... 2·20 2·20
First Day Cover .... 2·75
Presentation Pack .... 2·75
    Plate Nos.: All values 1A, 1B, 1C, 1D (each×4).
    Sheets: 20 (5×4).
    Imprint: Central, left-hand margin.
    Quantities sold: 23p. 422,536; 28p. 340,206; 39p. 230,510.
    Withdrawn: 30.4.94.

598 1943 Occupation ½d. Stamp

599 1943 1d. Stamp

600 1943 1½d. Stamp

601 1943 2d. Stamp

602 1943 2½d. Stamp

603 1943 3d. Stamp

50th Anniversary of Edmund Blampied's Occupation Stamps

(Des G. Drummond. Litho Cartor)

1993 (2 June) P 13½ (C).

628	**598**	17p. myrtle-green, pale grn & blk	35	35
629	**599**	23p. vermilion, salmon-pink & blk	50	50
630	**600**	28p. chocolate, cinnamon & black	70	70
631	**601**	33p. reddish orge, salmon & blk	85	85
632	**602**	39p. royal blue, cobalt and black	1·20	1·20
633	**603**	50p. bright magenta, pale mauve and black	1·40	1·40

628/33 *Set of 6* .... 4·50 4·50
First Day Cover .... 4·75
Presentation Pack .... 5·25
    Plate Nos.: All values 1A, 1B, 1C, 1D (each×3).
    Sheets: 20 (4×5).
    Imprint: Central, left-hand margin.
    Quantities sold: 17p. 549,708; 23p. 565,711; 28p. 174,159; 33p.
    120,570; 39p. 93,502; 50p. 99,135.
    Withdrawn: 30.6.94.

604 Queen Elizabeth II (from painting by Mara McGregor)

40th Anniversary of Coronation

(Litho Questa)

1993 (2 June). P 14½ (C).

634	**604**	£1 multicoloured (ab)	2·75	2·75
First Day Cover				3·00
Presentation Pack			3·50	

No. 634 was retained in use as part of the current definitive series until replaced by No. 804.

Printings: (a) 2.6.93; (b) 1.9.95.
Plate Nos.: 1A, 1B, 1C, 1D (each×4).
Sheets: 20 (5×4).
Imprint: Central, left-hand margin.
Withdrawn: 31.3.99 but used again by the Philatelic Bureau for a Millennium cover, issued 31.12.99.

605 Short-toed Treecreeper **606** Dartford Warbler **607** Northern Wheatear

608 Cirl Bunting **609** Jay

Summer Birds

(Des W. Oliver. Litho Cartor)

1993 (7 Sept). P 13½×14 (C).

635	**605**	17p. multicoloured	45	50
636	**606**	23p. multicoloured	70	75
637	**607**	28p. multicoloured	80	85
638	**608**	39p. multicoloured	1·20	1·20
639	**609**	57p. multicoloured	1·70	1·70
635/9 *Set of 5*			4·50	4·50
First Day Cover				5·25
Presentation Pack			5·00	

Plate Nos.: All values 1A, 1B, 1C, 1D (each×4).
Sheets: 20 (5×4).
Imprint: Central, left-hand margin.
Quantities sold: 17p. 495,975; 23p. 496,942; 28p. 170,135; 39p. 139,630; 57p. 138,994.
Withdrawn: 30.9.94.

610 Two Angels holding 'Hark the Herald Angels Sing' Banner **611** Two Angels playing Harps

612 Two Angels playing Violins **613** Two Angels holding 'Once in Royal David's City' Banner

Christmas. Stained Glass Windows by Henry Bosdet from St. Aubin on the Hill Church

(Des N. Mackenzie. Litho Enschedé)

1993 (2 Nov). P 14×13 (C).

640	**610**	17p. multicoloured	40	35
641	**611**	23p. multicoloured	60	60
642	**612**	39p. multicoloured	1·10	1·20
643	**613**	57p. multicoloured	1·70	1·90
640/3 *Set of 4*			3·50	3·75
First Day Cover				4·00
Presentation Pack			4·25	

Plate Nos.: All values 1A, 1B, 1C (each×4).
Sheets: 20 (5×4).
Imprint: Central, left-hand margin.
Quantities sold: 17p. 877,806; 23p. 744,661; 39p. 110,131; 57p. 108,703.
Withdrawn: 30.11.94.

Post Office Yearbook

1993 (2 Nov). Comprises Nos. 601/43 (price £16.50).

Yearbook		33·00

Sold out: By 9.97.

614 *Coprinus comatus* **615** *Amanita muscaria*

616 *Cantharellus cibarius* **617** *Macrolepiota procera*

618 *Clathrus ruber*

Fungi (1st series)

(Des W. Oliver. Litho Questa)

1994 (11 Jan). P 14½ (C).					
644	**614**	18p. multicoloured		45	40
645	**615**	23p. multicoloured		65	70
646	**616**	30p. multicoloured		80	85
647	**617**	41p. multicoloured		1·20	1·20
648	**618**	60p. multicoloured		1·60	1·60
644/8 *Set of 5*				4·00	4·00
First Day Cover					4·25
Presentation Pack				4·50	

See also Nos.1240/**MS**1246 and 1464/9.
Plate Nos.: 18p. 1A (×4); 23p. 1B (×4); 30p. 1C (×4); 41p. 1D. (×4); 60p. 1E (×4).
Sheets: 20 (5×4).
Imprint: Central, left-hand margin.
Quantities sold: 18p. 735,158; 23p. 482,461; 30p. 188,095; 41p. 184,418; 60p. 137,309.
Withdrawn: 30.1.95.

619 Pekingnese (*Illustration reduced. Actual size* 110×75 mm)

'Hong Kong 94' International Stamp Exhibition. Chinese Year of the Dog

(Des P. Layton, adapted A. Copp. Litho Questa)

1994 (18 Feb). Sheet 110×75 mm. P 15×14½ (C).			
MS649 **619** £1 multicoloured		2·50	2·75
First Day Cover			4·00
Presentation Pack		3·50	

Quantity sold: 120,029.
Withdrawn: 28.2.95.

620 Maine Coon

621 British Shorthair

622 Persian

623 Siamese

624 Non-pedigree

Cats (1st series). 21st Anniversary of Jersey Cat Club

(Des P. Layton. Litho BDT)

1994 (5 Apr). P 14 (C).					
650	**620**	18p. multicoloured		40	30
651	**621**	23p. multicoloured		60	50
652	**622**	35p. multicoloured		80	80
653	**623**	41p. multicoloured		1·20	1·20
654	**624**	60p. multicoloured		1·20	1·50
650/4 *Set of 5*				3·75	3·75
First Day Cover					4·50
Presentation Pack				4·50	

See also Nos. 1060/**MS**1066.
Plate Nos.: 35p. 1A, 1B, 1C, 1D (each×4); others 1A, 1B (each×4).
Sheets: 20 (5×4) 18p., 35p., 60p.; (4×5) 23p., 41p.
Imprint: Central, left-hand margin.
Quantities sold: 18p. 491,500; 23p. 490,820; 35p. 221,769; 41p. 185,206; 60p. 132,276.
Withdrawn: 29.4.95.

625 Mammoth Hunt, La Cotte de St. Brelade

626 Stone Age Hunters pulling Mammoth into Cave

627 Chambered Passage, La Hougue Bie

628 Transporting Stones

Europa. Archaeological Discoveries

(Des A. Copp. Litho Enschedé)

1994 (5 Apr). P 13½×14 (C).					
655	**625**	23p. multicoloured		50	55
		a. Horiz pair. Nos. 655/6		1·00	1·10
656	**626**	23p. multicoloured		50	55
657	**627**	30p. multicoloured		75	85
		a. Horiz pair. Nos. 657/8		1·50	1·70
658	**628**	30p. multicoloured		75	85
655/8 *Set of 4*				2·20	2·50
First Day Cover					3·00
Presentation Pack				3·00	

Plate Nos.: Both values 1A, 1B (each×4).
Sheets: 20 (4×5) the two horizontal designs for each value printed together, *se-tenant*, in horizontal pairs throughout the sheets.
Imprint: Central, left-hand margin.
Quantities sold: No. 655, 371,149; No. 656, 373,190; No. 657, 273,889; No. 658, 275,833.
Withdrawn: 29.4.95.

629 Gliders and Towing Aircraft approaching France

630 Landing Craft approaching Beaches

631 Disembarking from Landing Craft on Gold Beach

632 British Troops on Sword Beach

633 Spitfires over Beaches

634 Invasion Map

50th Anniversary of D-Day

(Des A. Theobald. Litho BDT)

1994 (6 June). P 13½×14 (C).

659	**629**	18p. multicoloured	55	50
		a. Booklet pane. Nos. 659/60, each×3, with margins all round	3·00	
		b. Booklet pane. Nos. 659/64, with margins all round	4·50	
660	**630**	18p. multicoloured	55	50
661	**631**	23p. multicoloured	75	70
		a. Booklet pane. Nos. 661/2, each×3, with margins all round	5·00	
662	**632**	23p. multicoloured	75	70
663	**633**	30p. multicoloured	80	75
		a. Booklet pane. Nos. 663/4, each×3, with margins all round	5·00	
664	**634**	30p. multicoloured	80	75
659/64 *Set of 6*			3·75	3·50
First Day Cover				4·25
Presentation Pack			4·50	

No. 659b was also available as a loose pane (with no stitch holes) from the Philatelic Bureau.

Plate Nos.: All values 1A, 1B (each×4).
Sheets: 20 (4×5).
Imprint: Central, left-hand margin.
Quantities sold: No. 659, 361,667; No. 660, 365,169; No. 661, 377,546; No. 662, 367,033; No. 663, 229,455; No. 664, 226,520.
Withdrawn: 30.6.95.

635 Sailing   **636** Rifle Shooting

637 Hurdling   **638** Swimming

639 Hockey

Sports (1st series). Centenary of International Olympic Committee

(Des A. Theobald. Litho Questa)

1994 (6 June). P 14 (C).

665	**635**	18p. multicoloured	40	35
666	**636**	23p. multicoloured	55	55
667	**637**	30p. multicoloured	75	75
668	**638**	41p. multicoloured	1·10	1·10
669	**639**	60p. multicoloured	1·50	1·60
665/9 *Set of 5*			4·00	4·00
First Day Cover				4·50
Presentation Pack			4·50	

See also Nos. 746/50.
Plate Nos.: All values 1A (×4).
Sheets: 20 (5×4).
Imprint: Central, left-hand margin.
Quantities sold: 18p. 279,163; 23p. 276,438; 30p. 178,234; 41p. 183,875; 60p. 133,357.
Withdrawn: 30.6.95.

640 Strawberry Anemone

641 Hermit Crab and Parasitic Anemone

642 Velvet Swimming Crab

643 Common Jellyfish

Marine Life (2nd series)

(Des W. Oliver. Litho Cartor)

1994 (2 Aug). P 13½ (C).

670	**640**	18p. multicoloured	40	45
671	**641**	23p. multicoloured	60	65
672	**642**	41p. multicoloured	1·20	1·40
673	**643**	60p. multicoloured	1·60	1·60
670/3 *Set of 4*			3·50	3·75
First Day Cover				4·25
Presentation Pack			4·50	

Plate Nos.: All values 1A, 1B, 1C, 1D (each×4).
Sheets: 20 (4×5).
Imprint: Central, left-hand margin.
Quantities sold: 18p. 465,890; 23p. 453,750; 41p. 171,459; 60p. 175,656.
Withdrawn: 31.8.95.

644 *Condor 10* (catamaran)

645 Map of Jersey and Pillar Box

646 Vicker's Type 953 Vanguard of B.E.A.

647 Short 360 of Aurigny Air Services

648 *Caesarea* (Sealink ferry)

25th Anniversary of Jersey Postal Administration

(Des A. Copp. Litho Questa)

1994 (1 Oct). P 14 (C).

674	**644**	18p. multicoloured	50	45
675	**645**	23p. multicoloured	60	50
676	**646**	35p. multicoloured	85	85
677	**647**	41p. multicoloured	1·10	1·00
678	**648**	60p. multicoloured	1·60	1·50
674/8 *Set of 5*			4·25	4·00
First Day Cover				4·50
Presentation Pack			5·00	

MS679 150×100 mm. Nos. 674/8 .... 4·50   4·50
First Day Cover .... 5·25
Presentation Pack .... 4·75
    Plate Nos.: All values 1A (×5).
    Sheets: 20 (5×4).
    Imprint: Central, left-hand margin.
    Quantities sold: 18p. 473,837; 23p. 472,468; 35p. 184,871; 41p. 186,653; 60p. 182,108; miniature sheet 76,623.
    Withdrawn: 31.10.95.

649 'Away in a Manger'

650 'Hark! the Herald Angels Sing'

651 'While Shepherds watched'

652 'We Three Kings of Orient Are'

Christmas. Carols

(Des A. Copp. Litho Questa)

1994 (8 Nov). P 14 (C).

680	**649**	18p. multicoloured	40	40
681	**650**	23p. multicoloured	50	50
682	**651**	41p. multicoloured	1·20	1·20
683	**652**	60p. multicoloured	1·50	1·50

680/3 *Set of 4* .... 3·25   3·25
First Day Cover .... 4·25
Presentation Pack .... 4·25
    Plate Nos.: All values 1A, 1B (each×4).
    Sheets: 20 (5×4).
    Imprint: Central, left-hand margin.
    Quantities sold: 18p. 981,010; 23p. 883,715; 41p. 174,413; 60p. 179,888.
    Withdrawn: 30.11.95.

Post Office Yearbook

1994 (8 Nov). Comprises Nos. **MS**248 and 644/83 (price £18.50).
Yearbook .... 30·00
    Sold out: By 2.2000.

653 Dog and 'GOOD LUCK'

654 Rose and 'WITH LOVE'

655 Chick and "CONGRATULATIONS'

656 Bouquet of Flowers and 'THANK YOU'

657 Dove with Letter and 'WITH LOVE'

658 Cat with 'GOOD LUCK'

659 Carnations and 'THANK YOU'

660 Parrot and 'CONGRATULATIONS'

661 'Pig and 'HAPPY NEW YEAR'

Greetings Stamps

(Des A. Copp. Litho BDT)

1995 (24 Jan). P 13 (C).

684	**653**	18p. multicoloured	30	20
		a. Horiz strip of 4. Nos. 684/7	2·00	2·00
		b. Booklet pane of 9. Nos. 684/92	6·00	
685	**654**	18p. multicoloured	30	20
686	**655**	18p. multicoloured	30	20
687	**656**	18p. multicoloured	30	20
688	**657**	23p. multicoloured	45	25
		a. Horiz strip of 4. Nos. 688/91	2·40	2·40
689	**658**	23p. multicoloured	45	25
690	**659**	23p. multicoloured	45	25
691	**660**	23p. multicoloured	45	25
692	**661**	60p. multicoloured	45	25

684/92 *Set of 9* .... 5·50   5·50
First Day Cover (Nos. 684/91) .... 6·00
First Day Cover (Nos. 692) .... 2·40
Presentation Pack .... 5·75
    No. 684a was available as a loose pane from the Philatelic Bureau and was also included in the presentation pack. No. 692 commemorates the Chinese New Year of the Pig.
    Plate Nos.: All values 1A, 1B, 1C, 1D (each×4).
    Sheets: 60p. 10 (5×2); others 20 (4×5) the four designs for each value printed together, *se-tenant*, in horizontal strips of 4 throughout the sheets.
    Imprint: Central, left-hand margin.
    Quantities sold: 18p. 369,217; 23p. 338,047; 60p. 101,753.
    Withdrawn: 31.1.96 (sheets).

662 'Captain Rawes'

663 'Brigadoon'

664 'Elsie Jury'

665 'Augusto L' Gouveia Pinto'

666 'Bella Romana'

Camellias

(Des and litho Questa)

1995 (21 Mar). P 14½ (C).

693	**662**	18p. multicoloured	55	50
694	**663**	23p. multicoloured	80	70
695	**664**	30p. multicoloured	90	85
696	**665**	35p. multicoloured	1·10	1·20
697	**666**	41p. multicoloured	1·20	1·30
693/7 *Set of 5*			4·00	4·00
First Day Cover				4·50
Presentation Pack			4·50	

Plate Nos.: All values 1A (×5).
Sheets: 20 (5×4).
Imprint: Central, left-hand margin.
Quantities sold: 18p. 398,810; 23p. 480,040; 30p. 187,651; 35p. 160,765; 41p. 133,208.
Withdrawn: 31.3.96.

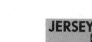

667 'Liberation' (sculpture, Philip Jackson)

Europa. Peace and Freedom

(Des A. Theobald. Litho Cartor)

1995 (9 May). P 13½ (C).

698	**667**	23p. black and dull violet-blue	55	55
699		30p. black and rose-pink	70	95
698/9 *Set of 2*			1·20	1·50
First Day Cover				2·20
Presentation Pack			2·00	

Plate Nos.: Both values 1A, 1B, 1C (each×2).
Sheets: 10 (5×2).
Imprint: Bottom margin.
Quantities sold: 19p. 251,352; 30p. 278,162.
Withdrawn: 31.5.96.

668 Baliff and Crown Officers in Launch

669 *Vega* (Red Cross supply ship)

670 H.M.S. *Beagle* (destroyer)

671 British Troops in Ordnance Yard, St. Helier

672 King George VI and Queen Elizabeth in Jersey

673 Unloading Supplies from Landing Craft, St. Aubin's

674 Royal Family with Winston Churchill on Buckingham Palace Balcony, V.E. Day (*Illustration reduced. Actual size 110×75 mm*)

50th Anniversary of Liberation

(Des A. Theobald. Litho BDT)

1995 (9 May). P 15×14 (C).

700	**668**	18p. multicoloured	40	40
		a. Booklet pane. Nos. 700/1, each×3, with margins all round	2·00	
701	**669**	18p. multicoloured	40	40
702	**670**	23p. multicoloured	60	60
		a. Booklet pane. Nos. 702/3, each×3, with margins all round	2·75	
703	**671**	23p. multicoloured	60	60
704	**672**	60p. multicoloured	1·50	1·50
		a. Booklet pane. Nos. 704/5, each×3, with margins all round	7·50	
705	**673**	60p. multicoloured	1·50	1·50
700/5 *Set of 6*			4·50	4·50
First Day Cover				5·25
Presentation Pack			5·50	
MS706 110×75 mm. **674** £1 multicoloured			2·75	2·75
		a. Booklet pane. As No. **MS**706 with additional margins all round showing arms, mace and inscriptions	2·50	
First Day Cover				3·50
Presentation Pack			3·50	

Plate Nos.: All values 1A, 1B (each×4).
Sheets: 20 (4×5).
Imprint: Central, left-hand margin.
Quantities sold: 18p. (No. 700) 207,666; 18p. (No. 701) 214,869; 23p. (No. 702) 279,930; 23p. (No. 703) 274,379; 60p. (No. 704) 131,342; 60p. (No. 705) 136,508; £1 122,855.
Withdrawn: 31.5.96 (sheets).

675 Bell Heather

676 Sea Campion

677 Spotted Rock-rose

678 Thrift

679 Sheep's-bit Scabious

680 Field Bind-weed

681 Common Bird's-foot Trefoil

682 Sea holly

683 Common Centaury

684 Dwarf Pansy

European Nature Conservation Year. Wild Flowers

(Des N. Parlett. Litho BDT)

1995 (4 July). P 13 (C).

707	**675**	19p. multicoloured	40	20
		a. Horiz strip of 5. Nos. 707/11	3·00	3·00
708	**676**	19p. multicoloured	40	20
709	**677**	19p. multicoloured	40	20
710	**678**	19p. multicoloured	40	20
711	**679**	19p. multicoloured	40	20
712	**680**	23p. multicoloured	50	25
		a. Horiz strip of 5. Nos. 712/16	3·50	3·50
713	**681**	23p. multicoloured	50	25
714	**682**	23p. multicoloured	50	25
715	**683**	23p. multicoloured	50	25
716	**684**	23p. multicoloured	50	25
707/16	*Set of 10*		6·00	6·00
First Day Cover				6·25
Presentation Pack			6·50	

Plate Nos.: Both values 1A, 1B (each×4).
Sheets: 20 (5×4) the five designs for each value printed together, *se-tenant*, in horizontal strips of 5 throughout the sheets, the backgrounds forming composite designs.
Imprint: Central, left-hand margin.
Quantities sold: 19p. 454,143; 23p. 554,070.
Withdrawn: 31.7.96.

685 *Precis almana*

686 *Papilio palinurus*

687 *Catopsilia scylla*

688 *Papilio rumanzovia*

689 *Troides helena*

Exotic Butterflies

(Des W. Oliver. Litho Questa)

1995 (1 Sept). P 14 (C).

717	**685**	19p. multicoloured	50	55
718	**686**	23p. multicoloured	55	60
719	**687**	30p. multicoloured	80	85
720	**688**	41p. multicoloured	1·00	1·10
721	**689**	60p. multicoloured	1·60	1·70
717/21	*Set of 5*		4·00	4·25
First Day Cover				4·75
Presentation Pack			4·50	
MS722 150×100 mm. Nos. 720/1			2·40	2·50
	a. 41p. value imperforate			
First Day Cover				3·25
Presentation Pack			3·25	

No. **MS**722 includes the 'Singapore '95' International Stamp Exhibition logo on the sheet margin and shows the two stamp designs without frames.
Plate Nos.: All values 1A (×4).
Sheets: 20 (5×4).
Imprint: Central, left-hand margin.
Quantities sold: 19p. 475,496; 23p. 466,880; 30p. 246,270; 41p. 117,354; 60p. 133,026; miniature sheet 76,062.
Withdrawn: 30.9.96.

690 Peace Doves and United Nations Anniversary Emblem

691 Symbolic Wheat and Anniversary Emblem

50th Anniversary of United Nations

(Des A. Copp. Litho Enschedé)

1995 (24 Oct). P 13×14½ (C).

723	**690**	19p. cobalt and royal blue	60	50
724	**691**	23p. turq-green & dp blue-green	70	70
725		41p. dp blue-green & turq-green	1·20	1·20
726	**690**	60p. royal blue and cobalt	1·50	1·50
723/6	*Set of 4*		3·50	3·50
First Day Cover				4·50
Presentation Pack			4·50	

Plate Nos.: 19p., 23p. 1A, 1B (each×2); others 1A (×2).
Sheets: 20 (5×4).
Imprint: Central, left-hand margin.
Quantities sold: 19p. 152,550; 23p. 201,977; 41p. 75,032; 60p. 73,943.
Withdrawn: 31.10.96.

692 'Puss in Boots'

693 'Cinderella'

694 'Sleeping Beauty'

695 'Aladdin'

Christmas. Pantomimes

(Des V. Ambrus. Litho Cartor)

1995 (24 Oct). P 13½ (C).

727	**692**	19p. multicoloured	50	40
728	**693**	23p. multicoloured	55	45
729	**694**	41p. multicoloured	1·00	1·00
730	**695**	60p. multicoloured	1·60	1·50
727/30 *Set of 4*			3·25	3·00
First Day Cover				4·25
Presentation Pack			4·50	

Plate Nos.: All values 1A, 1B, 1C, 1D (each×4).
Sheets: 20 (5×4).
Imprint: Central, left-hand margin.
Quantities sold: 19p. 986,299; 23p. 716,510; 41p. 118,699; 60p. 131,497.
Withdrawn: 31.10.96.

Post Office Yearbook

1995 (24 Oct). Comprises Nos. 491c and 684/730 (price £20.50).
Yearbook .... 32·00
Sold out: 12.99.

696 Rat with Top Hat (*Illustration reduced. Actual size 110×75 mm*)

Chinese New Year ('Year of the Rat')

(Des V. Ambrus. Litho Questa)

1996 (19 Feb). Sheet 110×75 mm. P 13½×14 (C).

MS731	**696**	£1 multicoloured	2·50	2·50
First Day Cover				3·25
Presentation Pack			3·50	

Withdrawn: 28.2.97.

697 African Child and Map

698 Children and Globe

699 European Child and Map

700 South American Child and Map

701 Asian Child and Map

702 South Pacific Child and Map

50th Anniversary of U.N.I.C.E.F.

(Des A. Copp. Litho Questa)

1996 (19 Feb). P 14½ (C).

732	**697**	19p. multicoloured	45	40
733	**698**	23p. multicoloured	55	45
734	**699**	30p. multicoloured	70	65
735	**700**	35p. multicoloured	90	95
736	**701**	41p. multicoloured	1·00	1·10
737	**702**	60p. multicoloured	1·50	1·60
732/7 *Set of 6*			4·50	4·50
First Day Cover				5·25
Presentation Cover			5·25	

Plate Nos.: All values 1A (×4).
Sheets: 20 (4×5).
Imprint: Central, left-hand margin.
Quantities sold: 19p. 464,379; 23p. 413,906; 30p. 152,043; 35p. 84,359; 41p. 86,886; 60p. 90,074.
Withdrawn: 28.2.97.

703 Queen Elizabeth II (*from photo by T. O.' Neill*)

70th Birthday of Queen Elizabeth II

(Litho Questa)

1996 (21 Apr). P 14×15 (C).

738	**703**	£5 multicoloured	10·00	10·00
First Day Cover				12·00
Presentation Pack			11·00	

After one year No. 738 was retained as a definitive.
Plate Nos.: 1A (×5).
Sheets: 10 (2×5).
Imprint: Central, left-hand margin.

704 Elizabeth Garrett (first British woman doctor)

705 Emmeline Pankhurst (suffragette)

Europa. Women of Achievement (1st series)

(Des Jennifer Toombs. Litho BDT)

1996 (25 Apr). P 13½×14 (C).

739	**704**	23p. multicoloured	60	60
740	**705**	30p. multicoloured	90	90
739/40 *Set of 2*			1·50	1·50
First Day Cover				2·00
Presentation Pack			2·00	

See also Nos. 1563/6.
Plate Nos.: 23p. 1A, 1B, 1C (each×4); 30p. 1A, 1B, 1C, 1D, 1E (each×4).
Sheets: 10 (5×2).
Imprint: Bottom margin.
Quantities sold: 23p. 245,907; 30p. 432,935.
Withdrawn: 30.4.97.

706 Player shooting at Goal

707 Two Players chasing Ball

708 Player avoiding Tackle

709 Two Players competing for Ball

710 Players heading Ball

Football (1st series). European Football Championship, England

(Des A. Theobald. Litho BDT)

1996 (25 Apr). P 13½×14 (C).

741	**706**	19p. multicoloured	50	40
742	**707**	23p. multicoloured	60	50
743	**708**	35p. multicoloured	95	90
744	**709**	41p. multicoloured	1·00	1·00
745	**710**	60p. multicoloured	1·60	1·60
741/5	*Set of 5*		4·25	4·00
First Day Cover				4·50
Presentation Pack			4·75	

See also Nos. **MS**1201 and **MS**1274.
Plate Nos.: 19p., 23p. 1A, 1B (each×4); others 1A (×4).
Sheets: 20 (5×4).
Imprint: Central, left-hand margin.
Quantities sold: 19p. 450,588; 23p. 458,412; 35p. 105,519; 41p. 106,826; 60p. 109,092.
Withdrawn: 30.4.97.

711 Rowing

712 Judo

713 Fencing

714 Boxing

715 Basketball

716 Olympic Torch and Stadium (*Illustration reduced. Actual size 150×100 mm*)

Sports (2nd series). Sporting Anniversaries

(Des A. Theobald. Litho Questa)

1996 (8 June). P 13½ (No. **MS**751) or 14 (others), both comb.

746	**711**	19p. multicoloured	50	40
747	**712**	23p. multicoloured	60	50
748	**713**	35p. multicoloured	95	95
749	**714**	41p. multicoloured	1·00	1·00
750	**715**	60p. multicoloured	1·60	1·60
746/50	*Set of 5*		4·25	4·25
First Day Cover				5·00
Presentation Pack			5·00	
MS751 150×100 mm. **716** £1 multicoloured			2·50	2·50

First Day Cover	3·50
Presentation Pack	3·50

Anniversaries:—Nos. 746/8, 750/1, Centenary of Modern Olympic Games; No. 749, 50th anniversary of International Amateur Boxing Association.
No. **MS**751 also includes the 'CAPEX '96' International Stamp Exhibition logo.
Plate Nos.: All values 1A (×4).
Sheets: 20 (5×4).
Imprint: Central, left-hand margin.
Withdrawn: 30.6.97.

717 Bay on North Coast

718 Portelet Bay

719 Greve de Lecq Bay

720 Beauport Beach

721 Plemont Bay

722 St. Brelade's Bay

Tourism. Beaches

(Des A. Copp. Litho BDT)

1996 (8 June). P 14 (C).

752	**717**	19p. multicoloured	50	50
		a. Booklet pane. Nos. 752/3, each×3, with margins all round	2·50	
		b. Booklet pane. Nos. 752/7, with margins all round	4·25	
753	**718**	23p. multicoloured	60	60
754	**719**	30p. multicoloured	80	80
		a. Booklet pane. Nos. 754/5, each×3, with margins all round	4·00	
755	**720**	35p. multicoloured	95	95
756	**721**	41p. multicoloured	1·10	1·10
		a. Booklet pane. Nos. 756/7, each×3, with margins all round	6·25	
757	**722**	60p. multicoloured	1·60	1·60
752/7	*Set of 6*		5·00	5·00
First Day Cover				5·25
Presentation Pack			5·25	
Postcards (set of 6)			3·00	8·50

Plate Nos.: 19p., 23p. 1A, 1B (each×4); others 1A (×4).
Sheets: 20 (5×4).
Imprint: Central, left-hand margin.
Withdrawn: 30.6.97 (sheets).

723 Drag Hunt

724 Pony and Trap

725 Training Racehorses on Beach

726 Show-jumping

727 Pony Club Event   **728** Shire Mare and Foal

Horses

(Des P. Layton. Litho Enschedé)

1996 (13 Sept). P 13½×14 (C).

758	**723**	19p. multicoloured	50	50
759	**724**	23p. multicoloured	60	60
760	**725**	30p. multicoloured	80	80
761	**726**	35p. multicoloured	95	95
762	**727**	41p. multicoloured	1·10	1·10
763	**728**	60p. multicoloured	1·60	1·60
758/63 *Set of* 6			5·00	5·00
First Day Cover				5·25
Presentation Pack			5·25	
Postcards (set of 6)			3·00	8·50

Plate Nos.: All values 1A, 1B (each×4).
Sheets: 20 (4×5).
Imprint: Central, left-hand margin.
Withdrawn: 30.9.97.

729 The Journey to Bethlehem   **730** The Shepherds

731 The Nativity   **732** The Three Kings

Christmas

(Des V. Ambrus. Litho Cartor)

1996 (12 Nov). P 13×13½ (C).

764	**729**	19p. multicoloured	50	50
765	**730**	23p. multicoloured	60	70
766	**731**	30p. multicoloured	90	95
767	**732**	60p. multicoloured	1·40	1·50
764/7 *Set of* 4			3·00	3·25
First Day Cover				4·25
Presentation Pack			4·25	

Plate Nos.: All values 1A, 1B, 1C (each×4).
Sheets: 20 (4×5).
Imprint: Central, left-hand margin.
Withdrawn: 28.11.97.

Post Office Yearbook

1996 (12 Nov). Comprises Nos. **MS**731/67 (price £23).

Yearbook	36·00	

Sold out: 12.99.

733 Jersey Cow wearing Scarf (*Illustration reduced. Actual size* 110×75 *mm*)

Chinese New Year ('Year of the Ox')

(Des V. Ambrus. Litho Questa)

1997 (7 Feb). Sheet 110×74 mm. P 14×13½ (C).

MS768	**733**	£1 multicoloured	3·25	3·75
First Day Cover				4·50
Presentation Pack			4·50	

Withdrawn: 28.2.98.

'HONG KONG '97' International Stamp Exhibition

1997 (7 Feb). No. **MS**768 optd with exhibition emblem in black and 'JERSEY AT HONG KONG '97' in red, both on sheet margin.

MS769	**733**	£1 multicoloured	3·75	4·00
First Day Cover				5·00
Presentation Pack			4·00	

Withdrawn: 28.2.98.

734 Lillie the Cow on   **735** Lillie taking
the Beach   Photograph

736 Carrying Bucket   **737** Eating Meal at
and Spade   Mont Orgueil

Tourism. 'Lillie the Cow'

(Des A. Copp. Litho BDT)

1997 (12 Feb)–**99**. Self-adhesive. P 9½ (C).

770	**734**	(23p). multicoloured (a)	80	85
		a. With copyright symbol after date (bc)	4·50	4·50
771	**735**	(23p). multicoloured (a)	80	85
		a. With copyright symbol after date (bc)	4·50	4·50
772	**736**	(23p). multicoloured (a)	80	85
		a. With copyright symbol after date (bc)	4·50	4·50
773	**737**	(23p). multicoloured (a)	80	85
		a. With copyright symbol after date (bc)	4·50	4·50
770/3 *Set of* 4			2·75	3·00
770a/3a *Set of* 4			16·00	16·00
First Day Cover				4·50
Presentation Pack			4·00	

Nos. 770/3, which are inscribed 'UK MINIMUM POSTAGE PAID', come, *se-tenant*, in strips of 4 or rolls of 100 with the surplus self-adhesive paper around each stamp removed. Nos. 770/3 were initially sold at 23p. each; this was increased to 24p. on 10 March 1997.

Initially released with '1997' imprint dates, Nos. 770a/3a were subsequently reissued inscribed '1999' (price per set, mint or used, £18) and '2000' (price £16).

Printings: (a) 12.2.97. Inscr '1997'; (b) 16.4.99. Inscr '1999'; (c). 9.12.00. Inscr '2000'.
Sold out: By 5.2001.

738 Red-breasted   **739** Sanderling
Merganser

740 Northern Gannet   **741** Great Crested Grebe

742 Common Tern

743 Black-headed Gull

744 Dunlin

745 Sandwich Tern

746 Ringed Plover

747 Bar-tailed Godwit

748 Atlantic Puffin

749 Brent Goose

750 Grey Plover

751 Black Scoter

752 Lesser Black-backed Gull

753 Little Egret

754 Fulmar

755 Golden Plover

756 Common Greenshank

757 Little Grebe

758 Great Cormorant

759 Western Curlew

760 Oystercatcher

761 Ruddy Turnstone

762 Herring Gull

763 Rock Pipit

764 Greater Black-backed Gull

765 Pied Avocet

766 Grey Heron

767 Common Redshank

768 Razorbill

769 Shag

Seabirds and Waders

(Des N. Parlett. Litho Questa)

1997 (12 Feb)–**99**. P 14½ (C).

774	**738**	1p. multicoloured (a)	10	10
775	**739**	2p. multicoloured (b)	10	10
776	**740**	4p. multicoloured (d)	10	10
777	**741**	5p. multicoloured (b)	10	15
778	**742**	10p. multicoloured (a)	20	25
779	**743**	15p. multicoloured (a)	30	35
780	**744**	20p. multicoloured (a)	60	45
		a. With copyright symbol after date (c)	40	45
781	**745**	21p. multicoloured (b)	40	45
782	**746**	22p. multicoloured (d)	45	50
783	**747**	23p. multicoloured (e)	45	50
784	**748**	24p. multicoloured (a)	70	50
		a. With copyright symbol after date (c)	45	50
785	**749**	25p. multicoloured (b)	50	55
786	**750**	26p. multicoloured (d)	50	55
787	**751**	27p. multicoloured (e)	55	60
788	**752**	28p. multicoloured (e)	60	65
789	**753**	29p. multicoloured (e)	60	65
790	**754**	30p. multicoloured (b)	60	65
791	**755**	31p. multicoloured (d)	60	65
792	**756**	32p. multicoloured (d)	65	70
793	**757**	33p. multicoloured (e)	65	70
794	**758**	34p. multicoloured (e)	70	75
795	**759**	35p. multicoloured (d)	70	75
796	**760**	37p. multicoloured (a)	75	80
797	**761**	40p. multicoloured (b)	80	85
798	**762**	44p. multicoloured (a)	90	95
799	**763**	45p. multicoloured (e)	90	95
800	**764**	50p. multicoloured (d)	1·00	1·10
801	**765**	60p. multicoloured (b)	1·20	1·40
802	**766**	65p. multicoloured (e)	1·20	1·40
803	**767**	75p. multicoloured (a)	2·00	2·10
804	**768**	£1 multicoloured (b)	2·50	2·50
805	**769**	£2 multicoloured (a)	5·00	5·25
774/805 *Set of 32*			24·00	26·00

First Day Covers (4) .... 30·00
Presentation Packs (4) .... 28·00
Postcards (set of 32) .... 13·00   40·00
MS806 Four sheets, each 136×130 mm. (a) Nos. 774,
778/80, 784, 796, 803 and 805 (a). (b) Nos. 775,
777, 781, 785, 790, 797, 801 and 804 (b). (c).
Nos. 776, 782, 786, 791/2, 795, 798 and 800 (d). (d)
Nos. 783, 787/9, 793/4, 799 and 802 (e) ....
Set of 4 sheets .... 25·00   25·00
First Day Covers (4) ....   40·00
Souvenir Folders (4) .... 32·00
Complete series Souvenir Folder .... 28·00

 Printings: (a) 12.2.97. Inscr '1997' without copyright symbol; (b)
28.1.98. Inscr '1998' with copyright symbol; (c) 2.4.98. Inscr '1998'
with copyright symbol; (d) 11.8.98. Inscr '1998' with copyright
symbol; (e) 21.8.99. Inscr '1999' with copyright symbol.
 Plate Nos.: 1p., 2p., 22p., 25p., 26p., £2 1A, 1B, 1C, 1D (each×4)
20p., 24p. 1A, 1B, 1C, 1D (each×4), 2A, 2B, 2C, 2D. (each×4)
(Nos. 780a, 784x); 4p., 21p., 50p., 60p. 1A, 1B, 1C, 1D, 1E, 1F, 1G,
1H (each×4); **MS**806 1A (each×4); others 1A, 1B (each×4).
 The 2p. (No. 775) from plate 1D has 1A (×4) in the top margin.
 Sheets: 20 (4×5).
 Imprint: Central, left-hand margin.
 Withdrawn: 31.12.2007.

770 de Havilland D.H.95
Flamingo

771 Handley Page
H.P.R.5 Marathon

772 de Havilland D.H.114 Heron

773 Boeing 737-236

774 Britten Norman Trislander

775 BAe 146-200

**Jersey Aviation History (6th series). 60th Anniversary of Jersey
Airport**

(Des A. Theobald. Litho Enschedé)

1997 (10 Mar). P 13½×14 (C).
807	**770**	20p. multicoloured	45	40
808	**771**	24p. multicoloured	55	40
809	**772**	31p. multicoloured	65	65
810	**773**	37p. multicoloured	95	95
811	**774**	43p. multicoloured	1·10	1·10
812	**775**	63p. multicoloured	1·70	1·70
807/12	*Set of 6*	....	5·00	5·00
	First Day Cover	....		5·25
	Presentation Pack	....	5·50	

 Plate Nos.: All values 1A, 1B, 1C (each×4).
 Sheets: 20 (4×5).
 Imprint: Central, left-hand margin.
 Withdrawn: 31.3.98.

776 The Bull of St. Clement

777 The Black Horse of
St. Ouen

778 The Black Dog of Bouley
Bay

779 Les Fontainnes des Mittes

Europa. Tales and Legends

(Des Jennifer Toombs. Litho BDT)

1997 (15 Apr). P 15×14 (C).
813	**776**	20p. multicoloured	65	60
814	**777**	24p. multicoloured	75	70
815	**778**	31p. multicoloured	1·00	1·10
816	**779**	63p. multicoloured	1·25	1·80
813/16	*Set of 4*	....	3·00	3·75
	First Day Cover	....		4·50
	Presentation Pack	....	4·50	

 Nos. 814/15 include the 'EUROPA' emblem.
 Plate Nos.: All values 1A, 1B (each×5).
 Sheets: 10 (5×2).
 Imprint: Bottom margin.
 Withdrawn: 30.4.98.

'Pacific 97' International Stamp Exhibition, San Francisco

1997 (29 May). No. **MS**806a optd with exhibition emblem on sheet
margin.
MS817 136×130 mm. Nos. 774, 778/80, 784, 796, 803
and 805 .... 7·50   8·50
Souvenir Folder .... 9·50

780 Cycling

781 Archery

782 Windsurfing

783 Gymnastics

784 Volleyball

785 Running

Seventh Island Games, Jersey

(Des A. Theobald. Litho BDT)

1997 (28 June). P 13½ (C).
818	**780**	20p. multicoloured	55	55
		a. Booklet pane. Nos. 818/19,		
		each×3, with margins all round	2·50	
		b. Booklet pane. Nos. 818/23, with		
		margins all round	5·25	
819	**781**	24p. multicoloured	65	65
820	**782**	31p. multicoloured	80	80
		a. Booklet pane. Nos. 820/1, each×3,		
		with margins all round....................	4·00	
821	**783**	37p. multicoloured	1·00	1·00
822	**784**	43p. multicoloured	1·10	1·10
		a. Booklet pane. Nos. 822/3, each×3,		
		with margins all round....................	6·25	
823	**785**	63p. multicoloured	1·70	1·70
818/23	*Set of 6*	....	5·25	5·25

First Day Cover .... 5·75
Presentation Pack .... 6·00
    Plate Nos.: 20p., 24p. 1A, 1B (each×4); others 1A (×4).
    Sheets: 20 (5×4).
    Imprint: Central, left-hand margin.
    Withdrawn: 30.6.98 (sheets).

786 Mallorcan Midwife Toad   787 Aye-Aye

788 Mauritius Parakeet   789 Pigmy Hog

790 St. Lucia Whip-tail   791 Madagascar Teal

Wildlife Preservation Trust (6th series)

(Des W. Oliver. Litho Cartor)

1997 (2 Sept). P 13 (C).

824	786	20p. multicoloured	50	45
825	787	24p. multicoloured	60	50
826	788	31p. multicoloured	90	90
827	789	37p. multicoloured	1·00	1·10
828	790	43p. multicoloured	1·10	1·20
829	791	63p. multicoloured	1·70	1·80
824/9	*Set of 6*		5·25	5·25

First Day Cover .... 5·50
Presentation Pack .... 6·00
    Plate Nos.: All values 1A, 1B (each×4).
    Sheets: 20 (5×4).
    Imprint: Central, left-hand margin.
    Withdrawn: 30.9.98.

792 Ash   793 Elder

794 Beech   795 Sweet Chestnut

796 Hawthorn   797 Common Oak

Trees

(Des Norah Bryan. Litho Questa)

1997 (2 Sept). P 14½ (C).

830	792	20p. multicoloured	50	45
831	793	24p. multicoloured	60	50
832	794	31p. multicoloured	90	90
833	795	37p. multicoloured	1·00	1·10
834	796	43p. multicoloured	1·10	1·20
835	797	63p. multicoloured	1·70	1·80
830/5	*Set of 6*		5·25	5·25

First Day Cover .... 5·50
Presentation Pack .... 6·00
    Plate Nos.: 20p., 24p. 1A, 1B (each×4); others 1A (×4).
    Sheets: 20 (5×4).
    Imprint: Central, left-hand margin.
    Withdrawn: 30.9.98.

798 Father Christmas and   799 Father Christmas with
Reindeer outside Jersey Airport   Presents, St. Aubin's Harbour

800 Father Christmas in Sleigh,   801 Father Christmas with
Mont Orgueil Castle   Children, Royal Square, St. Helier

Christmas

(Des Colleen Corlett. Litho BDT)

1997 (11 Nov). P 14 (C).

836	798	20p. multicoloured	60	60
837	799	24p. multicoloured	70	70
838	800	31p. multicoloured	1·00	1·00
839	801	63p. multicoloured	1·90	1·90
836/9	*Set of 4*		3·75	3·75

First Day Cover .... 4·50
Presentation Pack .... 4·50
    Plate Nos.: 20p., 31p. 1A, 1B (each×5); others 1A, 1B (each×4).
    Sheets: 20 (4×5).
    Imprint: Central, left-hand margin.
    Withdrawn: 30.11.98.

802 Wedding Photograph, 1947   803 Queen Elizabeth and
Prince Philip, 1997

804 Full-length Wedding Photograph, 1947
(*Illustration reduced, Actual size 150×100 mm*)

Golden Wedding of Queen Elizabeth and Prince Philip

(Des G. Drummond. Litho Questa)

1997 (20 Nov). P 13½ (**MS**842) or 14½ (others), both comb.

840	**802**	50p. multicoloured	1·00	60
		a. Horiz pair. Nos. 840/1	3·00	3·00
841	**803**	50p. multicoloured	1·00	60
840/1	*Set of 2*		3·00	3·00
	First Day Cover			3·75
	Presentation Pack		3·75	
MS842	150×100 mm. **804** £1.50 multicoloured		4·50	4·50
	First Day Cover			5·00
	Presentation Pack		4·75	

Plate Nos.: 1A, 1B, 1C, 1D (each×5).
Sheets: 20 (4×5). The two designs were printed together, *se-tenant*, in horizontal pairs throughout the sheets.
Imprint: Central, left-hand margin.
Withdrawn: 30.11.98.
Sold out: By 7.04.

Year Pack 1997

1997 (20 Nov). Comprises Nos. **MS**768, 770/4, 778/80, 784, 796, 803, 805, 807/16 and 818/42 (price £22).

Year Pack		45·00

Sold out: By 11.02.

Post Office Yearbook 1997

1997 (20 Nov). Comprises Nos. **MS**768, 770/4, 778/80, 784, 796, 803, 805, 807/16 and 818/42 (price £25).

Yearbook		45·00

Sold out: By 7.04.

805 Tiger wearing Scarf (*Illustration reduced. Actual size 110×75 mm*)

Chinese New Year ('Year of the Tiger')

(Des V. Ambrus. Litho Questa)

1998 (28 Jan). Sheet 110×75 mm. P 14×13½ (C).

MS843 **805** £1 multicoloured		2·50	2·75
First Day Cover			3·75
Presentation Pack		4·25	

Withdrawn: 30.1.99.

806 J.M.T. Bristol 4 Tonner, 1923 **807** Safety Coach Service Regent Double Decker, 1934

808 Slade's Dennis Lancet, circa 1936 **809** Tantivy Leyland PLSC, Lion, 1947

810 J.B.S. Morris, circa 1958 **811** J.M.T. Titan TD4 Double Decker, circa 1961

75th Anniversary of Jersey Motor Transport Company. Buses (1st series)

(Des A. Copp. Litho BDT)

1998 (2 Apr). P 14 (C).

844	**806**	20p. multicoloured	55	50
		a. Booklet pane. Nos. 844/5, each×3, with margins all round	2·50	
		b. Booklet pane. Nos. 844/9, with margins all round	4·50	
845	**807**	24p. multicoloured	65	50
846	**808**	31p. multicoloured	75	70
		a. Booklet pane. Nos. 846/7, each×3, with margins all round	4·00	
847	**809**	37p. multicoloured	1·00	1·00
848	**810**	43p. multicoloured	1·10	1·10
		a. Booklet pane. Nos. 848/9, each×3, with margins all round	7·00	
849	**811**	63p. multicoloured	1·50	1·60
844/9	*Set of 6*		5·00	5·00
	First Day Cover			5·75
	Presentation Pack		5·75	

See also Nos. 1364/**MS**1370, 1553/8 and 1736/41.
Plate Nos.: 20p., 24p. 1A, 1B (each×4); others 1A (×4).
Sheets: 20 (4×5).
Imprint: Central, left-hand margin.
Withdrawn: 30.4.99 (sheets).

812 Creative Arts Festival **813** Jazz Festival

814 Good Food Festival **815** Floral Festival

Europa. National Festivals

(Des A. Copp. Litho Enschedé)

1998 (2 Apr). P 14×13½ (C).

850	**812**	20p. multicoloured	65	45
851	**813**	24p. multicoloured	70	55
852	**814**	31p. multicoloured	90	1·00
853	**815**	63p. multicoloured	1·70	1·90
850/3	*Set of 4*		3·50	3·50

First Day Cover .... 4·00
Presentation Pack .... 4·00

Nos. 851/2 include the 'EUROPA' emblem.
Plate Nos.: All values 1A, 1B (each×4).
Sheets: 10 (5×2).
Imprint: Bottom, left-hand corner margin.
Withdrawn: 30.4.99.

816 Hobie Cat and *Duke of Normandy* (launch)

817 Hobie Cat with White, Yellow, Red and Green Sails

818 Hobie Cats with Pink, Purple and Orange Sails

819 Bow of Hobie Cat with Yellow, Blue and Purple Sails

820 Hobie Cat Heeling

821 Yacht with Red, White and Blue Spinnaker

822 Yacht with Pink Spinnaker

823 Yacht with Two White Sails

824 Trimaram

825 Yacht with Blue, White and Yellow Spinnaker in Foreground

Jersey Yachting (1st series). Opening of Elizabeth Marina, St. Helier

(Des A. Theobald. Litho Cartor)

1998 (15 May). P 13 (C).

854	**816**	20p. multicoloured	40	20
		a. Horiz strip of 5. Nos. 854/8................	2·50	2·50
855	**817**	20p. multicoloured	40	20
856	**818**	20p. multicoloured	40	20
857	**819**	20p. multicoloured	40	20
858	**820**	20p. multicoloured	40	20
859	**821**	24p. multicoloured	45	25
		a. Horiz strip of 5. Nos. 859/63...............	3·00	3·00
860	**822**	24p. multicoloured	45	25
861	**823**	24p. multicoloured	45	25
862	**824**	24p. multicoloured	45	25
863	**825**	24p. multicoloured	45	25
854/63 *Set of 10*..			5·00	5·00
First Day Cover				6·00
Presentation Pack			6·00	

See also No. **MS**1319.
Plate Nos.: Both values 1A (×4).
Sheets: 20 (5×4), the designs were each printed together, *se-tenant*, in horizontal strips of five throughout the sheets, each strip forming a composite design.
Imprint: Central, left-hand margin.
Withdrawn: 31.5.99.

826 Bass

827 Red Gurnard

828 Skate

829 Mackerel

830 Tope

831 Cuckoo Wrasse

Marine Life (3rd series). International Year of the Ocean. Fish

(Des W. Oliver. Litho BDT)

1998 (11 Aug). P 15×14 (C).

864	**826**	20p. multicoloured	50	50
865	**827**	24p. multicoloured	65	65
866	**828**	31p. multicoloured	80	80
867	**829**	37p. multicoloured	1·00	1·00
868	**830**	43p. multicoloured	1·10	1·10
869	**831**	63p. multicoloured	1·50	1·50
864/9 *Set of 6*			5·00	5·00
First Day Cover				6·00
Presentation Pack			6·00	

Plate Nos.: 20p., 24p. 1A, 1B (each×4); others 1A (×4).
Sheets: 20 (4×5).
Imprint: Central, left-hand margin.
Withdrawn: 31.8.99.

832 Cider-making

833 Potato Barrels on Cart

834 Collecting Seaweed for Fertiliser

835 Milking Jersey Cows

Days Gone By

(Des A. Copp. Litho SNP Cambec, Melbourne)

1998 (11 Aug). Self-adhesive. With copyright symbol after date. P 11½×11 (Die-cut).

870	**832**	(20p). multicoloured (abcde)	90	90
871	**833**	(20p). multicoloured (abcde)	90	90
872	**834**	(20p). multicoloured (abcde)	90	90
873	**835**	(20p). multicoloured (abcde)	90	90
870/3	*Set of 4*		3·25	3·25
First Day Cover				3·50
Presentation Pack			3·50	

Nos. 870/3, which are inscribed 'BAILIWICK MINIMUM POSTAGE PAID' and were initially sold at 20p. each, come, *se-tenant*, in strips of 4 or rolls of 100 with the surplus self-adhesive paper around each stamp removed. Initially released with '1998' imprint dates, Nos. 870/3 were subsequently reissued inscribed '1999' (price per set, unused or used, £18), '2000' (price £16), '2001' (price £10) and 2003 (price £6).

Printings: (a) 11.8.98, Inscr '1998'; (b) 16.7.99, Inscr '1999'; (c). 3.11.2000. Inscr '2000'; (d) 19.11.2001. Inscr '2001'; (e) 4.4.2003. Inscr '2003'.

836 Irises

837 Carnations

838 Chrysanthemums

839 Pinks

840 Roses

841 Lilies

842 Lilium 'Star Gazer' (*Illustration reduced. Actual size 150×100 mm*)

Seasonal Flowers (1st series). Autumn

(Des Wendy Tait. Litho Questa)

1998 (23 Oct). P 14×13½ (No. **MS**880) or 14½ (others), both comb.

874	**836**	20p. multicoloured	50	40
875	**837**	24p. multicoloured	60	50
876	**838**	31p. multicoloured	75	70
877	**839**	37p. multicoloured	90	90
878	**840**	43p. multicoloured	1·00	1·10
879	**841**	63p. multicoloured	1·40	1·50
874/9	*Set of 6*		4·75	4·75
First Day Cover				5·50
Presentation Pack			5·50	
MS880	150×100 mm. **842** £1.50 multicoloured		3·25	3·75
First Day Cover				4·50
Presentation Pack			4·50	

No. **MS**880 includes the 'ITALIA' 98 stamp exhibition emblem on the margin.

See also Nos. 1119/24, 1320/5 and 1427/32.
Plate Nos.: 20p., 24p. 1A, 1B (each×6); 31p., 37p. 1A (×6); 43p., 63p. 1A, 1B, 1C (each×6).
Sheets: 20 (4×5).
Imprint: Central, left-hand margin.
Withdrawn: 30.10.99.

843 Central Market Crib

844 St. Thomas's Church Crib

845 Trinity Parish Church Crib

846 Royal Square Crib

Christmas. Cribs

(Des Colleen Corlett. Litho Cartor)

1998 (10 Nov). P 13 (C).

881	**843**	20p. multicoloured	40	40
882	**844**	24p. multicoloured	50	55
883	**845**	31p. multicoloured	65	65
884	**846**	63p. multicoloured	1·60	1·60
881/4	*Set of 4*		3·00	3·00
First Day Cover				4·00
Presentation Pack			4·00	

Plate Nos.: All values 1A (×5).
Sheets: 20 (4×5).
Imprint: Central, left-hand margin.
Withdrawn: 30.11.99.

Year Pack 1998

1998 (10 Nov). Comprises Nos. 775/7, 781/2, 785/6, 790/2, 795, 797/8, 800/1, 804 and **MS**843/84 (price £22.50).
Year Pack .... 45·00
Sold out: By 7.04.

Post Office Yearbook

1998 (10 Nov). Comprises Nos. 775/7, 781/2, 785/6, 790/2, 795, 797/8, 800/1, 804 and **MS**843/84 (price £22.50).
Yearbook .... 45·00
Sold out: By 7.04.

847 Rabbit (*Illustration reduced. Actual size 110×75 mm*)

Chinese New Year ('Year of the Rabbit')

(Des V. Ambrus. Litho Questa)

1999 (16 Feb). Sheet 110×75 mm. P 14×13½ (C).

MS885 **847** £1 multicoloured			2·50	2·75
First Day Cover				4·00
Presentation Pack			3·75	

Withdrawn: 29.2.2000.

848 Jersey Eastern Railway Mail Train

849 Brighton (paddle-steamer)

850 de Havilland D.H.86 Dragon Express at Jersey Airport

851 Jersey Postal Service Morris Minor Van

125th Anniversary of Universal Postal Union

(Des A. Theobald. Litho BDT)

1999 (16 Feb). P 14 (C).

886	**848**	20p. multicoloured	55	50
887	**849**	24p. multicoloured	65	60
888	**850**	43p. multicoloured	95	1·10
889	**851**	63p. multicoloured	1·40	1·70
886/9 Set of 4			3·25	3·50
First Day Cover				4·50
Presentation Pack			4·50	

Plate Nos.: All values 1A (×4).
Sheets: 20 (4×5).
Imprint: Central, left-hand margin.
Withdrawn: 29.2.2000.

852 Jessie Eliza, St. Catherine

853 Alexander Coutanche, St. Helier

Jersey Lifeboats (2nd series). 175th Anniversary of Royal National Lifeboat Institution

(Litho Questa)

1999 (16 Feb). P 14½ (C).

890	**852**	75p. multicoloured	2·00	80
		a. Horiz pair. Nos. 890/1	4·50	4·50
891	**853**	£1 multicoloured	2·50	1·00
890/1 Set of 2			4·50	4·50
First Day Cover				5·00
Presentation Pack			5·00	

Plate Nos.: 1A, 1B, 1C, 1D (each×7).
Sheets: 20 (4×5), the two values printed together, se-tenant, in horizontal pairs throughout the sheet.
Imprint: Central, left-hand margin.
Withdrawn: 29.2.2000.

854 Cymbidium Maufant 'Jersey'

855 Miltonia Millbrook 'Jersey'

856 Paphiopedilum Transvaal

857 Paphiopedilum Elizabeth Castle

858 Calanthe Five Oaks

859 Cymbidium Icho Tower 'Trinity'

860 Miltonia Portelet (Illustration reduced. Actual size 150×100 mm)

Jersey Orchids (4th series)

(Litho Enschedé)

1999 (19 Mar). P 13½ (No. MS898) or 14×13, both comb.

892	**854**	21p. multicoloured	55	50
893	**855**	25p. multicoloured	55	50
894	**856**	31p. multicoloured	75	70
895	**857**	37p. multicoloured	85	80
896	**858**	43p. multicoloured	90	90
897	**859**	63p. multicoloured	2·00	2·00
892/7 Set of 6			5·00	5·00
First Day Cover				5·50
Presentation Pack			5·50	
MS898 150×100 mm. **860** £1.50, multicoloured			4·00	4·50
First Day Cover				6·00
Presentation Pack			4·50	

No. **MS**898 also includes the 'Australia '99' World Stamp Exhibition, Melbourne, emblem on the margin at top left.
Plate Nos.: 21p, 25p. 1A, 1B (each×5); others 1A (×5).
Sheets: 20 (5×4).
Imprint: Central, left-hand margin.
Withdrawn: 31.3.2000.

861 Howard Davis Park

862 Sir Winston Churchill Memorial Park

863 Coronation Park

864 La Collette Gardens

Europa. Parks and Gardens

(Des Ariel Luke. Litho Cartor)

1999 (27 Apr). P 13×13½ (C).

899	**861**	21p. multicoloured	50	50
900	**862**	25p. multicoloured	70	70
901	**863**	31p. multicoloured	1·00	1·00
902	**864**	63p. multicoloured	2·00	2·00
899/902 Set of 4			4·00	4·00

First Day Cover... 4·50
Presentation Pack.. 4·50

Nos. 900/1 include the 'EUROPA' logo at top left and all four values show the 'ibra '99' International Stamp Exhibition, Nuremberg, emblem at top right.
    Plate Nos.: All values 1A (×4).
    Sheets: 10 (2×5).
    Imprint: Central, left-hand margin.
    Withdrawn: 29.4.2000.

865 Prince Edward and Miss Sophie Rhys-Jones

Royal Wedding

(Des A. Copp. Litho Questa)

1999 (19 June). P 14½ (C).
903	**865**	35p. mult (yellow background)...............	75	75
		a. Pair. Nos. 903/4..............................	1·50	1·50
904		35p. mult (blue background)................	75	75
903/4	*Set of 2*		1·50	1·50
First Day Cover...				2·00
Presentation Pack...		2·00		

    Plate Nos.: 1A, 1B, 1C, 1D (each×4).
    Sheets: 20 (4×5) with the two designs printed together, *se-tenant*, in horizontal or vertical pairs throughout the sheet.
    Imprint: Central, left-hand margin.
    Withdrawn: 30.6.2000.

866 Jersey-built Benz, 1899   **867** Star Tourer, 1910

868 Citroen 'Traction Avant', 1938   **869** Talbot BG110 Tourer, 1937

870 Morris Cowley Six Special Coupé, 1934   **871** Ford Anglia Saloon, 1946

Vintage Cars (3rd series). Centenary of Motoring in Jersey

(Des A. Copp. Litho BDT)

1999 (2 July). P 14 (C).
905	**866**	21p. multicoloured............................	45	45
		a. Booklet pane. Nos. 905/6, each×3, with margins all round....................	2·50	
		b. Booklet pane. Nos. 905/10, with margins all round	4·50	
906	**867**	25p. multicoloured............................	55	55
907	**868**	31p. multicoloured............................	65	65
		a. Booklet pane. Nos. 907/8, each×3, with margins all round....................	4·50	
908	**869**	37p. multicoloured............................	1·00	1·00
909	**870**	43p. multicoloured............................	1·20	1·20
		a. Booklet pane. Nos. 909/10, each×3, with margins all round	7·50	
910	**871**	63p. multicoloured............................	1·50	1·50
905/10	*Set of 6*...		5·00	5·00

First Day Cover... 5·50
Presentation Pack.. 5·50

Nos. 905a/b, 907a and 909a also include the 'PhilexFrance 99' International Stamp Exhibition emblem on the margins at top right.
    Plate Nos.: 21p, 25p. 1A, 1B (each×4); others 1A (×4).
    Sheets: 20 (4×5).
    Imprint: Central, left-hand margin.
    Withdrawn: 31.7.2000 (sheets).

872 West European Hedgehog   **873** Eurasian Red Squirrel

874 Nathusius Pipistrelle   **875** Jersey Bank Vole

876 Lesser White-toothed Shrew   **877** Common Mole

Jersey Nature. Small Mammals

(Des W. Oliver. Litho Cartor)

1999 (21 Aug). P 13½×13 (C).
911	**872**	21p. multicoloured............................	45	45
912	**873**	25p. multicoloured............................	55	55
913	**874**	31p. multicoloured............................	65	65
914	**875**	37p. multicoloured............................	1·00	1·10
915	**876**	43p. multicoloured............................	1·00	1·10
916	**877**	63p. multicoloured............................	2·00	2·20
911/16	*Set of 6*...		5·25	5·50
First Day Cover...				6·00
Presentation Pack...		6·00		

No. 913 is inscribed 'Pipestrelle' in error.
    Plate Nos.: All values 1A (×4).
    Sheets: 20 (4×5).
    Imprint: Central, left-hand margin.
    Withdrawn: 31.8.2000.

878 Gorey Pierhead Light   **879** La Corbière

880 Noirmont Point   **881** Demie de Pas

882 Greve d'Azette   **883** Sorel Point

Jersey Lighthouses (1st series). 150th Anniversary of First Lighthouse on Jersey

(Des A. Copp. Litho Walsall)

1999 (5 Oct). P 14 (C).

917	**878**	21p. multicoloured	45	45
918	**879**	25p. multicoloured	55	55
919	**880**	34p. multicoloured	75	75
920	**881**	38p. multicoloured	1·00	1·00
921	**882**	44p. multicoloured	1·20	1·20
922	**883**	64p. multicoloured	2·00	2·00
917/22	*Set of 6*		5·50	5·50

First Day Cover .... 6·00
Presentation Pack .... 6·00

See also Nos. 1086/91.
Plate Nos.: All values 1A, 1B (each×4).
Sheets: 20 (5×4).
Imprint: Central, left-hand margin.
Withdrawn: 31.10.2000.

884 Mistletoe   **885** Holly

886 Ivy   **887** Christmas Rose

Christmas. Festive Foliage

(Des Colleen Corlett. Litho BDT)

1999 (9 Nov). P 14 (C).

923	**884**	21p. multicoloured	45	45
924	**885**	25p. multicoloured	55	55
925	**886**	34p. multicoloured	1·10	75
926	**887**	64p. multicoloured	1·60	2·00
923/6	*Set of 4*		3·50	3·50

First Day Cover .... 4·50
Presentation Pack .... 4·50

Plate Nos.: All values 1A, 1B (each×4).
Sheets: 20 (5×4).
Imprint: Central, left-hand margin.
Withdrawn: 30.11.2000.

Year Pack 1999

1999 (1 Dec). Comprises Nos. 783, 787/9, 793/4, 799, 802 and **MS**885/926 (price £23.50).
Year Pack .... 48·00

Post Office Yearbook

1999 (1 Dec). Comprises Nos. 783, 787/9, 793/4, 799, 802 and **MS**885/926 (price £27).
Yearbook .... 50·00
Sold out: By 11.03.

888 Jersey Crest

New Millennium

(Des A. Copp. Litho, die-stamped and embossed Cartor)

2000 (1 Jan). P 13½ (C).

927	**888**	£10 gold, bright red and deep carmine	20·00	22·00

First Day Cover .... 23·00
Presentation Pack .... 21·00

The printing of No. 927 incorporates metallic die-stamping and embossing using 22 carat gold.
No. 927 was retained in use as a definitive stamp.
Plate Nos.: 1A (×3).
Sheets: 10 (5×2).
Imprint: Upper left-hand margin.
Withdrawn: 31.5.2013.

889 Dragon (*Illustration reduced. Actual size 110×75 mm*)

Chinese New Year ('Year of the Dragon')

(Des V. Ambrus. Litho Questa)

2000 (5 Feb). Sheet 110×75 mm. P 14½×13½ (C).

MS928	**889**	£1 multicoloured	3·00	3·00

First Day Cover .... 4·00
Presentation Pack .... 4·00
Withdrawn: 29.2.2001.

890 'Ocean Adventure' (Gemma Carré)   **891** 'Solar Power' (Chantal Varley-Best)

892 'Floating City and Space Cars' (Nicola Singleton)

893 'Conservation' (Carly Logan)

'Stampin' the Future (children's stamp design competition) Winners

(Litho Questa)

2000 (9 May). P 14 (C).

929	**890**	22p. multicoloured	65	65
930	**891**	22p. multicoloured	65	65
931	**892**	22p. multicoloured	65	65
932	**893**	22p. multicoloured	65	65
929/32		*Set of 4*	2·40	2·40
		First Day Cover		3·50
		Presentation Pack	3·50	
MS933		150×100 mm. Nos. 929/32	3·00	3·50
		First Day Cover		5·00
		Presentation Pack	5·00	

Plate Nos.: All designs 1A (×4).
Sheets: 10 (2×5).
Imprint: Central, left-hand margin.
Withdrawn: 31.5.2001.

894 'Jersey in Europe'

895 'Building Europe'

Europa

(Des A. Copp (26p.), J.-P. Cousin (34p.). Litho Cartor)

2000 (9 May). P 13½×13 (C).

934	**894**	26p. multicoloured	2·00	2·00
935	**895**	34p. multicoloured	3·00	3·50
934/5		*Set of 2*	4·50	4·75
		First Day Cover		6·00
		Presentation Pack	5·50	

Only the 34p. includes the 'EUROPA' emblem.
Plate Nos.: Both values 1A (×4).
Sheets: 10 (2×5) 26p.; (5×2) 34p.
Imprint: Central, left-hand margin (26p.); upper left-hand margin (34p.).
Withdrawn: 31.5.2001.

896 Roman Merchant Ship
897 Viking Longship
898 13th-century Warship

899 14th-15th century Merchant Ship
900 Tudor Warship
901 17th-century Warship

902 18th-century Naval Cutter
903 19th-century Barque

904 19th-century Oyster Cutter
905 10th-century Ketch

Millennium Maritime Heritage. Opening of 'The Stamp Show 2000' International Stamp Exhibition, London.

(Des A. Theobald. Litho BDT)

2000 (22 May). P 14×13½ (C).

936	**896**	22p. multicoloured	45	25
		a. Horiz strip of 5. Nos. 936/40	3·00	3·00
		b. Booklet pane. Nos. 936/9 and 941/4	4·00	
		c. Booklet pane. Nos. 936/7, 939/41 and 943/5	4·00	
		d. Booklet pane. Nos. 936, 938/42 and 944/5	4·00	
		e. Booklet pane. Nos. 936/8, 940/3 and 945	4·00	
937	**897**	22p. multicoloured	45	25
		a. Booklet pane. Nos. 937/40 and 942/5	4·00	
938	**898**	22p. multicoloured	45	25
939	**899**	22p. multicoloured	45	25
940	**900**	22p. multicoloured	45	25
941	**901**	26p. multicoloured	50	30
		a. Horiz strip of 5. Nos. 941/5	3·25	3·25
942	**902**	26p. multicoloured	50	30
943	**903**	26p. multicoloured	50	30
944	**904**	26p. multicoloured	50	30
945	**905**	26p. multicoloured	50	30
936/45		*Set of 10*	6·00	6·00
		First Day Cover		6·50
		First Day Cover (set of 5 booklet panes)		31·00
		Presentation Pack	6·50	
		Souvenir Folder	13·00	
MS946		174×104 mm. Nos. 936/45	6·00	6·00
		a. With 'The Stamp Show 2000' logo added to top margin	6·00	6·00
		First Day Cover		7·00
		Presentation Pack	7·00	

Plate Nos.: Both values and miniature sheet 1A (×5).
Sheet: 10 (5×2). The five designs for each value printed together, *se-tenant*, in horizontal strips of 5 throughout the sheets, with 'The Stamp Show 2000' logo on the bottom sheet margin.
Withdrawn: 31.5.2001 (sheets).

906 Bottle-nosed Dolphins

907 Long-finned Pilot Whales

908 Common Porpoises

909 Grey Seals

910 Risso's Dolphins

911 White-beaked Dolphin

912 Common Dolphins (*Illustration reduced. Actual size 150×100 mm*)

Marine Life (4th series). World Environment Day. Marine Mammals

(Des W. Oliver. Litho BDT)

2000 (5 June). P 15×14 (C).

947	**906**	22p. multicoloured	50	55
948	**907**	26p. multicoloured	55	60
949	**908**	34p. multicoloured	80	85
950	**909**	38p. multicoloured	1·00	1·10
951	**910**	44p. multicoloured	1·10	1·20
952	**911**	64p. multicoloured	1·50	1·70

947/52 *Set of 6* ... 5·00 / 5·50
First Day Cover ... 6·00
Presentation Pack ... 6·50
MS953 150×100 mm. **912** £1.50 multicoloured ... 4·00 / 4·50
First Day Cover ... 6·00
Presentation Pack ... 6·00
  Plate Nos.: All values 1A, 1B, 1C (each×4).
  Sheets: 10 (2×5).
  Imprint: Central, left-hand margin.
  Withdrawn: 30.6.2001.

913 Prince William and Alps

914 Prince William and Polo Player

915 Prince William and Beaumaris Castle

916 Prince William and Fireworks

18th Birthday of Prince William

(Des W. Wall. Litho Questa)

2000 (21 June). P 14½ (C).

954	**913**	75p. multicoloured	1·75	1·50
955	**914**	75p. multicoloured	1·75	1·50
956	**915**	75p. multicoloured	1·75	1·50
957	**916**	75p. multicoloured	1·75	1·50

954/7 *Set of 4* ... 7·00 / 6·00
First Day Cover ... 7·00
Presentation Pack ... 7·75
  Plate Nos.: All designs 1A (×4).
  Sheets: 10 (2×5).
  Imprint: Central, left-hand margin.
  Withdrawn: 30.6.2001.

'World Stamp Expo 2000', Anaheim, U.S.A.

(Litho BDT)

2000 (7 July). As No. **MS**953, but with multicoloured exhibition logo added to top left corner of sheet margin. P 15×14 (C).
MS958 150×100 mm. **912** £1.50 multicoloured ... 4·00 / 4·00
First Day Cover ... 6·00
  Withdrawn: 31.7.2001.

917 Queen Elizabeth the Queen Mother with Roses

918 Queen Elizabeth the Queen Mother with Daisies

Queen Elizabeth the Queen Mother's 100th Birthday

(Des Colleen Corlett. Litho and die-stamped Questa)

2000 (4 Aug). P 14½ (C).

959	**917**	50p. multicoloured	1·20	1·20
960	**918**	50p. multicoloured	1·20	1·20

959/60 *Set of 2* ... 2·50 / 2·50
First Day Cover ... 3·25
Presentation Pack ... 3·25
MS961 150×100 mm. Nos. 959/60 ... 2·50 / 3·00
First Day Cover ... 4·50
Presentation Pack ... 3·50
Souvenir Folder (containing **MS**961, first day cover and presentation pack) ... 16·00
  Plate Nos.: Both designs 1A (×6).
  Sheets: 10 (5×2).
  Imprint: Bottom margin.
  Withdrawn: 31.8.2001.

919 Supermarine Spitfire MK Ia

920 Hawker Hurricane Mk I

921 Bristol Blenheim Mk IV

922 Vickers Wellington Mk Ic

923 Boulton Paul Defiant Mk I

924 Short Sunderland Mk I

Jersey Aviation History (7th series). 60th Anniversary of Battle of Britain

(Des A. Theobald. Litho Questa BDT)

2000 (15 Sept). P 14 (C).

962	**919**	22p. multicoloured	50	55
963	**920**	26p. multicoloured	60	65
964	**921**	36p. multicoloured	80	85
965	**922**	40p. multicoloured	90	95
966	**923**	45p. multicoloured	1·00	1·10
967	**924**	65p. multicoloured	1·50	1·60
962/7	*Set of 6*		4·75	5·00
First Day Cover				5·50
Presentation Pack			6·00	

Plate Nos.: All values 1A, 1B (each×5).
Sheets: 10 (2×5).
Imprint: Bottom margin.
Withdrawn: 29.9.2001.

925 Virgin Mary

926 Shepherd

927 Angel

928 Magi with Gift

Christmas. Children's Nativity Play

(Des F. Venton. Litho Cartor)

2000 (7 Nov). P 13 (C).

968	**925**	22p. multicoloured	55	55
969	**926**	26p. multicoloured	65	65
970	**927**	36p. multicoloured	1·00	1·00
971	**928**	65p. multicoloured	1·60	1·60
968/71	*Set of 4*		3·50	3·50
First Day Cover				4·50
Presentation Pack			4·50	

Plate Nos.: All values 1A (each×4).
Sheets: 10 (5×2).
Imprint: Bottom margin.
Withdrawn: 30.11.2001.

Year Pack 2000

2000 (1 Dec). Comprises Nos. 927/32, 934/45, 947/57 and 959/71 (price £27).
Year Pack .... 50·00
Sold out: By 4.05.

Post Office Yearbook

2000 (1 Dec). Comprises Nos. 927/32, 934/45, 947/57 and 959/71 (price £29.95).
Yearbook .... 55·00
Sold out: By 8.05.

929 Snake (*Illustration reduced. Actual size 110×75 mm*)

Chinese New Year ('Year of the Snake')

(Des V. Ambrus. Litho Questa)

2001 (24 Jan). Sheet 110×75 mm. P 14×13½ (C).

MS972	**929**	£1 multicoloured	2·75	3·00
First Day Cover				4·50
Presentation Pack			4·75	

Withdrawn: 31.1.2002.

930 Rose (1851–61)

931 Comete (1856–67)

932 Cygne (1894–1912)

933 Victoria (1896–1918)

934 Attala (1920–25)

935 Brittany (1933–62)

Maritime Links with France. Mail Packet Ships

(Des I. Boyd. Litho Cartor)

2001 (24 Jan). P 13×13½ (C).

973	**930**	22p. multicoloured	50	55
974	**931**	26p. multicoloured	60	65
975	**932**	36p. multicoloured	80	85
976	**933**	40p. multicoloured	90	95
977	**934**	45p. multicoloured	1·20	1·30
978	**935**	65p. multicoloured	1·70	1·80
973/8	*Set of 6*		5·25	5·50
First Day Cover				6·00
Presentation Pack			6·00	

Plate Nos.: All values 1A (×4).
Sheets: 10 (2×5).
Imprint: Central, left-hand margin.
Withdrawn: 31.1.2002.

936 H.H.S. *Jersey* (4th Rate), 1654–91

937 H.M.S. *Jersey* (6th Rate), 1694–98

938 H.M.S. *Jersey* (4th Rate), 1698–1731

939 H.M.S. *Jersey* (4th Rate), 1736–83

940 H.M.S. *Jersey* (cutter), 1860–73

941 H.M.S. *Jersey* (destroyer), 1938–41

Jersey Naval Connections (1st series). Royal Navy Ships named after Jersey

(Des A. Theobald. Litho BDT)

2001 (3 Apr). P 14 (C).

979	**936**	23p. multicoloured	50	55
980	**937**	26p. multicoloured	60	65
981	**938**	37p. multicoloured	80	85
982	**939**	41p. multicoloured	1·00	95
983	**940**	46p. multicoloured	1·20	1·10
984	**941**	66p. multicoloured	1·50	1·60
979/84 Set of 6			5·00	5·00
First Day Cover				6·00
Presentation Pack			5·50	

See also Nos. 1380/**MS**1386 and 1470/5

Plate Nos.: 23p., 26p. 1A, 1B (each×4); others 1A (×4).
Sheets: 10 (2×5).
Imprint: Bottom, left-hand corner margin.
Withdrawn: 30.4.2002.

942 Jersey Cows   **943** Potatoes   **944** Tomatoes

945 Cauliflower and Purple-sprouting Broccoli   **946** Peppers and Courgettes

Jersey Cows and Farm Produce

(Des Colleen Corlett. Litho SNP Ausprint, Melbourne)

2001 (3 Apr). Self-adhesive. P 11½ (C).

985	**942**	(26p.) multicoloured (abcd)	1·50	1·50
986	**943**	(26p.) multicoloured (abcd)	1·50	1·50
987	**944**	(26p.) multicoloured (abcd)	1·50	1·50
988	**945**	(26p.) multicoloured (abcd)	1·50	1·50
989	**946**	(26p.) multicoloured (abcd)	1·50	1·50
985/9 Set of 5			7·00	7·00
First Day Cover				10·00
Presentation Pack			9·00	

Nos. 985/9, which are inscribed 'UK MINIMUM POSTAGE PAID' and were initially sold at 26p. each, come, *se-tenant*, in strips of 5 or rolls of 100 with the surplus self-adhesive paper around each stamp removed.

Initially released with '2001' imprint dates (price per set, £10 unused, £11 used), Nos. 985/9 were subsequently reissued inscribed '2002' (price, unused or used, £9), '2003' (price, unused or used, £8) and '2005' (price £7).

Printings: (a) 3.4.2001. Inscr '2001'; (b) 4.10.2002. Inscr '2002'; (c) 4.4.2003. Inscr '2003'; (d) 21.10.2005. Inscr '2005'.

947 Queen Elizabeth II

75th Birthday of Queen Elizabeth II

(Des W. Wall. Litho Questa)

2001 (21 Apr). P 14×15 (C).

990	**947**	£3 multicoloured	6·00	6·50
First Day Cover				7·00
Presentation Pack			7·00	

No. 990 was retained in use as part of the current definitive series.
Plate Nos.: 1A, 1B, 1C, 1D, 1E, 1F (each×4).
Sheets: 10 (2×5).
Imprint: Bottom margin.
Withdrawn: 30.11.2008.

948 Agile Frog   **949** Trout

950 White Water-Lily   **951** Common Blue Damselfly

952 Palmate Newt   **953** Tufted Duck

954 Common Kingfisher (*Illustration reduced. Actual size 150×100 mm*)

Europa. Water, a Natural Treasure. Pond Life

(Des N. Parlett. Litho BDT)

2001 (22 May). P 14 (No. MS997) or 14½×14 (others), both comb.

991	948	23p. multicoloured	60	65
992	949	26p. multicoloured	70	75
993	950	37p. multicoloured	1·00	1·10
994	951	41p. multicoloured	1·10	1·20
995	952	46p. multicoloured	1·20	1·40
996	953	66p. multicoloured	2·00	2·20
991/6 Set of 6			6·00	6·50
First Day Cover				7·00
Presentation Pack			7·00	
MS997 150×100 mm. 954 £1.50, multicoloured			5·00	5·00
First Day Cover				5·50
Presentation Pack			5·25	

The 26p. and 37p. values include the 'EUROPA' emblem.
Plate Nos.: All values 1A, 1B (each×4).
Sheets: 10 (2×5).
Imprint: Central, left-hand margin.
Withdrawn: 31.5.2002.

'Belgica 2001' International Stamp Exhibition, Brussels

(Litho BDT)

2001 (9 June). No. MS997 optd 'JERSEY AT BELGICA 2001' on sheet margin. P 14 (C).

MS998 954 £1.50 multicoloured			5·00	4·50
First Day Cover				5·50
Presentation Pack			5·50	

Withdrawn: 29.6.2002.

955 Long-eared Owl

956 Peregrine Falcon

957 Short-eared Owl

958 Western Marsh Harrier

959 Northern Sparrow Hawk

960 Tawny Owl

961 Barn Owl (Illustration reduced. Actual size 110×75 mm)

Birds of Prey

(Des M. Chester. Litho Cartor)

2001 (3 July). P 13½×13 (C).

999	955	23p. multicoloured	50	55
		a. Booklet pane. Nos. 999/1004	3·50	
		b. Booklet pane. Nos. 999, 1001 and 1004, each×2	3·75	

		c. Booklet pane. Nos. 999×2, 1000/1 and 1003×2	3·00	
		d. Booklet pane. Nos. 999/1001, 1002×2 and 1004	3·75	
1000	956	26p. multicoloured	60	65
1001	957	37p. multicoloured	80	85
1002	958	41p. multicoloured	1·00	95
1003	959	46p. multicoloured	1·20	1·10
1004	960	66p. multicoloured	1·50	1·60
999/1004 Set of 6			5·00	5·00
First Day Cover				6·00
Presentation Pack			5·75	
MS1005 110×75 mm. 961 £1.50, multicoloured			5·00	5·00
		a. Booklet pane. As No. MS1005, but 153×100 mm with line of roulettes at left	9·00	
First Day Cover				6·50
Presentation Pack			6·50	

Nos. 999a/d each have margins all round and a bird Illustration on the tab at left.

No. MS1005a also differs from the normal miniature sheet by the owl on the post being centred on the stamp. No. MS1005 shows the '£1.5' of the face value across the post, but on the booklet pane the figures are to the right of the post.
Plate Nos.: All values 1A (×4).
Sheets: 10 (5×2).
Imprint: Bottom margin.
Withdrawn: 31.7.2002 (sheets).

962 Jersey Clipper (yacht) (Illustration reduced. Actual size 150×100 mm)

The Times Clipper 2000 Round the World Yacht Race

(Des B. Ozard. Litho Questa)

2001 (17 Sept). Sheet 150×100 mm. P 13½×14 (C).

MS1006 962 £1.50 multicoloured		4·00	5·00
First Day Cover			6·00
Presentation Pack		5·50	

Withdrawn: 30.9.2002.

963 Tilley 26 Manual Fire Engine, circa 1845

964 Albion Merryweather, circa 1935

965 Dennis Ace, circa 1940

966 Dennis F8 Pump Escape, circa 1952

967 Landrover Merry-weather, circa 1968

968 Dennis Carmichael, circa 1989

Centenary of Jersey Fire and Rescue Service. Fire Engines

(Des A. Copp. Litho Cartor)

2001 (25 Sept). P 13×13½ (C).

1007	**963**	23p. multicoloured	50	55
1008	**964**	26p. multicoloured	60	65
1009	**965**	37p. multicoloured	80	85
1010	**966**	41p. multicoloured	90	95
1011	**967**	46p. multicoloured	1·00	1·10
1012	**968**	66p. multicoloured	1·50	1·60
1007/12 *Set of 6*			4·75	5·00
First Day Cover				6·00
Presentation Pack			6·00	

Plate Nos.: All values 1A (×4).
Sheets: 10 (2×5).
Imprint: Central, left-hand margin.
Withdrawn: 30.9.2002.

'Hafnia 01' International Stamp Exhibition, Copenhagen

(Litho Cartor)

2001 (16 Oct). As No. **MS**1005, but with brown-red exhibition logo added to bottom left corner of sheet margin and additionally inscr 'Jersey visits Hafnia 01 Denmark'. P 13½×13 (C).

MS1013	**961**	£1.50, multicoloured	4·00	4·00
First Day Cover				5·00
Presentation Pack			5·50	

Withdrawn: 31.10.2002.

969 Nativity

970 Street Decorations

971 Carol Singers with Hand Bells

972 Father Christmas

973 Christmas Tree Decorations

974 Adoration of the Shepherds

975 Carol Singers and Father Christmas in Sleigh

976 Paper Bell, Chains and Christmas Tree

977 Church Bells ringing

978 Christmas Cracker

Christmas. Bells

(Des M. Pollard. Litho SNP Ausprint, Melbourne)

2001 (6 Nov). Self-adhesive. P 11×11½ (die-cut).

1014	**969**	(23p.) multicoloured (abc)	1·00	70
		a. Booklet pane. Nos. 1014, 1016/18,		
		1019/20 and 1022/3, each×2 (a)	9·00	
1015	**970**	(23p.) multicoloured (abc)	1·00	70
1016	**971**	(23p.) multicoloured (abc)	1·00	70
1017	**972**	(23p.) multicoloured (abc)	1·00	70
1018	**973**	(23p.) multicoloured (abc)	1·00	70
1019	**974**	(26p.) multicoloured (ab)	1·00	70
1020	**975**	(26p.) multicoloured (ab)	1·00	70
1021	**976**	(26p.) multicoloured (ab)	1·00	70
1022	**977**	(26p.) multicoloured (ab)	1·00	70
1023	**978**	(26p.) multicoloured (ab)	1·00	70
1014/23 *Set of 10*			9·00	6·50
First Day Cover				7·00
Presentation Pack			11·00	

Nos. 1014/18 are inscribed 'JERSEY MINIMUM POSTAGE PAID' and were initially sold for 23p., and Nos. 1019/23 are inscribed 'U.K. MINIMUM POSTAGE PAID' and were initially sold for 26p. The 5 designs for each value were printed together, *se-tenant*, in strips of 5 or rolls of 100. Nos. 1014, 1016/20 and 1022/3 also come from £3.92 booklets, containing pane No. 1014a on which the surplus self-adhesive paper was retained.

Initially released with '2001' imprint dates Nos. 1014/23 were subsequently reissued inscribed '2002' and Nos. 1014/8 only inscribed '2003' (all the same price).

Printings: (a) 6.11.2001. Inscr '2001'; (b) 23.11.2002. Inscr '2002'; (c) 10.11.2003. Inscr '2003'.

Sold out: By 6.2003 (booklets) or by end of 2005 (coils).

Post Office Yearbook

2001 (1 Dec). Comprises Nos. **MS**972/97, 999/1012 and 1014/23 (price £29).

Yearbook		55·00

Sold out: By 7.1.2008.

979 Duchess of Normandy (launch)

980 Duke of Normandy (tug)

981 Challenger (customs patrol boat)

982 Le Fret (pilot boat)

983 Norman le Brocq (fisheries protection vessel)

States Vessels

(Des A. Theobald. Litho Cartor)

2002 (22 Jan). P 13×13½ (C).

1024	**979**	23p. multicoloured	50	55
1025	**980**	29p. multicoloured	65	70
1026	**981**	38p. multicoloured	80	85
1027	**982**	47p. multicoloured	1·20	1·30
1028	**983**	68p. multicoloured	1·70	1·90
1024/8 *Set of 5*			4·50	4·75
First Day Cover				5·75
Presentation Pack			5·75	

Plate Nos.: All values 1A (×4).
Sheets: 10 (2×5).
Imprint: Bottom, left-hand margin.
Withdrawn: 31.1.2003.

984 Queen Elizabeth in Coronation Robes (after Cecil Beaton)

Golden Jubilee

(Litho with gold and silver embossing Cartor)

2002 (6 Feb). P 13½ (C).
1029	**984**	£3 multicoloured	6·25	6·50

First Day Cover .... 7·50
Presentation Pack .... 6·75
  Plate Nos.: 1A (×5).
  Sheets: 4 (2×2).
  Imprint: Upper left-hand margin.
No. 1029 was retained in use as a definitive.
  Withdrawn: 31.5.2013.

985 Horse (*Illustration reduced. Actual size 110×75 mm*)

Chinese New Year ('Year of the Horse')

(Des V. Ambrus. Litho Questa)

2002 (12 Feb). Sheet 110×75 mm. P 14×13½ (C).
MS1030	**985**	£1 multicoloured	2·50	2·50

First Day Cover .... 4·50
Presentation Pack .... 4·50
  Withdrawn: 28.2.2003.

986 Elephant Float, Parish of St. John, 1980

987 Clown with Red Hair, Grouville, 1996

988 Clown with White Hat, Optimists, 1988

989 Porming Seal, Grouville, 1996

Europa. Circus. Carnival Floats

(Des N. Shewring. Litho BDT)

2002 (12 Mar). P 14 (C).
1031	**986**	23p. multicoloured	50	55
1032	**987**	29p. multicoloured	65	70
1033	**988**	38p. multicoloured	1·00	1·10
1034	**989**	68p. multicoloured	1·70	2·00
1031/4	*Set of 4*		3·50	4·00

First Day Cover .... 4·00
Presentation Pack .... 4·50
  The 29p. and 38p. values include the 'EUROPA' emblem.
  Plate Nos.: All values 1A, 1B (each×4).
  Sheets: 10 (5×2).
  Imprint: Bottom margin, right-hand side.
  Withdrawn: 31.3.2003.

990 Aubrey Boomer   **991** Harry Vardon

992 Sir Henry Cotton   **993** Diagram of Golf Swing

994 Putting

Jersey Golf (2nd series). Centenary of La Moye Golf Club

(Des Jennifer Toombs. Litho Questa)

2002 (16 Apr). P 14 (C).
1035	**990**	23p. multicoloured	55	55
1036	**991**	29p. multicoloured	70	70
1037	**992**	38p. multicoloured	85	85
1038	**993**	47p. multicoloured	1·10	1·10
1039	**994**	68p. multicoloured	1·75	1·75
1035/9	*Set of 5*		4·50	4·50

First Day Cover .... 5·50
Presentation Pack .... 5·50
  Plate Nos.: 23p., 29p. 1A, 1B, 1C, 1D, 1E, 1F (each×7); 38p. 1A, 1B, 1C, 1D, 1E, 1F, 1G, 1H, 1J (each×7); 47p., 68p. 1A, 1B, 1C (each×7).
  Sheets: 10 (2×5) with enlarged illustrated right margins.
  Imprint: Lower left-hand margin.
  Withdrawn: 30.4.2003.

995 Vauxhall 12, 1952   **996** Jaguar 2.4 MkII, 1959–60

997 Austin 1800 1972–73   **998** Ford Cortina MkIV, 1978

999 Honda ST 1100
Motorcycle, 1995–2000

1000 Vauxhall Vectra,
1998–2000

50th Anniversary of States of Jersey Police. Patrol Vehicles

(Des A. Copp. Litho Cartor)

2002 (24 May). P 13 (C).

1040	**995**	23p. multicoloured	55	55
1041	**996**	29p. multicoloured	70	70
1042	**997**	38p. multicoloured	95	85
1043	**998**	40p. multicoloured	1·00	90
1044	**999**	47p. multicoloured	1·10	1·10
1045	**1000**	68p. multicoloured	1·75	1·75
1040/5	*Set of 6*		5·50	5·25
First Day Cover				6·25
Presentation Pack			6·00	

Plate Nos.: All values 1A (each×4).
Sheets: 10 (2×5).
Imprint: Bottom, left-hand margin.
Withdrawn: 31.5.2003.

1001 Honey Bee

1002 Seven-spot Ladybird

1003 Great Green Bush-cricket

1004 Greater Horn-tail

1005 Emperor Dragonfly

1006 Hawthorn Shield Bug

Insects (1st series)

(Des W. Oliver. Litho BDT)

2002 (18 June). P 15×14 (C).

1046	**1001**	23p. multicoloured	55	55
1047	**1002**	29p. multicoloured	70	70
1048	**1003**	38p. multicoloured	85	85
1049	**1004**	40p. multicoloured	90	90
1050	**1005**	47p. multicoloured	1·25	1·25
1051	**1006**	68p. multicoloured	1·75	1·75
1046/51	*Set of 6*		5·50	5·50
First Day Cover				6·50
Presentation Pack			6·00	

See also Nos. 1393/8.
Plate Nos.: All values 1A, 1B (each×4).
Sheets: 10 (2×5).
Imprint: Bottom margin, left-hand corner.
Withdrawn: 30.6.2003.

1007 Queen Elizabeth the Queen
Mother in 1910, 1923 and 2002

Queen Elizabeth the Queen Mother Commemoration

(Des W. Wall. Litho Questa)

2002 (4 Aug). P 14×15 (C).

1052	**1007**	£2 multicoloured	4·25	4·50
First Day Cover				5·50
Presentation Pack			5·50	

Plate Nos.: 1A, 1B, 1C, 1D, 1E, 1F (each×4).
Sheets: 10 (2×5).
Imprint: Lower left-hand margin.
Withdrawn: 30.8.2003.

1008 Hydrangeas

1009 Chrysanthemums

1010 Hare's Tails and Pampas
Grasses

1011 Asters

1012 Carnations

1013 Gladioli

1014 'Zanzibar' Float (winner of Prix d'Honneur, 1999)
(*Illustration reduced. Actual size 150×100 mm*)

Centenary of 'Battle of Flowers' Parade

(Des M. Pollard. Litho Cartor)

2002 (8 Aug). P 13 (C).

1053	**1008**	23p. multicoloured	55	55
		a. Booklet pane. Nos. 1053/8, with		
		margins all round	5·25	
1054	**1009**	29p. multicoloured	70	70
1055	**1010**	38p. multicoloured	95	85

1056	**1011**	40p. multicoloured	1·00	90
1057	**1012**	47p. multicoloured	1·10	1·10
1058	**1013**	68p. multicoloured	1·75	1·75
1053/8		*Set of 6*	5·50	5·25
		First Day Cover		6·00
		Presentation Pack	6·00	
MS1059		150×100 mm. **1014** £2 multicoloured	4·25	4·50
		a. Booklet pane. As No. **MS**1059, but with line of roulettes at left..	4·25	
		First Day Cover		5·50
		Presentation Pack	5·00	

Booklet pane No. 1053a exists in three versions which differ in the order of the stamps within the block of six.
Plate Nos.: All values 1A (×4).
Sheets: 10 (2×5).
Imprint: Central, left-hand margin.
Withdrawn: 30.8.2003 (sheets).

1015 British Dilute Tortoiseshell

1016 Cream Persian

1017 Blue Exotic Shorthair

1018 Black Smoke Devon Rex

1019 British Silver Tabby

1020 Usual Abyssinian

1021 British Cream/White Bi-colour Cross (*Illustration reduced. Actual size 110×75 mm*)

Cats (2nd series). 25th Anniversary of Caesarea Cat Club

(Des G. Vasarhelyi. Litho BDT)

2002 (12 Oct). P 14 (No. **MS**1066) or 15×14 (others), both comb.

1060	**1015**	23p. multicoloured	55	55
1061	**1016**	29p. multicoloured	70	70
1062	**1017**	38p. multicoloured	95	85
1063	**1018**	40p. multicoloured	1·00	90
1064	**1019**	47p. multicoloured	1·10	1·10
1065	**1020**	68p. multicoloured	1·75	1·75
1060/5		*Set of 6*	5·50	5·25
		First Day Cover		6·00
		Presentation Pack	5·75	
MS1066		110×75 mm. **1021** £2 multicoloured	4·25	4·50
		First Day Cover		6·00
		Presentation Pack	5·50	

Plate Nos.: All values 1A, 1B (each×4).
Sheets: 10 (2×5).
Imprint: Lower left-hand margin.
Withdrawn: 31.10.2003.

1022 Victorian Pillar Box in Central Market

1023 Edward VII Wall Box, Colomberie

1024 George V Wall Box, St. Clement's Inner Road

1025 George V 'Boite Mobile' Ship Box

1026 Elizabeth II Pillar Box, Parade

1027 Modern Pillar Boxes, La Collette

1028 Posting Letter in First Pillar Box, David Place (*Illustration reduced. Actual size 150×100 mm*)

Jersey Postal History (1st series). 150th Anniversary of the First Pillar Box

(Des Colleen Corlett. Litho Questa)

2002 (23 Nov). P 14½ (No. **MS**1073) or 14½×14 (others), both comb.

1067	**1022**	23p. multicoloured	55	55
1068	**1023**	29p. multicoloured	70	70
1069	**1024**	38p. multicoloured	95	85
1070	**1025**	40p. multicoloured	1·00	90
1071	**1026**	47p. multicoloured	1·10	1·10
1072	**1027**	68p. multicoloured	1·75	1·60
1067/72		*Set of 6*	5·50	5·25
		First Day Cover		6·00
		Presentation Pack	5·75	
MS1073		150×100 mm. **1028** £2 multicoloured	4·25	4·50
		First Day Cover		7·00
		Presentation Pack	5·50	

See also Nos. 1286/92, **MS**1442, 1503/**MS**1510 and 1511/**MS**1517.
Plate Nos.: All values 1A (×5).
Sheets: 10 (5×2).
Imprint: Bottom, right-hand corner margin.
Withdrawn: 31.10.2003.
MS1073 was supplied free to bureau customers with a standing order account.

Post Office Yearbook

2002 (2 Dec). Comprises Nos. 1024/73 (price £33).
Yearbook .... 60·00

1029 Sanchez-Besa Hydroplane

1030 Supermarine S.6B Seaplane

1031 de Havilland DH84 Dragon

1032 de Havilland DH89a Rapide

1033 Vickers 701 Viscount

1034 BAC One Eleven

1035 Jacob Ellehammer's Biplane, 1906 (*Illustration reduced. Actual size 112×76 mm*)

Jersey Aviation History (8th series). Centenary of Powered Flight

(Des T. Theobald. Litho Cartor)

2003 (21 Jan). P 13½×13 (No. MS1080) or 13×13½ (others), both comb.

1074	**1029**	23p. multicoloured	55	55
		a. Booklet pane. Nos. 1074/9 with margins all round	5·50	
1075	**1030**	29p. multicoloured	70	70
1076	**1031**	38p. multicoloured	95	85
1077	**1032**	40p. multicoloured	1·00	90
1078	**1033**	47p. multicoloured	1·10	1·10
1079	**1034**	68p. multicoloured	1·75	1·60
1074/9		*Set of 6*	5·50	5·25
First Day Cover				6·75
Presentation Pack			6·75	
MS1080		112×76 mm. **1035** £2 multicoloured	4·25	4·50
		a. Booklet pane. As No. MS1080, but 153×100 mm with line of roulettes at left	6·50	
First Day Cover				6·50
Presentation Pack			4·75	

No. 1074a comes with three different Illustrations on the margins.

The stamp in booklet pane No. MS1080a differs from that in the normal miniature sheet by having the imprint date centred, rather than ranged to the left.

Plate Nos.: All values 1A (×4).
Sheets: 10 (2×5).
Imprint: Bottom, right-hand corner margin.
Withdrawn: 31.1.2004 (Sheets).

1036 Ram (*Illustration reduced. Actual size 110×75 mm*)

Chinese New Year ('Year of the Ram')

(Des V. Ambrus. Litho Questa)

2003 (1 Feb). Sheet 110×75 mm. P 14×13½ (C).

MS1081	**1036**	£1 multicoloured	2·50	2·75
First Day Cover				4·00
Presentation Pack			3·25	

Withdrawn: 28.2.2004.

1037 'Portelet' (Adrian Allinson)

1038 'Jersey' (Lander)

1039 'Channel Islands Map'

1040 'Jersey, the Sunny Channel Island' (A. Allinson)

Europa. Poster Art. Travel Posters

(Des N. Shewring. Litho Cartor)

2003 (11 Mar). P 13½ (C).

1082	**1037**	23p. multicoloured	50	55
1083	**1038**	29p. multicoloured	80	80
1084	**1039**	38p. multicoloured	1·25	1·50
1085	**1040**	68p. multicoloured	1·75	2·00
1082/5		*Set of 4*	4·00	4·50
First Day Cover				5·00
Presentation Pack			5·00	

The 29p. and 38p. values include the 'EUROPA' emblem.
Plate Nos.: All values 1A (×4).
Sheets: 10 (2×5) 23p., 68p.; (5×2) 29p., 38p.
Imprint: Lower left-hand margin.
Withdrawn: 31.3.2004.

1041 Violet Channel Light Buoy

1042 St. Catherine's Breakwater Light

1043 Frouquie Aubert Light Buoy

1044 Mont Ube Lighthouse

1045 Banc des Ormes Light Buoy

1046 Gronez Point Lighthouse

Jersey Lighthouses (2nd series)

(Des A. Copp. Litho BDT)

2003 (15 Apr). P 13½ (C).

1086	**1041**	29p. multicoloured	50	30
		a. Pair. Nos. 1086/7	1·30	1·30
1087	**1042**	29p. multicoloured	50	30
1088	**1043**	30p. multicoloured	55	35
		a. Pair. Nos. 1088/9	1·30	1·30
1089	**1044**	30p. multicoloured	55	35
1090	**1045**	48p. multicoloured	85	50
		a. Pair. Nos. 1090/1	2·00	2·10
1091	**1046**	48p. multicoloured	85	50
1086/91		Set of 6	4·25	4·50
		First Day Cover		5·50
		Presentation Pack	5·50	

The two designs for each value were printed together, *se-tenant*, both horizontally and vertically in sheets of ten stamps.

Plate Nos.: All values 1A (×4).
Sheets: 10 (5×2).
Imprint: Lower left-hand margin.
Withdrawn: 30.4.2004.

1053 Loose-flowered Orchid (*Illustration reduced. Actual size 110×75 mm*)

Wild Orchids

(Des B. Ozard. Litho Cartor)

2003 (13 May). P 13 (C).

1092	**1047**	29p. multicoloured	70	65
1093	**1048**	30p. multicoloured	75	65
1094	**1049**	39p. multicoloured	95	85
1095	**1050**	50p. multicoloured	1·25	1·10
1096	**1051**	53p. multicoloured	1·25	1·25
1097	**1052**	69p. multicoloured	1·75	1·50
1092/7		Set of 6	6·00	5·75
		First Day Cover		6·50
		Presentation Pack	6·50	
MS1098		110×75 mm. **1053** £2 multicoloured	4·00	4·25
		First Day Cover		5·25
		Presentation Pack	5·25	

Plate Nos.: All values 1A (×4).
Sheets: 10 (5×2).
Imprint: Lower left-hand margin.
Withdrawn: 31.5.2004.

1047 Southern-marsh Orchid

1048 Loose-flowered Orchid

1054 Sovereign's Orb

1055 St. Edward's Crown

1049 Spotted Orchid

1050 Autumn Ladies Tresses

1056 Sceptre with Cross

1057 Ampulla and Spoon

1058 Sovereign's Ring

1059 Armills

50th Anniversary of Coronation. Coronation Regalia

(Des Jennifer Toombs. Litho and die-stamped BDT)

2003 (2 June). P 15×14 (C).

1099	**1054**	29p. multicoloured	70	65
1100	**1055**	30p. multicoloured	75	65
1101	**1056**	39p. multicoloured	95	85
1102	**1057**	50p. multicoloured	1·25	1·10
1103	**1058**	53p. multicoloured	1·25	1·10
1104	**1059**	69p. multicoloured	1·75	1·50
1099/1104		Set of 6	6·00	5·75
		First Day Cover		6·50
		Presentation Pack	6·50	
MS1105		150×100 mm. Nos. 1099/1104	6·00	5·75
		First Day Cover		6·50
		Presentation Pack	6·50	

1051 Green-winged Orchid

1052 Pyramidal Orchid

Nos. 1099/1104 were each printed in sheets of 10 (2×5) with enlarged illustrated right-hand margins.

Plate Nos.: All values 1A (×6).
Sheets: 10 (2×5) with enlarged illustrated right-hand margins.
Imprint: Lower left-hand margin.
Withdrawn: 30.6.2004.

1060 Prince William, Prince Charles and Queen Elizabeth (*Illustration reduced. Actual size 110×75 mm*)

Royal Links

(Des The Partnership. Litho Questa)

2003 (21 June). Sheet 110×75 mm. P 14×13½ (C).

MS1106 **1060** £2 multicoloured		5·00	4·25
First Day Cover			5·25
Presentation Pack		5·25	

Withdrawn: 30.6.2004.

1061 Rock Samphire and Paternosters **1062** Bluebells and Les Ecrehous **1063** Tree-mallow and Les Ecrehous

1064 Smooth Sow-thistle and Les Minquiers **1065** Thrift and Les Minquiers

Offshore Reefs

(Des Colleen Corlett. Photo Questa)

2003 (5 Aug). Self-adhesive. P 11 (die-cut).

1107	**1061** (29p.) multicoloured	1·10	1·25
1108	**1062** (29p.) multicoloured	1·10	1·25
1109	**1063** (29p.) multicoloured	1·10	1·25
1110	**1064** (29p.) multicoloured	1·10	1·25
1111	**1065** (29p.) multicoloured	1·10	1·25
1107/11 Set of 5		5·00	5·50
First Day Cover			6·00
Presentation Pack		5·50	

Nos. 1107/11, which are inscribed 'JERSEY MINIMUM POSTAGE PAID' and were initially sold at 29p. each, come *se-tenant* in strips of 5 or rolls of 100 with the surplus self-adhesive paper around each stamp removed.

Nos. 1107/11 are inscr '2003' with copyright symbol before date.

For designs as Nos. 1107/11 printed in lithography by Sprintpak see Nos. 1180/4.

1066 Albino RexRabbit **1067** Black Labrador Puppy **1068** Canary and Budgerigar

1069 Hamster **1070** Guinea Pig

1071 Border Collie (*Illustration reduced. Actual size 150×100 mm*)

Pets

(Des N. Parlett. Litho BDT)

2003 (9 Sept). P 13×13½ (No. **MS**1117) or 13½ (others), both comb.

1112	**1066**	29p. multicoloured	95	95
1113	**1067**	30p. multicoloured	95	95
1114	**1068**	38p. multicoloured	1·20	1·20
1115	**1069**	53p. multicoloured	1·70	1·70
1116	**1070**	69p. multicoloured	2·20	2·20
1112/16 Set of 5			6·00	6·00
First Day Cover				7·00
Presentation Pack			7·00	
MS1117 150×100 mm. **1071** £2 multicoloured			5·50	5·50
First Day Cover				7·00
Presentation Pack			6·50	

Nos.: All values 1A (×4).
Sheets: 10 (2×5).
Imprint: Central, bottom margin.
Withdrawn: 30.9.2004.

'Bangkok 2003' International Stamp Exhibition

2003 (4 Oct). No. **MS**1098 optd with 'Jersey at Bangkok 2003' and emblem on sheet margin. P 13 (C).

MS1118 110×75 mm. **1053** £2 multicoloured		5·50	5·50
First Day Cover			7·00
Presentation Pack		6·50	

Withdrawn: 31.10.2004.

1072 Japanese Quince **1073** Winter Jasmine

1074 Snowdrop **1075** Winter Heath

1076 Chinese Witch-hazel

1077 Winter Daphne

Seasonal Flowers (2nd series). Winter

(Des Wendy Tait. Litho Questa)

2003 (10 Nov). P 14½ (C).

1119	1072	29p. multicoloured	70	65
1120	1073	30p. multicoloured	75	65
1121	1074	39p. multicoloured	95	85
1122	1075	48p. multicoloured	1·10	1·00
1123	1076	53p. multicoloured	1·25	1·10
1124	1077	69p. multicoloured	1·75	1·50
1119/24 Set of 6			6·00	5·75
First Day Cover				6·75
Presentation Pack			6·50	

See also Nos. 1204/9 and 1359/63.
Plate Nos.: 29p. 1A, 1B, 1C, 1D; 30p. 1A, 1B, 1C, 1D, 1E, 1F; others 1A, 1B (each×5).
Sheets: 10 (5×2).
Imprint: Right-hand side, bottom margin.
Withdrawn: 30.11.2004.

Post Office Yearbook

2003 (1 Dec). Comprises Nos. 1074/1104 and **MS**1106/17 and 1119/24 (price £33).

Yearbook		60·00

Sold out: By 11.04.

1078 Rook

1079 Knight

1080 Bishop

1081 Pawn

1082 Queen

1083 King

Jersey Festivals (1st issue). Festival of Chess

(Des Jennifer Toombs. Litho BDT)

2004 (22 Jan). P 14×13½ (C).

1125	1078	29p. multicoloured	95	95
1126	1079	30p. multicoloured	1·00	1·00
1127	1080	39p. multicoloured	1·30	1·30

1128	1081	48p. multicoloured	1·60	1·60
1129	1082	53p. multicoloured	1·70	1·70
1130	1083	69p. multicoloured	2·20	2·20
1125/30 Set of 6			8·75	8·75
First Day Cover				10·00
Presentation Pack			9·50	

See also Nos. 1204/9 and 1359/63.
Plate Nos.: All values 1A (×5).
Sheets: 10 (5×2).
Imprint: Bottom margin.
Withdrawn: 31.1.2005.

1084 Monkey (Illustration reduced. Actual size 110×75 mm)

Chinese New Year ('Year of the Monkey')

(Des V. Ambrus. Litho Questa)

2004 (22 Jan). Sheet 110×75 mm. P 14×13½ (C).

MS1131	1084	£1 multicoloured	3·25	3·25
First Day Cover				5·25
Presentation Pack			5·25	

Withdrawn: 31.1.2008.

1085 St. Aubin's Harbour

1086 Mont Orgueil Castle

1087 Corbiere Lighthouse

1088 Rozel Harbour

Europa. Holidays

(Des A. Copp. Litho Cartor)

2004 (9 Mar). P 13×13½ (C).

1132	1085	29p. multicoloured	95	95
1133	1086	30p. multicoloured	95	95
1134	1087	39p. multicoloured	1·30	1·30
1135	1088	69p. multicoloured	2·30	2·30
1132/5 Set of 4			5·50	5·50
First Day Cover				6·00
Presentation Pack			6·50	

The 30p. and 39p. values include the 'EUROPA' emblem.
Plate Nos.: All values 1A (×4).
Sheets: 10 (2×5).
Imprint: Upper left-hand margin.
Withdrawn: 31.3.2005.

1089 Green-winged Teal ('Eurasian Teal')

1090 Mute Swan

1091 Northern Shoveler

1092 Common Pochard

1093 Black Swan

1094 European Wigeon ('Eurasian Wigeon')

1095 Mallard (*Illustration reduced. Actual size 150×100 mm*)

Jersey Nature. Ducks and Swans

(Des N. Parlett. Litho BDT)

2004 (6 Apr). P 15×14 (C).

1136	**1089**	32p. multicoloured	1·00	1·00
1137	**1090**	33p. multicoloured	1·10	1·10
1138	**1091**	40p. multicoloured	1·30	1·30
1139	**1092**	49p. multicoloured	1·60	1·60
1140	**1093**	62p. multicoloured	2·00	2·00
1141	**1094**	70p. multicoloured	2·30	2·30
1136/41		Set of 6	9·25	9·25
First Day Cover				11·25
Presentation Pack			11·25	
MS1142		150×100 mm. **1095** £2 multicoloured. P 14...	6·50	6·50
First Day Cover				7·50
Presentation Pack			7·50	

Plate Nos.: All values 1A (×4).
Sheets: 10 (2×5).
Imprint: Central, left-hand margin.
Withdrawn: 30.4.2005.

1096 Cymbidium lowianum 'Concolor'

1097 Phragmipedium besseae var. flavum

1098 Peristeria elata

1099 Cymbidium tracyanum

1100 *Paphiopedilum* Victoria Village 'Isle of Jersey'

1101 *Paphiopedilum hirsutissimum*

1102 *Phragmipedium* 'Jason Fischer' (*Illustration reduced. Actual size 110×75 mm*)

Jersey Orchids (5th series)

(Des S. Giovinazzi. Litho Cartor)

2004 (25 May). P 13×13½ (C).

1143	**1096**	32p. multicoloured	1·00	1·00
		a. Booklet pane. Nos. 1143/8 with margins all round	9·50	
1144	**1097**	33p. multicoloured	1·10	1·10
1145	**1098**	40p. multicoloured	1·30	1·30
1146	**1099**	54p. multicoloured	1·80	1·80
1147	**1100**	62p. multicoloured	2·00	2·00
1148	**1101**	70p. multicoloured	2·30	2·30
1143/8		Set of 6	9·50	9·50
First Day Cover				11·00
Presentation Pack			11·50	
MS1149		110×75 mm. **1102** £2 multicoloured	6·50	6·50
		a. Booklet pane. No. **MS**1149, but 151×100 mm with line of roulettes at left	6·50	
First Day Cover				7·50
Presentation Pack			7·00	

Booklet pane No. 1143a exists in three versions which differ in the order of the stamps within the block of six.
Plate Nos.: All values 1A (×5).
Sheets: 10 (2×5).
Imprint: Lower left-hand margin.
Withdrawn: 31.5.2005 (Sheets).

1103 Invasion Map (*Illustration reduced. Actual size 110×75 mm*)

60th Anniversary of D-Day

(Des A. Theobald. Litho Cartor)

2004 (6 June). Sheet 110×75 mm. P 13 (C).

MS1150	**1103**	£2 multicoloured	6·50	6·50
First Day Cover				8·75
Presentation Pack			7·50	

Withdrawn: 30.6.2005.

1104 Mont Orgueil Castle in 13th Century

1105 King John, c. 1204

1106 Mont Orgueil Castle in 17th Century

1107 King Charles II, c. 1684

1108 Mont Orgueil Castle, 2004

1109 Queen Elizabeth II, 2002

Jersey — 'A Peculiar of the Crown'

(Des V. Ambrus. Litho Questa)

2004 (25 June). P 14½×15 (C).

1151	**1104**	32p. multicoloured	60	35
		a. Horiz pair. Nos. 1151/2	2·00	2·00
1152	**1105**	32p. multicoloured	60	35
1153	**1106**	33p. multicoloured	60	35
		a. Horiz pair. Nos. 1153/4	2·00	2·00
1154	**1107**	33p. multicoloured	60	35
1155	**1108**	40p. multicoloured	80	45
		a. Horiz pair. Nos. 1155/6	2·50	2·50
1156	**1109**	40p. multicoloured	80	45
1151/6	Set of 6		6·50	6·50
First Day Cover				7·75
Presentation Pack			7·00	

No. 1156 has wrongly spelled inscription "Queen Elizbeth c 2002".
Plate Nos.: All values 1A (×4).
Sheets: 10 (2×5). Nos. 1151/2, 1153/4 and 1155/6 were each printed together, se-tenant, in horizontal pairs.
Imprint: Upper left-hand margin (32p., 33p.) or central, left-hand margin (40p.).
Withdrawn: 30.6.2005.

Salon du Timbre Stamp Exhibition, Paris

2004 (26 June). As No. **MS**1149, but optd with 'Jersey at Le Salon du Timbre 2004' at top left corner of sheet margin. P 13×13½ (C).

MS1157 110×75 mm. **1102** £2 multicoloured	6·50	6·50
First Day Cover		7·50
Presentation Pack	7·50	

Withdrawn: 30.6.2005.

1110 Wall Lizard

1111 Ant Lion

1112 Field Cricket

1113 Dartford Warbler

Jersey Rare Fauna (2nd series). Endangered Species of Jersey

(Des W. Oliver. Litho BDT)

2004 (27 July). P 15×14 (C).

1158	**1110**	32p. multicoloured	1·00	1·00
1159	**1111**	33p. multicoloured	1·10	1·10
1160	**1112**	49p. multicoloured	1·60	1·60
1161	**1113**	70p. multicoloured	2·30	2·30
1158/61	Set of 4		6·00	6·00
First Day Cover				8·25
Presentation Pack			7·50	
MS1162 141×174 mm. Nos. 1158/61 each×2			12·00	12·00

Plate Nos.: All values 1A (×4).
Sheets: 10 (2×5).
Imprint: Bottom margin.
Withdrawn: 30.7.2005.

1114 Dead Man's Fingers

1115 Devonshire Cup

1116 White Sea Fan

1117 Pink Sea Fan

1118 Sunset Cup

1119 Red Fingers

Marine Life (5th series). Corals

(Des Colleen Corlett. Litho Cartor)

2004 (28 Sept). P 13×13½ (C).

1163	**1114**	32p. multicoloured	1·00	1·00
1164	**1115**	33p. multicoloured	1·10	1·10
1165	**1116**	40p. multicoloured	1·30	1·30
1166	**1117**	54p. multicoloured	1·80	1·80
1167	**1118**	62p. multicoloured	2·00	2·00
1168	**1119**	70p. multicoloured	2·30	2·30
1163/8	Set of 6		9·50	9·50
First Day Cover				11·50
Presentation Pack			10·50	
MS1169 150×100 mm. Nos. 1166/8			6·00	6·00
First Day Cover				8·25
Presentation Pack			7·00	

Plate Nos.: All values 1A (×4).
Sheets: 10 (2×5).
Imprint: Lower left-hand margin.
Withdrawn: 30.9.2005.

1120 Nativity Scene

1121 Fairy Lights over Busy Streets

1122 Santa Claus, Children and Christmas Tree

1123 Candles in Church

1124 Three Candles and Holly

1125 Mary and Jesus

1126 Stockings and Candle on Mantlepiece

1127 Five Candles

1128 Angel and Candle

1129 Candles in Window

Christmas Illuminations

(Des M. Pollard. Litho SNP Sprint)

2004 (2 Nov). Self-adhesive. P 11½ (die-cut).

1170	**1120**	(32p.) multicoloured (abc)	1·00	1·00
1171	**1121**	(32p.) multicoloured (abc)	1·00	1·00
1172	**1122**	(32p.) multicoloured (abc)	1·00	1·00
1173	**1123**	(32p.) multicoloured (abc)	1·00	1·00
1174	**1124**	(32p.) multicoloured (abc)	1·00	1·00
1175	**1125**	(33p.) multicoloured (abc)	1·10	1·10
1176	**1126**	(33p.) multicoloured (abc)	1·10	1·10
1177	**1127**	(33p.) multicoloured (abc)	1·10	1·10
1178	**1128**	(33p.) multicoloured (abc)	1·10	1·10
1179	**1129**	(33p.) multicoloured (abc)	1·10	1·10
1170/9	*Set of 10*		10·50	10·50
First Day Cover				12·75
Presentation Pack			12·75	

Nos. 1170/4, which are inscribed 'JERSEY MINIMUM POSTAGE PAID' and Nos. 1175/9, inscribed 'U.K. MINIMUM POSTAGE PAID' were sold at 32p. and 33p. respectively and were available in strips of five and rolls of 100 with the surplus self-adhesive paper around each stamp removed.

Initially released with '2004' imprint dates, Nos. 1170/9 were subsequently reissued inscribed '2005' and '2006' (all prices the same).

Printings: (a) 2.11.2004. Inscr '2004'; (b) 21.10.2005. Inscr '2005'; (c) 31.10.2006. Inscr '2006'.

(Litho SNP Sprint, Australia)

2004 (3 Nov). Designs as Nos. 1107/11 (Offshore Reefs). Self-adhesive. P 11½ (die-cut).

1180	**1061**	(32p.) multicoloured (ab)	1·25	1·50
1181	**1062**	(32p.) multicoloured (ab)	1·25	1·50
1182	**1063**	(32p.) multicoloured (ab)	1·25	1·50
1183	**1064**	(32p.) multicoloured (ab)	1·25	1·50
1184	**1065**	(32p.) multicoloured (ab)	1·25	1·50
1180/4	*Set of 5*		6·00	6·50

Nos. 1180/4, which are inscribed 'JERSEY MINIMUM POSTAGE PAID' and were initially sold at 32p. each, come *se-tenant* in strips of five or rolls of 100 with the surplus self-adhesive paper around each stamp removed.

Nos. 1180/4 are inscr '2004' or '2006' with copyright symbol after date.

Initially released with '2004' imprint dates, Nos. 1180/4 were subsequently reissued inscribed '2006' (prices the same).

Printings: (a) 3.11.2004. Inscr '2004'; (b) 16.11.2006. Inscr '2006'.

Post Office Yearbook

2004 (1 Dec). Comprises Nos. 1125/56, 1158/61, 1163/8 and 1170/9 (price £34).

Yearbook	55·00

1130 C 1 Air Search Aircraft

1131 Burby Helicopter

1132 Beach Lifeguard Service

1133 Fire Rescue Inflatable

1134 RAF Sea King Helicopter

Rescue Craft

(Des A. Theobald. Litho Cartor)

2005 (18 Jan). P 13×13½ (C).

1185	**1130**	32p. multicoloured	65	70
1186	**1131**	33p. multicoloured	65	70
1187	**1132**	40p. multicoloured	80	85
1188	**1133**	49p. multicoloured	1·50	1·50
1189	**1134**	70p. multicoloured	1·75	1·75
1185/9	*Set of 5*		5·00	5·00
First Day Cover				6·00
Presentation Pack			5·75	

Plate Nos.: All values 1A (×4).
Sheets: 10 (2×5).
Imprint: Right-hand side, bottom margin.
Withdrawn: 31.1.2006.

1135 Rooster (*Illustration reduced. Actual size 110×75 mm*)

Chinese New Year ('Year of the Rooster')

(Des V. Ambrus. Litho BDT)

2005 (9 Feb). Sheet 110×75 mm. P 14½ (C).
MS1190 **1135** £1 multicoloured .... 2·50 2·75
First Day Cover .... 3·50
Presentation Pack .... 3·50
   Withdrawn: 28.2.2006.

1136 Conger Eel Soup

1137 Oysters

1138 Bean Crock

1139 Bourdélots with Black Butter

Europa. Gastronomy

(Des Jennifer Toombs. Litho BDT)

2005 (8 Mar). P 14 (C).
1191 **1136** 32p. multicoloured 65 70
1192 **1137** 33p. multicoloured 65 70
1193 **1138** 40p. multicoloured 80 85
1194 **1139** 70p. multicoloured .... 1·40 1·50
1191/4 *Set of 4* .... 3·50 3·75
First Day Cover .... 5·50
Presentation Pack .... 5·00
   The 33p. and 40p. values include the 'EUROPA' emblem.
   Plate Nos.: All values 1A (×5).
   Sheets: 10 (5×2).
   Imprint: Right-hand side, bottom margin.
   Withdrawn: 31.3.2006.

1140 Little Red Riding Hood

1141 The Little Mermaid

1142 Beauty and the Beast

1143 Rumplestiltskin

1144 Goose that laid the Golden Egg

1145 The Ugly Duckling (*Illustration reduced. Actual size 110×75 mm*)

Fairy Tales

(Des M. Pollard. Litho Cartor)

2005 (2 Apr). P 13½ (**MS**1200) or 13×13½ (others), both comb.
1195 **1140** 33p. multicoloured 65 70
1196 **1141** 34p. multicoloured 70 75
1197 **1142** 41p. multicoloured 80 85
1198 **1143** 50p. multicoloured .... 1·50 1·50
1199 **1144** 73p. multicoloured .... 2·00 2·00
1195/9 *Set of 5* .... 5·50 5·50
First Day Cover .... 6·00
Presentation Pack .... 5·75
MS1200 110×75 mm. **1145** £2 multicoloured .... 4·50 4·75
First Day Cover .... 6·50
Presentation Pack .... 5·50
   Nos. 1195/**MS**1200 commemorate the birth bicentenary of Hans
Christian Andersen.
   Plate Nos.: All values 1A (×4).
   Sheets: 10 (2×5).
   Imprint: Lower left-hand margin.
   Withdrawn: 30.4.2006.

1146 Muratti Vase Medal (*Illustration reduced. Actual size 110×75 mm*)

Football (2nd series). Centenary of Jersey Football Association and Muratti Vase

(Des A. Robinson. Litho Cartor)

2005 (27 Apr). Sheet 110×75 mm. P 14½ (C).
MS1201 **1146** £2 brown-ochre, black and orange-
   brown .... 4·50 4·50
First Day Cover .... 6·00
Presentation Pack .... 5·50
   Withdrawn: 29.4.2006.

1147 Peace Dove (*Illustration reduced. Actual size 110×75 mm*)

60th Anniversary of Liberation of Channel Islands. Peace and Reconciliation

(Des A. Robinson. Litho BDT)

2005 (9 May). Sheet 110×75 mm. P 14½ (C).
MS1202 1147 £2 multicoloured .... 4·50   4·50
First Day Cover ....   5·50
Presentation Pack .... 5·00
    Withdrawn: 31.5.2006.

'Nordia 2005' Stamp Exhibition, Göteborg, Sweden

2005 (26 May). No. MS1200 optd 'Jersey at Nordia 2005' in blue and 'Göteborg 26–29 mai SVENSKA FRIMÄRKET 150 ÅR' in black on bottom sheet margin. P 13½ (C).
MS1203 110×75 mm. 1147 £2 multicoloured .... 4·00   4·25
    Withdrawn: 31.5.2006.

1148 MGB GT

1149 Mini Cooper

1150 Citroën DS

1151 Jaguar E Type

1152 Volkswagen Beetle

1153 Aston Martin DB5

Jersey Festivals (2nd issue). Motor Festival. Classic Cars

(Des A. Copp. Litho Cartor)

2005 (6 June). P 13×13½ (C).

1204	**1148**	33p. multicoloured	65	70
		a. Booklet pane. Nos. 1204/9	6·00	
1205	**1149**	34p. multicoloured	70	75
1206	**1150**	41p. multicoloured	80	85
1207	**1151**	50p. multicoloured	1·00	1·10
1208	**1152**	56p. multicoloured	1·10	1·20
1209	**1153**	73p. multicoloured	1·50	1·60
1204/9 Set of 6			5·75	6·00
First Day Cover				7·00
Presentation Pack			7·00	

    Booklet pane No. 1204a exists in three versions which differ in the order of the stamps within the block of six.
    Plate Nos.: All values 1A (×4).
    Sheets: 10 (2×5).
    Imprint: Lower left-hand margin.
    Withdrawn: 30.6.2006 (sheets).

1154 Yellow Bartsia   **1155** Scarlet Pimpernel   **1156** Wild Angelica   **1157** Common Knapweed

1158 Marsh St. Johnswort   **1159** Black Bryony   **1160** Bog Pimpernel   **1161** Greater Stitchwort

1162 Horseshoe Vetch   **1163** Common Mallow   **1164** English Stonecrop   **1165** White Campion

1166 Tutsan   **1167** Common Dog-violet   **1168** Ox Eye Daisy   **1169** Rock Sea Spurrey

1170 Herb-Robert   **1171** Ragged Robin   **1172** Brooklime   **1173** Mouse Ear Hawkweed

1174 Cuckoo Flower   **1175** Yellow Iris   **1176** Three-cornered Garlic   **1177** Devil's-bit Scabious

Wild Flowers

(Des N. Parlett. Litho Cartor)

2005 (19 July)–07. P 13½ (C).

1210	**1154**	1p. multicoloured (b)	10	10
1211	**1155**	2p. multicoloured (a)	10	10
1212	**1156**	3p. multicoloured (b)	10	10
1213	**1157**	4p. multicoloured (a)	10	10
1214	**1158**	5p. multicoloured (b)	10	15
1215	**1159**	10p. multicoloured (c)	30	30
1216	**1160**	15p. multicoloured (b)	30	35
1217	**1161**	20p. multicoloured (a)	40	45
1218	**1162**	25p. multicoloured (c)	75	75
1219	**1163**	30p. multicoloured (a)	60	65
1220	**1164**	35p. multicoloured (a)	1·00	1·00
1221	**1165**	40p. multicoloured (a)	80	85
1222	**1166**	45p. multicoloured (c) (d)	1·30	1·30
1223	**1167**	50p. multicoloured (c)	1·00	1·10
1224	**1168**	55p. multicoloured (c)	1·60	1·60
1225	**1169**	60p. multicoloured (c)	1·80	1·80
1226	**1170**	65p. multicoloured (a)	1·30	1·40
1227	**1171**	70p. multicoloured (b)	1·40	1·50
1228	**1172**	75p. multicoloured (b)	1·50	1·60
1229	**1173**	80p. multicoloured (c)	2·30	2·30
1230	**1174**	85p. multicoloured (b)	1·70	1·80
1231	**1175**	90p. multicoloured (b)	1·80	1·90
1232	**1176**	£1 multicoloured (a)	2·00	2·10
1233	**1177**	£1.50 multicoloured (c)	4·50	4·50
1210/33 Set of 24			25·00	26·00
First Day Covers (3)				29·00
Presentation Packs (3)			29·00	

MS1234 Three sheets, each 150×100 mm. (a) Nos. 1211, 1213, 1217, 1219, 1221, 1223, 1226 and 1232 (a). (b) Nos. 1210, 1212, 1214, 1216, 1227/8 and 1230/1 (b). (c) Nos. 1215, 1218, 1220, 1222, 1224/5, 1229 and 1233 (C)

Set of 3 sheets	26·00	27·00
First Day Covers (3)		29·00
Presentation Packs (3)	29·00	

Printings: (a) 19.7.2005. Inscr '2005' with copyright symbol. (b) 26.9.2006. Inscr '2006' with copyright symbol. (c) 25.7.2007. Inscr '2007' with copyright symbol. (d) 16.6.2011. Inscr '2011' with copyright symbol.

Plate Nos.: 1p. to 5p., 15p., 20p., 30p., 40p., 50p., 65p. to 75p., 85p. to £1 1A (×4); 10p., 25p., 35p., 45p., 55p., 60p., 80p., £1.50 1A (×5). Sheets: 10 (5×2).

Imprint: Right-hand side, bottom margin.

BONUS GIFTS. Starting in 2006, Jersey Post has provided 'bonus gifts' to standing order customers spending over a certain amount during the previous year. These gifts consist of a miniature sheet or a first day cover bearing that sheet. In 2006 the sheet comprised the 2p. and 5p. Wild Flowers stamps (Nos. 2011 and 2014); subsequent sheets have comprised the 3p. and 25p. (2007), 4p. and 10p. (2008), 1p. and 2p. (2009) and 15p. and 45p. (2010).

1178 Le Hocq Tower   **1179** Seymour Tower   **1180** Archirondel Tower

1181 Kempt Tower   **1182** Le Rocco Tower

Coastal Towers (1st series)

(Des N. Shewring. Litho BDT)

2005 (9 Aug). P 14 (C).

1235	1178	33p. multicoloured	65	70
1236	1179	34p. multicoloured	70	75
1237	1180	41p. multicoloured	1·00	85
1238	1181	56p. multicoloured	1·50	1·75
1239	1182	73p. multicoloured	2·00	2·25
1235/9 Set of 5			5·50	5·50
First Day Cover				6·25
Presentation Pack			6·00	

See also Nos. 1694/9.
Plate Nos.: All values 1A (×4).
Sheets: 10 (5×2).
Imprint: Upper left-hand margin.
Withdrawn: 31.8.2006.

1183 Hygrocybe calyptriformis   **1184** Boletus luridiformis   **1185** Inocybe godeyi

1186 Myriostoma coliforme   **1187** Helvella crispa   **1188** Hygrocybe coccinea

1189 Marasmius oreades (Illustration reduced. Actual size 150×100 mm)

Fungi (2nd series)

(Des W. Oliver. Litho BDT)

2005 (13 Sept). P 14 (C).

1240	1183	33p. multicoloured	65	70
1241	1184	34p. multicoloured	70	75
1242	1185	41p. multicoloured	80	85
1243	1186	50p. multicoloured	1·00	1·10
1244	1187	56p. multicoloured	1·10	1·20
1245	1188	73p. multicoloured	1·50	1·60
1240/5 Set of 6			5·75	6·00
First Day Cover				7·50
Presentation Pack			6·00	

MS1246 150×100 mm. 1189 £2. multicoloured P 14½ (C)

	4·50	4·75
First Day Cover		7·50
Presentation Pack	5·00	

Plate Nos.: All values 1A (×4).
Sheets: 10 (5×2).
Imprint: Upper left-hand margin.
Withdrawn: 30.9.2006.

1190 H.M.S. Belleisle   **1191** H.M.S. Royal Sovereign

1192 H.M.S. Neptune   **1193** H.M.S. Euryalus

1194 H.M.S. Mars

1195 H.M.S. *Victory* (*Illustration reduced. Actual size 110×75 mm*)

Bicentenary of the Battle of Trafalgar

(Des A. Theobald. Litho BDT)

2005 (21 Oct). P 14 (C).

1247	**1190**	33p. multicoloured	65	70
1248	**1191**	34p. multicoloured	70	75
1249	**1192**	41p. multicoloured	80	95
1250	**1193**	50p. multicoloured	1·50	1·50
1251	**1194**	73p. multicoloured	2·00	2·00
1247/51	*Set of 5*		5·50	5·75

First Day Cover .... 6·50
Presentation Pack .... 6·50
MS1252 110×75 mm. **1195** £2 multicoloured .... 5·00   5·00
First Day Cover .... 6·50
Presentation Pack .... 6·50

Plate Nos.: All values 1A (×4).
Sheets: 10 (2×5).
Imprint: Lower left-hand margin.
Withdrawn: 31.10.2006.

Post Office Yearbook

2005 (1 Dec). Comprises Nos. 1185/**MS**1202, 1204/9, 1211, 1213, 1217, 1219, 1221, 1223, 1226, 1232 and 1235/52 (price £37).
Yearbook .... 75·00

1196 Royal Jersey Regiment, c. 1830

1197 Royal Jersey Regiment, c. 1844

1198 Royal Jersey Artillery, c. 1881

1199 Royal Jersey Light Infantry, c. 1890

1200 Royal Engineers (modern)

Royal Jersey Militia (2nd series)

(Des A. Robinson. Litho Enschedé)

2006 (6 Jan). P 13½×14 (C).

1253	**1196**	33p. multicoloured	65	70
1254	**1197**	34p. multicoloured	70	75
1255	**1198**	41p. multicoloured	80	85
1256	**1199**	50p. multicoloured	1·50	1·50
1257	**1200**	73p. multicoloured	2·00	2·00
1253/7	*Set of 5*		5·50	5·50

First Day Cover .... 6·25
Presentation Pack .... 6·25

Plate Nos.: All values 1A, 1B (each×4).
Sheets: 10 (2×5).
Imprint: Bottom, left-hand corner margin.
Withdrawn: 31.1.2007.

1201 Victoria Cross (*Illustration reduced. Actual size 110×75 mm*)

150th Anniversary of the Victoria Cross

(Des A. Robinson. Litho Enschedé)

2006 (29 Jan). Sheet 110×75 mm. P 13½×14 (C).
MS1258 **1201** £2 multicoloured .... 5·00   5·00
First Day Cover .... 6·00
Presentation Pack .... 6·00
Withdrawn: 31.1.2007.

1202 Dog (*Illustration reduced. Actual size 110×75 mm*)

Chinese New Year ('Year of the Dog')

(Des V. Ambrus. Litho BDT)

2006 (29 Jan). Sheet 110×75 mm. P 14½ (C).
MS1259 **1202** £1 multicoloured .... 3·50   3·75
First Day Cover .... 4·00
Presentation Pack .... 4·00
Withdrawn: 31.1.2008.

1203 Chinese National Costumes and Mask (Elliott Grimes)

1204 Portuguese Fado Music Festival (Liam Reynolds)

1205 Polish Pisanki painted Easter Egg Design (Kelly Reynolds)

1206 Indian National Costumes (Olivia Grimes)

Europa. Integration. Winning Entries in Children's Stamp Design Competition

(Adapted A. Copp. Litho BDT)

2006 (7 Mar). P 14 (C).

1260	**1203**	33p. multicoloured	65	70
1261	**1204**	34p. multicoloured	70	75
1262	**1205**	41p. multicoloured	1·75	1·50
1263	**1206**	73p. multicoloured	2·25	2·25
1260/3 *Set of 4*			5·00	5·00
First Day Cover				6·50
Presentation Pack			6·50	

Plate Nos.: All values 1A (×4).
Sheets: 10 (2×5) with enlarged illustrated margins.
Imprint: Lower left-hand margin.
Withdrawn: 31.3.2007.
The 34p. and 41p. values include the 'EUROPA' emblem.

1207 Flat Periwinkle

1208 Painted Top Shell

1209 Dog Cockle

1210 Variegated Scallop

1211 Blue Rayed Limpet

1212 European Cowrie

1213 Ormer Shell (*Illustration reduced. Actual size 150×100 mm*)

Marine Life (6th series). Sea Shells

(Des N. Parlett. Litho (with thermography (Nos. 1264/9)) or embossing (**MS**1270) Cartor)

2006 (4 Apr). P 13×13½ (C).

1264	**1207**	34p. multicoloured	70	75
1265	**1208**	37p. multicoloured	75	80
1266	**1209**	42p. multicoloured	85	90
1267	**1210**	51p. multicoloured	1·00	1·10
1268	**1211**	57p. multicoloured	1·10	1·20
1269	**1212**	74p. multicoloured	1·50	1·60
1264/9 *Set of 6*			6·00	6·25
First Day Cover				7·75
Presentation Pack			7·75	
MS1270 150×100 mm. **1213** £2 multicoloured.				
P 13½			4·50	4·50
First Day Cover				5·50
Presentation Pack			5·50	

Plate Nos.: All values 1A (×4).
Sheets: 10 (2×5) with enlarged illustrated margins.
Imprint: Lower left-hand margin.
Withdrawn: 30.4.2007.

1214 Prince Charles and Duchess of Cornwall Wedding Photograph

First Wedding Anniversary of Prince Charles and Duchess of Cornwall

(Des A. Robinson. Litho Cartor)

2006 (9 Apr). P 13½ (C).

1271	**1214**	£2 multicoloured	4·50	4·50
First Day Cover				5·50
Presentation Pack			5·50	

No. 1271 was retained in use as a definitive stamp.
Plate Nos.: 1A (×5).
Sheets: 4 (2×2).
Imprint: Lower left-hand margin.

1215 Queen Elizabeth II

1216 Queen Elizabeth II (£5; New Zealand $5) (*Illustration reduced. Actual size 150×100 mm*)

80th Birthday of Queen Elizabeth II

(Litho and embossed Cartor)

2006 (21 Apr). P 13½ (C).

1272	**1215**	£5 multicoloured	10·00	10·50
First Day Cover				13·00
Presentation Pack			13·50	
MS1273 150×100 mm. **1216** £5 multicoloured; New				
Zealand $5 multicoloured (sold at £7)			13·00	15·00
a. Silver foil (country names, values				
and borders) omitted			£3250	
First Day Cover				17·00
Presentation Pack			17·00	

The background colour of the sheet stamp, No. 1272, is deep ultramarine, but both the stamps in the miniature sheet have a deep turquoise-blue background.

The miniature sheet contains a £5 Jersey stamp and a $5 New Zealand stamp. The same miniature sheet and a stamp in a similar design to No. 1272 was also issued by New Zealand.

No. 1272 was retained in use as a definitive stamp.
Plate Nos.: 1A (×6).
Sheets: 4 (2×2).
Imprint: Upper left-hand margin.

1217 Football and World Cup Trophy (*Illustration reduced. Actual size 110×75 mm*)

Football (3rd series). World Cup Football Championship, Germany

(Des N. Shewring. Litho BDT)

2006 (9 June). Sheet 110×75 mm. P 14½ (C).

MS1274	**1217**	£2 multicoloured	4·75	5·00
	First Day Cover			5·50
	Presentation Pack		5·50	

Withdrawn: 30.6.2007.

1218 Greve de Lecq

1219 La Rocque

1220 Portelet

1221 St. Brelade's Bay

Island Views

(Des Colleen Corlett. Litho SEP Sprint, Australia)

2006 (11 July). Self-adhesive. P 11½ (die-cut).

1275	**1218**	(37p.) multicoloured (ab)	1·50	1·50
1276	**1219**	(37p.) multicoloured (ab)	1·50	1·50
1277	**1220**	(37p.) multicoloured (ab)	1·50	1·50
1278	**1221**	(37p.) multicoloured (ab)	1·50	1·50
1275/8	*Set of 4*		5·00	5·00
	First Day Cover			6·00
	Presentation Pack		5·50	

Nos. 1275/8, which are inscribed 'UK MINIMUM POSTAGE PAID' and were initially sold at 37p. each, come *se-tenant* in strips of 4 or rolls of 100 with the surplus self-adhesive paper around each stamp removed.
Printings: (a) 11.7.2006. Inscr '2006'; (b) 10.3.2009. Inscr '2009'.

1222 Red Underwing Moth

1223 Comma Butterfly

1224 Black Arches Moth

1225 Small Copper Butterfly

1226 Holly Blue Butterfly

1227 Orange-tip Butterfly

Butterflies and Moths (2nd series)

(Des W. Oliver. Litho BDT)

2006 (1 Aug). P 15×14 (C).

1279	**1222**	34p. multicoloured	70	75
1280	**1223**	37p. multicoloured	75	80
1281	**1224**	42p. multicoloured	85	90
1282	**1225**	51p. multicoloured	1·00	1·10
1283	**1226**	57p. multicoloured	1·10	1·20
1284	**1227**	74p. multicoloured	1·50	1·60
1279/84	*Set of 6*		5·75	6·25
	First Day Cover			7·75
	Presentation Pack		7·75	
MS1285	150×100 mm. Nos. 1282/4		4·50	4·50
	First Day Cover			5·25
	Presentation Pack		5·25	

Stamps from **MS**1285 have no white borders.
Plate Nos.: All values 1A (×4).
Sheets: 10 (2×5) with enlarged illustrated margins.
Imprint: Lower left-hand margin.
Withdrawn: 31.8.2007.

1228 LDV Luton Van, c. 2004

1229 Renault Kangoo, 1999–2004

1230 LDV Pilot, 1994–2004

1231 Ford Transit, Luton Body, 1988–96

1232 Morris Marina, 440/575, c. 1978

1233 Morris Minor, c. 1969

Jersey Postal History (2nd series). Postal Vehicles

(Des A. Theobald. Litho Cartor)

2006 (31 Oct). P 13×13½ (C).

1286	**1228**	34p. multicoloured	70	75
		a. Booklet pane. Nos. 1286/91 with margins all round	6·00	
1287	**1229**	37p. multicoloured	75	80
1288	**1230**	42p. multicoloured	85	90
1289	**1231**	51p. multicoloured	1·00	1·10
1290	**1232**	57p. multicoloured	1·10	1·20
1291	**1233**	74p. multicoloured	1·50	1·60
1286/91	*Set of 6*		5·75	6·25
	First Day Cover			7·75
	Presentation Pack		7·75	
MS1292	150×100 mm. Nos. 1289/91		4·50	4·75
		a. Booklet pane. No. **MS**1292, but with line of roulettes at left	4·00	
	First Day Cover			5·50
	Presentation Pack		5·50	

Booklet pane No. 1286a exists in three versions which differ in the order of the stamps within the block of six.

Plate Nos.: All values 1A (×4).
Sheets: 10 (2×5).
Imprint: Right-hand side, bottom margin.
Withdrawn: 31.10.2007 (Sheets).

Belgica '06 International Stamp Exhibition, Brussels

2006 (16 Nov). No. **MS**1270 optd with 'Jersey at' and Belgica emblem on bottom left sheet margin.

MS1293 150×100 mm. **1213** £2 multicoloured			5·00	5·50
First Day Cover				6·00
Presentation Pack			5·50	

Withdrawn: 31.10.2007.

Post Office Yearbook

2006 (1 Dec). Comprises Nos. 1210, 1212, 1214, 1216, 1227/8, 1230/1, 1253/72, **MS**1274/84 and 1286/91 (price £40).

Yearbook	80·00

1234 Molybdenite

1235 Muscovite in Pegmatite Vein, Feldspar + Quartz

1236 Orthoclase and Plagioclase

1237 Quartz coated with Manganese Oxide

1238 Smoky Quartz

Mineralogy

(Des Jennifer Toombs. Litho Cartor)

2007 (23 Jan). P 13×13½ (C).

1294	**1234**	34p. multicoloured	1·00	1·00
1295	**1235**	37p. multicoloured	1·10	1·10
1296	**1236**	42p. multicoloured	1·20	1·20
1297	**1237**	51p. multicoloured	1·50	1·50
1298	**1238**	74p. multicoloured	2·20	2·20
1294/8	Set of 5		7·00	7·00
First Day Cover				7·50
Presentation Pack			7·50	

Plate Nos.: All values 1A (×5).
Sheets: 10 (2×5) with enlarged illustrated margins.
Imprint: Lower left-hand margin.
Withdrawn: 31.1.2008.

1239 Pig (*Illustration reduced. Actual size 110×75 mm*)

Chinese New Year ('Year of the Pig')

(Des V. Ambrus. Litho BDT)

2007 (18 Feb). Sheet 110×75 mm. P 14½ (C).

MS1299 **1239** £1 multicoloured			3·25	3·50
First Day Cover				4·50
Presentation Pack			3·75	

Omnibus Folder (*containing Nos.* **MS**731, **MS**768, **MS**843, **MS**885, **MS**928, **MS**972, **MS**1030, **MS**1081, **MS**1131, **MS**1190, **MS**1259, **MS**1299). 25·00

Withdrawn: 29.2.2008 (**MS**1299 only).

1240 Windsurfing canoeing and land yachting ('Adventure')

1241 Scouts playing Trumpets and National Flags ('International Friendship')

1242 Climbing and go-karting ('Developing Young People')

1243 Scouts and Badges ('Changing the World for Good')

Europa. Centenary of Scouting

(Des Colleen Corlett. Litho Austrian State Ptg Wks, Vienna)

2007 (6 Mar). P 14 (C).

1300	**1240**	34p. multicoloured	1·00	1·00
1301	**1241**	37p. multicoloured	1·10	1·10
1302	**1242**	42p. multicoloured	1·20	1·20
1303	**1243**	74p. multicoloured	2·20	2·20
1300/3	Set of 4		5·50	5·50
First Day Cover				6·00
Presentation Pack			6·00	

Plate Nos.: All values 1A (×4).
Sheets: 10 (2×5) with enlarged illustrated margins.
Imprint: Lower left-hand margin.
Withdrawn: 31.3.2008.
The 37p. and 42p. values include the 'EUROPA' emblem.

1244 Long-tailed Field Mouse

1245 Rabbits

1246 Polecat

1247 Common Shrew

1248 Stoat

1249 Brown Rat

Jersey Nature. Countryside Animals

(Des W. Oliver. Litho BDT)

2007 (10 Apr). P 15×14 (C).

1304	**1244**	34p. multicoloured	1·00	1·00
1305	**1245**	37p. multicoloured	1·10	1·10

1306	**1246**	42p. multicoloured	1·30	1·30
1307	**1247**	51p. multicoloured	1·50	1·50
1308	**1248**	57p. multicoloured	1·70	1·70
1309	**1249**	74p. multicoloured	2·20	2·20
1304/9	*Set of 6*		8·75	8·75
First Day Cover				9·25
Presentation Pack			9·25	
MS1310 150×100 mm. As Nos. 1307/9			5·50	5·50
First Day Cover				6·00
Presentation Pack			6·00	

Stamps from **MS**1310 have no white borders.
Plate Nos.: All values 1A (×4).
Sheets: 10 (2×5) with enlarged illustrated margins.
Imprint: Lower left-hand margin.
Withdrawn: 30.4.2008.

1250 House Sparrow

1251 Chaffinch

1252 Blue Tit

1253 Blackbirds (pair)

1254 Magpie   **1255** Great Tit

Jersey Birdlife (1st series). Garden Birds

(Des Nick Parlett. Litho Cartor)

2007 (19 June). P 13×13½ (C).

1311	**1250**	34p. multicoloured	1·00	1·00
1312	**1251**	37p. multicoloured	1·10	1·10
1313	**1252**	42p. multicoloured	1·30	1·30
1314	**1253**	51p. multicoloured	1·50	1·50
1315	**1254**	57p. multicoloured	1·70	1·70
1316	**1255**	74p. multicoloured	2·20	2·20
1311/16	*Set of 6*		8·75	8·75
First Day Cover				9·25
Presentation Pack			9·25	
MS1317 150×100 mm. As Nos. 1314/16			5·25	5·25
First Day Cover				5·75
Presentation Pack			5·75	
MS1318 150×100 mm. Nos. 1311/16			8·75	8·75
First Day Cover				9·25
Presentation Pack			9·25	

Stamps from **MS**1317 have no white borders.
See also Nos. 1400/**MS**1407, 1450/**MS**1457, 1495/**MS**1502, 1584/
MS1591 and 1681/6.
Plate Nos.: All values 1A (×5).
Sheets: 10 (2×5) with enlarged illustrated margins.
Imprint: Lower left-hand margin.
Withdrawn: 30.6.2008 (except **MS**1318).

1256 Gorey Regatta (*Illustration reduced. Actual size* 110×75 *mm*)

Jersey Yachting (2nd issue). 150th Anniversary of Gorey Regatta

(Des Andrew Robinson. Litho Enschedé)

2007 (22 June). Sheet 110×75 mm. P 13×13½ (C).

MS1319 **1256** £2 multicoloured			6·00	6·00
First Day Cover				6·50
Presentation Pack			6·50	

Withdrawn: 30.6.2008.

1257 Clematis 'Nelly Moser' and 'The President'

1258 Rose 'Just Joey'

1259 Honeysuckle *Lonicera × americana*

1260 Fuchsia 'Swingtime'

1261 Sweet Peas

1262 Lilac

Seasonal Flowers (3rd series). Summer

(Des Wendy Tait. Litho Enschedé)

2007 (25 July). P 13½ (C).

1320	**1257**	34p. multicoloured	1·00	1·00
1321	**1258**	37p. multicoloured	1·10	1·10
1322	**1259**	42p. multicoloured	1·30	1·30
1323	**1260**	51p. multicoloured	1·50	1·50
1324	**1261**	57p. multicoloured	1·70	1·70
1325	**1262**	74p. multicoloured	2·20	2·20
1320/5	*Set of 6*		8·75	8·75
First Day Cover				9·25
Presentation Pack			9·25	

Plate Nos.: 34p., 37p. 1A, 1B; others 1A (each×5).
Sheets: 10 (5×2).
Imprint: Bottom margin.
Withdrawn: 31.7.2008.

1263 Dornier Do 24 ATT   **1264** Avro Vulcan B.2

1265 Junkers Ju 52   **1266** Sukhoi Su-27 'Flanker'

1267 Boeing B-52 Stratofortress

1268 Anglo-French Concorde

1269 Red Arrows (*Illustration reduced. Actual size 110×75 mm*)

Jersey Aviation History (9th series). 60th Anniversary of Jersey International Air Display

(Des Tony Theobald. Litho Cartor)

2007 (13 Sept). P 13×13½ (C).

1326	**1263**	34p. multicoloured	1·00	1·00
		a. Booklet pane. Nos. 1326/31 with margins all round	6·00	
1327	**1264**	37p. multicoloured	1·10	1·10
1328	**1265**	42p. multicoloured	1·30	1·30
1329	**1266**	51p. multicoloured	1·50	1·50
1330	**1267**	57p. multicoloured	1·70	1·70
1331	**1268**	74p. multicoloured	2·20	2·20
1326/31 *Set of 6*			8·75	8·75
First Day Cover				9·25
Presentation Pack			9·25	
MS1332	110×75 mm. **1269** £2·50 multicoloured. P 13½×13		7·25	7·25
		a. Booklet pane. No. **MS**1332 but 150×100 mm with line of roulettes at left	5·00	
First Day Cover				7·75
Presentation Pack			7·75	

Booklet pane No. 1326a exists in three versions which differ in the order of the stamps within the block of six.

Plate Nos.: All values 1A (×4).
Sheets: 10 (2×5) with enlarged illustrated margins.
Imprint: Lower left-hand margin.
Withdrawn: 30.9.2008 (sheets).

1270 Queen's Valley Reservoir

1271 Mont Orgueil Castle

1272 Bonne Nuit Harbour

1273 La Hougue Bie

1274 Bouley Bay

1275 La Corbière Lighthouse

Jersey Scenery (1st series) (sepac)

(Des Andrew Robinson. Litho Enschedé)

2007 (1 Oct). P 14×13½ (C).

1333	**1270**	34p. multicoloured	1·00	1·00
1334	**1271**	37p. multicoloured	1·10	1·10
1335	**1272**	42p. multicoloured	1·30	1·30
1336	**1273**	51p. multicoloured	1·50	1·50
1337	**1274**	57p. multicoloured	1·70	1·70
1338	**1275**	74p. multicoloured	2·20	2·20
1333/8 *Set of 6*			8·75	8·75
First Day Cover				9·25
Presentation Pack			9·25	

The 42p. value No. 1335 is inscr 'sepac' and was also available in a souvenir folder with ten other Sepac logo stamps issued by other administrations (original selling price £10.75).

See also Nos. 1458/63 and 1612/17.

Plate Nos.: 34p., 37p. 1A, 1B, 1C; 42p., 74p. 1A, 1B; 51p., 57p. 1A (each×4).
Sheets: 10 (2×5) with enlarged illustrated margins.
Imprint: Lower left-hand margin.
Withdrawn: 31.10.2008.

1276 'Minuit Chrétiens'

1277 'While Shepherds Watched'

1278 'O Come All Ye Faithful'

1279 'O Christmas Tree'

1280 'Jingle Bells'

1281 'Hark the Herald Angels Sing'

1282 'We Three Kings'

1283 'Ding Dong Merrily on High'

1284 'Holly and the Ivy'

1285 'Good King Wenceslas'

Christmas Carols

(Des Michael Pollard. Litho SNP Sprint, Australia)

2007 (7 Nov). Self-adhesive. P 11½ (die-cut).

1339	**1276**	(35p.) multicoloured (abc)	1·00	1·00
1340	**1277**	(35p.) multicoloured (abc)	1·00	1·00
1341	**1278**	(35p.) multicoloured (abc)	1·00	1·00
1342	**1279**	(35p.) multicoloured (abc)	1·00	1·00
1343	**1280**	(35p.) multicoloured (abc)	1·00	1·00
1344	**1281**	(39p.) multicoloured (abc)	1·20	1·20
1345	**1282**	(39p.) multicoloured (abc)	1·20	1·20
1346	**1283**	(39p.) multicoloured (abc)	1·20	1·20
1347	**1284**	(39p.) multicoloured (abc)	1·20	1·20
1348	**1285**	(39p.) multicoloured (abc)	1·20	1·20
1339/48 *Set of 10*			11·00	11·00
First Day Cover				12·00
Presentation Pack			12·00	

Nos. 1339/43 which are inscribed 'JERSEY MINIMUM POSTAGE PAID' were sold for 35p., and Nos. 1344/8 which are inscribed 'U.K. MINIMUM POSTAGE PAID' were sold for 39p. Nos. 1339/43 and 1344/8 were each printed together, *se-tenant*, in strips of 5 from rolls of 100, from which the surplus self-adhesive backing paper around each stamp was removed.

Printings: (a) 7.11.2007. Inscr '2007'; (b) 14.11.2008. Inscr '2008'; (c) 10.11.2009. Inscr '2009'.

1286 Queen Elizabeth II and Duke of Edinburgh

Diamond Wedding of Queen Elizabeth II and Duke of Edinburgh

(Des Andrew Robinson. Litho Cartor)

2007 (20 Nov). P 13½ (C).

1349	**1286**	£3 multicoloured	8·75	8·75
First Day Cover				9·25
Presentation Pack			9·25	

No. 1349 was retained in use as a definitive stamp.
Plate Nos.: 1A (or A1) (×5).
Sheets: 4 (2×2).
Imprint: Lower left-hand margin.

Post Office Yearbook

2007 (1 Dec). Comprises Nos. 1215, 1218, 1220, 1222, 1224/5, 1229, 1233, 1294/309, 1311/16 and **MS**1319/49 (price £43).
Yearbook .... 82·00

1287 Sunshine

1288 Strong Wind Signals

1289 Weather Signals

1290 Temperature

1291 Tides and Wave Signals

300th Anniversary of Jersey Signal Station

(Des Nick Shewring. Litho Austrian State Ptg Wks, Vienna)

2008 (15 Jan). P 14 (C).

1350	**1287**	35p. multicoloured	1·00	1·00
1351	**1288**	39p. multicoloured	1·20	1·20
1352	**1289**	43p. multicoloured	1·30	1·30
1353	**1290**	58p. multicoloured	1·70	1·70
1354	**1291**	76p. multicoloured	2·30	2·30
1350/4 *Set of 5*			7·50	7·50
First Day Cover				10·00
Presentation Pack			10·00	

Plate Nos.: All values 1A (each×4).
Sheets: 10 (2×5) with enlarged illustrated margins.
Imprint: Lower left-hand margin.
Withdrawn: 31.1.2009.

1292 Thank You Letter

1293 Love Letter

1294 Letter to Santa Claus

1295 Family Letter

Europa. The Letter

(Des Jennifer Toombs. Litho Enschedé)

2008 (14 Feb). P 13½×14 (C).

1355	**1292**	35p. multicoloured	1·00	1·00
1356	**1293**	39p. multicoloured	1·20	1·20
1357	**1294**	43p. multicoloured	1·30	1·30
1358	**1295**	76p. multicoloured	2·30	2·30
1355/8 *Set of 4*			5·75	5·75
First Day Cover				8·25
Presentation Pack			8·25	

The 39p. and 43p. values include the 'EUROPA' emblem.
Plate Nos.: 35p., 39p. 1A, 1B; 43p., 76p. 1A (each×6).
Sheets: 10 (2×5) with enlarged inscribed margins.
Imprint: Lower left-hand margin.
Withdrawn: 28.2.2009.

1296 Arts and Crafts

1297 Dance and Drama

1298 Speech

1299 Films and Photography

1300 Music

Jersey Festivals (3rd issue). Centenary of Jersey Eisteddfod

(Des Jennifer Toombs. Litho Austrian State Ptg Wks, Vienna)

2008 (3 Mar). P 14 (C).

1359	**1296**	35p. multicoloured	1·00	1·00
1360	**1297**	39p. multicoloured	1·20	1·20
1361	**1298**	43p. multicoloured	1·30	1·30
1362	**1299**	58p. multicoloured	1·70	1·70
1363	**1300**	76p. multicoloured	2·30	2·30
1359/63 *Set of 5*			7·50	7·50
First Day Cover				10·00
Presentation Pack			10·00	

Plate Nos.: All values 1A (each×4).
Sheets: 10 (2×5) with enlarged illustrated margins.
Imprint: Lower left-hand margin.
Withdrawn: 31.3.2009.

1301 Grey Bus Services Daimler CB, c. 1920

1302 SCS Ex LGOC 'K' Single Decker, c. 1930

1303 JMT Town Bus Service, c. 1941

1304 JMT Leyland Lion Charcoal Burner, c. 1941

1305 JBS Bedford WLB, c. 1956

1306 JMT Commer Commando, c. 1963

1307 JMT Ford Willowbrook, c. 1977 (*Illustration reduced. Actual size 110×75 mm*)

Jersey Transport. Buses (2nd series)

(Des Alan Copp. Litho Enschedé)

2008 (8 Apr). P 14 (C).

1364	**1301**	35p. multicoloured	85	85
1365	**1302**	39p. multicoloured	95	95
1366	**1303**	43p. multicoloured	1·00	1·00
1367	**1304**	52p. multicoloured	1·30	1·30
1368	**1305**	58p. multicoloured	1·40	1·40
1369	**1306**	76p. multicoloured	1·80	1·80
1364/9 *Set of 6*			7·25	7·25
First Day Cover				11·50
Presentation Pack			11·50	
MS1370 110×75 mm. **1307** £2·50 multicoloured. P 13½×14 (C).			7·25	7·25
First Day Cover				10·00
Presentation Pack			10·00	

Plate Nos.: 35p., 39p., 43p. 1A, 1B, 1C; 52p., 58p., 76p. 1A (each×5).
Sheets: 10 (2×5) with enlarged illustrated margins.
Imprint: Lower left-hand margin.
Withdrawn: 30.4.2009.

1308 Jersey Bull 'Mermaid's Warrior Count' (*Illustration reduced. Actual size 110×75 mm*)

18th World Jersey Cattle Bureau Conference, Jersey

(Des William Oliver. Litho Cartor)

2008 (18 May). Sheet 110×75 mm. P 13½×13½ (C).

MS1371 **1308** £2 multicoloured		5·75	5·75
First Day Cover			8·50
Presentation Pack		8·50	

Withdrawn: 31.5.2009.

1309 *Cymbidium* Averanches 'Victoria Village'

1310 *Miltonia* 'Tesson Mill'

1311 *Anguloa* Victoire 'Trinity'

1312 *Phragmipedium* La Hougette

1313 *Phragmipedium* Havre de Pas 'Jersey'

1314 *Paphiopedilum* Rolfei 'Trinity'

1315 *Paphiopedilum* Rocco Tower (*Illustration reduced. Actual size* 110×75 *mm*)

Jersey Orchids (6th series)

(Des Andrew Robinson. Litho Cartor)

2008 (20 May). P 13×13½ (C).

1372	**1309**	35p. multicoloured	1·00	1·00
1373	**1310**	39p. multicoloured	1·20	1·20
1374	**1311**	43p. multicoloured	1·30	1·30
1375	**1312**	52p. multicoloured	1·50	1·50
1376	**1313**	58p. multicoloured	1·70	1·70
1377	**1314**	76p. multicoloured	2·30	2·30
1372/7	*Set of 6*		9·00	9·00
First Day Cover				11·50
Presentation Pack			11·50	
MS1378	110×75 mm. **1315** £2.50 multicoloured		7·25	7·25
First Day Cover				10·00
Presentation Pack			10·00	

Plate Nos.: All values 1A (each×5).
Sheets: 10 (2×5) with enlarged illustrated margins.
Imprint: Lower left-hand margin.
Withdrawn: 31.5.2009.

1316 Jersey Cricket Board Ball hitting Stumps (*Illustration reduced. Actual size* 110×75 *mm*)

World Cricket League Division 5 Tournament, Jersey

(Des Andrew Robinson. Litho Cartor)

2008 (23 May). Sheet 110×75 mm. P 13×13½ (C).

MS1379 **1316** £2 multicoloured		5·75	5·75
First Day Cover			8·50
Presentation Pack		8·50	

Withdrawn: 31.5.2009.

1317 HMS *Roebuck*   **1318** HMS *Monmouth*

1319 HMS *Edinburgh*   **1320** HMS *Express*

1321 HMS *Severn*   **1322** HMS *Cottesmore*

1323 HMY *Britannia* (*Illustration reduced. Actual size* 110×75 *mm*)

Jersey Naval Connections (2nd series). Visiting Naval Vessels

(Des Tony Theobald. Litho Cartor)

2008 (24 June). P 13×13½ (C).

1380	**1317**	35p. multicoloured	1·00	1·00
		a. Booklet pane. Nos. 1380/5 with margins all round	9·00	
1381	**1318**	39p. multicoloured	1·20	1·20
1382	**1319**	43p. multicoloured	1·30	1·30
1383	**1320**	52p. multicoloured	1·50	1·50
1384	**1321**	58p. multicoloured	1·70	1·70
1385	**1322**	76p. multicoloured	2·30	2·30
1380/5	*Set of 6*		9·00	9·00
First Day Cover				11·50
Presentation Pack			11·50	
MS1386	110×75 mm. **1323** £2.50 multicoloured. P 13½×13 (C)		7·00	7·00
		a. Booklet pane. No. **MS**1386, but 150×100 mm with line of roulettes at left	7·00	
First Day Cover				10·00
Presentation Pack			10·00	

Booklet pane No. 1380a exists in three versions which differ in the order of the stamps within the block of six.
Plate Nos.: All values 1A (each×4).
Sheets: 10 (2×5) with enlarged illustrated margins.
Imprint: Lower left-hand margin.
Withdrawn: 30.6.2009 (Sheets).

1324 Daimler Dart (*Illustration reduced. Actual size* 110×75 *mm*)

Jersey Festival of Speed

(Des Alan R. Copp. Litho Cartor)

2008 (23 Aug). Sheet 110×75 mm. P 13×13½ (C).

MS1387 **1324** £2.50 multicoloured		7·25	7·25
First Day Cover			10·00
Presentation Pack		10·00	

Withdrawn: 31.8.2009.

1325 Cockerel, Hen and Chicks

1326 Ewe and Lambs

1327 Sow and Piglets

1328 Geese and Goslings

1329 Jersey Cows and Calf

Farm Animals

(Des Colleen Corlett. Litho SEP Sprint, Australia)

2008 (26 Aug). Self-adhesive. P 11½ (die-cut).

1388	**1325**	(35p.) multicoloured (ab)	1·00	1·00
1389	**1326**	(35p.) multicoloured (ab)	1·00	1·00
1390	**1327**	(35p.) multicoloured (ab)	1·00	1·00
1391	**1328**	(35p.) multicoloured (ab)	1·00	1·00
1392	**1329**	(35p.) multicoloured (ab)	1·00	1·00
1388/92	*Set of 5*		5·00	5·00
First Day Cover				7·75
Presentation Pack			7·75	

Nos. 1388/92 are inscribed 'JERSEY MINIMUM POSTAGE PAID' and were sold for 35p. each. They were printed together, *se-tenant*, in strips of five from rolls of 100, from which the surplus self-adhesive backing paper around each stamp was removed.

Nos. 1388/92 commemorate the 175th anniversary of the Royal Jersey Agricultural and Horticultural Society.

Printings: (a) 26.8.2008. Inscr '2008'; (b) 2.4.2010. Inscr '2010'.

1330 Carpenter Bee

1331 Buff-tailed Bumblebee

1332 Clown-faced Bug

1333 Large Migrant Hoverfly

1334 Ruby-tailed Wasp

1335 22-spot Ladybird

Insects (2nd series)

(Des William Oliver. Litho Cartor)

2008 (8 Sept). P 13×13½ (C).

1393	**1330**	35p. multicoloured	1·00	1·00
1394	**1331**	39p. multicoloured	1·20	1·20
1395	**1332**	43p. multicoloured	1·30	1·30
1396	**1333**	52p. multicoloured	1·50	1·50
1397	**1334**	58p. multicoloured	1·70	1·70
1398	**1335**	76p. multicoloured	2·30	2·30
1393/8	*Set of 6*		9·00	9·00
First Day Cover				11·50
Presentation Pack			11·50	

Plate Nos.: All values 1A (each×4).
Sheets: 10 (2×5) with enlarged illustrated margins.
Imprint: Lower left-hand margin.
Withdrawn: 30.9.2009.

Wipa08 International Stamp Exhibition, Vienna

2008 (18 Sept). No. **MS**1370 optd 'Jersey at WIPA08' on bottom right sheet margin.

MS1399	110×75 mm. **1307** £2·50 multicoloured.		
P 13½×14 (C)		7·25	7·25
First Day Cover			9·50

Withdrawn: 30.9.2009.

1336 Northern Wheatear

1337 Whinchat

1338 Pied Flycatcher

1339 Yellow Wagtail

1340 Ring Ouzel

1341 Common Redstart

Jersey Birdlife (2nd series). Migrating Birds

(Des Nick Parlett. Litho Cartor)

2008 (21 Oct). P 13×13½ (C).

1400	**1336**	35p. multicoloured	1·00	1·00
1401	**1337**	39p. multicoloured	1·20	1·20
1402	**1338**	43p. multicoloured	1·30	1·30
1403	**1339**	52p. multicoloured	1·50	1·50
1404	**1340**	58p. multicoloured	1·70	1·70
1405	**1341**	76p. multicoloured	2·30	2·30
1400/5	*Set of 6*		9·00	9·00
First Day Cover				11·50
Presentation Pack			11·50	
MS1406	150×100 mm. Nos. 1400/5		9·00	9·00
First Day Cover				11·50
Presentation Pack			11·50	
MS1407	150×100 mm. Nos. 1403/5		5·50	5·50
First Day Cover				8·00
Presentation Pack			8·00	

Stamps from **MS**1407 have no white borders.
Plate Nos.: All values 1A (each×5).
Sheets: 10 (2×5) with enlarged illustrated margins.
Imprint: Lower left-hand margin.
Withdrawn: 31.10.2009.

1342 Prince Charles

60th Birthday of Prince Charles

(Des Andrew Robinson. Litho Cartor)

2008 (14 Nov). P 13½ (C).

1408	**1342**	£4 multicoloured	12·00	12·00
First Day Cover				14·50
Presentation Pack			14·50	

MS1409 150×100 mm. £4 multicoloured............................ 12·00   12·00
First Day Cover ....   14·50
Presentation Pack.. 14·50
After one year No. 1408 was retained as a definitive.
Plate Nos.: 1A (×5).
Sheets: 4 (2×2).
Imprint: Lower left-hand margin.

Post Office Yearbook

2008 (1 Dec). Comprises Nos. 1350/98, 1400/5 and 1408 (price £48).
Yearbook .... 95·00

1343 Douglas C-47 Dakota 3 'Pionair'

1344 Vickers Viscount 833

1345 Handley Page HPR7 Dart-Herald

1346 Bristol SuPreighter 32

1347 Fokker F-27 Friendship

1348 Bombardier Q400 Dash 8

1349 de Havilland D.H.84 Dragon 2 (Illustration reduced. Actual size 110×75 mm)

Jersey Aviation History (10th series). 75th Anniversary of the First Flight from Jersey to Southampton

(Des Tony Theobald. Litho Austrian State Ptg Wks, Vienna)
2009 (13 Jan). P 14 (C).
1410   **1343**   35p. multicoloured .... 1·00   1·00
1411   **1344**   39p. multicoloured .... 1·25   1·25
1412   **1345**   43p. multicoloured .... 1·25   1·25
1413   **1346**   52p. multicoloured .... 1·50   1·50
1414   **1347**   58p. multicoloured .... 1·75   1·75
1415   **1348**   76p. multicoloured .... 2·25   2·25
1410/15 Set of 6 .... 9·00   9·00
First Day Cover..   10·00
Presentation Pack.. 10·00
MS1416 110×75 mm. **1349** £3 multicoloured.................. 9·00   9·00
First Day Cover..   10·00
Presentation Pack.. 10·00
Plate Nos.: All values 1A (each×4).
Sheets: 10 (2×5) with enlarged illustrated margins.
Imprint: Lower left-hand margin.
Withdrawn: 31.1.2010.

1350 Io, Ursa Major and Cassiopeia

1351 Europa, Boötes and Corona Borealis

1352 Ganymede, Cygnus and Pegasus

1353 Callisto, Perseus and Orion

Europa. Astronomy. Satellites of Jupiter and Constellations

(Des Jennifer Toombs. Litho and embossed in silver (stars) Cartor)
2009 (10 Feb). P 13 (C).
1417   **1350**   35p. multicoloured .... 1·00   1·00
1418   **1351**   39p. multicoloured .... 1·25   1·25
1419   **1352**   43p. multicoloured .... 1·25   1·25
1420   **1353**   76p. multicoloured .... 2·25   2·25
1417/20 Set of 4 .... 5·75   5·75
First Day Cover..   6·75
Presentation Pack.. 6·75
The 39p. and 43p. values include the 'EUROPA' emblem.
Plate Nos.: All values 1A (each×6).
Sheets: 10 (2×5) with enlarged illustrated margins.
Imprint: Lower left-hand margin.
Withdrawn: 28.2.2010.

1354 Blue Iguana (Cyclura lewisi)

1355 Madagascan Giant Jumping Rat (Hypogeomys antimena)

1356 Mountain Chicken Frog (Leptodactylus fallax)

1357 Livingstone's Fruit Bat (Pteropus livingstonii)

1358 Andean Bear (Tremarctos ornatus)

1359 Western Lowland Gorilla (Gorilla g. gorilla)

Endangered Species (1st series). 50th Anniversary of the Durrell Wildlife Conservation Trust

(Des William Oliver. Litho BDT)
2009 (10 Mar). P 14½×14 (C).
1421   **1354**   35p. multicoloured............................ 1·00   1·00
1422   **1355**   39p. multicoloured............................ 1·25   1·25
1423   **1356**   43p. multicoloured............................ 1·25   1·25
1424   **1357**   52p. multicoloured............................ 1·50   1·50
1425   **1358**   58p. multicoloured............................ 1·75   1·75
1426   **1359**   76p. multicoloured............................ 2·25   2·25
1421/6 Set of 6.. 9·00   9·00

First Day Cover.. 10·00
Presentation Pack...   10·00
   Plate Nos.: All values 1A (each×4).
   Sheets: 10 (2×5) with enlarged illustrated margins.
   Imprint: Lower left-hand margin.
   Withdrawn: 31.3.2010.

1360 Crocus and Grape Hyacinths

1361 Daffodils

1362 Anemones de Caen

1363 Tulips

1364 Hyacinths

1365 Polyanthus and Primulas

Seasonal Flowers (4th series). Spring

(Des Wendy Tait. Litho Enschedé)

2009 (1 Apr). P 13 (C).
1427	**1360**	35p. multicoloured	1·00	1·00
1428	**1361**	39p. multicoloured	1·25	1·25
1429	**1362**	43p. multicoloured	1·25	1·25
1430	**1363**	52p. multicoloured	1·50	1·50
1431	**1364**	58p. multicoloured	1·75	1·75
1432	**1365**	76p. multicoloured	2·25	2·25

1427/32 Set of 6 .... 9·00 9·00
First Day Cover ....   10·00
Presentation Pack ....   10·00
   Plate Nos.: 35p., 39p. 1A, 1B; others 1A (each×5).
   Sheets: 10 (5×2).
   Imprint: Bottom margin.
   Withdrawn: 30.4.2010.

1366 *Mont Orgueil*

1367 *Corbière*

1368 *Carteret*

1369 Railcar *Pioneer*

1370 *La Moye*

1371 *St. Brelades*

1372 Locomotive No. 5 *La Moye* awaits Departure from St. Aubin (*Illustration reduced. Actual size 110×75 mm*)

Jersey Railway History (3rd series). Jersey Railways

(Des Tony Theobald. Litho Cartor)

2009 (6 May). P 13 (C).
1433	**1366**	37p. multicoloured	1·10	1·10
		a. Booklet pane. Nos. 1433/8 with margins all round	9·25	
1434	**1367**	42p. multicoloured	1·25	1·25
1435	**1368**	45p. multicoloured	1·40	1·40
1436	**1369**	55p. multicoloured	1·60	1·60
1437	**1370**	61p. multicoloured	1·75	1·75
1438	**1371**	80p. multicoloured	2·40	2·40

1433/8 Set of 6 .... 9·25 9·25
First Day Cover ....   10·00
Presentation Pack .... 10·00
MS1439 110×75 mm. **1372** £3 multicoloured............... 9·25 9·25
   a. Booklet pane. No. **MS**1439, but 150×100 mm, with line of roulettes at left .... 9·25
First Day Cover ....   10·00
Presentation Pack .... 10·00
 Booklet pane No. 1433a exists in three versions which differ in the order of the stamps within the block of six.
   Plate Nos.: All values 1A (each×4).
   Sheets: 10 (2×5) with enlarged illustrated margins.
   Imprint: Lower left-hand margin.
   Withdrawn: 31.5.2010 (Sheets).

IBRA International Stamp Exhibition, Essen, Germany

2009 (6 May). No. **MS**1439 optd 'JERSEY AT iBRA' on upper left sheet margin.
MS1440 110×75 mm. **1372** £3 multicoloured............... 9·00 9·00
First Day Cover ....   10·00
Presentation Pack .... 10·00
   Withdrawn: 31.5.2010.

1373 Surfboards (*Illustration reduced. Actual size 110×75 mm*)

50th Anniversary of Jersey Surfboard Club

(Des Andrew Robinson. Litho BDT)

2009 (2 June). Sheet 110×75 mm. P 13 (C).

MS1441 **1373** £3 multicoloured		9·00	9·00
First Day Cover			10·00
Presentation Pack		10·00	

Withdrawn: 30.6.2010.

1374 Post Office, Broad Street, St. Helier, 1909 *(Illustration reduced. Actual size 110×75 mm)*

Jersey Postal History (3rd series). Post Office Buildings

(Des Colleen Corlett. Litho Austrian State Ptg Wks, Vienna)

2009 (21 June). Sheet 110×75 mm. P 14 (C).

MS1442 **1374** £3 multicoloured		9·00	9·00
First Day Cover			10·00
Presentation Pack		10·00	

No. **MS**1442 commemorates the centenary of Jersey's Head Post Office at Broad Street, St. Helier.
Withdrawn: 30.6.2010.

1375 Investiture of the Prince of Wales at Caernarfon Castle, 1969 *(Illustration reduced. Actual size 110×75 mm)*

40th Anniversary of the Investiture of Prince Charles as the Prince of Wales

(Des Andrew Robinson. Litho Cartor)

2009 (1 July). Sheet 110×75 mm. P 13 (C).

MS1443 **1375** £3 multicoloured		8·75	8·75
First Day Cover			9·75
Presentation Pack		9·75	

Withdrawn: 31.7.2010.

1376 *Ascophyllum nodosum* (Egg Wrack)

1377 *Enteromorpha* sp. (Gutweed)

1378 *Dilsea carnosa* (Red Rags)

1379 *Ulva lactuca* (Sea Lettuce)

1380 *Laminaria hyperborea* (Tangle and Cuvie)

1381 *Codium tomentosum* (Velvet Horn)

Marine Life (7th series). Seaweed

(Des Nick Parlett. Litho Cartor)

2009 (7 July). P 13 (C).

1444	**1376**	37p. multicoloured	1·00	1·00
1445	**1377**	42p. multicoloured	1·25	1·25
1446	**1378**	45p. multicoloured	1·40	1·40
1447	**1379**	55p. multicoloured	1·50	1·50
1448	**1380**	64p. multicoloured	2·00	2·00
1449	**1381**	80p. multicoloured	2·40	2·40
1444/9 Set of 6			9·50	9·50
First Day Cover				10·50
Presentation Pack			10·50	

Plate Nos.: All values 1A (each×5).
Sheets: 10 (2×5).
Lower left-hand margin.
Withdrawn: 31.7.2010.

1382 Dunnock

1383 Song Thrush

1384 Wren

1385 Blackcap

1386 Mistle Thrush

1387 Robin

Jersey Birdlife (3rd series). Songbirds

(Des Nick Parlett. Litho Cartor)

2009 (4 Aug). P 13 (C).

1450	**1382**	37p. multicoloured	1·00	1·00
1451	**1383**	42p. multicoloured	1·25	1·25
1452	**1384**	45p. multicoloured	1·40	1·40
1453	**1385**	55p. multicoloured	1·50	1·50
1454	**1386**	61p. multicoloured	2·00	2·00
1455	**1387**	80p. multicoloured	2·40	2·40
1450/5 Set of 6			9·50	9·50
First Day Cover				10·50
Presentation Pack			10·50	
MS1456 150×100 mm. Nos. 1450/5			9·50	9·50
First Day Cover				10·50
Presentation Pack			10·50	
MS1457 150×100 mm. Nos. 1453/5			5·75	5·75
First Day Cover				6·50
Presentation Pack			6·50	

Stamps from **MS**1457 have no white borders.
Plate Nos.: All values 1A (each×5).
Sheets: 10 (2×5) with enlarged illustrated margins.
Imprint: Lower left-hand margin.
Withdrawn: 31.8.2010.

1388 Green Island

1389 Gorey Castle at Night

1390 St. Aubin's Harbour

1391 St. Peter's Valley

1392 La Rocque Harbour

1393 Grève de Lecq

Jersey Scenery (2nd series) (sepac)

(Des Andrew Robinson. Litho Enschedé)

2009 (16 Sept). P 14×13 (C).

1458	**1388**	37p. multicoloured	1·00	1·00
1459	**1389**	42p. multicoloured	1·25	1·25
1460	**1390**	45p. multicoloured	1·40	1·40
1461	**1391**	55p. multicoloured	1·50	1·50
1462	**1392**	61p. multicoloured	2·00	2·00
1463	**1393**	80p. multicoloured	2·40	2·40
1458/63 *Set of 6*			9·50	9·50
First Day Cover				10·50
Presentation Pack			10·50	

The 45p. value is inscr 'sepac' and was also available in a souvenir folder with ten other sepac logo stamps issued by other postal administrations (original selling price £14.75).
Plate Nos.: All values 1A (each×4).
Sheets: 10 (2×5) with enlarged illustrated margins.
Imprint: Lower left-hand margin.
Withdrawn: 30.9.2010.

1394 Parrot Wax-cap (*Hygrocybe psittacina*)

1395 Primrose Brittlegill (*Russula sardonia*)

1396 Velvet Foot (*Flammulina velutipes*)

1397 Honey Fungus (*Armillaria mellea*)

1398 Orange Peel Fungus (*Aleuria aurantia*)

1399 Jewelled Deathcap (*Amanita gemmata*)

Fungi (3rd series)

(Des William Oliver. Litho Cartor)

2009 (15 Oct). P 13½×13 (C).

1464	**1394**	37p. multicoloured	1·10	1·10
1465	**1395**	42p. multicoloured	1·25	1·25
1466	**1396**	45p. multicoloured	1·25	1·25
1467	**1397**	55p. multicoloured	1·60	1·60
1468	**1398**	61p. multicoloured	1·75	1·75
1469	**1399**	80p. multicoloured	2·25	2·25
1464/9 *Set of 6*			9·00	9·00
First Day Cover				10·00
Presentation Pack			10·00	

Plate Nos.: All values 1A (each×4).
Sheets: 10 (5×2) with enlarged illustrated margins.
Imprint: Lower left-hand margins.
Withdrawn: 31.10.2010.

1400 HMS *Garland*

1401 HMS *Eighth Lion's Whelp*

1402 HMS *Unicorn*

1403 HMS *Mary Rose*

1404 HMS *Antelope*

1405 HMS *Rainbow*

Jersey Naval Connections (3rd series). 400th Birth Anniversary of Sir George Carteret

(Des A. Theobald. Litho Cartor)

2009 (10 Nov). P 13 (C).

1470	**1400**	37p. multicoloured	1·10	1·10
1471	**1401**	42p. multicoloured	1·25	1·25
1472	**1402**	45p. multicoloured	1·25	1·25
1473	**1403**	55p. multicoloured	1·60	1·60
1474	**1404**	61p. multicoloured	1·75	1·75
1475	**1405**	80p. multicoloured	2·25	2·25
1470/5 *Set of 6*			9·00	9·00
First Day Cover				10·00
Presentation Pack			10·00	

Plate Nos.: All values 1A (each×4).
Sheets: 10 (2×5) with enlarged illustrated margins.
Imprint: Lower left-hand margin.
Withdrawn: 30.11.2010.

Post Office Yearbook

2009 (1 Dec). Comprises Nos. 1410/39, **MS**1441/55 and **MS**1458/75 (price £52).

Yearbook	£100

1406 Gymnast and Cyclist ('Healthy Lifestyles')

1407 Broken Globe, Tap and Young Child Drinking ('global awareness')

1408 Guide Salute and Handshake ('Skills & Relationships')

1409 Guides holding Hands around Globe ('Celebrating Diversity')

1410 Guides doing Handicrafts and on Climbing Wall ('Discovery')

Centenary of the Girl Guide Association

(Des Colleen Corlett. Litho Austrian State Ptg Wks, Vienna)

2010 (12 Jan). P 14.

1476	**1406**	37p. multicoloured	1·00	1·00
1477	**1407**	42p. multicoloured	1·25	1·25
1478	**1408**	45p. multicoloured	1·25	1·25
1479	**1409**	61p. multicoloured	1·75	1·75
1480	**1410**	80p. multicoloured	2·25	2·25
1476/80 Set of 5			7·50	7·50
First Day Cover				8·50
Presentation Pack			8·50	

Plate Nos.: All values 1A (each×4).
Sheets: 10 (2×5).
Imprint: Lower left-hand margin.
Withdrawn: 31.1.2011.

1411 A Pushmi-Pullyu (*The Story of Doctor Dolittle* by Hugh Lofting)

1412 *How the Elephant got his Trunk* (Rudyard Kipling)

1413 The Mad Hatter's Tea Party (*Alice's Adventures in Wonderland* by Lewis Carroll)

1414 *The Dong with a Luminous Nose* (Edward Lear)

Europa. Children's Books

(Des Michael Pollard. Litho Cartor)

2010 (9 Feb). P 13 (C).

1481	**1411**	37p. multicoloured	1·50	1·50
1482	**1412**	42p. multicoloured	1·60	1·60
1483	**1413**	45p. multicoloured	1·75	1·75
1484	**1414**	80p. multicoloured	3·25	3·25
1481/4 Set of 4			8·00	8·00

First Day Cover		9·00
Presentation Pack	9·00	

The 42p. and 45p. values are inscr 'EUROPA'.

Luminous ink has been applied to the end of the dong's long nose on No. 1484.

Plate Nos.: All values 1A (each×4).
Sheets: 10 (2×5) with enlarged illustrated margins.
Imprint: Lower left-hand margin.
Withdrawn: 28.2.2011.

1415 Map, c. 1685   **1416** Map, c. 1844   **1417** Map, c. 1980s

1418 Map, c. 2000   **1419** Satellite View

Maps

(Des Andrew Robinson. Litho Australia Post Sprintpak)

2010 (9 Feb). Self-adhesive. P 11 (die-cut).

1485	**1415**	(42p.) multicoloured	1·25	1·25
1486	**1416**	(42p.) multicoloured	1·25	1·25
1487	**1417**	(42p.) multicoloured	1·25	1·25
1488	**1418**	(42p.) multicoloured	1·25	1·25
1489	**1419**	(42p.) multicoloured	1·25	1·25
1485/9 Set of 5			6·25	6·25
First Day Cover				7·00
Presentation Pack			7·00	

Nos. 1485/9 were inscribed 'UK LETTER' and originally sold for 42p. each. They were printed together, *se-tenant*, in strips of five from rolls of 100, from which the surplus self-adhesive backing paper around each stamp was removed.

1420 Brecciated Pegmatite, Orthoclase Feldspar Crystals, re-cemented with Chalcedony

1421 Diorite with Incipient Orbicular Structure

1422 Granite

1423 Jasper in Andesite

1424 Pebbles of Granite, Andesite and Shale in Rozel Conglomerate

Petrology

(Des Jennifer Toombs. Litho Cartor)

2010 (9 Mar). P 13×13½ (C).

1490	**1420**	37p. multicoloured	1·10	1·10
1491	**1421**	42p. multicoloured	1·25	1·25
1492	**1422**	45p. multicoloured	1·25	1·25

1493	**1423**	61p. multicoloured	1·75	1·75
1494	**1424**	80p. multicoloured	2·40	2·40
1490/4 Set of 5			7·75	7·75
First Day Cover				8·50
Presentation Pack			8·50	

Plate Nos.: All values 1A (each×4).
Sheets: 10 (2×5) with enlarged illustrated margins.
Imprint: Lower left-hand margin.
Withdrawn: 31.3.2011.

1425 Jay   **1426** Great Spotted Woodpecker

1427 Short-toed Treecreeper   **1428** Chiffchaff

1429 Long-tailed Tit   **1430** Turtle Dove

Jersey Birdlife (4th series). Woodland Birds

(Des Nick Parlett. Litho Cartor)

2010 (1 Apr). P 13×13½ (C).

1495	**1425**	37p. multicoloured	1·10	1·10
1496	**1426**	42p. multicoloured	1·25	1·25
1497	**1427**	45p. multicoloured	1·40	1·40
1498	**1428**	55p. multicoloured	1·60	1·60
1499	**1429**	61p. multicoloured	1·75	1·75
1500	**1430**	80p. multicoloured	2·40	2·40
1495/500 Set of 6			9·50	9·50
First Day Cover				10·00
Presentation Pack			10·00	
MS1501 150×100 mm. Nos. 1495/500			9·50	9·50
First Day Cover				10·00
Presentation Pack			10·00	
MS1502 150×100 mm. As Nos. 1498/500			5·75	5·75
First Day Cover				7·00
Presentation Pack			6·00	

Stamps from **MS**1502 have no white borders.
Plate Nos.: All values 1A (each×5).
Sheets: 10 (2×5) with enlarged illustrated margins.
Imprint: Lower left-hand margin.
Withdrawn: 30.4.2011.

1431 *Royal Charlotte*   **1432** *Dispatch*

1433 *Diana*   **1434** *Reindeer*

1435 *Caesarea* (II)   **1436** *St. Patrick* (III)

1437 *Watersprite* (*Illustration reduced. Actual size 110×75 mm*)

Jersey Postal History (4th series). Mail Ships

(Des Tony Theobald. Litho Cartor)

2010 (8 MAY). P 13½×13 (**MS**1510) or 13×13½ (others), all comb.

1503	**1431**	39p. multicoloured	1·10	1·10
		a. Booklet pane. Nos. 1503/8 with margins all round	10·50	
1504	**1432**	45p. multicoloured	1·40	1·40
1505	**1433**	55p. multicoloured	1·60	1·60
1506	**1434**	60p. multicoloured	1·75	1·75
1507	**1435**	72p. multicoloured	2·25	2·25
1508	**1436**	80p. multicoloured	2·40	2·40
1503/8 Set of 6			10·50	10·50
First Day Cover				11·00
Presentation Pack			11·00	
MS1509 150×100 mm. Nos. 1503/8			10·50	10·50
First Day Cover				11·00
Presentation Pack			11·00	
MS1510 110×75 mm. **1437** £3 multicoloured			8·50	8·50
		a. Booklet pane. As No. **MS**1510 but 150×100 mm with line of roulettes at left	8·50	
First Day Cover				9·00
Presentation Pack			9·00	

Booklet pane No. 1503*a* exists in three versions which differ in the order of the stamps within the block of six.
Plate Nos.: All values 1A (each×4).
Sheets: 10 (2×5).
Imprint: Lower left-hand margin.
Withdrawn: 31.5.2011.

1438 1958 3d. Deep Lilac Stamp   **1439** 1964 2½d. Carmine-Red Stamp

1440 1966 4d. Ultramarine Stamp   **1441** 1968 4d. Olive-Sepia Stamp

1442 1968 5d. Royal Blue
Stamp

1443 1969 4d. Bright Vermilion
Stamp

**Jersey Postal History (5th series). British Regional Definitive
Stamps for Jersey 1958–69**

(Des Andrew Robinson. Litho Cartor)

2010 (8 May). P 13×13½ (C).

1511	**1438**	36p. multicoloured	1·10	1·10
1512	**1439**	39p. multicoloured	1·10	1·10
1513	**1440**	45p. multicoloured	1·40	1·40
1514	**1441**	55p. multicoloured	1·60	1·60
1515	**1442**	60p. multicoloured	1·75	1·75
1516	**1443**	72p. multicoloured	2·25	2·25
1511/16	*Set of 6*		9·00	9·00
First Day Cover				10·00
Presentation Pack			10·00	
MS1517	150×100 mm. Nos. 1511/16		9·25	9·25
First Day Cover				10·00
Presentation Pack			10·00	

Plate Nos.: All values 1A (each×5).
Sheets: 10 (2×5).
Imprint: Lower left-hand margin.
Withdrawn: 31.5.2011 (Sheets).

1444 'Nostalgia'

1445 'Mountbatten'

1446 'Royal William'

1447 'Elina'

1448 'New Dawn'

1449 'Lovers Meeting'

1450 'Pride of England' (*Illustration reduced. Actual size
110×75 mm*)

Roses

(Des Lizzie Harper. Litho Cartor)

2010 (8 June). P 13×13½ (C).

1518	**1444**	36p. multicoloured	1·10	1·10
1519	**1445**	39p. multicoloured	1·10	1·10
1520	**1446**	45p. multicoloured	1·40	1·40
1521	**1447**	55p. multicoloured	1·60	1·60
1522	**1448**	60p. multicoloured	1·75	1·75
1523	**1449**	72p. multicoloured	2·25	2·25
1518/23	*Set of 6*		9·00	9·00
First Day Cover				10·00
Presentation Pack			10·00	
MS1524	10×75 mm **1450** £3 multicoloured		8·50	8·50
First Day Cover				9·00
Presentation Pack			9·00	

Plate Nos.: All values 1A (each×4).
Sheets: 10 (2×5).
Imprint: Lower left-hand margin.
Withdrawn: 30.6.2011.

Planete Timbres National Stamp Exhibition, Paris

2010 (12 June). No. **MS**1524 inscr with emblem on top left margin.
P 13×13½.

MS1524a	£3 multicoloured	8·75	8·75

Withdrawn: 30.6.2011.

1451 Strawberry Anemone
(*Actinia fragacea*)

1452 Snakelocks Anemone
(*Anemonia viridis*)

1453 Jewel Anemone
(*Corynactis viridis*)

1454 Parasitic Anemone
(*Sagartia parasitica*)

1455 Tube Anemone
(*Pachycerianthus* 'Dorothy')

1456 Beadlet Anemone
(*Actinia equina*)

1457 Dahlia Anemone (*Urticina felina*) (*Illustration reduced.
Actual size 110×75 mm*)

Marine Life (8th series). Sea Anemones

(Des Nick Parlett. Litho Cartor)

2010 (6 July). P 13×13½ (C).

1525	**1451**	36p. multicoloured	1·10	1·10
1526	**1452**	39p. multicoloured	1·10	1·10
1527	**1453**	45p. multicoloured	1·40	1·40
1528	**1454**	55p. multicoloured	1·60	1·60
1529	**1455**	60p. multicoloured	1·75	1·75
1530	**1456**	72p. multicoloured	2·25	2·25
1525/30 *Set of 6*			9·00	9·00
First Day Cover				9·75
Presentation Pack			9·75	
MS1531 **1457** £3 multicoloured			9·00	9·00
First Day Cover				9·50
Presentation Pack			9·50	

No. 1526 was incorrectly inscribed 'Snakelock Anemone'.
Plate Nos.: All values 1A (each×4).
Sheets: 10 (2×5) with enlarged illustrated margins.
Imprint: Lower left-hand margin.
Withdrawn: 30.6.2011.

1458 Rolls Royce Silver Ghost, 1912   **1459** Bugatti Type 37, 1926

1460 Austin Seven, 1933   **1461** Citroën Light 15, 1938

1462 Morris 10, 1946   **1463** Rover 75 Sports Saloon, 1949

Vintage Cars (4th series)

(Des Alan Copp. Litho BDT)

2010 (3 Aug). P 14 (C).

1532	**1458**	39p. multicoloured	1·10	1·10
1533	**1459**	45p. multicoloured	1·10	1·10
1534	**1460**	55p. multicoloured	1·40	1·40
1535	**1461**	60p. multicoloured	1·60	1·60
1536	**1462**	72p. multicoloured	1·75	1·75
1537	**1463**	80p. multicoloured	2·25	2·25
1532/7 *Set of 6*			9·00	9·00
First Day Cover				10·50
Presentation Pack			10·50	

Plate Nos.: All values 1A (each×4).
Sheets: 10 (2×5) with enlarged illustrated margins.
Imprint: Lower left-hand margin.
Withdrawn: 31.8.2011.

1464 Perch (*Perca fluviatilis*)   **1465** Tench (*Tinca tinca*)

1466 Roach (*Rutilus rutilus*)   **1467** Rudd (*Scardinius erythrophthalmus*)

1468 Mirror Carp (*Cyprinus carpio*)   **1469** Common Bream (*Abramis brama*)

1470 Brown Trout (*Salmo trutta*) (*Illustration reduced. Actual size 110×75 mm*)

Freshwater Fish

(Des William Oliver. Litho BDT)

2010 (7 Sept). P 14½×14 (C).

1538	**1464**	36p. multicoloured	1·10	1·10
1539	**1465**	39p. multicoloured	1·10	1·10
1540	**1466**	45p. multicoloured	1·40	1·40
1541	**1467**	55p. multicoloured	1·60	1·60
1542	**1468**	60p. multicoloured	1·75	1·75
1543	**1469**	72p. multicoloured	2·25	2·25
1538/43 *Set of 6*			9·00	9·00
First Day Cover				9·75
Presentation Pack			9·75	
MS1544 110×75 mm. **1470** £3 multicoloured			9·00	9·00
First Day Cover				9·50
Presentation Pack			9·50	

Nos. 1538/43 commemorate the 50th anniversary of the Jersey Freshwater Angling Association.
Plate Nos.: All values 1A (each×4).
Sheets: 10 (2×5).
Imprint: Lower left-hand margin.
Withdrawn: 30.9.2011.

1471 Neanderthal Man and Teeth   **1472** Woolly Rhinoceros and Skull

1473 Woolly Mammoth, Tusks and Teeth   **1474** Flint Tools

1475 Giant Deer and Antler

Archaeology (1st series). La Cotte de St. Brelade

(Des Nick Shewring. Litho Austrian State Ptg Wks, Vienna)

2010 (12 Oct). P 14 (C).

1545	**1497**	39p. multicoloured	1·10	1·10
1546	**1472**	45p. multicoloured	1·40	1·40
1546	**1473**	55p. multicoloured	1·60	1·60
1548	**1474**	60p. multicoloured	1·75	1·75
1549	**1475**	80p. multicoloured	2·25	2·25
1545/9 Set of 5			8·00	8·00
First Day Cover				9·00
Presentation Pack			9·00	

See also Nos. 1605/10 and 1700/4.
Plate Nos.: All values 1A (each×4).
Sheets: 10 (2×5) with enlarged illustrated margins.
Imprint: Lower left-hand margin.
Withdrawn: 31.10.2011.

1476

1477

1478

Jersey Map with Lions from Crest of Jersey

(Des Andrew Robinson. Litho Walsall)

2010 (1 Nov). Self-adhesive. Die-cut perf 11½×11.

1550	**1476**	(36p.) multicoloured	1·10	1·10
1551	**1477**	(39p.) multicoloured	1·10	1·10
1552	**1478**	(45p.) multicoloured	1·40	1·40
1550/2 Set of 3			3·50	3·50
First Day Cover				5·00
Presentation Pack			5·00	

No. 1550 was inscribed 'STANDARD LETTER' and originally sold for 36p. each.
No. 1551 was inscribed 'PRIORITY LETTER' and originally sold for 39p. each.
No. 1552 was inscribed 'UK LETTER' and originally sold for 45p. each.
Nos. 1550/2 were each issued in rolls of 100, from which the surplus self-adhesive backing paper from around each stamp was removed.

Post Office Yearbook

2010 (11 Dec). Comprises Nos. 1476/500, 1503/8, 1511/16 and 1518/52 (price £52).

Yearbook		£100

1479 Paragon C10 AEC 'B', c. 1926

1480 Rambler Tours Chevrolet, c. 1935

1481 JMT Leyland Lioness C14, c. 1938

1482 JMT Leyland PLSC1 Lion, c. 1939

1483 Mascot Motors Morris CVF 13/5, c. 1948

1484 Mascot Motors AEC Regal 4, c. 1961

Jersey Transport (3rd series). Coaches

(Des Alan Copp. Litho BDT)

2011 (11 Jan). P 14 (C).

1553	**1479**	36p. multicoloured	1·10	1·10
1554	**1480**	45p. multicoloured	1·40	1·40
1555	**1481**	55p. multicoloured	1·60	1·60
1556	**1482**	60p. multicoloured	1·70	1·70
1557	**1483**	72p. multicoloured	2·25	2·25
1558	**1484**	80p. multicoloured	2·40	2·40
1553/8 Set of 6			10·00	10·00
First Day Cover				10·50
Presentation Pack			10·50	

Plate Nos.: All values 1A (each×4).
Sheets: 10 (2×5) with enlarged illustrated margins.
Imprint: Lower left-hand margins.
Withdrawn: 11.1.2013.

1485 Silver Birch (Betula pendula)

1486 English Oak (Quercus robur)

1487 Beech (Fagus sylvatica)

1488 Lime (Tilia cordata)

Europa. Forests

(Des Lizzie Harper. Litho Cartor)

2011 (8 Feb). P 13×13½ (C).

1559	**1485**	39p. multicoloured	1·10	1·10
1560	**1486**	45p. multicoloured	1·40	1·40
1561	**1487**	55p. multicoloured	1·60	1·60
1562	**1488**	80p. multicoloured	2·40	2·40
1559/62 Set of 4			6·50	6·50
First Day Cover				7·50
Presentation Pack			7·50	

The 45p. and 55p. values include the 'EUROPA' emblem.
Plate Nos.: All values 1A (each×4).
Sheets: 10 (2×5) with enlarged illustrated margins.
Imprint: Lower left-hand margins.
Withdrawn: 8.2.2013.

1489 Dame Margot Fonteyn

1490 Florence Nightingale

1491 Marie Curie

1492 Mother Teresa

Women of Achievement (2nd series)

(Des Colleen Corlett. Litho Cartor)

2011 (8 Mar). P 13×13½ (C).

1563	**1489**	36p. multicoloured	1·10	1·10
1564	**1490**	45p. multicoloured	1·40	1·40
1565	**1491**	60p. multicoloured	1·75	1·75
1566	**1492**	72p. multicoloured	2·25	2·25
1563/6 *Set of 4*			6·50	6·50
First Day Cover				7·50
Presentation Pack			7·50	

Plate Nos.: All values 1A (each×4).
Sheets: 10 (2×5) with enlarged illustrated margins.
Imprint: Lower left-hand margin.
Withdrawn: 8.3.2013.

1493 Gooseberry Sea Squirt (*Dendrodoa grossularia*)

1494 Finger Sponge (*Axinella dissimilis*)

1495 Purse Sponge (*Scypha ciliata*)

1496 Star Squirt (*Botryllus schlosseri*)

1497 Light Bulb Sea Squirt (*Clavelina lepadiformis*)

1498 Red Sea Squirt (*Polysyncraton lacazei*)

Marine Life (9th series). Sea Squirts and Sponges

(Des William Oliver. Litho BDT)

2011 (7 Apr). P 14½×14 (C).

1567	**1493**	(36p.) multicoloured	1·10	1·10
1568	**1494**	(39p.) multicoloured	1·10	1·10
1569	**1495**	(45p.) multicoloured	1·40	1·40
1570	**1496**	60p. multicoloured	1·75	1·75
1571	**1497**	72p. multicoloured	2·25	2·25
1572	**1498**	80p. multicoloured	2·40	2·40
1567/72 *Set of 6*			10·00	10·00
First Day Cover				10·50
Presentation Pack			10·50	
MS1573 150×100 mm. As Nos. 1570/2			10·00	10·00
First Day Cover				10·50
Presentation Pack			10·50	

No. 1567 was inscr 'LOCAL STANDARD LETTER' and originally sold for 36p.
No. 1568 was inscr 'LOCAL PRIORITY LETTER' and originally sold for 39p.
No. 1569 was inscr 'UK LETTER' and originally sold for 45p.
Stamps from **MS**1573 have no white borders.
Plate Nos.: All values 1A (each×4).
Sheets: 10 (2×5).
Imprint: Lower left-hand margin.
Withdrawn: 7.4.2013.

1499 Queen Elizabeth II in Jersey, 2005

85th Birthday of Queen Elizabeth II

(Des Sally Diamond Ferbrache. Litho Cartor)

2011 (21 Apr). P 13½ (C).

1574	**1499**	£3 multicoloured	7·00	7·00
First Day Cover				9·50
Presentation Pack			9·50	
MS1575 150×100 mm. No. 1574			7·00	7·00
First Day Cover				9·50
Presentation Pack			9·50	

No. 1574 was printed in sheetlets of four stamps.
Plate Nos.: 1A (each×5).
Sheets: 4 (2×2).
Imprint: Lower left-hand margin.
No. 1574 was retained in use as a definitive.

1500 Engagement of Prince William and Miss Catherine Middleton, 16 November 2010

Royal Wedding

(Des Andrew Robinson. Litho Cartor)

2011 (29 Apr). P 13½ (C).

1576	**1500**	£3.50 multicoloured	8·00	7·00
First Day Cover				9·00
Presentation Pack			9·00	

Plate Nos.: 1A (each×4).
Sheets: 4 (2×2).
Imprint: Lower left-hand margin.
No. 1576 was retained in use as a definitive.

1501 *Paphiopedilum* La Garenne 'St. John'

1502 *Odontioda* Les Brayes 'Pontac'

1503 *Phragmipedium* Don Wimber

1504 *Kriegerara* Kemp Tower 'Trinity'

1505 *Angulocaste* Noirmont 'Isle of Jersey'

1506 *Calanthe* Beresford 'Victoria Village'

1507 *Miltonia* Point des Pas 'Jersey' (*Illustration reduced. Actual size 110×75 mm*)

Jersey Orchids (7th series)

(Des Andrew Robinson. Litho Cartor)

2011 (17 May). P 13 (C).

1577	**1501**	(36p.) multicoloured	1·10	1·10
1578	**1502**	(39p.) multicoloured	1·10	1·10
1579	**1503**	(45p.) multicoloured	1·40	1·40
1580	**1504**	55p. multicoloured	1·60	1·60
1581	**1505**	60p. multicoloured	1·75	1·75
1582	**1506**	72p. multicoloured	2·25	2·25
1577/82 Set of 6			9·00	9·00
First Day Cover				9·75
Presentation Pack			9·75	
MS1583 110×75 mm. **1507** £3 multicoloured			7·00	7·00
First Day Cover				9·50
Presentation Pack			9·50	

No. 1577 was inscr 'LOCAL STANDARD LETTER' and originally sold for 36p.

No. 1578 was inscr 'LOCAL PRIORITY LETTER' and originally sold for 39p.

No. 1579 was inscr 'UK LETTER' and originally sold for 45p.

Plate Nos.: All values 1A (each×5).

Sheets: 10 (2×5) with enlarged illustrated margins.

Imprint: Lower left-hand margin.

Withdrawn: 17.5.2013.

1508 Barn Swallow (*Hirundo rustica*)

1509 Spotted Flycatcher (*Muscicapa striata*)

1510 Cuckoo (*Cuculus canorus*)

1511 Whitethroat (*Sylvia communis*)

1512 Linnet (*Carduelis cannabina*)

1513 Swift (*Apus apus*)

Jersey Birdlife (5th series). Summer Visiting Birds

(Des Nick Parlett. Litho Cartor)

2011 (16 June). P 13×13½ (C).

1584	**1508**	42p. multicoloured	1·25	1·25
1585	**1509**	50p. multicoloured	1·50	1·50
1586	**1510**	59p. multicoloured	1·75	1·75
1587	**1511**	64p. multicoloured	1·90	1·90
1588	**1512**	79p. multicoloured	2·40	2·40
1589	**1513**	86p. multicoloured	2·60	2·60
1584/9 Set of 6			11·00	11·00
First Day Cover				11·50
Presentation Pack			11·50	
MS1590 150×100 mm. Nos. 1584/9			11·50	11·50
First Day Cover				12·00
Presentation Pack			12·00	
MS1591 150×100 mm. Nos. 1587/9			7·00	7·00
First Day Cover				8·00
Presentation Pack			8·00	

Stamps from **MS**1591 have no white borders.

Plate Nos.: All values 1A (each×5).

Sheets: 10 (2×5) with enlarged illustrated margins.

Imprint: Lower left-hand margin.

Withdrawn: 16.6.2013.

1514 *Princess Ena*, 1935

1515 *Caledonia*, 1881

1516 *Ibex*, 1897

1517 *Schokland*, 1943

1518 USS PT509, 1944

1519 *Superb*, 1850

1520 *Roebuck*, 1911 (*Illustration reduced. Actual size 110×75 mm*)

Shipwrecks

(Des Tony Theobald. Litho Cartor)

2011 (12 July). P 13 (C).

1592	1514	37p. multicoloured	1·10	1·10
		a. Booklet pane. Nos. 1592/7 with		
		margins all round	11·00	
1593	1515	49p. multicoloured	1·50	1·50
1594	1516	59p. multicoloured	1·75	1·75
1595	1517	64p. multicoloured	1·90	1·90
1596	1518	79p. multicoloured	2·40	2·40
1597	1519	86p. multicoloured	2·50	2·50
1592/7 Set of			10·50	10·50
First Day Cover				11·50
Presentation Pack			11·50	
MS1598 110×75 mm. 1520 £3 multicoloured			9·00	9·00
		a. Booklet pane. No. MS1598,		
		but 150×100 mm with line of		
		roulettes at left	9·00	
First Day Cover				9·75
Presentation Pack			9·75	

Booklet pane No. 1592a exists in three versions which differ in the order of the stamps within the block of six.

Plate Nos.: All values 1A (each×4).
Sheets: 10 (2×5) with enlarged illustrated margins.
Imprint: Lower left-hand margin.
Withdrawn: 11.7.2013 (Sheets).

1521 Marsh Harrier (*Circus aeruginosus*) and La Caumine à Marie Best

1522 Swallowtail Butterfly (*Papilio machaon*) and Victoria Tower

1523 Dartford Warbler (*Sylvia undata*) and La Cotte Battery

1524 Red Squirrel (*Sciurus vulgaris*) and La Moulin de Quétivel

1525 Marsh Harrier (*Circus aeruginosus*) and La Caumine à Marie Best painted Green

1526 Puffin (*Fratercula arctica*) and North Coast Sea Cliffs

75th Anniv of the National Trust for Jersey

2011 (3 Aug). P 14½×14 (C).

1599	1521	42p. multicoloured	1·25	1·25
1600	1522	50p. multicoloured	1·50	1·50
1601	1523	59p. multicoloured	1·75	1·75
1602	1524	64p. multicoloured	1·90	1·90
1603	1525	75p. multicoloured	2·25	2·25
1604	1526	79p. multicoloured	2·40	2·40
1599/604 Set of 6			10·50	10·50
First Day Cover (excl. 75p.)				9·50
First Day Cover (75p.)				4·00
Presentation Pack (excl. 75p.)			9·50	

Plate Nos.: All values 1A (each×4).
Sheets: 10 (2×5) with enlarged illustrated margins.
Imprint: Lower left-hand margin.
Withdrawn: 3.8.2013.

1527 Billion Stater of the XN Series (c. 55-50 BC)

1528 Durotriges Base Gold Quarter Stater (c. 50-30 BC)

1529 Baiocasses Gold Stater (c. 50 BC)

1530 Gold Chute Type Stater (c. 50 BC)

1531 Southern British Silver Unit (c. 50-30 BC)

1532 Billion Stater of the Coriosolites Tribe (c. 55-50 BC)

Archaeology (2nd series). Buried Treasure. Celtic Coins

(Des Andrew Robinson. Litho BDT)

2011 (30 Aug). P 14½×14 (C).

1605	1527	37p. multicoloured	1·10	1·10
1606	1528	49p. multicoloured	1·50	1·50
1607	1529	59p. multicoloured	1·75	1·75
1608	1530	64p. multicoloured	1·90	1·90
1609	1531	79p. multicoloured	2·40	2·40
1610	1532	86p. multicoloured	2·50	2·50
1605/10 Set of 6			10·50	10·50
First Day Cover				11·50
Presentation Pack			11·50	

Plate Nos.: All values 1A (each×5).
Sheets: 10 (2×5) with enlarged illustrated margins.
Imprint: Lower left-hand margin.
Withdrawn: 30.8.2013.

1533 1960 Fourth of a Shilling Coin, Jersey Lilies and Crest (*Illustration reduced. Actual size 110×75 mm*)

50th Anniv of Jersey's Finance Industry

(Des Limegreen Ltd. Litho and embossed Cartor)

2011 (12 Sept). Sheet 110×75 mm. P 13 (C).

MS1611 1533 £3 multicoloured	7·00	7·00
First Day Cover		9·50
Presentation Pack	9·50	

Withdrawn: 30.8.2013.

1534 Beauport

1535 St. Ouen's Bay

1536 Ouaisné

1537 St. Brelade's Bay

1538 Mont Orgueil

1539 Portelet

Jersey Scenery (3rd series) (sepac)

(Des Andrew Robinson. Litho Enschedé)

2011 (28 Sept). P 13½ (C).

1612	**1534**	42p. multicoloured	1·25	1·25
1613	**1535**	49p. multicoloured	1·50	1·50
1614	**1536**	50p. multicoloured	1·50	1·50
1615	**1537**	64p. multicoloured	1·90	1·90
1616	**1538**	79p. multicoloured	2·40	2·40
1617	**1539**	86p. multicoloured	2·50	2·50
1612/17 *Set of 6*			10·50	10·50
First Day Cover				11·00
Presentation Pack			11·00	

The 49p. value includes the 'sepac' emblem and was also available in a souvenir folder with 11 other sepac logo stamps issued by other administrations (original selling price £14.68).
Plate Nos.: All values 1A (each×4).
Sheets: 10 (2×5) with enlarged illustrated margins.
Imprint: Lower left-hand margin.
Withdrawn: 28.9.2013.

1540 Rozel Mill, c. 1880

1541 Tesson Mill, c. 1880

1542 St. Peter's Mill, c. 1905

1543 Ponterrin Mill, 19th century

1544 Quétivel Mill, 20th century

1545 Gréve De Lecq Mill, 20th century

Jersey Architecture (1st series). Mills

(Des Nick Shewring. Litho Austrian State Ptg Wks, Vienna)

2011 (11 Oct). P 14 (C).

1618	**1540**	37p. multicoloured	1·10	1·10
1619	**1541**	42p. multicoloured	1·25	1·25
1620	**1542**	49p. multicoloured	1·50	1·50
1621	**1543**	50p. multicoloured	1·50	1·50
1622	**1544**	59p. multicoloured	1·75	1·75
1623	**1545**	79p. multicoloured	2·40	2·40
1618/23 *Set of 6*			9·00	9·00
First Day Cover				10·00
Presentation Pack			10·00	

Plate Nos.: All values 1A (each×4).
Sheets: 10 (2×5) with enlarged illustrated margins.
Imprint: Lower left-hand margin.
Withdrawn: 11.10.2013.

1546 Santa, Baubles and 1970s Light

1547 Bauble, Bells and Gold Glass Beaded Garland

1548 Baubles enclosing Nativity Scenes and Gold Beads

1549 Glass Baubles enclosing Santa scenes and 1980s Candle Lights

1550 Angel, Bauble and Glass Bead Garland

1551 Nativity Bauble and Silver Bead Garland

Christmas

(Des Colleen Corlett. Litho Cartor)

2011 (8 Nov). P 13×13½ (C).

1624	**1546**	37p. multicoloured	1·10	1·10
1625	**1547**	42p. multicoloured	1·25	1·25
1626	**1548**	49p. multicoloured	1·50	1·50
1627	**1549**	50p. multicoloured	1·50	1·50
1628	**1550**	79p. multicoloured	2·40	2·40
1629	**1551**	86p. multicoloured	2·50	2·50
1624/9 *Set of 6*			9·75	9·75
First Day Cover				10·50
Presentation Pack			10·50	

Plate Nos.: All values 1A (each×4).
Sheets: 10 (2×5) with enlarged illustrated margins.
Imprint: Lower left-hand margin.
Withdrawn: 8.11.2013.

1552 Violin and 'Hark! The Herald Angels Sing' (Mendelssohn)

1553 Trumpets and 'Pomp and Circumstance' (Elgar)

1554 Harp and 'Pini di Roma' (Respighi)

1555 Timpani and 'La Gazza Ladra' (Rossini)

1556 Bassoons and 'Slavonic Dances – Op. 46 No. 1' (Dvorak)

1557 French Horn and 'Slavonic Dances – Op. 46 No. 3' (Dvorak)

25th Anniv of Jersey Symphony Orchestra

(Des Nick Shewring. Litho Austrian State Ptg Wks, Vienna)

2011 (15 Nov). P 14 (C).

1630	**1552**	37p. multicoloured	1·10	1·10
1631	**1553**	50p. multicoloured	1·50	1·50
1632	**1554**	59p. multicoloured	1·75	1·75
1633	**1555**	64p. multicoloured	1·90	1·90
1634	**1556**	79p. multicoloured	2·40	2·40
1635	**1557**	86p. multicoloured	2·50	2·50
1630/5 *Set of 6*			10·50	10·50
First Day Cover				10·50
Presentation Pack			11·50	

Plate Nos.: All values 1A (each×4).
Sheets: 10 (5×2) with enlarged illustrated margins.
Imprint: Lower left-hand margin.
Withdrawn: 15.11.2013.

Post Office Yearbook

2011 (1 Dec). Comprises Nos. 1553/72, 1574, 1576/89 and 1592/635 (price £58.88).

Yearbook £110

1558 Jersey Produce

1559 Surfer, Dinghies and Sand Yachts

1560 Cyclist, Family walking and Hikers

1561 Re-enactment of 1781 Jersey Militia, Elizabeth Castle and La Hougue Bie

Europa. Visit Jersey

(Des Colleen Corlett. Litho Enschedé)

2012 (10 Jan). P 13 (C).

1636	**1558**	42p. multicoloured	1·25	1·25
1637	**1559**	49p. multicoloured	1·50	1·50
1638	**1560**	59p. multicoloured	1·75	1·75
1639	**1561**	86p. multicoloured	2·50	2·50
1636/9 *Set of 4*			7·00	7·00
First Day Cover				8·00
Presentation Pack			8·00	

The 49p. and 59p. values are inscr 'EUROPA'.
Plate Nos.: 42p., 49p., 1A, 1B; others 1A (each×4).
Sheets: 10 (2×5) with enlarged illustrated margins.
Imprint: Lower left-hand margin.
Withdrawn: 10.1.2014.

1562 Queen Elizabeth II, 1954

1563 King George VI

Diamond Jubilee (1st issue)

(Litho (**MS**1642 also embossed) Cartor)

2012 (6 Feb). P 13 (C).

1640	**1562**	£2 black and new blue	5·00	5·00
		a. Horiz pair. Nos. 1640/1	10·00	10·00
1641	**1563**	£2 black and new blue	5·00	5·00
First Day Cover				12·00
Presentation Pack			12·00	
MS1642 126×85 mm. Nos. 1640/1			10·00	10·00
First Day Cover				12·00
Presentation Pack			12·00	

A miniature sheet with a diamond attached to the crown was available at a cost of £125.
See also No. 1662.
Plate Nos.: 1A (×2).
Sheets: 4 Nos. 1640/1 were printed together, *se-tenant*, as horizontal pairs throughout the sheets.
Imprint: Lower left-hand margin.

1564 de Havilland DH.86, c. 1937

1565 Bristol 170 Wayfarer, c. 1946

1566 Airspeed Ambassador, c. 1953

1567 Hawker Siddeley Trident, c. 1966

1568 Britten-Norman Trislander, c. 1977

1569 Vickers VC10, c.1987

1570 Fairchild Dornier 328-110, c. 2009 *(Illustration reduced. Actual size 110×75 mm)*

Aviation History (11th series). 75th Anniversary of Jersey Airport

(Des Tony Theobald. Litho Cartor)

2012 (10 Mar). P 13×13½ (1643/8) or 13½×13 (**MS**1649) (both comb.).
1643	**1564**	37p. multicoloured	1·10	1·10
		a. Booklet pane. Nos. 1643/8 with margins all round	10·50	
1644	**1565**	49p. multicoloured	1·50	1·50
1645	**1566**	50p. multicoloured	1·50	1·50
1646	**1567**	64p. multicoloured	1·75	1·75
1647	**1568**	79p. multicoloured	2·25	2·25
1648	**1569**	86p. multicoloured	2·50	2·50
1643/8		*Set of 6*	10·50	10·50
		First Day Cover		11·00
		Presentation Pack	9·50	
MS1649	110×75 mm. **1570**	£3 multicoloured	6·50	6·50
		a. Booklet pane. As No. **MS**1649a but 151×100 mm with line of roulettes at left	6·50	
		First Day Cover		9·50
		Presentation Pack	9·50	

Booklet pane No. 1643a exists in three versions which differ in the order of the stamps within the block of six.
Plate Nos.: All values 1A (each×4).
Sheets: 10 (2×5) with enlarged illustrated margins.
Imprint: Lower left-hand margin.
Withdrawn: 9.3.2014 (Sheets).

1571 *Titanic (Illustration reduced. Actual size 150×100 mm)*

Centenary of the Sinking of the *Titanic*

(Des Mark Wilkinson. Litho BDT)

2012 (14 Apr). Sheet 150×100 mm. P 14 (C).
MS1650	**571**	£3 multicoloured	7·00	7·00
		First Day Cover		9·50
		Presentation Pack	9·50	

Withdrawn: 14.4.2014.

1572 Broad-bordered Yellow Underwing (moth) (*Noctua fimbriata*)

1573 Painted Lady (butterfly) (*Vanessa cardui*)

1574 Merveille du Jour (moth) (*Dichonia aprilina*)

1575 Queen of Spain Fritillary (butterfly) (*Issoria lathonia*)

1576 Large Emerald (moth) (*Geometra papilionaria*)

1577 Red Admiral (butterfly) (*Vanessa atalanta*)

Butterflies and Moths (3rd series)

(Des William Oliver. Litho Lowe-Martin, Canada)

2012 (8 May). P 13×13½ (C).
1651	**1572**	(45p.) multicoloured	1·25	1·25
1652	**1573**	(55p.) multicoloured	1·50	1·50
1653	**1574**	(60p.) multicoloured	1·75	1·75
1654	**1575**	(68p.) multicoloured	1·90	1·90
1655	**1576**	(70p.) multicoloured	2·00	2·00
1656	**1577**	(88p.) multicoloured	2·50	2·50
1651/6		*Set of 6*	10·50	10·50
		First Day Cover		11·50
		Presentation Pack	11·50	
MS1657	150×100 mm. Nos. 1654/6		6·25	6·25
		First Day Cover		7·75
		Presentation Pack	7·75	

Nos. 1651/6 were inscr 'Local Letter', 'UK Letter', 'Europe', 'Local Large', 'International' and 'UK Large' and were originally sold for 45p., 55p., 60p., 68p., 70p. and 88p. respectively.
Stamps from **MS**1657 have no white borders.
Plate Nos.: All values 1A (each×4).
Sheets: 10 (2×5) with enlarged illustrated margins.
Imprint: Lower left-hand margin.
Withdrawn: 8.5.2014.

1578 Archirondel Tower

1579 Mont Orgueil

1580 Corbiere Lighthouse

1581 Clasped Hands Sculpture

'Simply Jersey'. Landmarks

(Des Andrew Fothergill. Litho Cartor)

2012 (8 May). Self-adhesive. Die-cut perf 13½.
1658	**1578**	(45p.) multicoloured	1·25	1·25
		a. Booklet pane. No. 1658×10	12·00	
		b. Perf 12½	1·25	1·25

1659	**1579**	(45p.) multicoloured	1·25	1·25
		b. Perf 12½	1·25	1·25
1660	**1580**	(55p.) multicoloured	1·50	1·50
		b. Perf 12½	1·50	1·50
1661	**1581**	(55p.) multicoloured	1·50	1·50
		a. Booklet pane. No. 1661×10	14·00	
		b. Perf 12½	1·50	1·50
1658/61	Set of 4		5·50	5·50
First Day Cover				7·25
Presentation Pack			7·25	

Nos. 1658/9 were inscr 'Local letter' and originally sold for 45p. each.

Nos. 1660/1 were inscr 'UK letter' and originally sold for 55p. each.

Nos. 1658 and 1661 were issued in booklets of ten, Nos. SB72/3, originally sold for £4.50 (SB72) or £5.50 (SB73).

Nos. 1659/60 were issued in separate business sheets of 100 stamps.

Nos. 1658b/61b were issued in horizontal strips of the four designs

1582 *Equanimity* (official holographic portrait)

Diamond Jubilee (2nd issue)

(Des Chris Levine. Hologram by Rob Munday. Flat simili silver foiling Cartor)

2012 (1 June). P 13 (C).

1662	**1582**	£10 black and new blue	23·00	23·00
First Day Cover				26·00
Presentation Pack			26·00	

No. 1662 was retained in use as a definitive.
Plate Nos.: 1A (x2).
Sheets: 4 (2×2).
Imprint: Lower left-hand margin.

1583 Prince William as Helicopter Pilot

1584 Prince William as Officer cadet, Sandhurst

1585 Prince William in Irish Guards Uniform

1586 Prince William in Royal Navy Uniform

30th Birthday of Prince William

(Litho Austrian State Ptg Wks, Vienna)

2012 (21 June). P 14 (C).

1663	**1583**	45p. multicoloured	1·25	1·25
1664	**1584**	68p. multicoloured	1·90	1·90
1665	**1585**	70p. multicoloured	2·00	2·00
1666	**1586**	88p. multicoloured	2·50	2·50
1663/6	Set of 4		7·50	7·50
First Day Cover				9·00
Presentation Pack			9·00	

Plate Nos.: All values 1A (each×4).
Sheets: 10 (5×2) 45p., 88p.; (2×5) 68p., 70p. with enlarged illustrated margins.
Imprint: Lower right-hand margin (45p., 88p.) or top margin (68p., 70p.).
Withdrawn: 21.6.2014.

1587 *Magnolia campbellii*

1588 Swamp Cypress (*Taxodium distichum*)

1589 Flowering Cherry (*Prunus* 'Pink Perfection')

1590 Maidenhair (*Ginkgo biloba*)

1591 Hill Cherry (*Prunus jamasakura*)

1592 London Plane (*Platanus* × *hispanica*)

75th Anniv of Jersey Trees for Life (formerly Jersey branch of the Men of the Trees)

(Des Michael Pollard. Litho Enschedé)

2012 (3 July). P 13×14 (C).

1667	**1587**	45p. multicoloured	1·25	1·25
1668	**1588**	55p. multicoloured	1·50	1·50
1669	**1589**	60p. multicoloured	1·75	1·75
1670	**1590**	68p. multicoloured	1·90	1·90
1671	**1591**	70p. multicoloured	2·00	2·00
1672	**1592**	88p. multicoloured	2·50	2·50
1667/72	Set of 6		10·50	10·50
First Day Cover				11·50
Presentation Pack			11·50	

Plate Nos.: 45p., 55p., 1A, 1B; others 1A (each×4).
Sheets: 10 (5×2) with enlarged illustrated margins.
Imprint: Lower left-hand margin.
Withdrawn: 3.7.2014.

1593 Champagne Glasses   **1594** Flower   **1595** Coloured Ribbons   **1596** Teddy Bear

1597 Balloons   **1598** Candles on Birthday Cake   **1599** Rosette of Gold Ribbon   **1600** Red Ribbon Heart

Jersey Moments

(Des Andrew Fothergill. Litho Cartor)

2012 (2 Aug). Self-adhesive. Die-cut perf 12.

1673	**1593**	(45p.) multicoloured		1·25	1·25
		a. Sheetlet. Nos. 1673/80		10·00	10·00
1674	**1594**	(45p.) multicoloured		1·25	1·25
1675	**1595**	(45p.) multicoloured		1·25	1·25
1676	**1596**	(45p.) multicoloured		1·25	1·25
1677	**1597**	(55p.) multicoloured		1·25	1·25
1678	**1598**	(55p.) multicoloured		1·25	1·25
1679	**1599**	(55p.) multicoloured		1·25	1·25
1680	**1600**	(55p.) multicoloured		1·25	1·25
1673/80	*Set of 8*			10·00	10·00
First Day Cover					12·00
Presentation Pack				12·00	

1601 Lesser spotted Woodpecker (*Dendrocopos minor*)   **1602** Stonechat (*Saxicola torquata*)

1603 Yellowhammer (*Emberiza citronella*)   **1604** Serin (*Serinus serinus*)

1605 Bullfinch (*Pyrrhula pyrrhula*)   **1606** Cirl Bunting (*Emberiza cirlus*)

Jersey Birdlife (6th series). Threatened Birds

(Des Nick Parlett. Litho Cartor)

2012 (14 Aug). P 13×13½ (C).

1681	**1601**	45p. multicoloured	1·25	1·25
1682	**1602**	55p. multicoloured	1·50	1·50
1683	**1603**	60p. multicoloured	1·75	1·75
1684	**1604**	68p. multicoloured	1·90	1·90
1685	**1605**	70p. multicoloured	2·00	2·00
1686	**1606**	88p. multicoloured	2·50	2·50
1681/6	*Set of 6*		10·50	10·50
First Day Cover				11·50

Presentation Pack	11·50	
MS1687 1150×100 mm. Nos. 1684/6	6·25	6·25
First Day Cover		7·75
Presentation Pack	7·75	
MS1688 150×100 mm. Nos. 1681/6	10·50	10·50
First Day Cover		11·50
Presentation Pack	11·50	

Plate Nos.: All values 1A (each×5).
Sheets: 10 (2×5) with enlarged illustrated margins.
Imprint: Lower left-hand margin.
Withdrawn: 14.8.2014.

1607 Jambo the Gorilla   **1608** Jambo sitting in Tree

1609 Jambo with Female and Baby   **1610** Close-up of Jambo

1611 Jambo and his Family (*Illustration reduced. Actual size 110×75 mm*)

Jambo the Gorilla 1961-1992

(Des William Oliver. Litho BDT)

2012 (15 Sept). P 14½×14 (1689/92) or 14×14½ (**MS**1693), both comb.

1689	**1607**	45p. multicoloured	1·25	1·25
1690	**1608**	60p. multicoloured	1·75	1·75
1691	**1609**	80p. multicoloured	2·40	2·40
1692	**1610**	88p. multicoloured	2·50	2·50
1689/92	*Set of 4*		7·50	7·50
First Day Cover				9·00
Presentation Pack			9·00	
MS1693 110×75 mm. **1611** £1 multicoloured			2·50	2·50
First Day Cover				5·00
Presentation Pack			5·00	

Plate Nos.: All values 1A (each×4).
Sheets: 10 (2×5) with enlarged illustrated margins.
Imprint: Lower left-hand margin.
Withdrawn: 15.9.2014.

1612 Flicquet Tower   **1613** Portelet Tower

1614 Ouaisné Tower   **1615** Lewis Tower

1616 Noirmont Tower   **1617** St. Catherine's Tower

Coastal Towers (2nd series)

(Des Nick Shewring. Litho Austrian State Ptg Wks, Vienna)

2012 (12 Oct). P 14×13½ (C).

1694	**1612**	45p. multicoloured	1·25	1·25
1695	**1613**	55p. multicoloured	1·50	1·50
1696	**1614**	60p. multicoloured	1·75	1·75
1697	**1615**	68p. multicoloured	1·90	1·90
1698	**1616**	70p. multicoloured	2·00	2·00
1699	**1617**	80p. multicoloured	2·40	2·40
1694/9	Set of 6		10·50	10·50
First Day Cover				11·50
Presentation Pack			11·50	

Plate Nos.: All values 1A (each×4).
Sheets: 10 (2×5) with enlarged illustrated margins.
Imprint: Lower left-hand margin.
Withdrawn: 12.10.2014.

1618 Mont Ubé   **1619** Le Couperon

1620 Ville és Nouaux   **1621** Les Mont Grantez

1622 La Pouquelaye de Faldouet

Archaeology (3rd series). Dolmens

(Des Andrew Robinson. Litho Lowe-Martin, Canada)

2012 (2 Nov). P 13 (C).

(1700	**1618**	45p. multicoloured	1·25	1·25
1701	**1619**	55p. multicoloured	1·50	1·50
1702	**1620**	60p. multicoloured	1·75	1·75
1703	**1621**	68p. multicoloured	1·90	1·90
1704	**1622**	88p. multicoloured	2·50	2·50
1700/4	Set of 5		8·50	8·50
First Day Cover				10·00
Presentation Pack			10·00	

Plate Nos.: All values 1A (each×4).
Sheets: 10 (2×5) with enlarged illustrated margins.
Imprint: Lower left-hand margin.
Withdrawn: 2.11.2014.

1623 Reformed Scrooge ('A Merry Christmas one and all!')   **1624** Ebenezer Scrooge ('Bah Humbug!')

1625 Scrooge, Bob Cratchit and his Family ('The End of It')   **1626** Charles Dickens and Scrooge with Marley's Ghost

1627 Charles Dickens and Scrooge with the Ghost of Christmas Past   **1628** Charles Dickens and Scrooge with the Ghost of Christmas Present

1629 Charles Dickens, Scrooge and the Ghost of Christmas Future   **1630** Charles Dickens and Bob Cratchit and Tiny Tim

Christmas. *A Christmas Carol* by Charles Dickens

(Des Mark Wilkinson. Litho Lowe-Martin)

2012 (15 Nov). P 13 (C).

1705	**1623**	40p. multicoloured	1·10	1·10
1706	**1624**	45p. multicoloured	1·25	1·25
1707	**1625**	50p. multicoloured	1·50	1·50
1708	**1626**	55p. multicoloured	1·50	1·50
1709	**1627**	60p. multicoloured	1·75	1·75
1710	**1628**	68p. multicoloured	1·90	1·90
1711	**1629**	80p. multicoloured	2·40	2·40
1712	**1630**	88p. multicoloured	2·50	2·50
1705/12	Set of 8		13·50	13·50
First Day Cover				14·00
Presentation Pack			14·00	

A pack of postcards containing two each of the designs for Nos. 1705/7 and 1712 was issued (price £6).
Plate Nos.: All values 1A (each×5).
Sheets: 10 (2×5) with enlarged illustrated margins.
Imprint: Lower left-hand margin.
Withdrawn: 15.11.2014.

Post Office Yearbook

2012 (1 Dec). Comprises Nos. 1636/41, 1643/56, 1658/86 and 1689/712 (price £61.83).
Yearbook £120

1631 *Camellia sasanqua* 'Paradise Belinda'

1632 Butcher's Broom (*Ruscus aculeatus*)

1633 Snowdrop (*Galanthus nivalis*)

1634 Mistletoe (*Viscum album*)

1635 Bramble (*Rubus fruticosus*)

1636 Hawthorn (*Craetagus monogyna*)

Frosts and Nature

(Des Michael Pollard. Litho Cartor)

2013 (8 Jan). P 13×13½ (C).
1713	**1631**	45p. multicoloured	1·25	1·25
1714	**1632**	55p. multicoloured	1·50	1·50
1715	**1633**	60p. multicoloured	1·75	1·75
1716	**1634**	68p. multicoloured	1·90	1·90
1717	**1635**	80p. multicoloured	2·40	2·40
1718	**1636**	88p. multicoloured	2·50	2·50
1713/18 *Set of 6*			10·50	10·50
First Day Cover				12·00
Presentation Pack			12·00	

Plate Nos.: All values 1A (each×4).
Sheets: 10 (2×5) with enlarged illustrated margins.
Imprint: Lower left-hand margin.
Withdrawn: 8.1.2015.

1637 Statue of King Edward VII, Liverpool

1638 Statue of King Edward VII, Aberdeen

1639 Statue of King Edward VII, Birmingham

1640 Statue of King Edward VII, Reading

1641 Statue of King Edward VII, Bristol

1642 Statue of King Edward VII, London

1643 Statue of King Edward VII, Queen's Park, Toronto (*Illustration reduced. Actual size 110×75 mm*)

The Royal Legacy of Queen Victoria. King Edward VII

(Des True North. Litho Cartor)

2013 (5 Feb). P 13×13½ (C).
1719	**1637**	45p. multicoloured	1·25	1·25
1720	**1638**	55p. multicoloured	1·50	1·50
1721	**1639**	60p. multicoloured	1·75	1·75
1722	**1640**	68p. multicoloured	1·90	1·90
1723	**1641**	80p. multicoloured	2·40	2·40
1724	**1642**	88p. multicoloured	2·50	2·50
1719/24 *Set of 6*			10·50	10·50
First Day Cover				12·00
Presentation Pack			12·00	
MS1725 110×75 mm. **1643** £2 multicoloured			4·50	4·50
First Day Cover				7·50
Presentation Pack			7·50	

Plate Nos.: All values 1A (each×5).
Sheets: 10 (2×5) with enlarged illustrated left margins.
Imprint: Top margin at right.
Withdrawn: 5.2.2015.

1644 Boxer

1645 Lhasa Apso

1646 Irish Setter

1647 Kerry Blue Terrier

1648 Pomeranian

1649 Afghan Hound

125th Anniversary of the Kennel Club of Jersey (sepac)

(Des Andrew Beckett. Litho Lowe-Martin, Canada)

2013 (8 Mar). P 13½ (C).
1726	**1644**	45p. multicoloured	1·25	1·25
1727	**1645**	55p. multicoloured	1·50	1·50

1728	**1646**	60p. multicoloured	1·75	1·75
1729	**1647**	68p. multicoloured	1·90	1·90
1730	**1648**	80p. multicoloured	2·40	2·40
1731	**1649**	88p. multicoloured	2·50	2·50
1726/31 *Set of 6*			10·50	10·50
First Day Cover				12·00
Presentation Pack			12·00	

The 60p value is inscribed 'sepac' and was also available in a souvenir folder (24 Sept) with 11 other sepac logo stamps issued by other administrations, cost £13.95.

Plate Nos.: All values 1A (each×4).
Sheets: 10 (5×2).
Imprint: Lower left-hand margin.
Withdrawn: 8.3.2015.

1650 Postman's Bicycle, Mailbag and Trolley

1651 Jersey Post Lorry and Vans

1652 Jersey Post Van, Lorry and Ferry

1653 Loading Air Mail

Europa. Postal Vehicles

(Des Colleen Corlett. Litho Lowe-Martin, Canada)

2013 (19 Mar). P 13 (C).

1732	**1650**	45p. multicoloured	1·25	1·25
1733	**1651**	55p. multicoloured	1·50	1·50
1734	**1652**	60p. multicoloured	1·75	1·75
1735	**1653**	80p. multicoloured	2·40	2·40
1732/5 *Set of 4*			6·50	6·50
First Day Cover				8·50
Presentation Pack			8·50	

The 55p. and 80p. values are inscr 'EUROPA'.
Plate Nos.: All values 1A (each×4).
Sheets: 10 (2×5) with enlarged illustrated margins.
Imprint: Lower left-hand margin.
Withdrawn: 19.3.2015.

1654 Leyland, c. 1948

1655 Leyland, c. 1955

1656 Karrier Bantam, c. 1960

1657 Leyland Tiger Cub, c. 1962

1658 Leyland, c. 1963

1659 Dennis Triton, c. 1963

90th Anniversary of Jersey Motor Transport Company. Buses (4th series)

(Des Alan Copp. Litho BDT)

2013 (2 Apr). P 14½×14 (C).

1736	**1654**	45p. multicoloured	1·25	1·25
1737	**1655**	55p. multicoloured	1·50	1·50
1738	**1656**	60p. multicoloured	1·75	1·75
1739	**1657**	68p. multicoloured	1·90	1·90
1740	**1658**	80p. multicoloured	2·40	2·40
1741	**1659**	88p. multicoloured	2·50	2·50
1736/41 *Set of 6*			10·50	10·50
First Day Cover				12·00
Presentation Pack			12·00	

Plate Nos.: All values 1A (each×4).
Sheets: 10 (2×5).
Imprint: Lower left-hand margin.
Withdrawn: 2.4.2015.

1660 Corbiere lining up at Start of Race

1661 Corbiere leading Field in Race

1662 Corbiere jumping

1663 Corbiere winning Grand National

1664 Corbiere and Corbière Lighthouse (*Illustration reduced. Actual size 95×97 mm*)

Corbiere, Grand National Winner, 1983

(Des Nick Watton. Recess and litho (**MS**1746 only) or litho Enschedé)

2013 (11 Apr). P 14×13½ (C).

1742	**1660**	55p. multicoloured	1·50	1·50
1743	**1661**	60p. multicoloured	1·75	1·75
1744	**1662**	68p. multicoloured	1·90	1·90
1745	**1663**	80p. multicoloured	2·40	2·40
1742/5 *Set of 4*			7·00	7·00
First Day Cover				9·00
Presentation Pack			9·00	
MS1746 95×97 mm. **1664** £2 multicoloured			5·00	5·00
First Day Cover				7·50
Presentation Pack			7·50	

A limited edition of 200 uncut miniature sheets, each containing 12 perforated sheets, numbered by hand, was sold at face value, £24 each.

Plate Nos.: All values 1A (each×4).

Sheets: 10 (2×5).

Imprint: Upper left-hand margin.

Withdrawn: 11.4.2015.

1665 Tracing and Messaging (to reunite separated families)

1666 Red Cross Staff and Volunteers unloading Emergency Supplies

1667 Villagers drawing Water ('Water, shelter and food')

1668 First Aid Training

1669 South African Red Cross Helicopter ('Emergency response')

1670 Princess Diana visiting HALO Trust (landmine clearance organisation), Angola, 1997

1671 Red Cross Ship SS *Vega* arriving in Jersey, 1940–5 (*Illustration reduced. Actual size 115×80 mm*)

150th Anniversary of the International Red Cross and Red Crescent

(Des Nick Shewring. Litho BDT)

2013 (8 May). P 14 (C).

1747	**1665**	(45p.) multicoloured	1·25	1·25
1748	**1666**	(55p.) multicoloured	1·50	1·50
1749	**1667**	(60p.) multicoloured	1·75	1·75
1750	**1668**	(68p.) multicoloured	1·90	1·90
1751	**1669**	(80p.) multicoloured	2·40	2·40
1752	**1670**	(88p.) multicoloured	2·50	2·50
1747/52 *Set of 6*			10·50	10·50
First Day Cover				12·00
Presentation Pack			12·00	
MS1753 115×80 mm. **1671** £2 multicoloured			4·50	4·50
First Day Cover				7·50
Presentation Pack			7·50	

No. 1747 was inscr 'LOCAL LETTER', No. 1748 'UK LETTER', No. 1749 'EUROPE', No. 1750 'LOCAL LARGE', No. 1751 'INTERNATIONAL' and No. 1752 'UK LARGE' and they were originally sold for 45p., 55p., 60p., 68p., 80p. and 88p. respectively.

Plate Nos. All values 1A (each×4).

Sheets: 10 (2×5) with enlarged illustrated margins.

Imprint: Top margin at left.

Withdrawn: 8.5.2015.

1672 Queen Elizabeth II

1673 Queen Elizabeth II (Cecil Beaton) on 1971 9p. Stamp

60th Anniversary of the Coronation

(Des True North. Litho Cartor)

2013 (2 June). P 13 (C).

1754	**1672**	£2 multicoloured	5·00	5·00
		a. Horiz pair. Nos. 1754/5	10·00	10·00
1755	**1673**	£2 multicoloured	5·00	5·00
First Day Cover				12·00
Presentation Pack			12·00	
MS1756 125×85 mm. Nos. 1754/5			10·00	10·00
First Day Cover				12·00
Presentation Pack			12·00	

A limited edition of uncut miniature sheets, each containing six perforated sheets, was sold at face value, £24.

Sheets: 4 (2×2) Nos. 1754/5 were printed together, *se-tenant*, as horizontal pairs

Imprint: Lower left-hand margin.

1674 Henry Cavill as Man of Steel

1675 Henry Cavill as Man of Steel

1676 Henry Cavill as Man of Steel

1677 Man of Steel flying above Earth

1678 Man of Steel walking on Beauport Bay Pebbles

1679 Henry Cavill as Man of Steel

1680 Man of Steel flying (*Illustration reduced. Actual size 110×75 mm*)

Man of Steel (film)

(Des True North. Litho Cartor)

2013 (7 June). Self-adhesive (1758) or ordinary gum (others). P 13 (1758), 14 (**MS**1763) or 12½ (others), die-cut (1758), others comb.

1757	**1674**	45p. multicoloured	1·25	1·25
1758	**1675**	55p. multicoloured	1·50	1·50
1759	**1676**	60p. multicoloured	1·75	1·75
1760	**1677**	68p. multicoloured	1·90	1·90
1761	**1678**	80p. multicoloured	2·40	2·40
1762	**1679**	88p. multicoloured	2·50	2·50
1757/62 *Set of 6*			10·50	10·50
First Day Cover				12·00
Presentation Pack			12·00	
MS1763 110×75 mm. **1680** £3 multicoloured			7·50	7·50
First Day Cover				10·00
Presentation Pack			10·00	

No. 1757 can be scanned with a smartphone to trigger an augmented reality App with information about the stamps and film.

The self-adhesive stamp No. 1758 is transparent when peeled from backing paper.

No. 1759 is printed on flat simili silver foiling.

No. 1760 is printed with thermochromatic ink, and when warmth is applied to the face of the stamp the Earth is revealed beneath the flying Man of Steel.

No. 1761 has crushed granite from a Beauport Bay pebble applied to the face of the stamp.

No. 1762 has a message from the Man of Steel's father in phosphor ink visible under UV light.

The lenticular miniature sheet **MS**1763 when tilted shows the Man of Steel flying across the face of the sheet.

Sheets: 10 (2×5) with enlarged illustrated left margins.
Imprint: Upper right-hand margin.
Withdrawn: 7.6.2015.

1681 Beautiful Demoiselle (*Calopteryx virgo*)

1682 Golden-ringed Dragonfly (*Cordulegaster boltonii*)

1683 Dainty Damselfly (*Coenagrion scitulum*)

1684 Large Red Damselfly (*Pyrrhosoma nymphula*)

1685 Scarlet Darter (*Crocothemis erythraea*)

1686 Willow Emerald Damselfly (*Lestes viridis*)

Dragonflies and Damselflies

(Des Lizzie Harper. Litho Enschedé)

2013 (4 July). P 14×13½ (C).

1764	**1681**	45p. multicoloured	1·25	1·25
1765	**1682**	55p. multicoloured	1·50	1·50
1766	**1683**	60p. multicoloured	1·75	1·75
1767	**1684**	68p. multicoloured	1·90	1·90
1768	**1685**	80p. multicoloured	2·40	2·40
1769	**1686**	88p. multicoloured	2·50	2·50
1764/9 *Set of 6*			10·50	10·50
First Day Cover				12·00
Presentation Pack			12·00	

Plate Nos.: All values 1A (each×4).
Sheets: 10 (2×5) with enlarged illustrated margins.
Imprint: Lower right-hand margin.
Withdrawn: 4.7.2015.

1687 *Stavros S. Niarchos*

1688 HM Bark *Endeavour*

1689 STS *Tenacious*

1690 *Eye of the Wind*

1691 *Prince William*

1692 Sk/S *Christian Radich*

Visiting Tall Ships

(Des Tony Theobald. Litho Lowe-Martin, Canada)

2013 (8 Aug). P 13 (C).

1770	**1687**	45p. multicoloured	1·25	1·25
1771	**1688**	55p. multicoloured	1·50	1·50
1772	**1689**	60p. multicoloured	1·75	1·75
1773	**1690**	68p. multicoloured	1·90	1·90
1774	**1691**	80p. multicoloured	2·40	2·40
1775	**1692**	88p. multicoloured	2·50	2·50
1770/5 *Set of 6*			10·50	10·50
First Day Cover				12·00
Presentation Pack			12·00	
MS1776 150×100 mm. Nos. 1770/5			11·00	11·00
First Day Cover				12·00
Presentation Pack			12·00	

Plate Nos.: All values 1A (each×4).
Sheets: 10 (2×5) with margins all round.
Imprint: Lower right-hand margin.
Withdrawn: 8.8.2015.

1693 Stoewer R200 Radio Car

1694 Kettenkrad NSU HK 101 (1944)

1695 HMMWV M998

1696 Kubelwagen Type 82 (1944)

1697 Sd.Kfz 251-Ausf C Half Track

1698 Ford Willys Jeep GPW

Military Vehicles

(Des Alan Copp. Litho Enschedé)

2013 (30 Aug). P 14×13 (C).

1777	**1693**	45p. multicoloured	1·25	1·25
		a. Booklet pane. Nos. 1777/82 with		
		margins all round	10·50	
1778	**1694**	55p. multicoloured	1·50	1·50
1779	**1695**	60p. multicoloured	1·75	1·75
1780	**1696**	68p. multicoloured	1·90	1·90
1781	**1697**	80p. multicoloured	2·40	2·40
1782	**1698**	88p. multicoloured	2·50	2·50
1777/82 *Set of 6*			10·50	10·50
First Day Cover				12·00
Presentation Pack			12·00	

Booklet pane 1777a exists in four versions which differ in the order of the stamps within the block of six.
Plate Nos.: All values 1A (each×4).
Sheets: 10 (2×5).
Imprint: Upper left-hand margin.
Withdrawn: 30.8.2015 (Sheets).

1699 Clover

1700 Daisy

1701 Butterfly

1702 Florence

1703 Dolly Maud

1704 Buttercup

Jersey Cows. Paintings by Kathy Rondel

(Litho BDT)

2013 (20 Sept). P 14×14½ (C).

1783	**1699**	(45p.) multicoloured	1·25	1·25
1784	**1700**	(55p.) multicoloured	1·50	1·50
1785	**1701**	(60p.) multicoloured	1·75	1·75
1786	**1702**	(68p.) multicoloured	1·90	1·90
1787	**1703**	(80p.) multicoloured	2·40	2·40
1788	**1704**	(88p.) multicoloured	2·50	2·50
1783/8 *Set of 6*			10·50	10·50
First Day Cover				12·00
Presentation Pack			12·00	

No. 1783 was inscr 'LOCAL LETTER', No. 1784 'UK LETTER', No. 1785 'EUROPE', No. 1786 'LOCAL LARGE', No. 1787 'INTERNATIONAL' and No. 1788 'UK LARGE' and they were originally sold for 45p., 55p., 60p., 68p., 80p. and 88p. respectively.
Plate Nos.: All values 1A (each×4).
Sheets: 10 (5×2) with enlarged illustrated margins.
Imprint: Central, top margin.

1705 First Pole Position, Lotus 95T, US Grand Prix, 1984

1706 First Formula 1 Win, Williams Honda, European Grand Prix, 1985

1707 Winning Debut with Ferrari, Brazilian Grand Prix, 1989

1708 F1 World Champion, Williams Renault, Hungarian Grand Prix, 1992

1709 IndyCar Champion, Newman/ Haas Lola Ford, Nazareth Speedway, 1993

1710 The 'Mansell Taxi' giving Ayrton Senna a lift during Victory Lap, British Grand Prix, 1991

Legacy of a Formula One Champion - Nigel Mansell

(Des The Observatory. Litho Enschedé)

2013 (15 Oct). P 13×13½ (C).

1789	**1705**	45p. multicoloured	1·25	1·25
1790	**1706**	55p. multicoloured	1·50	1·50
1791	**1707**	60p. multicoloured	1·75	1·75
1792	**1708**	68p. multicoloured	1·90	1·90
1793	**1709**	80p. multicoloured	2·40	2·40
1794	**1710**	88p. multicoloured	2·50	2·50
1789/94 *Set of 6*			10·50	10·50
First Day Cover				12·00
Presentation Pack			12·00	
MS1795 150×100 mm. Nos. 1789/94			11·00	11·00
First Day Cover				12·00
Presentation Pack			12·00	

Plate Nos. All values 1A (each×5).
Sheets: 10 (2×5) with enlarged illustrated margins.
Imprint: Upper right-hand margin.
Withdrawn: 15.10.2015.

1711 Prince of Wales in Welsh Guards Uniform

65th Birthday of the Prince of Wales

(Des Andrew Robinson. Litho and varnish Cartor)

2013 (14 Nov). P 13½ (C).

1796	**1711**	£4 multicoloured	9·50	9·50
First Day Cover				12·00
Presentation Pack			12·00	
MS1797 100×100 mm. As No. 1796 (without white border)			9·50	9·50
First Day Cover				12·00
Presentation Pack			12·00	

Plate Nos.: 1A (each×4).
Sheets: 4 (2×2).
Imprint: Lower left-hand margin.
No. 1796 was retained in use as a definitive.

1712 Jersey Royal Mace (*Illustration reduced. Actual size 70×155 mm*)

350th Anniversary of the Jersey Royal Mace

(Des Andrew Robinson. Litho Cartor)

2013 (14 Nov). P 13½ (C).

MS1798 70×155 mm. **1712** £1 multicoloured	2·25	2·25
First Day Cover		5·00
Presentation Pack	5·00	

Withdrawn: 14.11.2015.

1713 Christmas Pudding

1714 Mulled Wine and Mince Pies

1715 Gingerbread

1716 Christmas Cake

1717 Stollen   **1718** Mixed Nuts

1719 Gingerbread House   **1720** Chocolate Yule Log

Christmas. Christmas Fayre

(Des Michael Pollard. Litho Enschedé)

2013 (27 Nov). P 14×13½ (C).

1799	**1713**	40p. multicoloured	1·10	1·10
1800	**1714**	45p. multicoloured	1·25	1·25
1801	**1715**	50p. multicoloured	1·50	1·50
1802	**1716**	55p. multicoloured	1·50	1·50
1803	**1717**	60p. multicoloured	1·75	1·75
1804	**1718**	68p. multicoloured	1·90	1·90
1805	**1719**	88p. multicoloured	2·50	2·50
1806	**1720**	95p. multicoloured	2·50	2·50
1799/806 *Set of 8*			13·50	13·50
First Day Cover				14·50
Presentation Pack			14·50	

Plate Nos.: All values 1A (each×4).
Sheets: 10 (2×5) with enlarged illustrated margins.
Imprint: Upper left-hand margin.
Withdrawn: 27.11.2015.

Post Office Yearbook

2013 (1 Dec). Comprises Nos. 1713/55, 1757/75, 1777/94, 1796 and
MS1798/806 (price £71.60).

Yearbook £140

1721 Trinity Manor   **1722** Longueville Manor

1723 Rosel Manor   **1724** St. John's Manor

1725 St. Ouen's Manor   **1726** Millbrook Manor

Jersey Architecture (2nd series). Manor Houses

(Des Nick Shewring. Litho Lowe-Martin, Canada)

2014 (7 Jan). P 13 (C).

1807	**1721**	45p. multicoloured	1·25	1·25
1808	**1722**	55p. multicoloured	1·50	1·50
1809	**1723**	60p. multicoloured	1·75	1·75
1810	**1724**	68p. multicoloured	1·90	1·90
1811	**1725**	80p. multicoloured	2·40	2·40

1812	**1726**	88p. multicoloured	2·50	2·50
1807/12 *Set of 6*			10·00	10·00
First Day Cover				11·50
Presentation Pack			11·50	

Plate Nos.: All values 1A (each×4)
Sheets: 10 (2×5)
Imprint: Upper left-hand margin

1727 Guitar and Audience   **1728** Piano and Concert
at Rock Concert   Hall (Classical)

1729 Trumpet and Jazz   **1730** Banjo and Jersey
Musicians   Landscape (Folk)

Europa. Musical Instruments

(Des Mark Wilkinson. Litho Cartor)

2014 (25 Mar). P 14.

1813	**1727**	45p. multicoloured	1·25	1·25
1814	**1728**	55p. multicoloured	1·50	1·50
1815	**1729**	60p. multicoloured	1·75	1·75
1816	**1730**	80p. multicoloured	2·40	2·40
1813/16 *Set of 4*			6·25	6·25
First Day Cover				7·75
Presentation Pack			7·75	

Plate Nos.: All values 1A (each×4)
Sheets: 10 (5×2)
Imprint: Upper left-hand margin

1731 Romeo and Juliet   **1732** Hamlet

1733 Macbeth   **1734** Othello

1742 Poppy Flower

1743 Poppy Flowers and Soldiers

1735 Twelfth Night   **1736** Midsummer Night's Dream

1744 In Flanders Fields (poem by John McCrae)

Remembrance 2014. Centenary of the First World War

(Des Katharine Asher. Litho Cartor.)

1737 William Shakespeare

2014 (6 May). P 13½ (C).

1824	**1738**	46p. multicoloured	1·25	1·25
1825	**1739**	56p. multicoloured	1·50	1·50
1826	**1740**	62p. multicoloured	1·75	1·75
1827	**1741**	70p. multicoloured	1·90	1·90
1828	**1742**	82p. multicoloured	2·40	2·40
1829	**1743**	91p. multicoloured	2·50	2·50
1824/9 Set of 6			10·00	10·00
First Day Cover				11·50
Presentation Pack			11·50	
MS1830 136×70 mm. **1744** £3 multicoloured			7·50	7·50
First Day Cover				9·00
Presentation Pack			9·00	

Nos. 1824/5 each had field poppy seeds affixed to them.
Plate Nos.: All values 1A (each×4)
Sheets: 10 (2×5)
Imprint: Upper right-hand margin

450th Birth Anniversary of William Shakespeare

(Des Chris Ede. Litho BDT)

2014 (23 Apr). P 14×14½ (C).

1817	**1731**	46p. multicoloured	1·25	1·25
1818	**1732**	56p. multicoloured	1·50	1·50
1819	**1733**	62p. multicoloured	1·75	1·75
1820	**1734**	70p. multicoloured	1·90	1·90
1821	**1735**	82p. multicoloured	2·40	2·40
1822	**1736**	91p. multicoloured	2·50	2·50
1817/22 Set of 6			10·00	10·00
First Day Cover				11·50
Presentation Pack			11·50	
MS1823 65×90 mm. **1737** £3 multicoloured			7·50	7·50
First Day Cover				9·00
Presentation Pack			9·00	

Plate Nos.: All values 1A (each×4)
Sheets: 10 (5×2)
Imprint: Lower right-hand margin

1745 Sword Beach, Normandy

1738 Poppies and Soldiers

1739 Poppy Flower

1746 Ste.-Mère-Eglise, Normandy

1740 Eternal Flame in Poppy Flower

1741 Poppy Flower and Soldier

1747 Gold Beach, Normandy

1748 Pegasus Bridge, Normandy

1749 Approaching Carentan, Normandy

1750 Off Gold Beach, Normandy

1751 Piper Bill, Pegasus Bridge, Normandy

70th Anniversary of D-Day

(Des David Pentland. Litho Lowe-Martin, Canada)

2014 (6 June). P 13 (C).

1831	**1745**	46p. multicoloured	1·25	1·25
1832	**1746**	56p. multicoloured	1·50	1·50
1833	**1747**	62p. multicoloured	1·75	1·75
1834	**1748**	70p. multicoloured	1·90	1·90
1835	**1749**	82p. multicoloured	2·40	2·40
1836	**1750**	91p. multicoloured	2·50	2·50
1831/6 *Set of 6*			10·00	10·00
First Day Cover				11·50
Presentation Pack			11·50	
MS1837 112×80 mm. **1751** £2 multicoloured			4·50	4·50
First Day Cover				7·00
Presentation Pack			7·00	

Plate Nos.: All values 1A (each×4)
Sheets: 10 (2×5)
Imprint: Lower right-hand margin

1752 Boat at Belcroute Bay

1753 Seymour Tower at High Tide

1754 Summer Calm at Beauport

1755 Fisherman's Chapel, St. Brelade's Bay

1756 The White House at Sunrise

1757 South Coast Rocks

1758 Reflections of Archirondel Tower   **1759** A View Underwater at Les Ecréhous

Jersey Seasons (1st series). Summer

(Litho Enschedé)

2014 (30 June). P 13×14 (C).

1838	**1752**	46p. multicoloured	1·25	1·25
1839	**1753**	56p. multicoloured	1·50	1·50
1840	**1754**	62p. multicoloured	1·75	1·75
1841	**1755**	69p. multicoloured	1·90	1·90
1842	**1756**	70p. multicoloured	1·90	1·90
1843	**1757**	82p. multicoloured	2·40	2·40
1844	**1758**	91p. multicoloured	2·50	2·50
1845	**1759**	£1.20 multicoloured	3·25	3·25
1838/45 *Set of 8*			15·00	15·00
First Day Cover				16·00
Presentation Pack			16·00	

Sheets: 10 (2×5)
Imprint: Upper left-hand margin

1760 Red Arrows Jet

1761 Four Red Arrows

1762 Red Arrows flying in Arrow Formation

1763 Seven Red Arrows

1764 Red Arrows Jet

1765 Two Red Arrows

50th Display Season of Red Arrows

(Litho Lowe-Martin, Canada)

2014 (11 July). P 13 (C).

1846	**1760**	46p. multicoloured	1·25	1·25
1847	**1761**	56p. multicoloured	1·60	1·60
1848	**1762**	62p. multicoloured	1·75	1·75
1849	**1763**	70p. multicoloured	2·00	2·00
1850	**1764**	82p. multicoloured	2·40	2·40
1851	**1765**	91p. multicoloured	2·50	2·50
1846/51 *Set of 6*			10·50	10·50
First Day Cover				11·50
Presentation Pack			11·50	
MS1852 170×90 mm. Nos. 1846/51			11·50	11·50
First Day Cover				11·50
Presentation Pack			11·50	

Sheets: 10 (2×5)
Imprint: Central, left-hand margin

1766 Jersey Militiaman

1767 V.A.D. Nurse

1768 French Reservist

1769 Land Worker

1770 Flag Seller

1771 Royal Navy Officer

1772 'Are YOU in this?' Poster by Lt. Gen.
Sir R. S. S. Baden-Powell

Centenary of the Great War (1st issue). Participation

(Des Martin Hargreaves. Litho Cartor)

2014 (4 Aug). P 13½ (**MS**1860) or 13 (others) (both comb).

1853	**1766**	46p. multicoloured	1·25	1·25
1854	**1767**	56p. multicoloured	1·60	1·60
1855	**1768**	62p. multicoloured	1·75	1·75
1856	**1769**	70p. multicoloured	2·00	2·00
1857	**1770**	82p. multicoloured	2·40	2·40
1858	**1771**	91p. multicoloured	2·50	2·50
1853/8 *Set of 6*			10·50	10·50
First Day Cover				11·50
Presentation Pack			11·50	
MS1859 125×98 mm. Nos. 1853/8			11·50	11·50
First Day Cover				11·50
Presentation Pack			11·50	
MS1860 66×98 mm. **1772** £1 multicoloured (50×36 mm)			3·00	3·00
First Day Cover				5·00
Presentation Pack			5·00	

Plate Nos.: All values 1A (each×4)
Sheets: 10 (2×5)
Imprint: Lower right-hand margin

1773 Roman Invasion

1774 Traders and Roman Temple

1775 Emperor Hadrian and
Building of Hadrian's Wall

1776 Conversion to Christianity

1777 Family and Roman Soldiers

1778 War Chariot

1779 Elephant ridden into Battle

Jersey's Roman Connections

(Des Victor Ambrus. Recess and litho Enschedé)

2014 (27 Aug). P 13½ (C).

1861	**1773**	46p. multicoloured	1·25	1·25
1862	**1774**	56p. multicoloured	1·60	1·60
1863	**1775**	62p. multicoloured	1·75	1·75
1864	**1776**	70p. multicoloured	2·00	2·00
1865	**1777**	82p. multicoloured	2·40	2·40
1866	**1778**	91p. multicoloured	2·50	2·50
1861/6 Set of 6			10·50	10·50
First Day Cover				11·50
Presentation Pack			11·50	
MS1867 105×75 mm. **1779** £2 multicoloured			5·75	5·75
First Day Cover				7·00
Presentation Pack			7·00	

Plate Nos.: All values 1A (each×4)
Sheets: 10 (2×5)
Imprint: Central, left-hand margin

1780 Barnegat Lighthouse, New Jersey

1781 Elizabeth Castle, Jersey

1782 Corbière Lighthouse, Jersey

1783 Seymour Tower, Jersey

1784 Statue of Liberty, New York/New Jersey

1785 George Washington Bridge, New Jersey

350th Anniversary of Founding of the US State of New Jersey

(Des True North. Litho Lowe-Martin, Canada)

2014 (15 Sept). P 12½×13 (1868/73) or 12½ (**MS**1874) (both comb).

1868	**1780**	46p. multicoloured	1·25	1·25
1869	**1781**	56p. multicoloured	1·60	1·60
1870	**1782**	62p. multicoloured	1·75	1·75
1871	**1783**	70p. multicoloured	2·00	2·00
1872	**1784**	82p. multicoloured	2·40	2·40
1873	**1785**	91p. multicoloured	2·50	2·50
1868/73 Set of 6			10·50	10·50

First Day Cover		11·50
Presentation Pack	11·50	
MS1874 124×97 mm. As Nos. 1868/73	11·50	11·50
First Day Cover		11·50
Presentation Pack	11·50	

Plate Nos.: All values 1A (each×4)
Sheets: 10 (2×5)
Imprint: Lower right-hand margin

1786 19th-century Oyster Fishing Boat

1787 19th-century Shore Workers

1788 19th-century Oyster Fishermen with Dredges

1789 Tending Modern Oyster Beds

1790 Tending Oyster Beds at Low Tide with Tractor and Trailer

1791 La Duchesse de Normandie (20th-century transport)

1792 Basket of Oysters

Oyster Fishing

(Des Nick Parlett. Litho Cartor)

2014 (9 Oct). P 13×13½ (C).

1875	**1786**	46p. multicoloured	1·25	1·25
		a. Booklet pane. Nos. 1875/80 with margins all round	11·00	
1876	**1787**	56p. multicoloured	1·60	1·60
1877	**1788**	62p. multicoloured	1·75	1·75
1878	**1789**	70p. multicoloured	2·00	2·00
1879	**1790**	82p. multicoloured	2·40	2·40
1880	**1791**	191p. multicoloured	2·50	2·50
1875/80 Set of 6			10·50	10·50
First Day Cover				11·50
Presentation Pack			11·50	
MS1881 151×100 mm. **1792** £2 multicoloured			5·75	5·75
		a. Booklet pane. As No. **MS**1881 but with line of roulettes at left..	5·75	
First Day Cover				7·00
Presentation Pack			7·00	

Booklet pane No. 1875a exists in three versions which differ in the order of the stamps within the block of six.
Plate Nos.: All values 1A (each×4)
Sheets: 10 (2×5)
Imprint: Lower right-hand margin

1793 Galleons

1794 Pirates on board Ship

1795 In Longboat

1796 Galleons

Pirates and Privateering

(Des Mark Wilkinson. Litho Enschedé)

2014 (30 Oct). P 13½ (C).
1882	**1793**	46p. multicoloured	1·25	1·25
1883	**1794**	56p. multicoloured	1·60	1·60
1884	**1795**	69p. multicoloured	2·00	2·00
1885	**1796**	£1.20 multicoloured	3·50	3·50
1882/5	*Set of 4*		7·50	7·50
First Day Cover				8·75
Presentation Pack			8·75	
MS1886 114×98 mm. Nos. 1882/5			8·25	8·25
First Day Cover				8·75
Presentation Pack			8·75	

Plate Nos.: All values 1A (each×4)
Sheets: 10 (2×5)
Imprint: Lower left-hand margin

1797 White
Teddy Bear

1798 Red and
Yellow Balloons

1799 Hands
forming Heart

1800 Wrapped
Present

1801 Arms

1802 Fireworks

1803 White
Teddy Bear

1804 "hello" in
Sand

1805 Heart-
shaped Stone
and Ribbon

1806 Champagne
Glasses

1807 Flag

1808 Globe
showing Western
Europe

Greetings Stamps. My Moments

(Des Andy Le Gresley. Litho Cartor)

2014 (12 Nov). Self-adhesive. Die-cut perf 14½×14 (with one elliptical
hole in each vert side).
1887	**1797**	(46p.) multicoloured	1·25	1·25
		a. Horiz strip of 6. Nos. 1887/92	7·50	7·50
1888	**1798**	(46p.) multicoloured	1·25	1·25
1889	**1799**	(46p.) multicoloured	1·25	1·25
1890	**1800**	(46p.) multicoloured	1·25	1·25
1891	**1801**	(46p.) multicoloured	1·25	1·25
1892	**1802**	(46p.) multicoloured	1·25	1·25
1893	**1803**	(56p.) multicoloured	1·60	1·60
		a. Horiz strip of 6. Nos. 1893/8	9·50	9·50
1894	**1804**	(56p.) multicoloured	1·60	1·60
1895	**1805**	(56p.) multicoloured	1·60	1·60
1896	**1806**	(56p.) multicoloured	1·60	1·60
1897	**1807**	(56p.) multicoloured	1·60	1·60
1898	**1808**	(56p.) multicoloured	1·60	1·60
1887/98	*Set of 12*		16·00	16·00
First Day Cover				17·00
Presentation Pack			17·00	

Nos. 1887/92 and 1893/8 were each issued in strips of six stamps.
Nos. 1887/92 were inscr 'Local letter' and originally sold for 46p. each.
Nos. 1893/8 were inscr 'UK letter' and originally sold for 56p. each.

1809 Father Christmas
talking with Child

1810 Carrying Tree

1811 Wrapping Presents

1812 On Top of Roof

1813 Eating Mince Pie

1814 Writing Christmas
Letter

1815 With Child carrying Tree

1816 Filling Sack with Presents

Christmas. The Story of Father Christmas

(Des Sharif Tarabay. Litho BDT)

2014 (27 Nov). P 14×14½ (C).

1899	**1809**	41p. multicoloured	1·10	1·10
1900	**1810**	46p. multicoloured	1·25	1·25
1901	**1811**	51p. multicoloured	1·50	1·50
1902	**1812**	56p. multicoloured	1·60	1·60
1903	**1813**	62p. multicoloured	1·75	1·75
1904	**1814**	70p. multicoloured	2·00	2·00
1905	**1815**	91p. multicoloured	2·50	2·50
1906	**1816**	£1.10 multicoloured	3·25	3·25
1899/906 Set of 8			13·50	13·50
First Day Cover				14·50
Presentation Pack			14·50	

Plate Nos.: All values 1A (each×4)
Sheets: 10 (5×2)
Imprint:Lower right-hand margin

Post Office Yearbook

2014 (5 Dec). Comprises Nos. 1807/51, 1853/8, **MS**1860/1873, 1875/85, 1887/906 (price £75).

Yearbook		£150

1817 The Beowulf Dragon

1818 St. George and the Dragon

1819 The Bakunawa

1820 The Colchian Dragon

1821 The Chinese Dragons

1822 The Welsh Dragon

Dragons

(Des Adrian Chesterman. Litho Lowe-Martin, Canada)

2015 (6 Jan). P 13 (C).

1907	**1817**	46p. multicoloured	1·25	1·25
1908	**1818**	56p. multicoloured	1·60	1·60
1909	**1819**	62p. multicoloured	1·75	1·75
1910	**1820**	70p. multicoloured	2·00	2·00
1911	**1821**	82p. multicoloured	2·40	2·40
1912	**1822**	91p. multicoloured	2·50	2·50
1907/12 Set of 6			10·50	10·50
First Day Cover				11·50
Presentation Pack			11·50	
MS1913 150×98 mm. Nos. 1907/12			11·50	11·50
First Day Cover				11·50
Presentation Pack			11·50	

Plate Nos.: All values 1A (each×5)
Sheets: 10 (2×5)
Imprint: Lower right-hand margin

1823 Crest of Jersey

1824 Crest of Jersey

Crest of Jersey

(Des True North. Litho, holography and embossed (£5) or litho (others) Kurz, Germany (£5) or Cartor (others))

2015 (18 Feb). P 13×13½ (£5) or 14×13½ (others) (both comb).

1914	**1823**	1p. bright reddish violet	10	10
1915		2p. bistre	10	10
1916		3p. ultramarine	10	10
1917		4p. deep bluish-green	10	10
1918		5p. brown-purple	15	15
1919		10p. bright magenta	30	30
1920		20p. bright orange	60	60
1921		40p. greenish blue	1·10	1·10
1922		50p. bright green	1·50	1·50
1923		£1 vermilion	3·00	3·00
1924	**1824**	£5 silver	14·50	14·50
1914/24 Set of 11			19·00	
First Day Cover				20·00
Presentation Pack			20·00	
Special Pack (Nos. 1662 and 1924) (sold for £16.96)			38·00	

Nos. 1914/24 have the names of all twelve Jersey parishes printed in micro text in the background waves on the stamps.
No. 1924 contains a hologram which has been embossed.
Plate Nos.: 1p. to 50p., £5 1A×2; £1 1A
Sheets: 1p. to £1 25 (5×5); £5 4 (2×2)
Imprint: 1p. to £1 Lower left-hand margin; £5 Bottom margin at right

1825 British Pullman

1826 GWR Passenger Freight

1827 Flying Scotsman

1828 The Cornishman

1829 Mixed Freight

1830 Caledonian Belle

Europa. Traditional Toys. Hornby Model Trains

(Des True North. Litho Cartor)

2015 (24 Mar). P 13×13½ (C).

1925	**1825**	46p. multicoloured	1·25	1·25
1926	**1826**	56p. multicoloured	1·60	1·60
1927	**1827**	62p. multicoloured	1·75	1·75
1928	**1828**	70p. multicoloured	2·00	2·00
1929	**1829**	82p. multicoloured	2·40	2·40
1930	**1830**	91p. multicoloured	2·50	2·50
1925/30 *Set of 6*			10·50	10·50
First Day Cover				11·50
Presentation Pack			11·50	

Plate Nos.: All values 1A (each×4)
Sheets: 10 (2×5)
Imprint: Lower left-hand margin

1831 Light Echo

1832 Spiral Galaxy

1833 Mystic Mountain

1834 Jupiter's New Red Spot, 2006

1835 Cat's Eye Nebula

1836 Mars

1837 A Rose of Galaxies

1838 The Pistol Star

1839 Hubble Telescope

25th Anniversary of Launch of Hubble Space Telescope

(Des Two Degrees North. Litho Lowe-Martin, Canada)

2015 (24 Apr). P 13 (C).

1931	**1831**	47p. multicoloured	1·25	1·25
1932	**1832**	57p. multicoloured	1·60	1·60
1933	**1833**	64p. multicoloured	1·75	1·75
1934	**1834**	71p. multi-coloured	2·00	2·00
1935	**1835**	73p. multicoloured	2·00	2·00
1936	**1836**	85p. multicoloured	2·40	2·40
1937	**1837**	95p. multicoloured	2·50	2·50
1938	**1838**	£1.25 multicoloured	3·50	3·50
1931/8 *Set of 8*			15·50	15·50
First Day Cover				16·50
Presentation Pack			16·50	
MS1939 110×75 mm. **1839** £2 multicoloured			5·75	5·75
First Day Cover				7·00
Presentation Pack			7·00	

Plate Nos.: All values 1A (each×5)
Sheets: 10 (5×2)
Imprint: Central, left-hand margin

1840 '9th May 1945' ('The Channel Islands were Liberated on this day')

1841 HMS *Beagle* ('The German occupying forces on Jersey signed the terms of surrender aboard HMS *Beagle*')

1842 Arms and Outline Map of Jersey ('Task Force 135 sailed into St Helier to Liberate the island')

1843 SS *Vega* and Map of its Voyage ('International Red Cross Ship SS *Vega* first arrived in Jersey from Lisbon 31st December 1944')

1844 Royal Square, St. Helier ('V for Victory was defiantly set in the paving stones of St Helier's Royal Square')

1845 *This is your Victory* (Winston Churchill) and Radio ('Churchill addressed the Nation on the Day of Victory')

1846 Winston Churchill, 30 December 1941

50th Death Anniversary of Sir Winston Churchill (1st issue).
70th Anniversary of Victory and Liberation

(Des Hat-Trick Design. Eng Martin Mörck (**MS**1947). Recess and litho
(**MS**1947) or litho (others) Cartor)

2015 (9 May). P 13 (C).

1940	**1840**	47p. multicoloured	1·25	1·25
1941	**1841**	57p. multicoloured	1·60	1·60
1942	**1842**	64p. multicoloured	1·75	1·75
1943	**1843**	73p. multicoloured	2·00	2·00
1944	**1844**	85p. multicoloured	2·40	2·40
1945	**1845**	95p. multicoloured	2·50	2·50
1940/5 *Set of 6*			10·50	10·50
First Day Cover				12·00
Presentation Pack			12·00	
MS1946 150×100 mm. Nos. 1940/5			11·00	11·00
First Day Cover				12·00
Presentation Pack			12·00	
MS1947 131×94 mm. **1846** £3 multicoloured			8·50	8·50
First Day Cover				9·50
Presentation Pack			9·50	

See also Nos. 1969/**MS**1976.
Plate Nos.: All values 1A (each×4)
Sheets: 10 (2×5)
Imprint: Upper right-hand margin

1847 Scales ('*800 Years of Justice*')

1848 Key ('*800 Years of Freedom*')

1849 Fist ('*800 Years of Human Rights*')

1850 Dove ('*800 Years of Liberty*')

1851 Outline Map of Jersey ('*800 Years of Citizenship*')

1852 Cross on Ballot Paper ('*800 Years of Democracy*')

1853 '*800 Years of Magna Carta 1215–2015*'

800th Anniversary of Magna Carta

(Des The Partnership Agency. Litho BDT)

2015 (15 June). P 13½ (1948/53) or 14 (**MS**1954) (C).

1948	**1847**	47p. multicoloured	1·25	1·25
1949	**1848**	57p. multicoloured	1·60	1·60
1950	**1849**	64p. multicoloured	1·75	1·75
1951	**1850**	73p. multicoloured	2·00	2·00
1952	**1851**	85p. multicoloured	2·40	2·40
1953	**1852**	95p. multicoloured	2·50	2·50
1948/53 *Set of 6*			10·50	10·50
First Day Cover				12·00
Presentation Pack			12·00	
MS1954 125×85 mm. **1853** £1.50 black and gold			4·50	4·50
First Day Cover				5·75
Presentation Pack			5·75	

Plate Nos.: All values 1A (each×5)
Sheets: 10 (2×5)
Imprint: Lower right-hand margin

1854 Table Tennis

1855 Archery

1856 Athletics

1857 Sailing

1858 Beach Volleyball

1859 Swimming

1860 Golf

1861 Shooting

1862 Triathlon

1863 Football

1864 Basketball

1865 Tennis

1866 Badminton

1867 Cycling

1868 Mk I Spitfire

1869 Radar

1870 RAF Wings and 'The Few

1871 Target and 'around 1,000 RAF planes were lost during the Battle of Britain. Luftwaffe losses exceeeded 1,800.'

1872 Barrage Balloons and Dome of St. Paul's Cathedral, London

1873 Hawker Hurricane Fighter Planes

Island Games, Jersey

(Litho Enschedé)

2015 (27 June). P 13½×14 (C).

1955	**1854**	(62p.) multicoloured	1·75	1·75
		a. Perf 13½	1·75	1·75
		ab. Booklet pane. Nos. 1955a and 1966a/7a, each×2	10·50	
1956	**1855**	(62p.) multicoloured	1·75	1·75
		a. Perf 13½	1·75	1·75
		ab. Booklet pane. Nos. 1956a and 1962a, each×2	7·00	
1957	**1856**	(62p.) multicoloured	1·75	1·75
		a. Perf 13½	1·75	1·75
		ab. Booklet pane. Nos. 1957a, 1961a and 1968a, each×2	10·50	
1958	**1857**	(62p.) multicoloured	1·75	1·75
		a. Perf 13½	1·75	1·75
		ab. Booklet pane. Nos. 1958a, 1960a and 1963, each×2	10·50	
1959	**1858**	(62p.) multi-coloured	1·75	1·75
		a. Perf 13½	1·75	1·75
		ab. Booklet pane. Nos. 1959a and 1964a/5a, each×2	10·50	
1960	**1859**	(62p.) multicoloured	1·75	1·75
		a. Perf 13½	1·75	1·75
1961	**1860**	(62p.) multicoloured	1·75	1·75
		a. Perf 13½	1·75	1·75
1962	**1861**	(62p.) multicoloured	1·75	1·75
		a. Perf 13½	1·75	1·75
1963	**1862**	(62p.) multicoloured	1·75	1·75
		a. Perf 13½	1·75	1·75
1964	**1863**	(62p.) multicoloured	1·75	1·75
		a. Perf 13½	1·75	1·75
1965	**1864**	(62p.) multicoloured	1·75	1·75
		a. Perf 13½	1·75	1·75
1966	**1865**	(62p.) multicoloured	1·75	1·75
		a. Perf 13½	1·75	1·75
1967	**1866**	(62p.) multicoloured	1·75	1·75
		a. Perf 13½	1·75	1·75
1968	**1867**	(62p.) multicoloured	1·75	1·75
		a. Perf 13½	1·75	1·75
1955/68		Set of 14	22·00	22·00
		First Day Cover		23·00
		Presentation Pack	23·00	

Nos. 1955/68 were all inscr 'POSTCARD' and were originally sold for 62p. each.

Nos. 1955a/68a come from £17.36 Island Games booklet, No. SB76.

All values: 1A (each×4)
Sheets: 10 (5×2)
Imprint: Upper margin

1874 Winston Churchill

50th Death Anniversary of Sir Winston Churchill (2nd issue).
75th Anniversary of the Battle of Britain

(Des Hat-Trick Design. Eng Martin Mörck (**MS**1976). Litho Recess and litho (**MS**1976) or litho (others))

2015 (10 July). P 13×13½ (C).

1969	**1868**	47p. multicoloured	1·25	1·25
1970	**1869**	57p. multicoloured	1·60	1·60
1971	**1870**	64p. multicoloured	1·75	1·75
1972	**1871**	73p. multicoloured	2·00	2·00
1973	**1872**	85p. multicoloured	2·40	2·40
1974	**1873**	95p. multicoloured	2·50	2·50
1969/74		Set of 6	10·50	10·50
		First Day Cover		12·00
		Presentation Pack	12·00	
MS1975		150×100 mm. Nos. 1969/74	11·00	11·00
		First Day Cover		12·00
		Presentation Pack	12·00	
MS1976		131×94 mm. **1874** £3 multicoloured	8·50	8·50
		First Day Cover		9·50
		Presentation Pack	9·50	
		Commemorative Book (Nos. **MS**1947 and **MS**1976)	40·00	

Plate Nos.: All values 1A (each×4)
Sheets: 10 (2×5)
Imprint: Upper right-hand margin

1875 Tank and Cavalryman (Mechanisation)

1876 Military Field Telephone and Signals with Flags (Communication)

1877 Ship painted with Dazzle Pattern (Camouflage and Deception)

1878 Uniforms

1879 Aeroplane and Observation Balloon (Observation)

1880 Helmet and Barbed Wire (Tactics of War)

1881 Flt Lt Charles Stanley Mossop and Wight Seaplane (first sinking of enemy submarine from the air, 1917)

Centenary of the Great War (2nd issue). Change

(Des Chris Ede. Litho Cartor)

2015 (4 Aug). P 13 (C).				
1977	**1875**	47p. multicoloured	1·25	1·25
1978	**1876**	57p. multicoloured	1·60	1·60
1979	**1877**	64p. multicoloured	1·75	1·75
1980	**1878**	73p. multicoloured	2·00	2·00
1981	**1879**	85p. multicoloured	2·40	2·40
1982	**1880**	95p. multicoloured	2·50	2·50
1977/82 *Set of 6*			10·50	10·50
First Day Cover				12·00
Presentation Pack			12·00	
MS1983 165×98 mm. Nos. 1977/82			11·00	11·00
First Day Cover				12·00
Presentation Pack			12·00	
MS1984 131×70 mm. **1881** £1 multicoloured			3·00	3·00
First Day Cover				7·00
Presentation Pack			7·00	

Plate Nos.: All values 1A (each×4)
Sheets: 10 (2×5)
Imprint: Central, left-hand margin

Sark - 450 years as a fief to the Crown
1565-2015

1882 De Carteret Coat of Arms and St. Ouen's Manor, Jersey

450th Anniversary of Island of Sark as a Fief to the Crown

(Des Nick Shewring. Litho BDT)

2015 (6 Aug). Sheet 150×100 mm. P 14×14½ (C).		
MS1985 **1882** £1.50 multicoloured	4·50	4·50
First Day Cover		5·75
Presentation Pack	5·75	

1883 Coronation Portrait (Cecil Beaton)

1884 Silver Jubilee Portrait (Peter Grugeon)

1885 Golden Jubilee Portrait (John Swannell)

1886 Diamond Jubilee Portrait (John Swannell)

1887 The Coronation Theatre, Westminster Abbey: A Portrait of Her Majesty Queen Elizabeth II (Ralph Heimans)

Queen Elizabeth II - Longest Reigning British Monarch

(Litho Cartor)

2015 (9 Sept). P 13½ (**MS**1991) or 13 (others) (both comb.).

1986	**1883**	47p. multicoloured	1·25	1·25
1987	**1884**	57p. multicoloured	1·60	1·60
1988	**1885**	71p. multicoloured	2·00	2·00
1989	**1886**	£1.25 multicoloured	3·50	3·50
1986/9 *Set of 4*			7·50	7·50
First Day Cover				9·00
Presentation Pack			9·00	
MS1990 148×85 mm. Nos. 1986/9			8·25	8·25
First Day Cover				9·00
Presentation Pack			9·00	
MS1991 22×84 mm. **1887** £3 multicoloured			8·50	8·50
First Day Cover				9·50
Presentation Pack			9·50	
*Commemorative Book (No. 1029 with cancellation and Nos.**MS**1990/1)*			45·00	

Plate Nos.: All values 1A (each×4)
Sheets: 10 (5×2)
Imprint: Upper left-hand margin

1888 Magnolia

1889 Camellia

1890 Azalea

1891 Hydrangea

1892 Chrysanthemum

1893 Peony

Links with China. Garden Flowers

(Des Drawn by Martin Mörck. Painted by Wang Huming. Litho Cartor)

2015 (22 Sept). P 13 (C).

1992	**1888**	47p. multicoloured	1·25	1·25
1993	**1889**	47p. multicoloured	1·25	1·25
1994	**1890**	47p. multicoloured	1·25	1·25
1995	**1891**	47p. multicoloured	1·25	1·25
1996	**1892**	47p. multicoloured	1·25	1·25
1997	**1893**	47p. multicoloured	1·25	1·25
1992/7 *Set of 6*			6·75	6·75
First Day Cover				8·50

Presentation Pack		8·50	
MS1998 125×96 mm. Nos. 1996/7		2·50	2·50
First Day Cover			4·75
Presentation Pack		4·75	

Plate Nos.: All values 1A (each×4)
Sheets: 10 (2×5)
Imprint: Lower right-hand margin

1894 Country Lane near St. John's Village

1895 Sun through the Clouds at Corbière

1896 Autumn in the Sand Dune

1897 Stormy Day at Noirmont Point

1898 High Tide Shore Break at St. Catherine's Bay

1899 Sunset at the Radio Tower, St. Brelade

1900 Woodland Path through St. Peter's Valley

1901 Kempt Tower through the Beach Grass, St. Ouen

Jersey Seasons (2nd series). Autumn

(Litho Enschede)

2015 (15 Oct). P 13½ (C).

1999	**1894**	47p. multicoloured	1·25	1·25
2000	**1895**	57p. multicoloured	1·60	1·60
2001	**1896**	64p. multicoloured	1·75	1·75
2002	**1897**	71p. multicoloured	2·00	2·00
2003	**1898**	73p. multicoloured	2·00	2·00
2004	**1899**	85p. multicoloured	2·40	2·40
2005	**1900**	95p. multicoloured	2·50	2·50
2006	**1901**	£1.25 multicoloured	3·50	3·50
1999/2006 *Set of 8*			15·50	15·50
First Day Cover				17·00
Presentation Pack			17·00	

Plate Nos. All values 1A (each×4)
Sheets: 10 (2×5)
Imprint: Upper left-hand margin

1902 Jersey Cow (Millie Foley)

1903 White House, St. Ouen's Bay, and Flowers (Jennifer Crocker)

1904 Sun, Surfboard and Sailing Boat (Matthew Brown)

1905 Girl and Boy Rock Pooling (Leah O'Brien)

1906 Seymour Tower (Anna Le Moine Gray)

1907 Puffin (Sophie Dixon)

1908 Jersey Royal Potato Farming (Ciaran Britton)

1909 Jersey Cow and Calf at Seaside (Allan Giles McCartney)

1910 Corbiére Lighthouse at Sunset (Skye Leather)

1911 Crest of Jersey, Liberation Sculpture, Mont Orgueil Castle and Corbiére Lighthouse (Claudia Dixon)

Greetings Stamps. My Jersey. Winning Designs from Design a Stamp Competition

(Litho Cartor)

2015 (9 Nov). Self-adhesive. Die-cut perf 12×13.

2007	**1902**	(47p.) multicoloured		1·25	1·25
2008	**1903**	(47p.) multicoloured		1·25	1·25
2009	**1904**	(47p.) multicoloured		1·25	1·25
2010	**1905**	(47p.) multicoloured		1·25	1·25
2011	**1906**	(47p.) multicoloured		1·25	1·25
2012	**1907**	(57p.) multicoloured		1·60	1·60
2013	**1908**	(57p.) multicoloured		1·60	1·60
2014	**1909**	(57p.) multicoloured		1·60	1·60
2015	**1910**	(57p.) multicoloured		1·60	1·60
2016	**1911**	(57p.) multicoloured		1·60	1·60
2007/2016 *Set of 10*				13·00	13·00
First Day Cover					14·00
Presentation Pack				14·00	

Nos. 2007/11 were inscr 'Local Letter' and originally sold for 47p. each.
Nos. 2012/16 were inscr 'UK Priority Letter' and originally sold for 57p. each.
Sheets: 50 (5×10). The five designs for each rate were issued together in folded sheets containing ten strips of the five designs

1912 Virgin Mary

1913 Archangel Gabriel

1914 Archangel Gabriel

1915 Virgin Mary

1916 Archangel Gabriel

1917 Virgin Mary

1918 Archangel Gabriel

1919 Virgin Mary

Christmas. Stained Glass Windows by Henry Thomas Bosdet depicting the Annunciation

(Litho Cartor)

2015 (27 Nov). P 13½ (C).

2017	**1912**	42p. multicoloured		1·10	1·10
2018	**1913**	47p. multicoloured		1·25	1·25
2019	**1914**	52p. multicoloured		1·50	1·50
2020	**1915**	57p. multicoloured		1·60	1·60
2021	**1916**	64p. multicoloured		1·75	1·75
2022	**1917**	73p. multicoloured		2·00	2·00
2023	**1918**	95p. multi-coloured		2·50	2·50
2024	**1919**	£1.15 multicoloured		3·00	3·00
2017/2024 *Set of 8*				13·00	13·00
First Day Cover					14·50
Presentation Pack				14·50	

Plate Nos.: All values 1A (each×5)
Sheets: 10 (5×2)
Imprint: Top margin

Post Office Yearbook

2014 (1 Dec). Comprises Nos. 1907/12, 1914/45, **MS**1947/74, **MS**1976/82, MS1984/9, **MS**1991/7 and 1999/2024 (*price £88*)
Yearbook... £175

POST & GO STAMPS

Jersey Post & Go stamps in the Flag design (Type FTJ **1**) were first introduced at Spring Stampex in London on 19 February 2014. They were available from the Philatelic Bureau and appeared at subsequent philatelic events, before being issued at the Broad Street post office, St Helier, on 4 September 2014.

FTJ **1** Jersey Flag

Jersey Flag

(Des True North. Gravure Walsall)

2014 (14 Sept). Multicoloured. Self-adhesive. Thermally printed service indicator. P 14×14½.

FSJ1	(Local Letter up to 100g)	2·00	2·00
FSJ2	(UK Letter up to 100g)	2·25	2·25
FSJ3	(Europe up to 20g)	2·50	2·50
FSJ4	(Local Large up to 100g)	2·75	2·75
FSJ5	(International up to 20g)	3·25	3·25
FSJ6	(UK Large up to 100g)	3·75	3·75
FSJ1/6 Set of 6		15·00	15·00
First Day Cover			16·00
Presentation Pack			16·00

Nos. FSJ1/6 were subsequently issued from Broad Street post office, inscribed 'Merry Christmas' and 'Churchill 24.1.65' and with other inscriptions and at stamp exhibitions and at Jersey Post Headquarters. These are outside the scope of this catalogue.

Royal Mail Post & Go stamps with Jersey inscriptions and Jersey stamps with UK 'values' are, similarly, not listed.

FTJ **2** Agile Frog

Jersey Protected Species

(Des Andrew Beckett. Gravure Walsall)

2015 (18 Feb). Multicoloured. Self-adhesive. Thermally printed service indicator. P 14×14½.

FSJ7	(Local Letter up to 100g)	2·00	2·00
FSJ8	(UK Letter up to 100g)	2·25	2·25
FSJ9	(Europew up to 20g)	2·50	2·50
FSJ10	(Local Large up to 100g)	2·75	2·75
FSJ11	(International up to 20g)	3·25	3·25
FSJ12	(UK Large up to 100g)	3·75	3·75
FSJ7/12 Set of 6		15·00	15·00
First Day Cover			16·00
Presentation Pack			16·00

Nos. FSJ7/12 were available in six different designs: Type FTJ **2**, Red Squirrel, Green Lizard, Hedgehog, Barn Owl and Puffin.

COMMEMORATIVE POSTAL STATIONERY ENVELOPE

40th Anniversary of Liberation

1985 (7 May). Cover showing imprinted stamp design as No. 36. Sold at 25p.

PS1	13p. multicoloured	1·00	2·00

Quantity sold: 79,744.
Sold out: 6.85.

POSTAGE DUE STAMPS

D **1** D **2** Map D **3** Map

(Des F. Guenier. Litho Bradbury, Wilkinson)

1969 (1 Oct). P 14×13½ (C).

D1	D **1**	1d. bluish violet (ab)	65	1·10
D2		2d. sepia (ad)	90	1·10
D3		3d. magenta (ad)	1·00	1·10
D4	D **2**	1s. bright emerald (acd)	5·50	5·00
D5		2s.6d. olive-grey (acd)	13·00	14·00
D6		5s. vermilion (ad)	15·00	16·00
D1/6 Set of 6			32·00	35·00

Sheets: 120 (2 panes 6×10).
Imprint: Central, bottom margin.
Printings: (a) 1.10.69; (b) 16.12.69; (c) 18.2.70; (d) 6.6.70.
Quantities sold: 1d. 98,535; 2d. 181,601; 3d. 155,832; 1s. 174,599; 2s.6d. 205,962; 5s. 200,698.
Withdrawn and Invalidated: 14.2.72.

Decimal Currency

(Des F. Guenier. Litho Bradbury, Wilkinson)

1971 (15 Feb)–75. P 14×13½ (C).

D7	D **3**	½p. black (a)	10	10
D8		1p. violet-blue (a)	10	10
D9		2p. olive-grey (a)	10	10
D10		3p. reddish purple (a)	10	10
D11		4p. pale red (a)	10	10
D12		5p. bright emerald (a)	10	10
D13		6p. yellow-orange (b)	10	10
D14		7p. bistre-yellow (b)	10	10
D15		8p. light greenish blue (c)	15	20
D16		10p. pale olive-grey (a)	15	20
D17		11p. ochre (a)	30	35
D18		14p. violet (a)	40	50
D19		25p. myrtle-green (b)	45	90
D20		50p. dull purple (a)	1·10	1·70
D7/20 Set of 14			3·00	4·50
Presentation Pack			5·00	

Printings: (a) 15.2.71; (b) 12.8.74; (c) 1.5.75.
Plate Nos.: 3p. 1a, 1d; 8p., 25p. 1b, 1c, 1d; 11p. 1a, 1b, 1d; others 1a, 1b, 1c, 1d.
Sheets: 50 (5×10).
Quantities sold: ½p. 313,604; 1p. 281,598; 2p. 205,263; 3p. 183,353; 4p. 180,948; 5p. 199,771; 6p. 161,580; 7p. 156,534; 8p. 154,904; 10p. 198,530; 11p. 151,638; 14p. 147,075; 25p. 158,663; 50p. 146,602.
Imprint: Central, bottom margin.
Withdrawn: 31.1.79.

D **4** Arms of St. Clement and Dovecote at Samares

D **5** Arms of St. Lawrence and Handois Reservoir

D **6** Arms of St. John and Sorel Point

D **7** Arms of St. Ouen and Pinnacle Rock

D **8** Arms of St. Peter and Quetivel Mill

D **9** Arms of St. Martin and St. Catherine's Breakwater

D **10** Arms of Harbour and St. Heller

D **11** Arms of St. Saviour and Highlands College

D **12** Arms of St. Brelade and Beauport Bay

D **13** Arms of Grouville and La Hougue Bie

D **14** Arms of St. Mary and Perry Farm

D **15** Arms of Trinity and Bouley Bay

Parish Arms and Views

(Des G. Drummond. Litho Questa)

1978 (17 Jan). P 14 (C).

D21	D **4**	1p. blue-green and black	10	10
D22	D **5**	2p. orange-yellow and black	10	10
D23	D **6**	3p. lake-brown and black	10	10
D24	D **7**	4p. orange-vermilion and black	10	10
D25	D **8**	5p. ultramarine and black	10	10
D26	D **9**	10p. brown-olive and black	10	10
D27	D **10**	12p. greenish blue and black	15	10
D28	D **11**	14p. red-orange and black	20	15
D29	D **12**	15p. bright magenta and black	25	30
D30	D **13**	20p. yellow-green and black	30	40

D31	D **14**	50p. deep brown and black	90	80
D32	D **15**	£1 chalky blue and black	1·40	1·40

D21/32 Set of 12 .... 3·25 3·25
Presentation Pack .... 3·75

Nos.: All values 1A–1A, 1B–1B, 1C–1C, 1D–1D, 1E–1E, 1F–1F.
Sheets: 50 (10×5).
Imprint: Right-hand corner, bottom margin.
Withdrawn: 30.9.83.

D **16** St. Brelade
D **17** St. Aubin
D **18** Rozel
D **19** Greve de Lecq

D **20** Bouley Bay
D **21** St. Catherine
D **22** Gorey
D **23** Bonne Nuit

D **24** La Rocque
D **25** St. Helier
D **26** Ronez
D **27** La Collette

D **28** Elizabeth Castle
D **29** Upper Harbour Marina

Jersey Harbours

(Des G. Drummond. Litho Questa)

1982 (7 Sept). P 14 (C).

D33	D **16**	1p. brt turquoise-green & black	10	10
D34	D **17**	2p. chrome yellow and black	10	10
D35	D **18**	3p. lake-brown and black	10	10
D36	D **19**	4p. red and black	10	10
D37	D **20**	5p. bright blue and black	10	10
D38	D **21**	6p. yellow-olive and black	10	15
D39	D **22**	7p. reddish mauve and black	15	20
D40	D **23**	8p. bright orange-red and black	15	20
D41	D **24**	9p. bright green and black	20	20
D42	D **25**	10p. turquoise-blue and black	20	20
D43	D **26**	20p. apple-green and black	40	40
D44	D **27**	30p. bright purple and black	60	60
D45	D **28**	40p. dull orange and black	80	80
D46	D **29**	£1 bright reddish violet & black	2·00	2·00

D33/46 Set of 14 .... 4·50 4·50
Presentation Pack .... 4·75

Plate Nos.: All values 1A, 1B, 1C, 1D, 1E, 1F, 1G, 1H (each×2).
Sheets: 50 (10×5).
Imprint: Right-hand corner, bottom margin.
Sold out: By 10.2005.

STAMP BOOKLETS

PRICES given are for complete booklets. All booklets are stitched unless otherwise stated.

B **1** Map

1969 (1 Oct)–**70**. 2s. Booklet. Blue cover as Type B **1**, 54×41 mm.
SB1   Containing 5×4d. (No. 19a), 4×1d. (No. 16a), all in panes of one with wide margins .... 2·00

B **2** Arms and Royal Mace

*7s. Booklet. Yellow cover as Type B **2**, 50×56 mm*
SB2   Containing 12×4d. (No. 19), 6×5d. (No. 20), 6×1d. (No. 16b), all in vertical pairs .... 13·00
SB2a   Containing 12×4d. (No. 19b), 6×5d. (No. 20a), 6×1d. (No. 16), all in vertical pairs (5.5.70) £130

*10s. Booklet. Pink cover as Type B **2** showing Mont Orgueil Castle, 50×55 mm*
SB3   Containing 14×4d. (No. 19), 12×5d. (No. 20), 4×1d. (No. 16b), all in vertical pairs .... 10·00
SB3a   Containing 14×4d. (No. 19b), 12×5d. (No. 20a), 4×1d. (No. 16), all in vertical pairs (5.5.70) .... 40·00

Special printings in sheets of 48 were made for manufacturing the 2s. booklets, but the 7s. and 10s. booklets were made up from ordinary sheets, using vertical pairs with stitching through the side margins. Stamps from both sides of the sheet were utilised so that the panes come either upright or inverted.

Decimal Currency

1971 (15 Feb).
*10p. Booklet. Blue cover as Type B **1** showing Martello Tower, 54×41 mm*
SB4   Containing 2×½p. (No. 42a), 2×2p. (No. 45a) and 2×2½p. (No. 46a). Each stamp with wide margin at bottom .... 1·00
SB4a   Containing 2×½p. (No. 42a), 2×2p. (No. 45a) and 2×2½p. (No. 46a). Each stamp with wide margin at top .... 2·75

*35p. Booklet. Yellow cover as Type B **2** showing The Royal Court, 50×56 mm*
SB5   Containing 10×2p. (No. 45) and 6×2½p. (No. 46) .... 1·20

*50p. Booklet. Pink cover as Type B **2** showing Elizabeth Castle, 50×56 mm*
SB6   Containing 10×2p (No. 45) and 12×2½p. (No. 46) .... 1·70

The panes for Nos. SB4/a were produced in sheets of 48, of which half were tête-bêche. In consequence, half the booklets have the blank margin at the bottom (SB4), and the other half at the top (SB4a).

Owing to the postal information printed in the booklets being out of date, supplies of Nos. SB4/a dispensed from machines between 10 July and early September 1972 bore an adhesive label on the front with the words 'RATE TO UNITED KINGDOM LETTERS' up to 4 ozs. and postcards 3p. in two lines. They were primarily to warn holiday-makers of the new rate and were issued only through the machines. Of these about 52,000 were sold.

Quantities sold: SB4/a 244,544; SB5 20,875; SB6 17,638.

1972 (15 May).
*20p. Booklet. Green cover as Type B **2** showing Jersey Cow, 50×56 mm*
SB7   Containing 8×2½p. (No. 46), all in vertical pairs .... 2·20

*30p. Booklet. Yellow cover as Type B **2** showing Portelet Bay, 50×56 mm*
SB8   Containing 10×3p. (No. 47), all in vertical pairs .... 25·00

*50p. Booklet. Pink cover as Type B **2** showing La Corbière Lighthouse, 50×56 mm*
SB9   Containing 8×2½p. (No. 46) and 10×3p. (No. 47), all in vertical pairs .... 1·70

1972 (1 Dec). 10p. Booklet. Orange cover as Type B **1** showing Legislative Chamber, 54×41 mm.
SB10   Containing 3×½p. (No. 42a), 1×2½p. (No. 45a) and 2×3p. (No. 47a). Each stamp with wide margin at bottom 90

SB10a   As SB10 but with margin at top 90
        Quantity sold: 126,877.
1973 (1 June). 10p. Booklet. Green cover as Type B **1** showing Mont Orgueil by night, 54×41 mm.
SB11   Contents as No. SB10. Each stamp with wide
            margin at bottom 90
SB11a   As SB11 but with margin at top 90
        Quantity sold: 109,129.

1973 (10 Sept).
        *20p. Booklet. Grey cover as Type B **2** showing Jersey Wildlife
        Preservation Trust species, 50×56 mm*
SB12   Containing 8×2½p. (No. 46) .... 2·50
        *30p. Booklet. Buff cover as Type B **2** showing
        Jersey Wild Flowers, 50×56 mm*
SB13   Containing 10×3p. (No. 47) .... 2·50
        *50p. Booklet. Blue cover as Type B **2** showing 'English Fleet
        in the Channel' by Peter Monamy, 50×56 mm*
SB14   Containing 8×2½p. (No. 46) and 10×3p.
            (No. 47) .... 2·00
        Quantites sold: SB12 8,790; SB13 11,450; SB14 14,145.

1974 (7 Jan). Jersey Wildlife Preservation Trust.
        *20p. Booklet. Green cover as Type B **2** showing
        Spectacled Bear, 50×56 mm*
SB15   Containing 8×2½p. (No. 46) .... 1·50
        *30p. Booklet. Yellow cover as Type B **2** showing
        White-eared Pheasant, 50×56 mm*
SB16   Containing 10×3p. (No. 47) .... 1·50
        *50p. Booklet. Red cover as Type B **2** showing
        Thick-billed Parrot, 50×56 mm*
SB17   Containing 8×2½p. (No. 46) and 10×3p.
            (No. 47) .... 2·20
        Quantities sold: SB15 14,283; SB16 14,049; SB17 15,976.

1974 (1 July). 10p. Booklet. Orange cover as Type B **1** showing Jersey Airport, 54×41 mm.
SB18   Containing 1×3p. (No. 47a) and 2×3½p.
            (No. 48a). Each stamp with wide margin at
            bottom 60
SB18a   As SB18 but with margin at top 60
        Quantity sold: 129,235.

1974 (1 July). Jersey Wildlife Preservation Trust. 60p. Booklet. Pink cover as Type B **2** showing Ring-tailed Lemur, 51×56 mm.
SB19   Containing 6×3p. (No. 47) and 12×3½p.
            (No. 48) .... 2·00
        Quantity sold: 22,274.

1974 (1 Oct). Jersey Wildlife Preservation Trust. 60p. Booklet. Green cover as Type B **2** showing Tuatara Lizard, 51×56 mm.
SB20   Contents as No. SB19 .... 2·00
        Quantity sold: 20,984.

B **3** Artillery Shako

1975 (25 Feb). Military Headgear.
        *10p. Booklet. Grey cover as Type B **3**, 54×41 mm*
SB21   Containing 1×½p. (No. 42a, 2×3p. (No. 47a)
            and 1×3½p. (No. 48a). Each stamp with wide
            margin at bottom 50
SB21a   As SB21 but with margin at top 50
        *20p. Booklet. Rose cover as Type B **3** showing Shako,
        2nd North Regt, 54×41 mm*
SB22   Containing 2×3p. (No. 47a) and 4×3½p. (No. 48a).
            Each stamp with wide margin at bottom 60
SB22a   As SB22 but with margin at top 50
        Quantities sold: SB21/a 37,849; SB22/a 38,854.

STAMP SACHETS These are booklet covers with the stamps loose inside and contained in clear plastic sachets. They are noted but not priced as such items are outside the scope of this checklist.

B **4** Post Office Crest

1975 (1 Apr). 20p. Stamp Sachet. Red cover as Type B **4**, 54×40 mm. Containing 2×1p. (No. 43), 2×4p. (No. 49) and 2×5p. (No. 50).

B **5** Astra Biplane (*Illustration reduced. Actual size 94×56 mm*)

1975 (21 Apr). Aviation History. Pale blue cover (SB23) or yellow cover (SB24).
        *50p. Booklet as Type B **2** showing Supermarine Sea Eagle*
SB23   Containing 6×1p. (No. 43), 6×4p. (No. 49) and
            4×5p. (No. 50) .... 1·70
        *£1 Booklet as Type B **5**, 94×56 mm*
SB24   Containing 8×1p. (No. 43), 8×4p. (No. 49) and
            12×5p. (No. 50) .... 3·00
        Quantites sold: SB23 29,872; SB24 29,608.

1976 (29 Jan). 20p. Stamp Sachet. Blue cover as Type B **4**, 52×41 mm. Containing 3×1p. (No. 138), 2×5p. (No. 139) and 1×7p. (No. 141).

B **6** Trinity Parish Crest (*Illustration reduced. Actual size 89×66 mm*)

1976 (5 Apr). Green cover (SB25) or magenta cover (SB26) as Type B **6**, 89×66 mm.
        50p. Booklet. Trinity Parish Crest
SB25   Containing booklet panes Nos. 138a, 139a and 141a ... 1·50
        £1 Booklet. St. Ouen's Parish Crest
SB26   Containing booklet panes Nos. 138b, 139a×2
            and 141a×2 .... 2·50
        Quantities sold: SB25 85,210; SB26 64,609.
1976 (2 Nov). 20p. Stamp Sachet. Green cover as Type B **4**, 53×40 mm.
            Containing 3×1p, 2×5p. and 1×7p. (Nos. 138/9
            and 141) ....
1977 (29 Sept). 20p. Stamp Sachet. Brown cover as Type B **4**, 53×40 mm.
            Containing 3×1p, 2×5p. and 1×7p. (Nos. 138/9
            and 141) ....

1978 (28 Feb). Orange-red cover (SB27) or pale blue cover (SB28) as Type B **6**, 90×65 mm.
        £1 Booklet. Grouville Parish Arms
SB27   Containing booklet panes Nos. 138b and
            140a×4 .... 2·50
        £1 Booklet. St. Saviour Parish Arms
SB28   Containing booklet panes Nos. 138b and
            142a×3 .... 2·50
        Quantities sold: SB27 43,446; SB28 45,015.

1978 (1 May). 30p. Stamp Sachet. Violet cover as Type B **4**, 53×40 mm.

Containing 2×1p., 2×6p. and 2×8p. (Nos. 138, 140 and 142)..

1979 (13 Aug). 30p. Stamp Sachet. Purple cover as Type B **4**.

Containing 2×1p., 2×6p. and 2×8p. (Nos. 138, 140 and 142)..

B **7** Jersey Post Office Headquarters, Mont Millais, St. Helier (*Illustration reduced. Actual size* 90×65 mm)

1979 (1 Oct). Bistre-brown on buff cover as Type B **7**. Stapled.
SB29   £1.20 booklet containing Nos. 138b, 140a and 142a each×2 .... 3·50
    Quantity sold: 82,738.

1980 (6 May). Black on red cover as Type B **6** showing St. Helier Parish Arms, 90×65 mm. Stapled.
SB30   £1.40 booklet containing Nos. 138b×3, 141a×2 and 143a×2 .... 4·00
    Quantity sold: 29,900.

1980 (6 May). 20p. Stamp Sachet. Black on red cover as Type B **4**, 53×40 mm.

Containing 4×1p., 1×7p. and 1×9p. (Nos. 138, 141 and 143).

1981 (24 Feb). Black on blue cover as Type B **6**, but 82×65 mm, showing De Bagot crest. Stapled.
SB31   £1.32 booklet containing Nos. 250a×2, 252a, 256a and 259a.. 4·00
    Quantity sold: 49,486.

1981 (24 Feb). 20p Stamp Sachet. Black on blue cover as Type B **4**, 52×40 mm.

Containing 2×3p. and 2×7p. (Nos. 252 and 256)..

1981 (1 Dec). Black on green cover as Type B **6**, but 82×65 mm, showing Poingdestre Arms. Stapled.
SB32   £1.20 booklet containing Nos. 250a, 251a, 256a and 259a.. 3·50
    Quantity sold: 43,434.

B **8** Jean Martell (*Illustration reduced. Actual size* 155×80 mm)

Martell Cognac

(Des Jersey Post Office)

1982 (7 Sept). Multicoloured cover 155×80 mm, as Type B **8**. Booklet contains text and Illustrations on labels attached to panes and on interleaving pages.
SB33   £3.08 booklet containing Nos. 293b, 295b and 297b each×2 .... 7·00
    Quantity sold: 54,654.

1983 (19 Apr). Black on orange-red cover as Type B **6**, but 82×65 mm, showing Bisson crest. Stapled.
SB34   £1.32 booklet containing Nos. 250a, 251a, 257a and 260a.. 3·50
    Quantity sold: 29,393.

1983 (19 Apr). 20p. Stamp Sachet. Black on turquoise-green cover as Type B **4**.

Containing 2×½p., 1×8p. and 1×11p. (Nos. 249, 257 and 260)....................................

1984 (3 Jan). 30p. Stamp Sachet. Black on pink cover as Type B **4**.

Containing 2×9p. and 1×12p. (Nos. 258 and 261)..

1984 (27 Apr). Black on rose-lilac cover as Type B **6**, but 80×65 mm, showing Robin crest. Stapled.
SB35   £2.16 booklet containing Nos. 252ba×2, 258ab×2 and 261ab.   6·00
    Quantity sold: 38,782.

1985 (15 Apr). 50p. Stamp Sachet. Black on light green cover as Type B **4**.

Containing 1×1p., 3×3p. and 4×10p. (Nos. 250, 252b and 259)....................................

B **9** Cross of Lorraine (*Illustration reduced. Actual size* 155×80 mm)

300th Anniversary of Huguenot Immigration

(Des Jersey Post Office)

1985 (10 Sept). Multicoloured cover, 155×80 mm, as Type B **9**.
SB36   £3.60 booklet containing Nos. 370a/5a............................. 9·00
    Quantity sold: 31,042.

1986 (1 Apr). Black on carmine cover as Type B **6**, but 81×65 mm, showing Messervy crest. Stapled.
SB37   £3.12 booklet containing Nos. 251ba, 259ba and 263ab, each×2.. 8·00
    Quantity sold 23,729.
    Withdrawn: 31.3.91.

B **10** Post Office Emblem (*Illustration reduced. Actual size* 52×40 mm)

1986 (1 Apr). 50p. Stamp Sachet. Black and orange-vermilion cover as Type B **10**, 52×40 mm.

Containing 1×2p., 2×4p. and 4×10p. (Nos. 251b, 253a and 259)....................................

1987 (6 Apr). Black on blue cover as Type B **6**, but 81×65 mm, showing Fiott crest. Stapled.
SB38   £3.60 booklet containing Nos. 253ab, 260ba and 264ab, each×2.. 8·50
    Quantity sold: 23,647.
    Withdrawn: 31.3.91.

1987 (6 Apr). 50p. Stamp Sachet. Black and orange-vermilion cover as Type B **10**.

Containing 1×2p., 1×3p., 3×4p. and 3×11p. (Nos. 251b, 252b, 253a and 260) ....

B **11** Vikings (*Illustration reduced. Actual size* 168×80 mm)

900th Death Anniversary of William the Conqueror

(Des Jersey Post Office)

1987 (16 Oct). Multicoloured cover, 168×80 mm, as Type B **11**. Booklet contains text and Illustrations on labels attached to panes and on interleaving pages.

SB39   £5.50 booklet containing Nos. 422a/7a............................ 15·00
          Quantity sold: 30,107.
          Sold out: 4.88.

1988 (17 May). Black on bright green cover as Type B **6**, but 81×56 mm, showing Malet crest. Stapled.

SB40   £3.84 booklet containing Nos. 253ab, 261ab and
          265a, each×2 .... 10·00
          Quantity sold: 16,566.
          Withdrawn: 31.3.91.

1988 (17 May). 50p. Stamp Sachet. Black and orange-vermilion cover as Type B **10**, 52×40 mm.
          Containing 1×2p., 3×4p. and 3×12p.
          (Nos. 251b, 253a and 261)..

B **12** Chouan Rebels (*Illustration reduced. Actual size* 155×80 *mm*)

Bicentenary of the French Revolution. Philippe D'Auvergne

(Des Jersey Post Office)

1989 (7 July). Multicoloured cover, 155×80 mm, as Type B **12**. Booklet contains text on labels attached to panes and on interleaving pages.

SB41   £6 booklet containing Nos. 501a/6a............................ 16·00
          Quantity sold: 31,052.
          Sold out: 7.8.99.

B **13** Flags of Jersey and Great Britain (*Illustration reduced. Actual size* 108×63 *mm*)

'Stamp World London 90' International Stamp Exhibition

1990 (3 May). Multicoloured cover, 108×63 mm, as Type B **13**.

SB42   £4.20 booklet containing Nos. 470a, 474a and 478a,
          each×2.. 10·00
          Withdrawn: 30.6.96.

B **14** (*Illustration reduced. Actual size* 52×41 *mm*)

1990 (3 May). 50p. Stamp Sachet. Multicoloured cover as Type B **14**, 52×41 mm, showing 18p. stamp (No. 478).
          Containing 2×4p. and 3×14p. (Nos. 470 and 474)..

B **15** Elizabeth Castle (*Illustration reduced. Actual size* 108×63 *mm*)

1991 (12 Feb). Jersey Scenes. Multicoloured, cover 108×63 mm, as Type B **15**.

SB43   £4.80 booklet containing Nos. 471a, 475a and 480a,
          each×2.. 11·50
          Withdrawn: 30.6.96.

1992 (25 Feb). £1 Stamp Sachet. Multicoloured cover as Type B **14**, 53×41 mm, showing design of 22p. stamp (No. 480).
          Containing 1×2p., 2×16p., 3×22p. (Nos. 467, 474 and 480)..

B **16** William Mesny on Horseback (*Illustration reduced. Actual size* 155×80 *mm*)

Jersey Adventures (3rd series). 150th Birth Anniversary of William Mesny

(Des Jersey Post Office)

1992 (25 Feb). Multicoloured cover, 155×80 mm, as Type B **16**. Booklet contains text on labels attached to panes and on interleaving pages.

SB44   £5.50 booklet containing Nos. 573b/8a .... 12·00
          Withdrawn: 30.6.96.

B **17** Jersey Post Logo (*Illustration reduced. Actual size* 67×52 *mm*)

1992 (25 May). Covers as Type B **17**, 67×52 mm. Panes attached by selvedge.

SB45   £1.12 booklet (scarlet on white cover) containing
          No. 474b.. 2·75
SB46   £1.28 booklet (bright yellow on scarlet cover)
          containing No. 476a.. 3·50
SB47   £1.76 booklet (scarlet on bright yellow cover)
          containing No. 482a.. 4·50
          Withdrawn: 30.6.96.

1993 (11 Jan). Covers as Type B **17**, 67×53 mm. Panes attached by selvedge.

SB48   (£1.36) booklet (bright yellow on green cover)
          containing pane No. 601a....................................... 5·00
SB49   (£1.84) booklet (scarlet on flesh cover) containing
          pane No. 605a... 5·50
SB50   (£2.24) booklet (white on bright new blue cover)
          containing pane No. 609a....................................... 7·00

Face values quoted for each booklet are those at which they were initially sold. The price of No. SB48 was increased to £1.44 and that of No. SB50 to £2.40 on 10 January 1994. No. SB48 was sold at £1.52 from 4 July 1995. On 10 March 1997, No. SB48 was increased to £1.60, No. SB49 to £1.92 and No. SB50 to £2.48.

Withdrawn: 30.9.99.

B **18** Invasion Map (*Illustration reduced. Actual size 162×98 mm*)

50th Anniversary of D-Day

(Des A. Theobald)

1994 (6 June). Multicoloured cover, 162×98 mm, as Type B **18**. Booklet contains text and illustrations on panes and interleaving pages.

SB51   £5.68 booklet containing Nos. 659a/b, 661a and 663a ..   17·00
Sold out: 12.94.

B **19** 'Greetings from JERSEY' (*Illustration reduced. Actual size 152×75 mm*)

Greetings Stamps

1995 (24 Jan). Multicoloured cover, 152×75 mm, as Type B **19**. Pane attached by selvedge.

SB52   £2.24 booklet containing pane No. 684b ....   6·50
Quantity sold: 65,810.
Withdrawn: 30.9.99.

B **20** Crowd Celebrating (*Illustration reduced. Actual size 162×97 mm*)

50th Anniversary of Liberation

(Des A. Theobald)

1995 (9 May). Multicoloured cover, 162×97 mm, as Type B **20**. Booklet contains text and illustrations on panes and interleaving pages.

SB53   £7.06 booklet containing Nos. 700a, 702a, 704a and
         MS706a ....   15·00

B **21** Mont Orgueil Castle, Gorey (*Illustration reduced. Actual size 164×97 mm*)

Tourism

(Des A. Copp)

1996 (8 June). Multicoloured cover, 164×97 mm, as Type B **21**. Booklet contains text and illustrations on panes and interleaving pages.

SB54   £8.32 booklet containing Nos. 752a/b, 754a and
         756a ....   17·00

B **22** Island Sports (*Illustration reduced. Actual size 163×98 mm*)

Seventh Island Games, Jersey

(Des A. Theobald)

1997 (28 June). Multicoloured cover, 163×98 mm, as Type B **22**. Booklet contains text and illustrations on panes and interleaving pages.

SB55   £8.72 booklet containing Nos. 818a/b, 820a and
         822a ....   18·00

B **23** Buses in Royal Square, St. Helier (*Illustration reduced. Actual size 164×98 mm*)

75th Anniversary of Jersey Motor Transport Company. Buses

(Des A. Copp)

1998 (2 Apr). Multicoloured cover, 164×98 mm, as Type B **23**. Booklet contains text and illustrations on panes and interleaving pages.

SB56   £8.72 booklet containing Nos. 844a/b, 846a and
         848a ....   18·00

B **24** Four Vintage Humbers at the Weighbridge, 1905 (*Illustration reduced. Actual size 164×98 mm*)

Centenary of Motoring in Jersey

(Des A. Copp)

1999 (2 July). Multicoloured cover, 164×98 mm, as Type B **24**. Booklet contains text and illustrations on panes and interleaving pages.

SB57   £8.80 booklet containing Nos. 905a/b, 907a and
         909a ....   19·00

B **25** Full-rigged Sailing Ship (*Illustration reduced. Actual size 164×100 mm*)

'The Stamp Show 2000' International Stamp Exhibition, London. Maritime Heritage

(Des A. Theobald)

2000 (22 May). Multicoloured cover, 164×100 mm, as Type B **25**. Booklet contains text and illustrations on interleaving pages. Stitched.
SB58   £9.60 booklet containing Nos. 936b/e and 937a ....   20·00

B **26** Two Tawny Owls on Gate (*Illustration reduced. Actual size 164×101 mm*)

Birds of Prey

(Des M. Chester)

2001 (3 July). Multicoloured cover, 164×101 mm, as Type B **26**. Booklet contains text and illustrations on panes and interleaving pages. Stitched.
SB59   £10.76 booklet containing Nos. 999a/d and **MS**1005a   23·00
     Sold out: By 7.2007.

B **27** Bells (*Illustration reduced. Actual size 83×60 mm*)

Christmas

2001 (6 Nov). Multicoloured cover, 83×60 mm, as Type B **27**. Self-adhesive.
SB60   £3.92 booklet containing No. 1014a ....   9·00
     Sold out: By 6.2003.

B **28** Mickey Mouse Float (*Illustration reduced. Actual size 165×100 mm*)

Centenary of 'Battle of Flowers' Parade

(Des M. Polland)

2002 (8 Aug). Multicoloured cover, 165×100 mm, as Type B **28**. Booklet contains text and illustrations on panes and interleaving pages. Stitched.
SB61   £9.35 booklet containing Nos. 1053a×3 and
         MS1059a ....   20·00

B **29** Ellehammer's Biplane and Space Shuttle (*Illustration reduced. Actual size 164×100 mm*)

Centenary of Powered Flight

(Des A. Theobald)

2003 (21 Jan). Multicoloured cover, 164×100 mm, as Type B **29**. Booklet contains text and illustrations on panes and interleaving pages. Stitched.
SB62   £9.35 booklet containing No. 1074a×3, with different
         marginal illustrations, and **MS**1080a ....   23·00

B **30** Paphiopedilum chamberlainianum (*Illustration reduced. Actual size 165×100 mm*)

Jersey Orchids (5th series)

(Des The Partnership)

2004 (25 May). Multicoloured cover, 165×100 mm, as Type B **30**. Booklet contains text and illustrations on panes and interleaving pages. Stitched.
SB63   £10.73 booklet containing No. 1143a×3 and
         MS1149a..   35·00

B **31** Jaguar E Type (*Illustration reduced. Actual size 165×100 mm*)

Jersey Festivals (2nd issue). Motor Festival. Classic Cars

(Des A. Copp)

2005 (6 June). Multicoloured cover, 165×100 mm, as Type B **31**. Booklet contains text and illustrations on panes and interleaving pages. Stitched.
SB64   £8.61 booklet containing No. 1204a×3 ....   18·00

B **32** Jersey Post Vehicles (*Illustration reduced. Actual size 164×100 mm*)

Jersey Postal History (2nd series). Postal Vehicles

(Des A. Theobald)

2006 (31 Oct). Multicoloured cover, 164×100 mm, as Type B **32**. Booklet contains text and illustrations on panes and interleaving pages. Stitched.

SB65   £10.67 booklet containing No. 1286a×3 and **MS**1292a.   22·00

B **33** Concorde (*Illustration reduced. Actual size 164×100 mm*)

60th Anniversary of Jersey International Air Display

(Des A. Theobald)

2007 (13 Sept). Multicoloured cover, 164×100 mm, as Type B **33**. Booklet contains text and illustrations on panes and interleaving pages. Stitched.

SB66   £11.35 booklet containing Nos. 1326a×3 and **MS**1332a ....   23·00

B **34** HMS Richmond (*Illustration reduced. Actual size 165×100 mm*)

Jersey Naval Connections (2nd series). Visiting Naval Vessels

(Des A. Theobald)

2008 (24 June). Multicoloured cover, 165×100 mm, as Type B **34**. Booklet contains text and illustrations on panes and interleaving pages. Stitched.

SB67   £11.59 booklet containing panes Nos. 1380×3 and **MS**1386a...   34·00

B **35** Locomotive *Caesarea* (*Illustration reduced. Actual size 150×100 mm*)

Jersey Railways (3rd issue)

(Des A. Theobald)

2009 (6 May). Multicoloured cover, 150×100 mm, as Type B **35**, 164×100 mm. Booklets contain text and illustrations on panes and interleaving pages. Stitched.

SB68   £12.60 booklet containing panes Nos. 1433a×3 and **MS**1439a...   37·00

B **36** Royal Charlotte (*Illustration reduced. Actual size 164×100 mm*)

Postal History (4th series). Mail Ships

(Des A. Theobald)

2010 (8 May). Multicoloured cover, 164×100 mm, as Type B **36**. Booklet contains text and illustrations on panes and interleaving pages. Stitched.

SB69   £13.53 booklet containing panes Nos. 1503a×3 and **MS**1510a...   40·00

B **37** Roebuck on Les Kaines Rock (*Illustration reduced. Actual size 164×100 mm*)

Shipwrecks

(Des A. Theobald)

2011 (12 July). Multicoloured cover, 164×100 mm, as Type B **37**. Booklet contains text and illustrations on panes and interleaving pages. Stitched.

SB70   £14.22 booklet containing panes Nos. 1592a×3 and **MS**1598a...   42·00

B **38** Jersey Airport

Aviation History (11th series). 75th Anniversary of Jersey Airport

(Des A. Theobald)

2012 (10 Mar). Multicoloured cover, 165×100 mm as Type B **38**. Booklet contains text and illustrations on panes and interleaving pages. Stitched.

SB71   £13.95 booklet containing panes Nos. 1643a×3 and **MS**1649a...   38·00

B **39**

B **42** Emblem

'Simply Jersey'. Landmarks

2012 (8 May). Vermilion (SB72) or grey (SB73) covers, 86×59 mm as Type B **39**. Self-adhesive.

SB72 (£4.50) booklet containing No. 1658a................................ 12.00
SB73 (£5.50) booklet containing No. 1661a................................ 14.00

Island Games, Jersey

2015 (27 Jun). Multicoloured cover, 164×101 mm, as Type B **42**. Stitched.

SB76 £17.36 booklet containing panes Nos. 1955ab/9ab 45.00

B **40** Abbot FV433 Armoured Fighting Vehicle (1970s) near Mont Orgueil Castle, Grouville Bay (*Illustration reduced. Actual size 165×101 mm*)

Military Vehicles

(Des A. Copp)

2013 (30 Aug). Military Vehicles. Multicoloured cover, 165×101 mm, as Type B **40**. Booklet contains text and illustrations on panes and interleaving pages. Stitched.

SB74 £15.84 booklet containing pane No. 1777a×4................. 40.00

B **41** Shore Worker with Baskets of Oysters

Oyster Fishing

2014 (9 Oct). Multicoloured cover, 165×100 mm, as Type B **41**. Booklet contains text and illustrations on panes and interleaving pages. Stitched.

SB75 £14.21 booklet containing panes Nos. 1875a×3 and
MS1881a... 38.00

Stanley Gibbons

399 Strand

Unsure how to progress your collection?

Visit 399 Strand to get advice from our experienced and knowledgeable staff. They will help you choose the stamps and philatelic accessories that will enhance and develop your collection. They will also offer guidance on techniques for the care and storage of your stamps and covers.

We have a superb range of stamps albums and philatelic accessories.

We strive to cater for every need a collector might have, and if we don't have the exact item you need, we will recommend an equivalent or an alternative.

Come in, browse our range and choose what's best for you.

Before you commit to a particular album, take the time to talk to our staff who will help you weigh up the pros and cons before you make your decision. We are always happy to demonstrate anything we sell from tweezers to Frank Godden luxury albums.

Everything for the philatelic collector.

Just down the road from the Savoy Hotel, two minutes from Charing Cross Tube station

For more information, please contact Stephen Bowyer on:
Tel. +44 (0)207 557 4436 or sbowyer@stanleygibbons.com
399 Strand opening hours **Mon-Fri 9am-5.30pm Sat 9:30am-5.30pm Sun Closed**

Est 1856
STANLEY GIBBONS

Stanley Gibbons Limited
399 Strand, London, WC2R 0LX
+44 (0)20 7557 4444
www.stanleygibbons.com

Stanley Gibbons
Auctions

Welcome consignments for future Auctions,
be it single items or complete collections.

If you are looking to sell your collection then come to
Stanley Gibbons Auctions where:

Outstanding realisations and percentage of lots sold
Mailing list and client list second to none
Stanley Gibbons Auctions is perfect for sellers and buyers alike.

Please contact Ryan Epps **repps@stanleygibbons.com**
or Steve Matthews **smatthews@stanleygibbons.com** or call **020 7836 8444**

Est 1856
STANLEY
GIBBONS
Auctions

Stanley Gibbons Limited
399 Strand, London, WC2R 0LX
+44 (0)20 7836 8444
www.stanleygibbons.com

Collect Channel Islands and Isle of Man Order Form

Est 1856
STANLEY GIBBONS

YOUR ORDER

Stanley Gibbons account number ☐ ☐ ☐ ☐ ☐ ☐

Condition (mint/UM/ used)	Country	SG No.	Description	Price	Office use only
			POSTAGE & PACK-ING	£3.60	
			TOTAL		

The lowest price charged for individual stamps or sets purchased from Stanley Gibbons Ltd, is £1.

Payment & address details

Name ....

Address (We cannot deliver to PO Boxes) ....

....

.... Postcode ....

Tel No. ....

Email ....

PLEASE NOTE Overseas customers MUST quote a telephone number or the order cannot be dispatched. Please complete ALL sections of this form to allow us to process the order.

☐ Cheque (made payable to Stanley Gibbons)

☐ I authorise you to charge my

☐ Mastercard ☐ Visa ☐ Diners ☐ Amex ☐ Maestro

Card No. ☐☐☐☐ ☐☐☐☐ ☐☐☐☐ ☐☐☐☐ ☐☐☐☐ (Maestro only)

Valid from ☐☐☐☐ Expiry date ☐☐☐☐ Issue No. (Maestro only) ☐☐ CVC No. (4 if Amex) ☐☐☐☐

CVC No. is the last three digits on the back of your card (4 if Amex)

Signature .... Date ....

4 EASY WAYS TO ORDER

Post to
Lesley Mourne,
Stamp Mail Order
Department, Stanley
Gibbons Ltd, 399
Strand, London,
WC2R 0LX, England

Call
020 7836 8444
+44 (0)20 7836 8444

Fax
020 7557 4499
+44 (0)20 7557 4499

Click
lmourne@
stanleygibbons.com

Delivering Your Dream Collection...
...can cost less than you think

MY favourite stamp is probably the same as my wife's – the GB PUC £1. Just take a look at the design / engraving – and in single monochrome – utterly magnificent. Strictly speaking I should say the 1d black – it's iconic and an amazing work of design/art in the first place as this stamp represents in communication terms the 'Apple i-phone' of its time – also barring damage to the actual paper – the 1d black is virtually indestructible … the colour is so 'fast' that you can soak a 1d black in a 1/10 part solution of 'milton/water' (nappy bleach) … the paper will turn white but the black will remain unaffected. This is the reason why you sometimes see a magnificent used 1d black but the paper is too white – simply it has been left too long in bleach … over-white paper will actually lower value … as with most things it is a question of degree …

Reader: That's all very interesting Andrew, but where is this going ..?

When I was, theoretically, growing up (in my teens) you could ask me the retail price of virtually any British commemorative set (think 'special issue' for the indoctrinated) and I would know it as black is to white. But nowadays, in value terms, what is black and what is white? – courtesy perhaps more than anything of the internet … so much is 'grey' and blurred around the edges … that 'retail' price depends more than ever upon the quality of what is being retailed and no longer does one price fit all … Just search on-line for an 'Agatha Christie' booklet – don't look at what sellers wish for – look at reality – click 'completed' – far fewer do … actual 'sold' prices can be 50% of each other

… now look at fixed retail prices,

consider the postally valid 'face value' and finally the 'catalogue' value … you could be forgiven for throwing your arms up in the air. The point is making sense of it all … not just for 'bog standard' commodity price items but for stamps with character – generally pre-QEII and pre 1950 / 1940 classic stamps of which they're not making any more (excepting on-line auction offers of modern fakes/reproductions) … so it follows that if you can be confident of just *four* things:
1. the supplier is real and reputable (and internet ratings only tell part of the story), **2.** the quality is as described, **3.** the price is realistic against comparison, **4.** You have a reliable guarantee … then that's the way for you to go …

But to realise your dream maybe there's another way for you to go so that …

1st
£55
FREE WINNINGS

Continued overleaf 🖝